A-Level Chemistry

Exam Board: Edexcel

Revising for Chemistry exams is stressful, that's for sure — even just getting your notes sorted out can leave you needing a lie down. But help is at hand...

This brilliant CGP book explains **everything you'll need to learn** (and nothing you won't), all in a straightforward style that's easy to get your head around. We've also included **exam questions** to test how ready you are for the real thing.

There's even a free Online Edition you can read on your computer or tablet!

How to get your free Online Edition

Go to **cgpbooks.co.uk/extras** and enter this code...

0328 8720 6385 1094

This code only works for one person. If somebody else has used this book before you, they might have already claimed the Online Edition.

A-Level revision? It has to be CGP!

Published by CGP

Editors:
Katie Braid, Katherine Faudemer, Robin Flello, Emily Howe, Paul Jordin, Sophie Scott and Ben Train.

Contributors:
Mike Bossart, Rob Clarke, Ian H. Davis, John Duffy, Emma Grimwood, Paddy Gannon, Lucy Muncaster, Antonio Angelosanto, Derek Swain, Paul Warren and Christopher Workman.

ISBN: 978 1 78908 130 5

With thanks to Jamie Sinclair for the proofreading.
With thanks to Jan Greenway for the copyright research.

Cover Photo © **Laguna Design**/Science Photo Library

Clipart from Corel®
Illustrations by: Sandy Gardner Artist, email sandy@sandygardner.co.uk
Printed by Elanders Ltd, Newcastle upon Tyne.

Based on the classic CGP style created by Richard Parsons.

Contents

If you're revising for the **AS exams**, you'll need Topics 1 – 10, and the Practical Skills section at the back.
If you're revising for the **A-Level exams**, you'll need the whole book.

The Scientific Process (AS)

Topic 1 — Atomic Structure and the Periodic Table (AS)

Topic 2 — Bonding and Structure (AS)

Topic 3 — Redox I (AS)

Topic 4 — Inorganic Chemistry and the Periodic Table (AS)

Topic 5 — Formulae, Equations & Amounts of Substances (AS)

Topic 14 — Redox II

Topic 15 — Transition Metals

Topic 16 — Kinetics II

Topic 17 — Organic Chemistry II

Topic 18 — Organic Chemistry III

Topic 19 — Modern Analytical Techniques II

Practical Skills (AS)

The Scientific Process

These pages are all about the scientific process — how we develop and test scientific ideas. It's what scientists do all day, every day (well except at coffee time — never come between scientists and their coffee).

Scientists Come Up with **Theories** — Then **Test Them**...

Science tries to explain **how** and **why** things happen. It's all about seeking and gaining **knowledge** about the world around us. Scientists do this by **asking** questions and **suggesting** answers and then **testing** them, to see if they're correct — this is the **scientific process**.

1) **Ask** a question — make an **observation** and ask **why or how** whatever you've observed happens.
   E.g. Why does sodium chloride dissolve in water?
2) **Suggest** an answer, or part of an answer, by forming a **theory** or a **model** (a possible **explanation** of the observations or a description of what you think is happening actually happening).
   E.g. Sodium chloride is made up of charged particles which are pulled apart by the polar water molecules.
3) Make a **prediction** or **hypothesis** — a **specific testable statement**, based on the theory, about what will happen in a test situation.
   E.g. A solution of sodium chloride will conduct electricity much better than water does.
4) Carry out **tests** — to provide **evidence** that will support the prediction or refute it.
   E.g. Measure the conductivity of water and of sodium chloride solution.

A theory is only scientific if it can be tested.

...Then They **Tell** Everyone About Their **Results**...

The results are **published** — scientists need to let others know about their work. Scientists publish their results in **scientific journals**. These are just like normal magazines, only they contain **scientific reports** (called papers) instead of the latest celebrity gossip.

1) Scientific reports are similar to the **lab write-ups** you do in school. And just as a lab write-up is **reviewed** (marked) by your teacher, reports in scientific journals undergo **peer review** before they're published.

   Scientists use standard terminology when writing their reports. This way they know that other scientists will understand them. For instance, there are internationally agreed rules for naming organic compounds, so that scientists across the world will know exactly what substance is being referred to. See page 70.

2) The report is sent out to **peers** — other scientists who are experts in the **same area**. They go through it bit by bit, examining the methods and data, and checking it's all clear and logical. When the report is approved, it's **published**. This makes sure that work published in scientific journals is of a **good standard**.
3) But peer review **can't guarantee** the science is **correct** — other scientists still need to **reproduce** it.
4) Sometimes **mistakes** are made and bad work is published. Peer review **isn't perfect** but it's probably the best way for scientists to self-regulate their work and to publish **quality reports**.

...Then **Other Scientists Will Test** the Theory Too

1) Other scientists read the published theories and results, and try to **test the theory** themselves. This involves:
   - Repeating the **exact same experiments**.
   - Using the theory to make **new predictions** and then testing them with **new experiments**.
2) If all the experiments in the world provide evidence to back it up, the theory is thought of as **scientific 'fact'**.
3) If **new evidence** comes to light that **conflicts** with the current evidence the theory is questioned all over again. More rounds of **testing** will be carried out to try to find out where the theory **falls down**.

This is how the **scientific process works** — **evidence** supports a theory, loads of other scientists read it and test it for themselves, eventually all the scientists in the world **agree** with it and then bingo, you get to **learn** it. When looking at experiments that give conflicting results, it's important to look at **all** the **evidence** to work out whether a theory is supported or not — this includes looking at the **methodology** (the techniques) used in the experiments and the **data** collected.

This is how scientists arrived at the structure of the atom (see page 4) — and how they came to the conclusion that electrons are arranged in shells and orbitals. As is often the case, it took years and years for these models to be developed and accepted.

The Scientific Process

If the Evidence Supports a Theory, It's Accepted — for Now

Our currently accepted theories have survived this '**trial by evidence**'. They've been tested **over and over again** and each time the results have backed them up. **BUT**, and this is a big but (teehee), they never become totally indisputable fact. Scientific **breakthroughs** or **advances** could provide new ways to question and test the theory, which could lead to **changes and challenges** to it. Then the testing starts all over again...

And this, my friend, is the **tentative nature of scientific knowledge** — it's always **changing** and **evolving**.

Evidence Comes From Lab Experiments...

1) Results from **controlled experiments** in **laboratories** are **great**.
2) A lab is the easiest place to **control variables** so that they're all **kept constant** (except for the one you're investigating).
3) This means you can draw meaningful **conclusions**.

For example, if you're investigating how temperature affects the rate of a reaction, you need to keep everything but the temperature constant, e.g. the pH of the solution, the concentration of the solution, etc.

...But You Can't Always do a Lab Experiment

There are things you **can't** study in a lab. And outside the lab, controlling the variables is tricky, if not impossible.

- *Are increasing CO_2 emissions causing climate change?* There are other variables which may have an effect, such as changes in solar activity. You can't easily rule out every possibility. Also, climate change is a very **gradual process**. Scientists won't be able to tell if their predictions are correct for donkey's years.
- *Does drinking chlorinated tap water increase the risk of developing certain cancers?* There are always differences between groups of people. The best you can do is to have a **well-designed study** using **matched groups** — **choose two groups** of people (those who drink tap water and those who don't) which are **as similar as possible** (same mix of ages, same mix of diets, etc). But you still can't rule out every possibility. Taking newborn identical twins and treating them identically, except for making one drink gallons of tap water and the other only pure water, might be a fairer test, but it would present huge **ethical problems**.

Samantha thought her study was very well designed — especially the fitted bookshelf.

Science Helps to Inform Decision-Making

Lots of scientific work eventually leads to **important discoveries** that **could** benefit humankind — but there are often **risks** attached (and almost always **financial costs**). **Society** (that's you, me and everyone else) must weigh up the information in order to **make decisions** — about the way we live, what we eat, what we drive, and so on. Information is also used by **politicians** to devise policies and laws.

- **Chlorine** is added to water in **small quantities** to disinfect it (see page 49). Some studies link drinking chlorinated water with certain types of cancer. But the risks from drinking water contaminated by nasty bacteria are far, far greater. There are other ways to get rid of bacteria in water, but they're heaps **more expensive**.
- Scientific advances mean that **non-polluting hydrogen-fuelled cars** can be made. They're better for the environment, but are really expensive. And it'd cost a lot to adapt filling stations to store hydrogen.
- Pharmaceutical drugs are really expensive to develop, and drug companies want to make money. So they put most of their efforts into developing drugs that they can sell for a good price. Society has to consider the **cost** of buying new drugs — the **NHS** can't afford the most expensive drugs without **sacrificing** something else.

So there you have it — how science works...

Hopefully these pages have given you a nice intro to how science works. You need to understand it for the exam, and for life. Once you've got it sussed it's time to move on to the really good stuff — the chemistry. Bet you can't wait...

The Atom

This stuff about atoms and elements should be ingrained in your brain from GCSE. You do need to know it perfectly though if you are to negotiate your way through the field of man-eating tigers and pesky atoms...

Atoms are made up of **Protons, Neutrons** and **Electrons**

Atoms are the stuff **all** elements and compounds are made of.
They're made up of 3 types of **subatomic** particle — **protons, neutrons** and **electrons**.

Electrons
1) Electrons have **–1** charge.
2) They whizz around the nucleus in **orbitals**. The orbitals take up most of the **volume** of the atom.

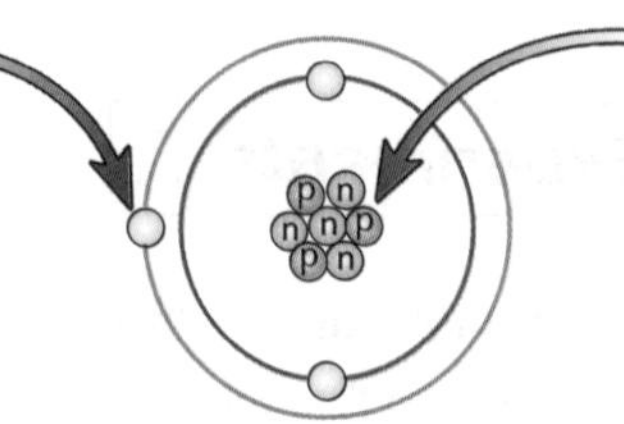

Nucleus
1) Most of the **mass** of the atom is concentrated in the nucleus.
2) The **diameter** of the nucleus is rather titchy compared to the whole atom.
3) The nucleus is where you find the **protons** and **neutrons**.

The mass and charge of these subatomic particles are **tiny**, so **relative mass** and **relative charge** are used instead.

Subatomic particle	Relative mass	Relative charge
Proton	1	+1
Neutron	1	0
Electron, e^-	0.0005	–1

The mass of an electron is negligible compared to a proton or a neutron — this means you can usually ignore it.

Nuclear Symbols Show Numbers of **Subatomic Particles**

You can figure out the **number** of protons, neutrons and electrons from the **nuclear symbol**, which is found in the periodic table.

$$^{A}_{Z}X$$

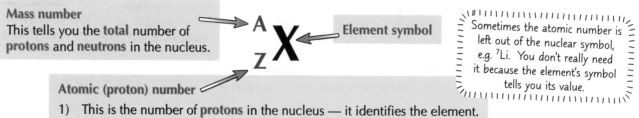

Mass number
This tells you the **total** number of **protons** and **neutrons** in the nucleus.

Element symbol

Atomic (proton) number
1) This is the number of **protons** in the nucleus — it identifies the element.
2) **All** atoms of the same element have the **same** number of protons.

Sometimes the atomic number is left out of the nuclear symbol, e.g. ^{7}Li. You don't really need it because the element's symbol tells you its value.

1) For **neutral** atoms, which have no overall charge, the number of electrons is **the same as** the number of protons.
2) The number of neutrons is just **mass number minus atomic number**, i.e. 'top minus bottom' in the nuclear symbol.

Nuclear symbol	Atomic number, Z	Mass number, A	Protons	Electrons	Neutrons
$^{7}_{3}Li$	3	7	3	3	7 – 3 = 4
$^{19}_{9}F$	9	19	9	9	19 – 9 = 10
$^{24}_{12}Mg$	12	24	12	12	24 – 12 = 12

To work out the number of each subatomic particle present in a molecule, just work out how many there are in each atom and then add them all up.

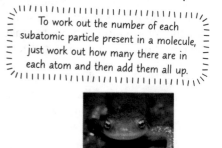

"Hello, I'm Newt Ron..."

Ions have **Different** Numbers of **Protons and Electrons**

Negative ions have **more electrons** than protons...

F^- — The **negative charge** means that there's **1 more** electron than there are protons. F has **9 protons** (see table above), so F^- must have **10 electrons**. The overall charge = +9 – 10 = –1.

...and **positive** ions have **fewer electrons** than protons.

Mg^{2+} — The **2+ charge** means that there are **2 fewer** electrons than there are protons. Mg has **12 protons** (see table above), so Mg^{2+} must have **10 electrons**. The overall charge = +12 – 10 = +2.

The Atom

*Isotopes are Atoms of the **Same Element** with Different Numbers of **Neutrons***

Isotopes of an element are atoms with the **same number of protons** but **different numbers of neutrons.**
Chlorine-35 and chlorine-37 are examples of isotopes:

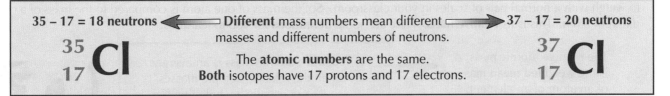

35 – 17 = 18 neutrons ⟵ **Different** mass numbers mean different masses and different numbers of neutrons. ⟶ 37 – 17 = 20 neutrons

$^{35}_{17}Cl$ The **atomic numbers** are the same. **Both** isotopes have 17 protons and 17 electrons. $^{37}_{17}Cl$

1) It's the **number** and **arrangement** of electrons that decides the **chemical properties** of an element. Isotopes have the **same configuration of electrons** (see pages 10-11), so they've got the **same** chemical properties.
2) Isotopes of an element do have slightly different **physical properties** though, such as different densities, rates of diffusion, etc. This is because **physical properties** tend to depend more on the **mass** of the atom.

Here's another example — naturally occurring **magnesium** consists of 3 isotopes.

^{24}Mg (79%)	^{25}Mg (10%)	^{26}Mg (11%)
12 protons	12 protons	12 protons
12 neutrons	**13** neutrons	**14** neutrons
12 electrons	12 electrons	12 electrons

The periodic table gives the atomic number for each element. The other number isn't the mass number — it's the relative atomic mass (see page 6). They're a bit different, but you can often assume they're equal — it doesn't matter unless you're doing really accurate work.

Practice Questions

Q1 Draw a diagram showing the structure of an atom, labelling each part.

Q2 Where is the mass concentrated in an atom, and what makes up most of the volume of an atom?

Q3 Draw a table showing the relative charge and relative mass of the three subatomic particles found in atoms.

Q4 Using an example, explain the terms 'atomic number' and 'mass number'.

Exam Questions

Q1 Hydrogen, deuterium and tritium are all isotopes of each other.

a) Identify one similarity and one difference between these isotopes. [2 marks]

b) Deuterium can be written as $^{2}_{1}H$. Determine the number of protons, neutrons and electrons in a deuterium atom. [1 mark]

c) Write the nuclear symbol for tritium, given that it has 2 neutrons. [1 mark]

Q2 This question relates to the atoms or ions A to D: **A** $^{32}_{16}S^{2-}$ **B** $^{40}_{18}Ar$ **C** $^{30}_{16}S$ **D** $^{42}_{20}Ca$

a) Identify the similarity for each of the following pairs, justifying your answer in each case.

i) A and B. [1 mark]

ii) A and C. [1 mark]

iii) B and D. [1 mark]

b) Which two of the atoms or ions are isotopes of each other? Explain your reasoning. [2 marks]

Q3 A molecule of propanol, C_3H_7OH, is made up of $^{1}_{1}H$, $^{16}_{8}O$ and $^{12}_{6}C$ atoms.
Calculate the number of electrons, protons and neutrons in one molecule of propanol. [2 marks]

Got it learned yet? — Isotope so...

This is a nice page to ease you into things. Remember that positive ions have fewer electrons than protons, and negative ions have more electrons than protons. Get that straight in your mind or you'll end up in a right mess.

Relative Mass

Relative mass... What? Eh?... Read on...

Relative Masses are Masses of Atoms Compared to **Carbon-12**

The actual mass of an atom is **very, very tiny**. Don't worry about exactly how tiny for now, but it's far **too small** to weigh with a normal pair of scales in your classroom. So, the mass of one atom is compared to the mass of a different atom. This is its **relative mass**. Here are some **definitions** for you to learn:

The **relative atomic mass**, A_r, is the weighted **mean mass** of an atom of an element, compared to 1/12th of the mass of an atom of **carbon-12**.

Relative isotopic mass is the mass of an atom of an **isotope**, compared with 1/12th of the mass of an atom of **carbon-12**.

1) Relative atomic mass is an **average** of all the relative isotopic masses, so it's not usually a whole number.
2) Relative isotopic mass is usually a **whole number**.

E.g. a natural sample of chlorine contains a mixture of ^{35}Cl (75%) and ^{37}Cl (25%), so the relative isotopic masses are **35** and **37**. But its relative atomic mass is **35.5**.

Jason's shirt was isotropical...

Relative Molecular Masses are Masses of **Molecules**

The **relative molecular mass** (or **relative formula mass**), M_r, is the average mass of a **molecule** or **formula unit**, compared to 1/12th of the mass of an atom of **carbon-12**.

Don't worry, this is one definition that you **don't** need to know for the exam.
But... you **do** need to know how to **work out** the **relative molecular mass**, and the **relative formula mass**, so it's probably best if you **learn** what they mean anyway.

1) **Relative molecular mass** is used when referring to **simple molecules**.
2) To find the relative molecular mass, just **add up** the **relative atomic mass values** of all the atoms in the molecule.

E.g. $M_r(C_2H_6O) = (2 \times 12.0) + (6 \times 1.0) + 16.0 = \mathbf{46.0}$

See page 22 for more on simple molecules, and pages 20 and 26-27 for more on giant structures.

1) **Relative formula mass** is used for compounds that are **ionic** (or **giant covalent**, such as SiO_2).
2) To find the relative formula mass, **add up** the **relative atomic masses** (A_r) of all the ions or atoms in the formula unit. (A_r of ion = A_r of atom. The electrons make no difference to the mass.)

E.g. $M_r(CaF_2) = 40.1 + (2 \times 19.0) = \mathbf{78.1}$

A_r Can Be Worked Out from **Isotopic Abundances**

You need to know how to calculate the **relative atomic mass** (A_r) of an element from its **isotopic abundances**.

1) Different isotopes of an element occur in different quantities, or isotopic abundances.
2) To work out the relative atomic mass of an element, you need to work out the **average** mass of all its atoms.
3) If you're given the isotopic abundances in **percentages**, all you need to do is follow these two easy steps:

Step 1: Multiply each **relative isotopic mass** by its % **relative isotopic abundance**, and **add up** the results.
Step 2: Divide by **100**.

Example: Find the relative atomic mass of boron, given that 20.0% of the boron atoms found on Earth have a relative isotopic mass of 10.0, while 80.0% have a relative isotopic mass of 11.0.

Step 1: $(20.0 \times 10) + (80.0 \times 11) = 1080$

Step 2: $1080 \div 100 = \mathbf{10.8}$

Relative Mass

Mass Spectrometry Can Tell Us About Isotopes

Mass spectra are produced by mass spectrometers — devices which are used to find out what samples are made up of by measuring the masses of their components. Mass spectra can tell us dead useful things, e.g. the **relative isotopic masses** and **abundances** of different elements.

Mass spectra can be used to work out the relative atomic masses of different elements.

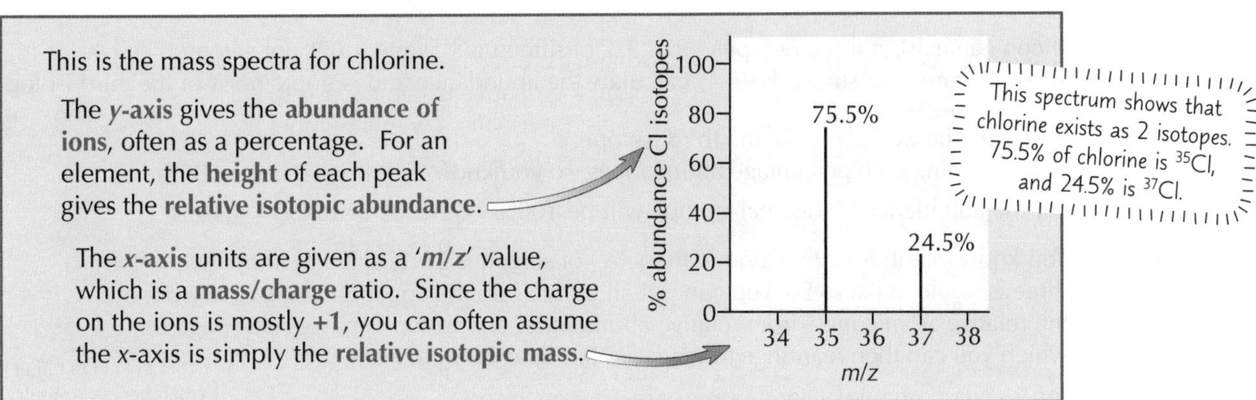

This is the mass spectra for chlorine.
The y-axis gives the abundance of ions, often as a percentage. For an element, the height of each peak gives the relative isotopic abundance.
The x-axis units are given as a 'm/z' value, which is a mass/charge ratio. Since the charge on the ions is mostly +1, you can often assume the x-axis is simply the relative isotopic mass.
% abundance Cl isotopes
100
80
60
40
20
0
75.5%
24.5%
34 35 36 37 38
m/z
This spectrum shows that chlorine exists as 2 isotopes. 75.5% of chlorine is 35Cl, and 24.5% is 37Cl.

The method for working out the relative atomic mass from a graph is a bit different to working it out from percentages (see previous page), but it starts off in the same way.

Step 1: Multiply each **relative isotopic mass** by its **relative isotopic abundance**, and **add up** the results.

Step 2: Divide by the **sum** of the isotopic abundances.

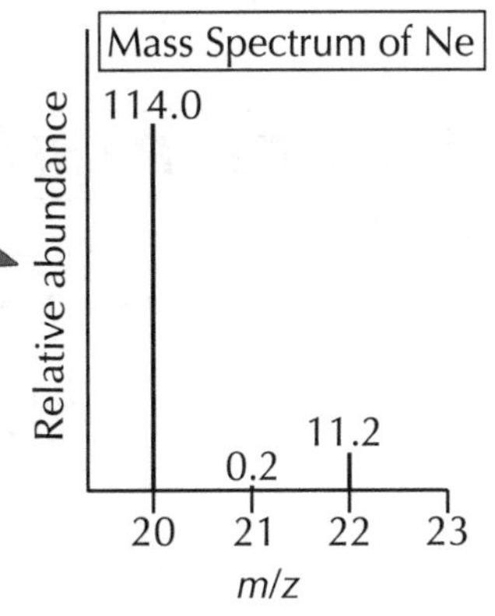

Example: Use the data from this mass spectrum to work out the relative atomic mass of neon. Give your answer to 1 decimal place.

Step 1: $(20 \times 114.0) + (21 \times 0.2) + (22 \times 11.2) = 2530.6$

Step 2: $(114.0 + 0.2 + 11.2 = 125.4)$
$2530.6 \div 125.4 = \mathbf{20.2}$

Practice Questions

Q1 Explain what relative atomic mass (A_r) and relative isotopic mass mean.

Q2 Explain the difference between relative molecular mass and relative formula mass.

Q3 Explain what relative isotopic abundance means.

Exam Questions

Q1 Copper exists in two main isotopic forms, ^{63}Cu and ^{65}Cu.

a) Calculate the relative atomic mass of copper using the information from the mass spectrum. [2 marks]

b) Explain why the relative atomic mass of copper is not a whole number. [2 marks]

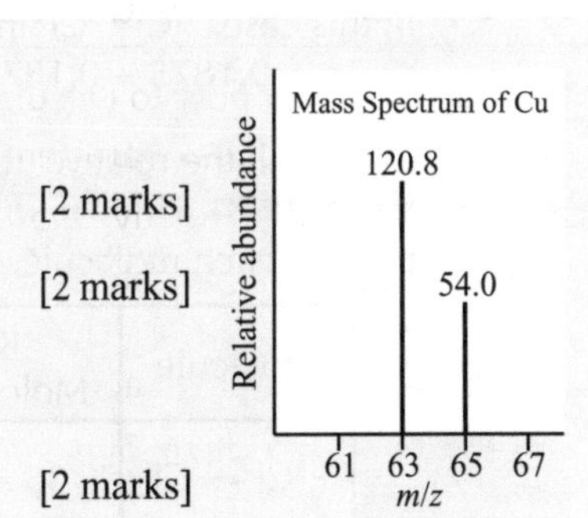

Q2 The percentage make-up of naturally occurring potassium is:
93.1% ^{39}K, 0.120% ^{40}K and 6.77% ^{41}K.
Use the information to determine the relative atomic mass of potassium. [2 marks]

You can't pick your relatives, you just have to learn them...

Isotopic masses are a bit frustrating. Why can't all atoms of an element just be the same? But the fact is they're not, so you're going to have to learn how to use those spectra to work out the relative atomic masses of different elements. The actual maths is pretty simple. A pinch of multiplying, a dash of addition, some division to flavour and you're away.

More on Relative Mass

"More relative mass?! How much more could there possibly be?" I hear you cry. Well, as you're about to see, there's plenty more. This is all dead useful to scientists and (more importantly) to you in your exams.

You Can Calculate **Isotopic Masses** from **Relative Atomic Mass**

If you know the **relative atomic mass** of an **element**, and you know all but one of the **abundances** and relative isotopic masses of its **isotopes**, you can work out the abundance and isotopic mass of the final isotope. Neat huh?

Example: Silicon can exist in three isotopes. 92.23% of silicon is ^{28}Si and 4.67% of silicon is ^{29}Si. Given that the A_r of silicon is 28.1, calculate the abundance and isotopic mass of the third isotope.

Step 1: First, find the **abundance** of the third isotope.
You're dealing with percentage abundances, so you know they need to total 100%.
So, the abundance of the final isotope will be 100% – 92.23% – 4.67% = **3.10%**

Step 2: You know that the **relative atomic mass** (A_r) of silicon is 28.1, and you know two of the three **isotopic masses**. So, you can put all of that into the equation you use to work out the relative atomic mass from relative abundances and isotopic masses (see page 6), which you can then rearrange to work out the **final isotopic mass**, *X*.

$28.1 = ((28 \times 92.23) + (29 \times 4.67) + (X \times 3.10)) \div 100$

$28.1 = (2717.87 + (X \times 3.10)) \div 100$

$2810 - 2717.87 = X \times 3.10$

$29.719 = X$ So the isotopic mass of the third isotope is **30** — ^{30}**Si**.

Remember — isotopic masses are usually whole numbers, so you should round your answer to the nearest whole number.

You Can **Predict** the Mass Spectra for **Diatomic Molecules**

Now, this is where it gets even more mathsy and interesting (seriously — I love it). You can use your knowledge to **predict** what the **mass spectra** of diatomic molecules (i.e. molecules containing two atoms) look like.

Example: Chlorine has two isotopes. ^{35}Cl has an abundance of 75% and ^{37}Cl has an abundance of 25%. Predict the mass spectrum of Cl_2.

To convert a percentage to a decimal, just divide by 100.

1) First, express each of the percentages as a decimal: 75% = 0.75 and 25% = 0.25.

2) Make a **table** showing all the different Cl_2 molecules. For each molecule, **multiply** the abundances (as decimals) of the isotopes to get the relative abundance of each one.

	^{35}Cl	^{37}Cl
^{35}Cl	$^{35}Cl-^{35}Cl$: $0.75 \times 0.75 = 0.5625$	$^{35}Cl-^{37}Cl$: $0.25 \times 0.75 = 0.1875$
^{37}Cl	$^{37}Cl-^{35}Cl$: $0.25 \times 0.75 = 0.1875$	$^{37}Cl-^{37}Cl$: $0.25 \times 0.25 = 0.0625$

3) Look for any molecules in the table that are the **same** and **add up** their abundances.
In this case, $^{37}Cl-^{35}Cl$ and $^{35}Cl-^{37}Cl$ are the same, so the actual abundance for this molecule is:
0.1875 + 0.1875 = **0.375**.

4) **Divide** all the relative abundances by the smallest relative abundance to get the **smallest whole number ratio**. And by working out the relative molecular mass of each molecule, you can **predict** the **mass spectrum** for Cl_2:

Molecule	Relative Molecular Mass	Relative abundance
$^{35}Cl-^{35}Cl$	35 + 35 = 70	0.5625 ÷ 0.0625 = 9
$^{35}Cl-^{37}Cl$	35 + 37 = 72	0.375 ÷ 0.0625 = 6
$^{37}Cl-^{37}Cl$	37 + 37 = 74	0.0625 ÷ 0.0625 = 1

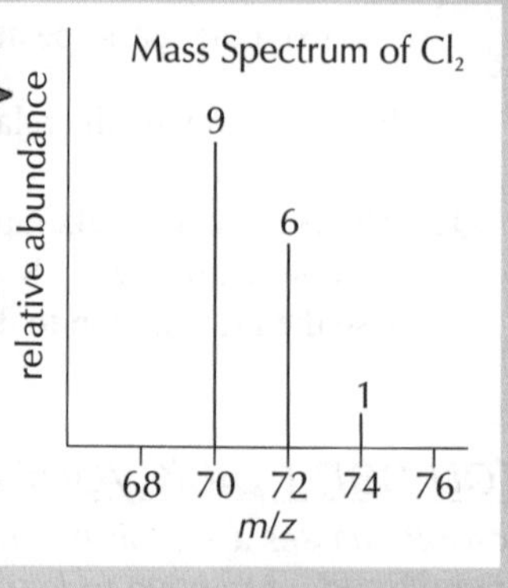

More on Relative Mass

Mass Spectrometry Can Also Help to Identify Compounds

1) You've seen how you can use a mass spectrum showing the relative isotopic abundances of an element to work out its relative atomic mass. You need to make sure you can remember how to do this. You can also get mass spectra for **molecules** made up from more than one element.
2) When the molecules in a sample are bombarded with electrons, an electron is removed from the molecule to form a **molecular ion, $M^+_{(g)}$**.

Assuming the ion has a 1+ charge, which it normally will have.

3) To find the relative molecular mass of a compound, you look at the **molecular ion peak** (the **M peak**) on the mass spectrum. This is the peak with the highest *m/z* value (ignoring any small M+1 peaks that occur due to the presence of any atoms of carbon-13). The mass/charge value of the molecular ion peak is the **molecular mass**.

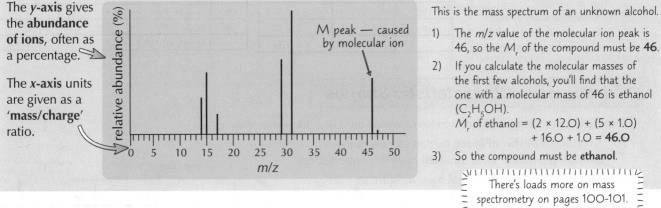

The *y*-axis gives the **abundance of ions**, often as a percentage.

The *x*-axis units are given as a **'mass/charge'** ratio.

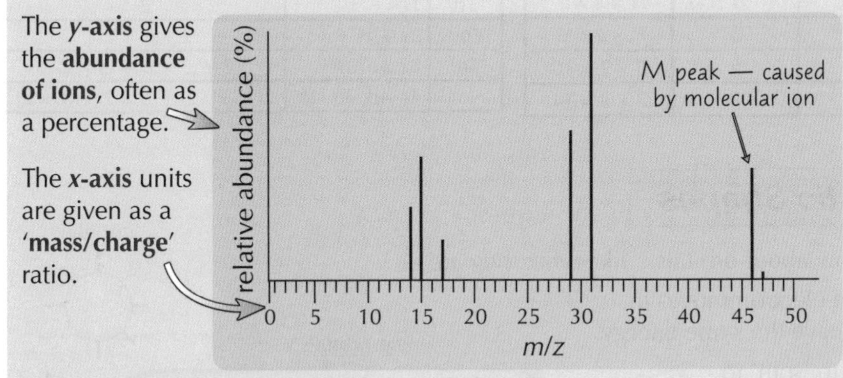

This is the mass spectrum of an unknown alcohol.

1) The *m/z* value of the molecular ion peak is 46, so the M_r of the compound must be **46**.
2) If you calculate the molecular masses of the first few alcohols, you'll find that the one with a molecular mass of 46 is ethanol (C_2H_5OH).
   M_r of ethanol = (2 × 12.0) + (5 × 1.0) + 16.0 + 1.0 = **46.0**
3) So the compound must be **ethanol**.

There's loads more on mass spectrometry on pages 100-101.

Practice Questions

Q1 Explain why diatomic molecules can have different relative molecular masses.

Q2 What is the significance of the molecular ion peak on a mass spectrum?

Exam Questions

Q1 The table below shows the percentage abundances of isotopes of oxygen found in a sample of O_2.

Isotopes	% Abundance
^{16}O	98
^{18}O	2

a) Calculate the relative abundances of all the possible molecules of O_2. [3 marks]

b) Sketch a mass spectrum of O_2. [4 marks]

Q2 Potassium (A_r = 39.1) can exist in one of three isotopes. 94.20% exists as ^{39}K and 0.012% exists as ^{40}K.

a) Calculate the abundance of the third isotope of potassium. [1 mark]

b) Calculate the isotopic mass of the third isotope of potassium. [2 marks]

Q3 A sample of an unknown straight-chain alkane is analysed using mass spectrometry. The molecular ion peak is seen at a *m/z* value of 58.

The structures of alkanes are covered on page 76.

a) What is the M_r of this compound? [1 mark]

b) Using your answer to part a), suggest a structure for this compound. [1 mark]

How do you make a colourful early noughties girl group? Diatomic Kitten...

Dye Atomic Kitten... Geddit...? Only nine pages into this revision guide and we already have a strong contender for world's worst joke. But don't be too dismayed, there are plenty more terrible puns on their way, I assure you. Before you go looking for them, make sure you know how to do all these relative mass calculations — they're pretty important.

Electronic Structure

Those little electrons prancing about like mini bunnies decide what'll react with what — it's what chemistry's all about.

Electron Shells** are Made Up of **Subshells** and **Orbitals

1) Electrons move around the nucleus in **quantum shells** (sometimes called **energy levels**). These shells are all given numbers known as **principal quantum numbers**.
2) Shells **further** from the nucleus have a greater energy level than shells closer to the nucleus.
3) The shells contain different types of **subshell**. These subshells have different numbers of **orbitals**, which can each hold up to **2 electrons**.

This table shows the number of electrons that fit in each type of subshell. You need to know how many electrons can fit into the s, p and d subshells for your exams.

Subshell	Number of orbitals	Maximum electrons
s	1	1 × 2 = 2
p	3	3 × 2 = 6
d	5	5 × 2 = 10
f	7	7 × 2 = 14

And this one shows the subshells and electrons in the first four quantum shells.

Shell	Subshells	Total number or electrons	
1st	1*s*	2	= 2
2nd	2*s* 2*p*	2 + (3 × 2)	= 8
3rd	3*s* 3*p* 3*d*	2 + (3 × 2) + (5 × 2)	= 18
4th	4*s* 4*p* 4*d* 4*f*	2 + (3 × 2) + (5 × 2) + (7 × 2)	= 32

*Orbitals Have **Characteristic Shapes***

There are a few things you need to know about orbitals... like what they are —

1) An orbital is the **bit of space** that an electron moves in. Orbitals within the same subshell have the **same energy**.
2) The electrons in each orbital have to 'spin' in **opposite** directions — this is called **spin-pairing**.
3) s-orbitals are **spherical** — p-orbitals have **dumbbell shapes**. There are 3 p-orbitals and they're at right angles to one another.
4) You can represent electrons in orbitals using arrows in boxes. Each of the boxes represents one orbital. Each of the arrows represents one electron.

s-orbital

p-orbitals

P_x orbital + P_y orbital + P_z orbital =

1s 2s 2p

The up and down arrows represent the electrons spinning in opposite directions.

*Work Out **Electronic Configurations** by Filling the **Lowest** Energy Levels First*

You can figure out most electronic configurations pretty easily, so long as you know a few simple rules —

1) Electrons fill up the **lowest** energy subshells first.

There's always got to be an exception to mess things up. The 4s subshell has a lower energy level than the 3d subshell, even though its principal quantum number is bigger. This means the 4s subshell fills up first.

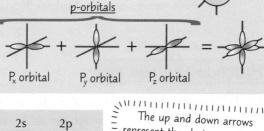

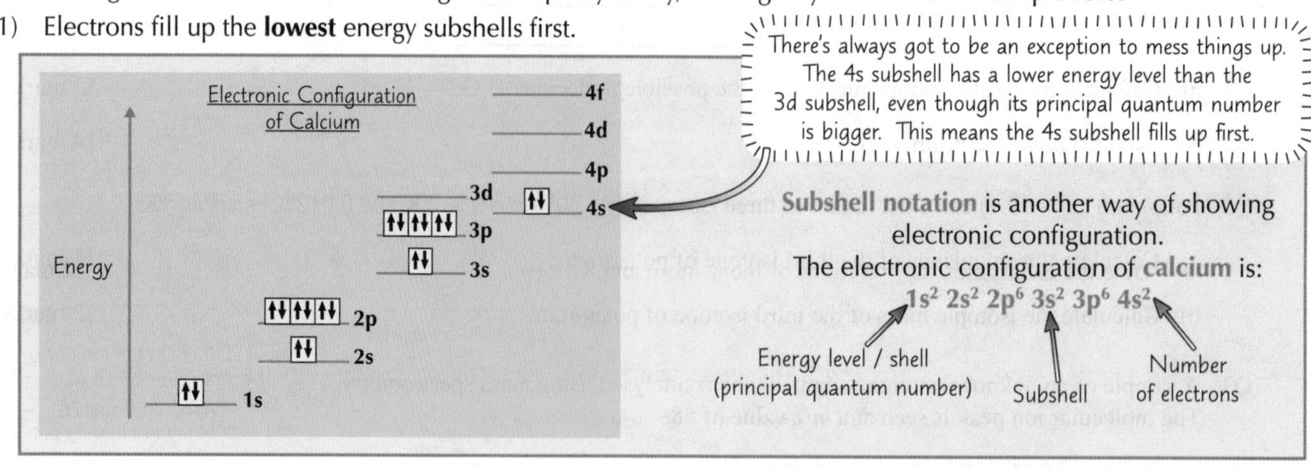

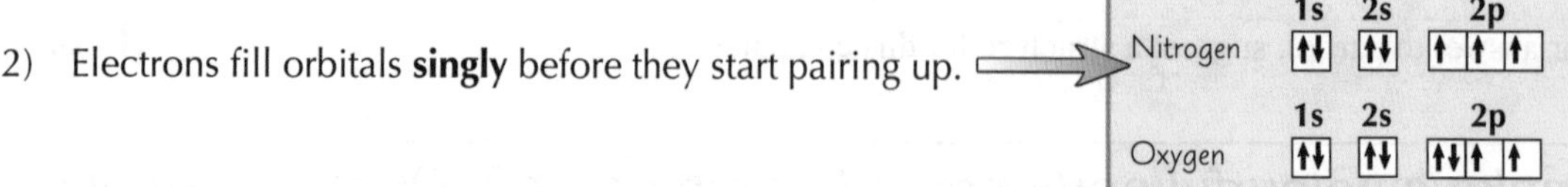

Watch out — **noble gas symbols**, like that of argon (Ar), are sometimes used in electronic configurations. For example, calcium ($1s^2\ 2s^2\ 2p^6\ 3s^2\ 3p^6\ 4s^2$) can be written as $[Ar]4s^2$, where $[Ar] = 1s^2\ 2s^2\ 2p^6\ 3s^2\ 3p^6$.

Electronic Structure

You can use the Periodic Table to work out *Electronic Configurations*

The periodic table can be split into an **s-block**, **d-block** and **p-block**.

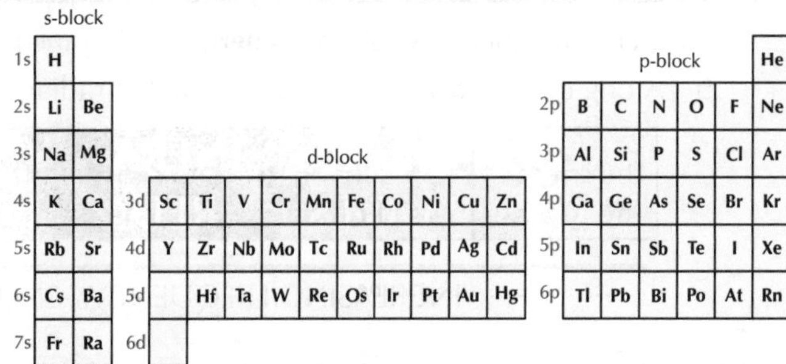

1) The **s-block** elements have an outer shell electronic configuration of s^1 or s^2.
   E.g. lithium ($1s^2$ $\mathbf{2s^1}$) and magnesium ($1s^2\ 2s^2\ 2p^6$ $\mathbf{3s^2}$).
2) The **p-block** elements have an outer shell configuration of s^2p^1 to s^2p^6.
   E.g. aluminium ($1s^2\ 2s^2\ 2p^6\ 3s^2$ $\mathbf{3p^1}$) and bromine ($1s^2\ 2s^2\ 2p^6\ 3s^2\ 3p^6\ 3d^{10}\ 4s^2$ $\mathbf{4p^5}$).

Example: Electronic configuration of phosphorus, P:

Period 1 — $1s^2$ ← Complete subshells
Period 2 — $2s^2\ 2p^6$ ← Complete subshells
Period 3 — $3s^2\ 3p^3$ ← Incomplete outer subshell

So it's: $\mathbf{1s^2\ 2s^2\ 2p^6\ 3s^2\ 3p^3}$

3) To work out the **configuration** of an **ion**, up to Ca, you just write the **electronic structure** of the atom and then **add** or **remove** electrons to or from the **highest-energy occupied subshell**.

Example: a) Give the electronic configuration a Ca^{2+} ion.

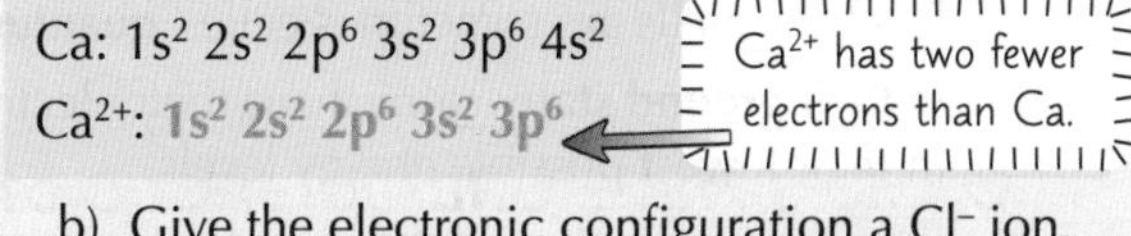

Ca: $1s^2\ 2s^2\ 2p^6\ 3s^2\ 3p^6\ 4s^2$
Ca^{2+}: $\mathbf{1s^2\ 2s^2\ 2p^6\ 3s^2\ 3p^6}$ ← Ca^{2+} has two fewer electrons than Ca.

b) Give the electronic configuration a Cl^- ion.

Cl: $1s^2\ 2s^2\ 2p^6\ 3s^2\ 3p^5$
Cl^-: $\mathbf{1s^2\ 2s^2\ 2p^6\ 3s^2\ 3p^6}$ ← Cl^- has one more electron than Cl.

4) The **d-block** elements are a bit trickier to work out — the 4s sub-shell fills **before** the 3d subshell.
   E.g. vanadium ($1s^2\ 2s^2\ 2p^6\ 3s^2\ 3p^6\ 3d^3\ 4s^2$) and nickel ($1s^2\ 2s^2\ 2p^6\ 3s^2\ 3p^6\ 3d^8\ 4s^2$).
5) **Chromium** (Cr) and **copper** (Cu) are badly behaved. They donate one of their **4s** electrons to the **3d subshell**. It's because they're **more stable** with a full or half-full d-subshell.

Cr atom (24 e^-): $1s^2\ 2s^2\ 2p^6\ 3s^2\ 3p^6\ 3d^5\ 4s^1$

Cu atom (29 e^-): $1s^2\ 2s^2\ 2p^6\ 3s^2\ 3p^6\ 3d^{10}\ 4s^1$

6) Different elements form ions with different **charges**.
   You can use the periodic table to **predict** what ion each element will form (see page 19 for more on this).

Practice Questions

Q1 How many electrons do full s-, p- and d-subshells contain?

Q2 What does the term 'spin-pairing' mean?

Q3 Draw diagrams to show the shapes of a s- and a p-orbital.

Q4 Write down the subshells in order of increasing energy up to 4p.

Exam Questions

Q1 Potassium reacts with oxygen to form potassium oxide, K_2O.

a) Give the electronic configurations of the K atom and K^+ ion. [2 marks]

b) Give the electronic configuration of the oxygen atom. [1 mark]

Q2 This question concerns electronic configurations in atoms and ions.

a) Identify the element with the 4th shell configuration of $4s^2\ 4p^2$. [1 mark]

b) Suggest the identities of an atom, a positive ion and a negative ion with the electronic configuration $1s^2\ 2s^2\ 2p^6\ 3s^2\ 3p^6$. [3 marks]

c) Give the electronic configuration of a Cu atom. [1 mark]

She shells sub-sells on the shesore...

The way electrons fill up the orbitals is kind of like how strangers fill up seats on a bus. Everyone tends to sit in their own seat till they're forced to share. Except for the scary man who comes and sits next to you. Make sure you learn the order that the subshells are filled up in, so you can write electronic configurations for any atom or ion they throw at you.

Atomic Emission Spectra

Atomic emission spectra, which you're about to meet, provide evidence for quantum shells. Read on...

Electromagnetic Spectrum — the Range of Electromagnetic Radiation

1) Electromagnetic radiation is **energy** that's transmitted as waves, with a **spectrum** of different frequencies.
2) Along the electromagnetic spectrum, the radiation increases in **frequency** and decreases in **wavelength**:

RADIO WAVES	MICRO-WAVES	INFRA-RED	VISIBLE LIGHT	ULTRA-VIOLET	X-RAYS	GAMMA RAYS

INCREASING FREQUENCY / ENERGY & DECREASING WAVELENGTH

Electrons Release Energy in Fixed Amounts

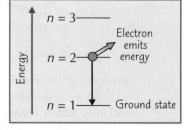

1) Electron shells are sometimes called **quantum shells**, or **energy levels** (see page 10).
2) In their **ground state**, atoms have their electrons in their **lowest** possible energy levels.
3) If an atom's electrons **take in energy** from their surroundings they can move to **higher energy levels**, further from the nucleus. At higher energy levels, electrons are said to be **excited**. (More excited than you right now, I'll bet.)
4) Electrons **release energy** by dropping from a higher energy level down to a **lower energy level**. The energy levels all have certain **fixed values** — they're **discrete**.

Energy
n = 3
n = 2
n = 1
Electron emits energy
Ground state

5) A **line spectrum** (called an **emission spectrum**) shows the frequencies of light emitted when electrons **drop down** from a higher energy level to a lower one. These frequencies appear as **coloured lines** on a dark background.

emission spectrum

6) Each element has a **different** electron arrangement, so the frequencies of radiation absorbed and emitted are different. This means the **spectrum** for each element is unique.

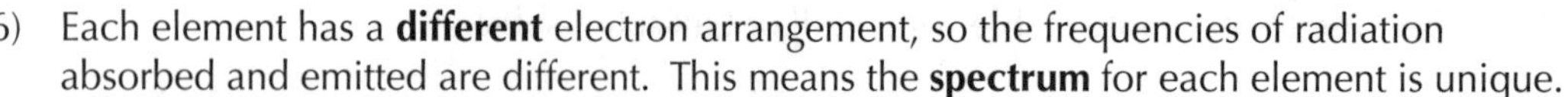

Emission Spectra are Made Up of Sets of Lines

1) You get lots of **sets of lines** in emission spectra — each set represents electrons moving to **a different energy level**. So, in an emission spectrum, you get one **set of lines** produced when electrons fall to the ***n* = 1** level, and another set produced when they fall to the ***n* = 2** level, and so on.
2) Each set of lines on emission spectra get **closer together** as the frequency **increases**.
3) Here's the emission spectrum of hydrogen (it only has **one** electron that can move). It has three important sets of lines:

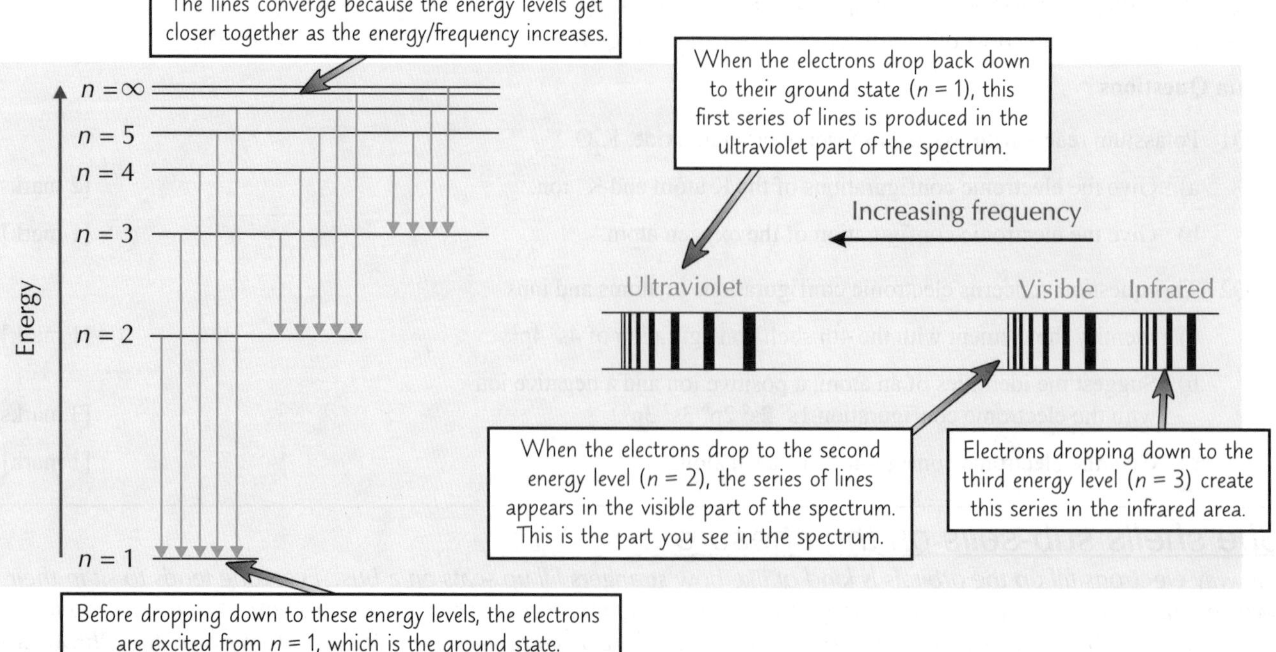

The lines converge because the energy levels get closer together as the energy/frequency increases.
n = ∞
n = 5
n = 4
n = 3
n = 2
n = 1
Energy
When the electrons drop back down to their ground state (n = 1), this first series of lines is produced in the ultraviolet part of the spectrum.
Increasing frequency
Ultraviolet
Visible
Infrared
When the electrons drop to the second energy level (n = 2), the series of lines appears in the visible part of the spectrum. This is the part you see in the spectrum.
Electrons dropping down to the third energy level (n = 3) create this series in the infrared area.
Before dropping down to these energy levels, the electrons are excited from n = 1, which is the ground state.

Atomic Emission Spectra

Emission Spectra Support the Idea of Quantum Shells

1) Our current understanding of **electronic configuration** involves the idea that electrons exist in **quantum shells** around the **nucleus**.
2) When it comes to electron shells, there are **four basic principles**:

- Electrons can only exist in **fixed orbits**, or **shells**, and not anywhere in between.
- Each shell has a **fixed energy**.
- When an electron moves between shells **electromagnetic radiation** is **emitted** or **absorbed**.
- Because the energy of shells is fixed, the radiation will have a **fixed frequency**.

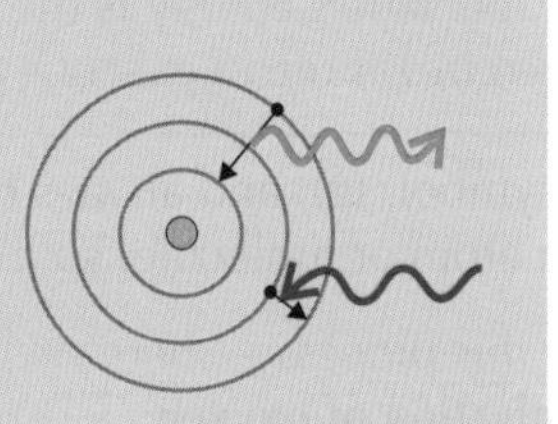

Brianna was a critically acclaimed expert in shells.

3) The emission spectrum of an atom has **clear lines** for different energy levels. This supports the idea that energy levels are discrete, i.e. **not continuous**. It means that an electron doesn't 'move' from one energy level to the next. It just **jumps**, with no in-between stage at all.
4) This is a really weird and quite confusing idea, but emission spectra and other **evidence** back up the idea that electrons exist in quantum shells.

Other evidence, such as ionisation energies (pages 14-15), supports the model of electrons in shells.

Practice Questions

Q1 Is energy absorbed or released when electrons drop from a higher energy level to a lower one?

Q2 Are energy levels discrete or continuous?

Exam Questions

Q1 The diagram below shows part of an atomic emission spectrum of a single element. The lines in the spectrum are labelled A to E.

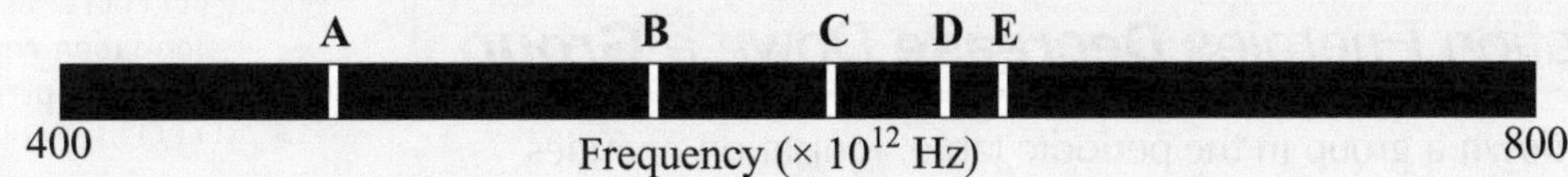

a) What happens in the atom when energy is emitted? [2 marks]

b) Which line in the spectrum represents the largest emission of energy? [1 mark]

c) Explain why the lines get closer together from A to E. [1 mark]

Q2 Many models of the atom have been presented in the past. One of the most widely used models currently relies on evidence provided by emission spectra, amongst other things.

a) What happens as an electron moves from a higher to a lower quantum shell? [1 mark]

b) Describe what the lines on an emission spectrum show. [1 mark]

c) Explain how emission spectra provide evidence that supports our current understanding of electrons existing in fixed energy levels. [2 marks]

d) Name one other factor that provides evidence that supports our current understanding of electrons existing in fixed energy levels. [1 mark]

Spectra — aren't they the baddies in those James Bond films?

All this stuff about fixed energy levels and electrons jumping up and down is a bit mind bending but it's actually pretty cool (if you're a Chemistry nerd like me). Emission spectra allow you to 'see' the gaps between these energy levels and show that the crazy idea of fixed energy levels dreamed up by an old, beardy chemist was actually spot on. Neat, huh?

Ionisation Energies

This page gets a trifle brain-boggling, so I hope you've got a few aspirin handy...

Ionisation** is the **Removal** of One or More **Electrons

You might see 'ionisation energy' referred to as 'ionisation enthalpy' instead.

When electrons have been removed from an atom or molecule, it's been **ionised**. The energy you need to remove the first electron is called the **first ionisation energy**.

The **first ionisation energy** is the energy needed to remove 1 electron from **each atom** in **1 mole** of **gaseous** atoms to form 1 mole of gaseous 1+ ions.

You **must** use the gas state symbol, **(g)**, and always refer to **1 mole** of atoms, as stated in the definition. Energy is put **in** to ionise an atom or molecule, so it's an **endothermic process** — there's more about this on page 104.

You can write **equations** for this process — here's the equation for the **first ionisation of oxygen**:

$$O_{(g)} \rightarrow O^{+}_{(g)} + e^{-} \quad \textbf{1st ionisation energy} = +1314\ \text{kJ mol}^{-1}$$

*These Three **Factors Affect Ionisation Energy***

Subshell structure also affects ionisation energy (see page 17).

Nuclear charge — The **more protons** there are in the nucleus, the more positively charged the nucleus is and the **stronger the attraction** for the electrons.

Electron shell — Attraction falls off very **rapidly with distance**. An electron in an electron shell **close** to the nucleus will be **much more** strongly attracted than one in a shell further away.

Shielding — As the number of electrons **between** the outer electrons and the nucleus **increases**, the outer electrons feel less attraction towards the nuclear charge. This lessening of the pull of the nucleus by inner shells of electrons is called **shielding** (or **screening**).

A **high ionisation energy** means there's a **strong attraction** between the **electron** and the **nucleus**, so **more energy** is needed to overcome the attraction and remove the electron.

*First Ionisation Energies **Decrease** Down a **Group***

Ionisation energy also increases across a period (see page 17).

1) As you **go down** a group in the periodic table, ionisation energies generally **fall**, i.e. it gets **easier** to remove outer electrons.
2) It happens because:
   - Elements further down a group have **extra electron shells** compared to ones above. The extra shells mean that the atomic radius is larger, so the outer electrons are **further away** from the nucleus, which greatly reduces their attraction to the nucleus.
   - The extra inner shells **shield** the outer electrons from the attraction of the nucleus.
3) A decrease in ionisation energy going down a group provides **evidence** that electron shells **really exist**.

The positive charge of the nucleus does increase as you go down a group (due to the extra protons), but this effect is overridden by the effect of the extra shells.

***Successive Ionisation Energies** Involve Removing **Additional** Electrons*

1) You can remove **all** the electrons from an atom, leaving only the nucleus. Each time you remove an electron, there's a **successive ionisation energy**. For example, the definition for the **second ionisation energy is**:

   The **second ionisation energy** is the energy needed to remove 1 electron from **each ion** in **1 mole** of **gaseous** 1+ ions to form 1 mole of gaseous 2+ ions.

   And here's the equation for the **second ionisation of oxygen**:

$$O^{+}_{(g)} \rightarrow O^{2+}_{(g)} + e^{-} \quad \textbf{2nd ionisation energy} = +3388\ \text{kJ mol}^{-1}$$

2) You need to be able to write equations for **any** successive ionisation energy. The equation for the ***n*^th^ ionisation energy** is...

$$X^{(n-1)+}_{(g)} \rightarrow X^{n+}_{(g)} + e^{-}$$

Ionisation Energies

Successive Ionisation Energies Show *Shell Structure*

A **graph** of successive ionisation energies (like this one for sodium) provides evidence for the **shell structure** of atoms.

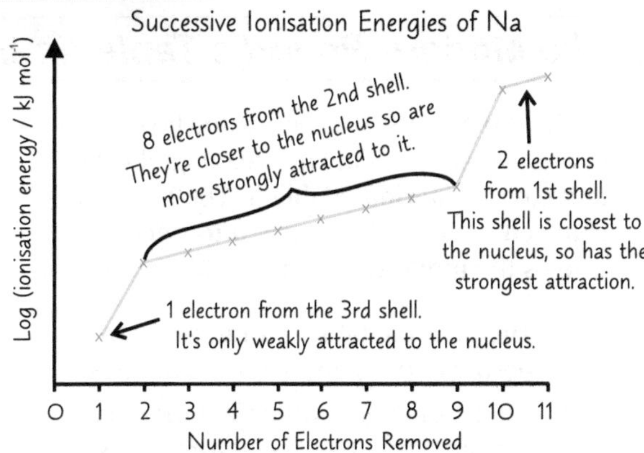

Successive Ionisation Energies of Na
Log (ionisation energy / kJ mol⁻¹)
8 electrons from the 2nd shell. They're closer to the nucleus so are more strongly attracted to it.
2 electrons from 1st shell. This shell is closest to the nucleus, so has the strongest attraction.
1 electron from the 3rd shell. It's only weakly attracted to the nucleus.
0 1 2 3 4 5 6 7 8 9 10 11
Number of Electrons Removed

- **Within each shell**, successive ionisation energies **increase**. This is because electrons are being removed from an **increasingly positive ion** — there's **less repulsion** amongst the remaining electrons, so they're **held more strongly** by the nucleus.
- The **big jumps** in ionisation energy happen when a new shell is broken into — an electron is being removed from a shell **closer** to the nucleus.

1) Graphs like this can tell you which **group** of the periodic table an element belongs to. Just count **how many electrons are removed** before the first big jump to find the group number.

E.g. In the graph for sodium, **one electron** is removed before the first big jump — sodium is in **group 1**.

2) These graphs can be used to predict the **electronic structure** of elements. Working from **right to left**, count how many points there are before each big jump to find how many electrons are in each shell, starting with the first.

E.g. The graph for sodium has **2 points** on the right-hand side, then a jump, then **8 points**, a jump, and **1 final point**. Sodium has **2 electrons** in the first shell, **8** in the second and **1** in the third.

Practice Questions

Q1 Define first ionisation energy and give an equation as an example.

Q2 Describe the three main factors that affect ionisation energies.

Q3 How is ionisation energy related to the force of attraction between an electron and the nucleus of an atom?

Exam Questions

Q1 This table shows the nuclear charge and first ionisation energy for four elements.

Element	B	C	N	0
Charge of Nucleus	+5	+6	+7	+8
1st Ionisation Energy (kJ mol^{-1})	801	1087	1402	1314

a) Write an equation, including state symbols, to represent the first ionisation energy of carbon (C). [2 marks]

b) In these four elements, what is the relationship between nuclear charge and first ionisation energy? [1 mark]

c) Explain why nuclear charge has this effect on first ionisation energy. [2 marks]

Q2 This graph shows the successive ionisation energies of a certain element.

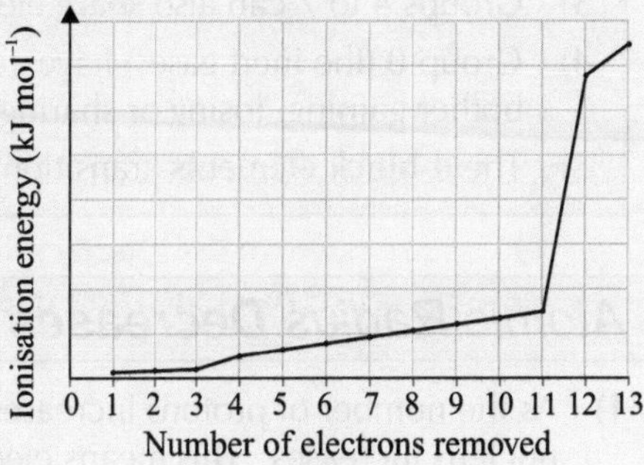

Ionisation energy (kJ mol⁻¹)
0 1 2 3 4 5 6 7 8 9 10 11 12 13
Number of electrons removed

a) To which group of the periodic table does this element belong? [1 mark]

b) Why does it takes more energy to remove each successive electron? [2 marks]

c) What causes the sudden increases in ionisation energy? [1 mark]

d) What is the total number of electron shells in this element? [1 mark]

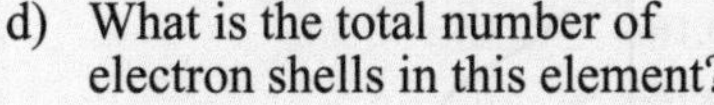

Shirt crumpled — ionise it...

When you're talking about ionisation energies in exams, always use the three main factors — shielding, nuclear charge and distance from nucleus. Recite the definition of the first ionisation energies to yourself until you can't take any more.

Periodicity

One last thing now in this Topic, and then you'll be onto the real juicy stuff. But first have a look at these pages about periodicity. Periodicity describes the trends of elements going across the Periodic Table.

*The **Modern Periodic Table** Arranges Elements by **Proton Number***

Dmitri Mendeleev was one of the first scientists to put the elements in any meaningful order to create the **periodic table** in 1869. It has **changed** a bit and been **added to** since then to give us the **modern** periodic table we use today:

	Grp 1	Grp 2											Grp 3	Grp 4	Grp 5	Grp 6	Grp 7	Grp 0
								1 H 1										4 He 2
2	7 Li 3	9 Be 4											11 B 5	12 C 6	14 N 7	16 O 8	19 F 9	20 Ne 10
3	23 Na 11	24 Mg 12											27 Al 13	28 Si 14	31 P 15	32 S 16	35.5 Cl 17	40 Ar 18
4	39 K 19	40 Ca 20	45 Sc 21	48 Ti 22	51 V 23	52 Cr 24	55 Mn 25	56 Fe 26	59 Co 27	59 Ni 28	63.5 Cu 29	65 Zn 30	70 Ga 31	73 Ge 32	75 As 33	79 Se 34	80 Br 35	84 Kr 36
5	86 Rb 37	88 Sr 38	89 Y 39	91 Zr 40	93 Nb 41	96 Mo 42	99 Tc 43	101 Ru 44	103 Rh 45	106 Pd 46	108 Ag 47	112 Cd 48	115 In 49	119 Sn 50	122 Sb 51	128 Te 52	127 I 53	131 Xe 54
6	133 Cs 55	137 Ba 56	139 La 57	179 Hf 72	181 Ta 73	184 W 74	186 Re 75	190 Os 76	192 Ir 77	195 Pt 78	197 Au 79	201 Hg 80	204 Tl 81	207 Pb 82	209 Bi 83	210 Po 84	210 At 85	222 Rn 86
7	223 Fr 87	226 Ra 88	227 Ac 89	261 Rf 104	262 Db 105	266 Sg 106	264 Bh 107	269 Hs 108	268 Mt 109	269 Ds 110	272 Rg 111	277 Cn 112	Uut 113	289 Fi 114	Uup 115	298 Lv 116	Uus 117	Uuo 118

140 Ce 58	141 Pr 59	144 Nd 60	145 Pm 61	150 Sm 62	152 Eu 63	157 Gd 64	159 Tb 65	163 Dy 66	165 Ho 67	167 Er 68	169 Tm 69	173 Yb 70	175 Lu 71
232 Th 90	231 Pa 91	238 U 92	237 Np 93	242 Pu 94	243 Am 95	247 Cm 96	245 Bk 97	251 Cf 98	254 Es 99	253 Fm 100	256 Md 101	254 No 102	257 Lr 103

f-block elements

1) The periodic table is arranged into **periods** (rows) and **groups** (columns).
2) All the elements **within a period** have the same number of **electron shells** (if you don't worry about the subshells). The elements of Period 1 (hydrogen and helium) both have 1 electron shell, the elements in Period 2 have 2 electron shells, and so on... This means there are **repeating trends** in the physical and chemical properties of the elements across each period (e.g. decreasing atomic radius). These trends are known as **periodicity**.
3) All the elements **within a group** have the same number of **electrons in their outer shell**. This means they have **similar chemical properties**. The group number tells you the number of electrons in the outer shell, e.g. Group 1 elements have 1 electron in their outer shell, Group 4 elements have 4 electrons, etc... (This isn't the case for Group 0 elements — they all have 8 electrons in their outer shell, except for helium, which has 2.)

*Electronic Configuration Decides the **Chemical Properties** of an Element*

The number of **outer shell electrons** decides the chemical properties of an element.

1) The **s-block** elements (Groups 1 and 2) have 1 or 2 outer shell electrons. These are easily **lost** to form positive ions with an **inert gas configuration**.
   E.g. Na: $1s^2\ 2s^2\ 2p^6\ 3s^1 \rightarrow Na^+: 1s^2\ 2s^2\ 2p^6$ (the electronic configuration of neon).
2) The elements in Groups 5, 6 and 7 (in the **p-block**) can **gain** 1, 2 or 3 electrons to form negative ions with an **inert gas configuration**.
   E.g. O: $1s^2\ 2s^2\ 2p^4 \rightarrow O^{2-}: 1s^2\ 2s^2\ 2p^6$.

Subshells and the Periodic Table

s	d	p
1s		1s
2s		2p
3s		3p
4s	3d	4p
5s	4d	5p
6s	5d	6p
7s		

3) Groups 4 to 7 can also **share** electrons when they form covalent bonds.
4) Group 0 (the inert gases) have **completely filled** s and p subshells and don't need to bother gaining, losing or sharing electrons — their full subshells make them **inert**.
5) The **d-block elements** (transition metals) tend to **lose** s and d electrons to form positive ions.

*Atomic Radius **Decreases** across a Period*

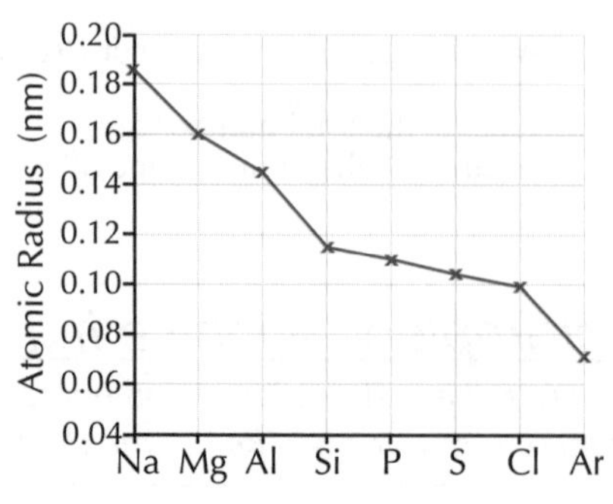

1) As the number of protons increases, the **positive charge** of the nucleus increases. This means electrons are **pulled closer** to the nucleus, making the atomic radius smaller.
2) The extra electrons that the elements gain across a period are added to the **outer energy level** so they don't really provide any extra shielding effect (shielding is mainly provided by the electrons in the inner shells).

Periodicity

Ionisation Energy Increases Across a Period

The graph below shows the first ionisation energies of the elements in **Period 2 and Period 3**.

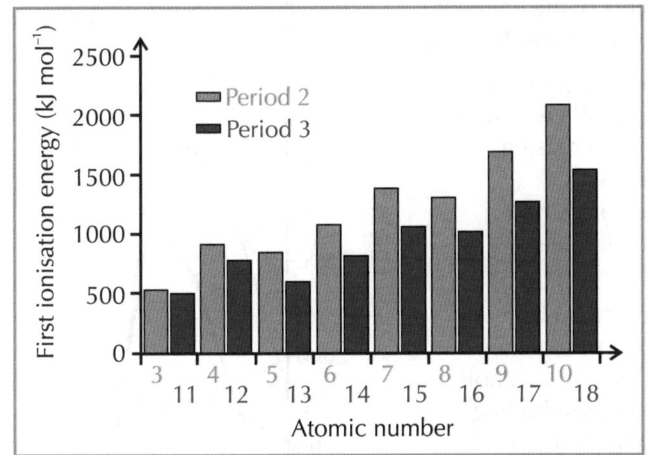

1) As you **move across** a period, the general trend is for the ionisation energies to **increase** — i.e. it gets harder to remove the outer electrons.
2) This can be explained because the number of protons is increasing, which means a stronger **nuclear attraction**.
3) All the extra electrons are at **roughly the same** energy level, even if the outer electrons are in different orbital types.
4) This means there's generally little **extra shielding** effect or **extra distance** to lessen the attraction from the nucleus.
5) But, there are **small drops** between Groups 2 and 3, and 5 and 6. Tell me more, I hear you cry. Well, alright then...

The Drop between Groups 2 and 3 Shows Subshell Structure

Generally, it requires **more energy** to remove an electron from a **higher energy subshell** than a **lower energy subshell** (see page 10 for a diagram showing the relative energies of subshells 1s to 4f).

Example: Mg $1s^2 2s^2 2p^6 3s^2$ 1st ionisation energy = 738 kJ mol^{-1}
Al $1s^2 2s^2 2p^6 3s^2 3p^1$ 1st ionisation energy = 578 kJ mol^{-1}

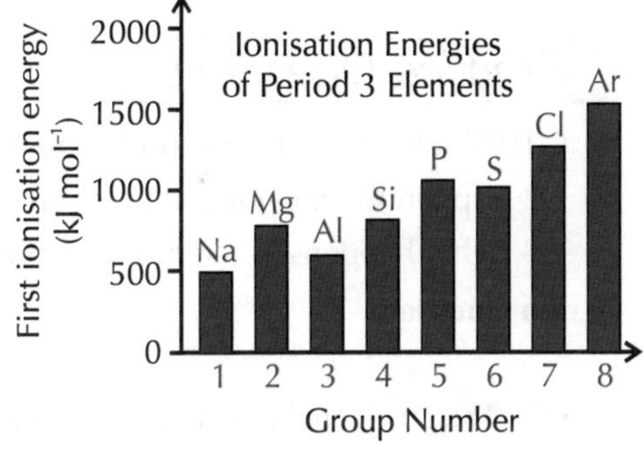

1) Aluminium's outer electron is in a **3p orbital** rather than a 3s. The 3p orbital has a **slightly higher** energy than the 3s orbital, so the electron is, on average, to be found **further** from the nucleus.
2) The 3p orbital has additional shielding provided by the **$3s^2$ electrons**.
3) Both these factors together are strong enough to **override** the effect of the increased nuclear charge, resulting in the ionisation energy **dropping** slightly.
4) This pattern in ionisation energies provides **evidence** for the theory of electron subshells.

The Drop between Groups 5 and 6 is due to Electron Repulsion

In general, elements with **singly filled** or **full** subshells are more **stable** than those with **partially filled subshells**, so have **higher** first ionisation energies.

Example: P $1s^2 2s^2 2p^6 3s^2\ 3p^3$ 1st ionisation energy = 1012 kJ mol^{-1}
S $1s^2 2s^2 2p^6 3s^2\ 3p^4$ 1st ionisation energy = 1000 kJ mol^{-1}

1) The **shielding is identical** in the phosphorus and sulfur atoms, and the electron is being removed from an identical orbital.
2) In phosphorus's case, the electron is being removed from a **singly-occupied** orbital. But in sulfur, the **electron** is being **removed** from an orbital containing two electrons.

This is the 'electrons-in-boxes' notation that you saw on page 10.

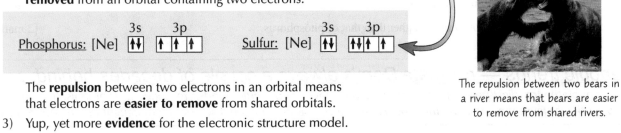

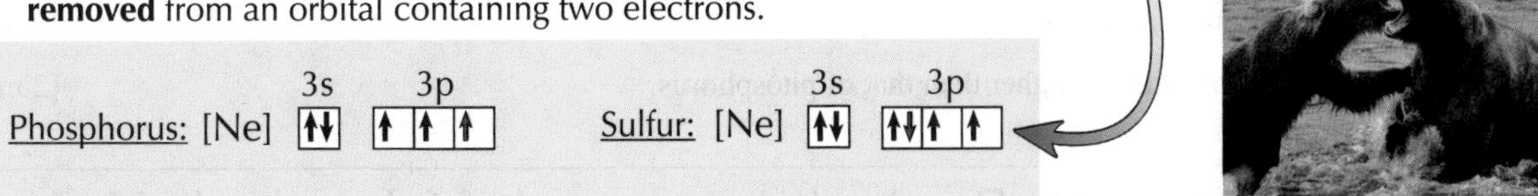

The repulsion between two bears in a river means that bears are easier to remove from shared rivers.

The **repulsion** between two electrons in an orbital means that electrons are **easier to remove** from shared orbitals.

3) Yup, yet more **evidence** for the electronic structure model.

Periodicity

Bond Strength Affects Melting and Boiling Points Across a Period

As you go across a period, the **type** of bond formed between the atoms of an element **changes**. This affects the **melting** and **boiling points** of the element. The graph on the right shows the trend in boiling points across **Periods 2 and 3**.

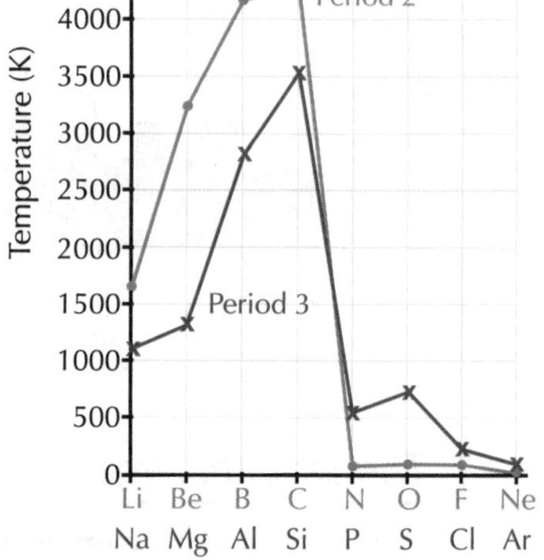

1) For the **metals** (Li, Be, Na, Mg and Al), melting and boiling points **increase** across the period because the **metallic bonds** (see page 27) get stronger. The bonds get stronger because the metal ions have an increasing number of **delocalised electrons** and a decreasing **radius** (i.e. the metal ions have a higher charge density — see page 19). This means there's a stronger attraction between the metal ions and delocalised electrons, so stronger metallic bonding.
2) The elements with **giant covalent lattice** structures (C and Si) have **strong covalent bonds** (see page 26) linking all their atoms together. **A lot** of energy is needed to break all of these bonds. So, for example, carbon (as graphite or diamond) and silicon have the highest boiling points in their periods. (The carbon data in the graph to the right is for graphite — diamond has an even higher boiling point.)
3) Next come the **simple molecular structures** (N_2, O_2 and F_2, P_4, S_8 and Cl_2). Their melting points depend upon the strength of the London forces (see page 30) between their molecules. London forces are weak and easily overcome, so these elements have low melting and boiling points.
4) More electrons in a molecule mean stronger London forces (see page 30). For example, in Period 3 a molecule of sulfur (S_8) has the most electrons, so it's got **higher** melting and boiling points than phosphorus and chlorine.
5) The noble gases (Ne and Ar) have the **lowest** melting and boiling points in their periods because they exist as **individual atoms** (they're monatomic) resulting in **very weak** London forces.

Practice Questions

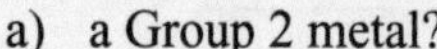

Q1 Which elements in Period 3 are found in the s-block of the periodic table?

Q2 Explain the meaning of the term 'periodicity'.

Q3 What happens to the first ionisation energy as you move across a period?

Exam Questions

Q1 The graph on the right shows first ionisation energy plotted against atomic number. Which of the labelled points on the graph shows the first ionisation energy of:

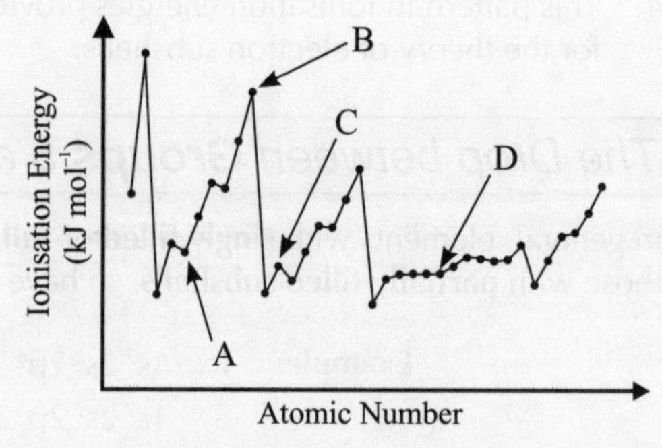

a) a Group 2 metal? [1 mark]

b) an element with a full outer electron shell? [1 mark]

c) an element in Period 3? [1 mark]

Q2 This table shows the melting points for the Period 3 elements.

Element	Na	Mg	Al	Si	P	S	Cl	Ar
Melting point / K	371	923	933	1687	317	392	172	84

In terms of structure and bonding explain why:

a) silicon has a high melting point. [2 marks]

b) the melting point of sulfur is higher than that of phosphorus. [2 marks]

Periodic trends — my mate Dom's always a couple of decades behind...

I may not be the trendiest person in the world, but I do love my periodic trends. Yes indeed. That ionisation energy one is my particular favourite. And whether you like it or not, you better learn it so you're not caught out in your exams...

Ionic Bonding

When different elements join or bond together, you get a compound. There are two main types of bonding in compounds — ionic and covalent. You need to make sure you've got them both totally sussed. Let's start with ionic.

Ions are Positively or Negatively Charged Atoms (or Groups of Atoms)

1) Ions are formed when electrons are **transferred** from one atom to another. They may be positively charged (**cations**) or negatively charged (**anions**).
2) The simplest ions are single atoms which have either lost or gained 1, 2 or 3 electrons so that they've got a **full outer shell**. Here are some examples of ions:

A sodium atom (Na) **loses** 1 electron to form a sodium ion (Na^+)	$Na \rightarrow Na^+ + e^-$
A magnesium atom (Mg) **loses** 2 electrons to form a magnesium ion (Mg^{2+})	$Mg \rightarrow Mg^{2+} + 2e^-$
A chlorine atom (Cl) **gains** 1 electron to form a chloride ion (Cl^-)	$Cl + e^- \rightarrow Cl^-$
An oxygen atom (O) **gains** 2 electrons to form an oxide ion (O^{2-})	$O + 2e^- \rightarrow O^{2-}$

3) You **don't** have to remember what ion **each element** forms — for a lot of them you just look at the periodic table. Elements in the same **group** all have the same number of **outer electrons**, so they have to **lose or gain** the same number to get the full outer shell. And this means that they form ions with the **same charges**. E.g. Mg and Sr are both in **Group 2**. They both lose **2 electrons** to form 2+ ions (Mg^{2+} and Sr^{2+}).
4) Generally the charge on a **metal ion** is equal to its **group number**. The charge on a **non-metal ion** is equal to its **group number minus eight**.

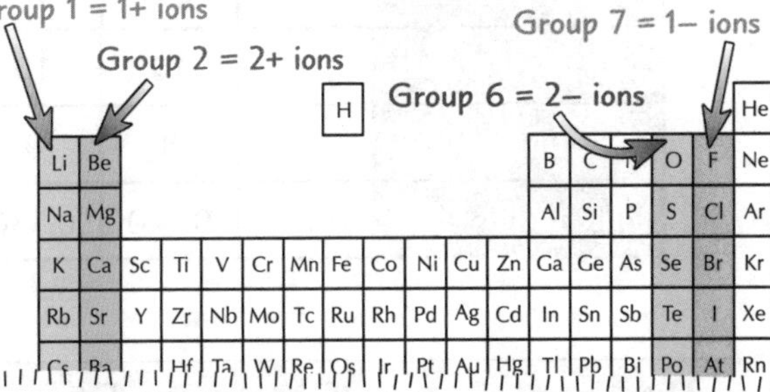
Group 1 = 1+ ions
Group 2 = 2+ ions
Group 6 = 2– ions
Group 7 = 1– ions
The Group numbers are the bold ones at the top of your periodic table.

Ionic Bonding is when Ions are Stuck Together by Electrostatic Attraction

Electrostatic attraction holds positive and negative ions together — it's **very** strong. When ions are held together like this, it's called **ionic bonding**. Here comes a definition for you to learn...

> An **ionic bond** is the strong **electrostatic attraction** between two **oppositely charged** ions.

When oppositely charged ions form an **ionic bond**, you get an **ionic compound**. The **formula** of an ionic compound tells you what **ions** that compound has in it.

Example: NaCl is made up of Na^+ and Cl^- ions in a 1 : 1 ratio.
$CaCl_2$ is made up of Ca^{2+} and Cl^- ions in a 1 : 2 ratio.

The positive charges in an ionic compound balance the negative charges exactly — so the total overall charge is zero. This is a dead handy way of checking the formula.

Ionic Charges and Ionic Radii Affect Ionic Bonding

Ionic bonds are all to do with the **attraction** between **oppositely charged ions**. So, the stronger the **electrostatic attraction**, the stronger the ionic bond. There are **two** things that affect the strength of an ionic bond:

IONIC CHARGES

In general, the **greater** the **charge** on an ion, the **stronger** the **ionic bond** and therefore, the higher the melting/boiling point.

E.g. the melting point of **NaF**, (which is made up of **singly charged** Na^+ and F^- ions) is **993 °C**, while **CaO** (which is made up of Ca^{2+} and O^{2-} ions) has a much higher melting point of **2572 °C**.

Generally, ions with a high charge density (they have a large charge spread over a small area) form stronger ionic bonds than ions with a low charge density (they have a small charge spread out over a large area).

IONIC RADII

Smaller ions can **pack closer** together than larger ions. Electrostatic attraction gets weaker with distance, so **small, closely packed ions** have **stronger** ionic bonding than larger ions, which sit further apart. Therefore, ionic compounds with small, closely packed ions have higher melting and boiling points than ionic compounds made of large ions.

E.g. the **ionic radius** of Cs^+ is **greater** than that of Na^+. NaF has a melting point of **993 °C**, whereas CsF has a melting point of **683 °C** since the Na^+ and F^- ions can pack closer together in NaF than the Cs^+ and F^- ions in CsF.

Ionic Bonding

The Size of an Ion Depends on its Electron Shells and Atomic Number

There are two trends in ionic radii you need to know about.

1) The **ionic radius increases** as you go **down a group**.

Ion	Li^+	Na^+	K^+	Rb^+
Ionic radius (nm)	0.060	0.095	0.133	0.148

All these Group 1 ions have the same charge.

As you go down the group the ionic radius increases as the atomic number increases.

This is because extra electron shells are added.

2) **Isoelectronic ions** are ions of different atoms with the **same number of electrons**. The **ionic radius** of a set of **isoelectronic ions decreases** as the **atomic number increases**.

See page 4 for how to work out the subatomic particles in an ion.

Ion	N^{3-}	O^{2-}	F^-	Na^+	Mg^{2+}	Al^{3+}
No. of electrons	10	10	10	10	10	10
No. of protons	7	8	9	11	12	13
Ionic radius (nm)	0.171	0.140	0.136	0.095	0.065	0.050

As you go through this series of ions the number of **electrons stays the same**, but the number of **protons increases**. This means that the electrons are **attracted** to the **nucleus** more strongly, pulling them in a little, so the **ionic radius decreases.**

Dot-and-Cross Diagrams Show Where the Electrons in a Bond Come From

Dot-and-cross diagrams show the **arrangement** of electrons in an atom or ion. Each electron is represented by a dot or a cross. They can also show which **atom** the electrons in a **bond** originally came from.

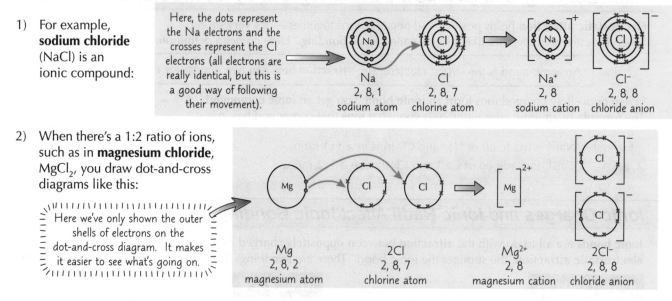

1) For example, **sodium chloride** (NaCl) is an ionic compound:

Here, the dots represent the Na electrons and the crosses represent the Cl electrons (all electrons are really identical, but this is a good way of following their movement).

Na
2, 8, 1
sodium atom

Cl
2, 8, 7
chlorine atom

Na^+
2, 8
sodium cation

Cl^-
2, 8, 8
chloride anion

2) When there's a 1:2 ratio of ions, such as in **magnesium chloride**, $MgCl_2$, you draw dot-and-cross diagrams like this:

Here we've only shown the outer shells of electrons on the dot-and-cross diagram. It makes it easier to see what's going on.

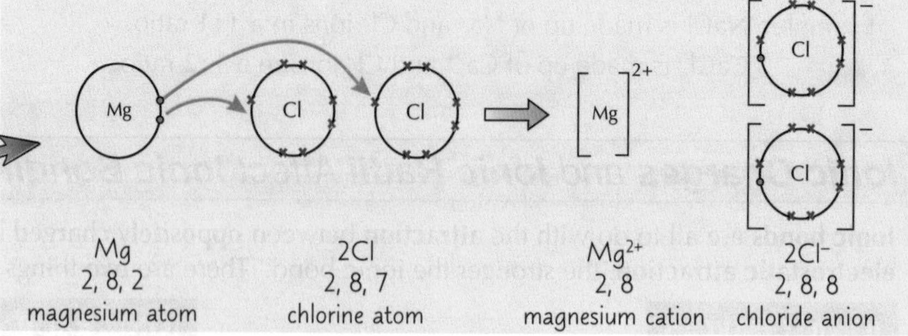

Ionic Compounds Form Giant Ionic Lattice Structures

1) Ionic crystals (e.g. crystals of common salt, such as NaCl) are giant lattices of ions. A lattice is just a regular structure. The structure's called '**giant**' because it's made up of the same basic unit repeated over and over again.
2) It forms because each ion is electrostatically attracted in **all directions** to ions of the **opposite** charge.
3) In **sodium chloride**, the Na^+ and Cl^- ions are packed together alternately in a **lattice**.
4) The sodium chloride lattice is **cube** shaped — different ionic compounds have different shaped structures, but they're all still giant lattices.

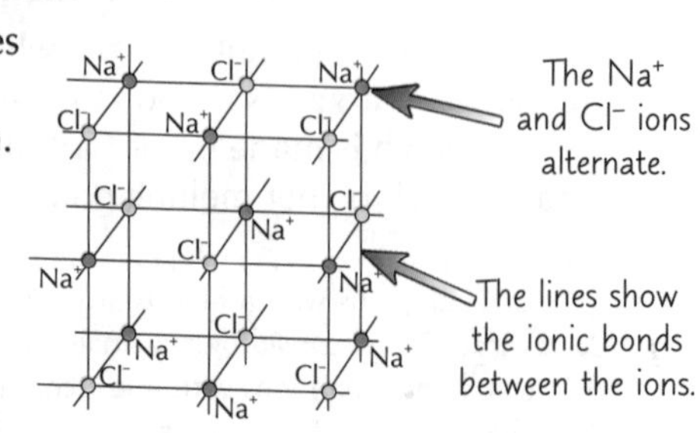

Ionic Bonding

The Theory of Ionic Bonding Fits the Evidence from Physical Properties

Scientists develop **models** of ionic bonding based on **experimental evidence** — they're an attempt to **explain observations** about how ionic compounds behave. Some evidence is provided by the **physical properties** of ionic compounds:

1) They have **high melting points** — this tells you that the ions are held together by a **strong attraction**. Positive and negative ions are strongly attracted, so the **model** fits the **evidence**.
2) They are often **soluble** in **water** but **not** in **non-polar solvents** — this tells you that the particles are **charged**. The ions are **pulled apart** by **polar molecules** like water, but **not** by **non-polar** molecules. Again, the **model** of ionic structures fits this evidence.
3) Ionic compounds **don't conduct electricity** when they're **solid** — but they **do** when they're **molten or dissolved**. This supports the idea that there are ions, which are **fixed** in position by strong ionic bonds in a solid, but are **free to move** (and carry a charge) as a liquid or in a solution.
4) Ionic compounds can't be **shaped** — for example, if you tried to pull layers of NaCl over each other, you'd get negative chlorine ions directly over other negative chlorine ions (and positive sodium ions directly over each other). The **repulsion** between these ions would be very **strong**, so ionic compounds are **brittle** (they **break** when they're **stretched** or **hammered**). This supports the lattice model.

The Migration of Ions is Evidence for the Presence of Charged Particles

- When you electrolyse a **green** solution of copper(II) chromate(VI) on a piece of wet filter paper, the filter paper turns **blue** at the **cathode** (the negative electrode) and **yellow** at the **anode** (the positive electrode).
- Copper(II) ions are **blue** in solution and chromate(VI) ions are **yellow**. Copper(II) chromate(VI) solution is **green** because it contains both ions.
- When you pass a current through the solution, the **positive** ions move to the **cathode** and the **negative** ions move to the **anode**.

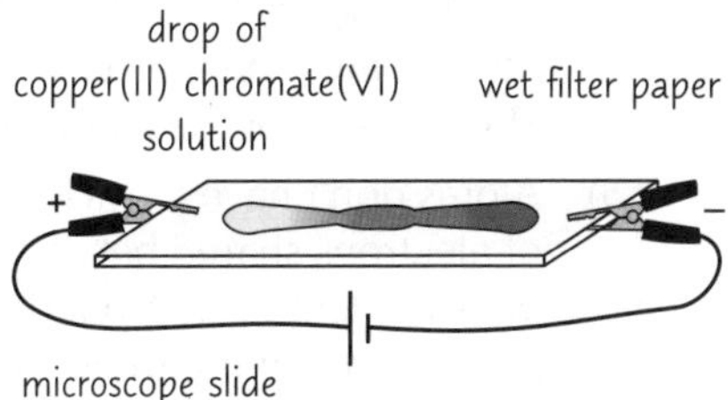

Practice Questions

Q1 What is an ionic bond?

Q2 What two factors affect the strength of ionic bonds?

Q3 Why do many ionic compounds dissolve in water?

Exam Questions

Q1 a) What type of structure does sodium chloride have? [1 mark]

b) Would you expect sodium chloride to have a high or a low melting point? Explain your answer. [2 marks]

c) How would you expect the melting point of sodium bromide (NaBr) to compare with sodium chloride? Explain your answer. [3 marks]

Q2 Calcium oxide is an ionic compound with ionic formula CaO.

a) Draw a dot-and-cross diagram to show the formation of a bond and subsequent bonding in calcium oxide. Show the outer electrons only. [2 marks]

b) Solid calcium oxide does not conduct electricity, but molten calcium oxide does. Explain this with reference to ionic bonding. [3 marks]

Q3 In terms of electron transfer, what happens when sodium reacts with fluorine to form sodium fluoride? [3 marks]

Q4 Which of the following sets of atoms and ions are isoelectronic?

A Ca^{2+}, K^+, Cl **B** Mg^+, Ne, Na^+ **C** Ar, S^{2-}, Sc^{3+} **D** Ti^{4+}, Cl^-, S [1 mark]

The name's Bond... Ionic Bond... Electrons taken, not shared...

It's all very well learning the properties of ionic compounds, but make sure you can also explain why they do what they do. And practise drawing dot-and-cross diagrams to show ionic bonding— they're easy marks in exams.

Covalent Bonding

And now for covalent bonding — this is when atoms share electrons with one another so they've all got full outer shells.

***Covalent Bonds** Hold Atoms in **Molecules** Together*

Molecules are formed when **2 or more** atoms bond together, and are held together by **covalent bonds**.
It doesn't matter if the atoms are the **same** or **different**.

Chlorine gas (Cl_2), carbon monoxide (CO), water (H_2O) and ethanol (C_2H_5OH) are all molecules.

In covalent bonding, two atoms **share** electrons, so they've **both** got full outer shells of electrons. A covalent bond is the **strong electrostatic attraction** between the two **positive nuclei** and the **shared electrons** in the bond.

E.g. two hydrogen atoms bond covalently to form a molecule of hydrogen.

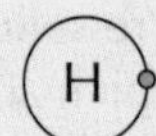

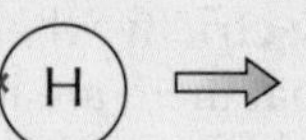

Covalent bonding usually happens between non-metals. Ionic bonding is usually between a metal and a non-metal.

*Make Sure You Can **Draw** the **Bonding** in These Molecules*

1) Dot-and-cross diagrams can be used to show how electrons behave in **covalent bonds**.
2) The bonded molecules are drawn with their outer atomic orbitals **overlapping**.
   The shared electrons that make up the covalent bond are drawn **within** the overlapping area.
3) To simplify the diagrams, not all the electrons in the molecules are shown — just the ones in the **outer shells**.
4) Most of the time the central atom ends up with **eight electrons** in its **outer shell**.
   This is good for the atom — it's a very **stable** arrangement.
5) Atoms don't have to stick with forming **single bonds** (when there's just **one** pair of electrons shared between two atoms). You can get atoms sharing multiple pairs of electrons. A bond containing **two** electron pairs is a **double bond**, a bond containing **three** electron pairs is a **triple bond** and so on...

The outer electrons in hydrogen are in the first electron shell, which only needs two electrons to be filled.

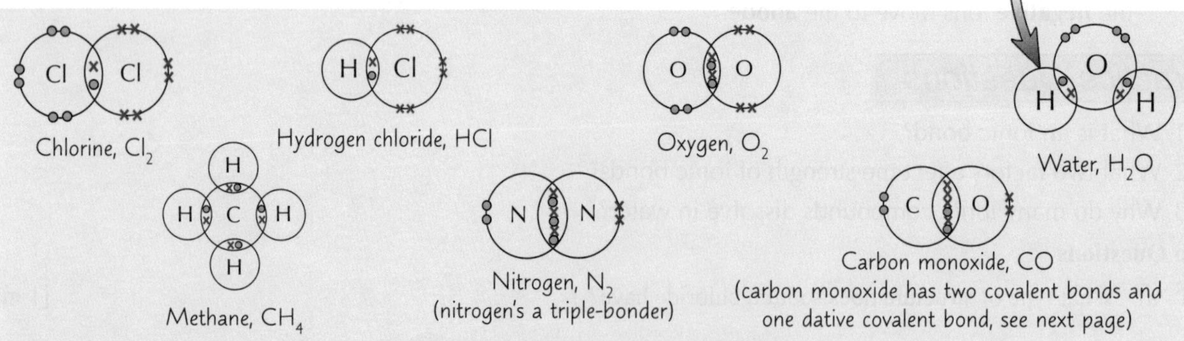

Chlorine, Cl_2

Hydrogen chloride, HCl

Oxygen, O_2

Water, H_2O

Methane, CH_4

Nitrogen, N_2 (nitrogen's a triple-bonder)

Carbon monoxide, CO (carbon monoxide has two covalent bonds and one dative covalent bond, see next page)

***Bond Enthalpy** is Related to the **Length** of a Bond*

1) In covalent molecules, the **positive nuclei** are attracted to the area of electron density between the two nuclei (where the shared electrons are). But there's also a repulsion. The two **positively charged nuclei repel** each other, as do the **electrons**. To maintain the covalent bond there has to be a **balance** between these forces.
2) The distance between the **two nuclei** is the distance where the **attractive** and **repulsive** forces balance each other. This distance is the **bond length**.
3) The **higher the electron density** between the nuclei (i.e. the more electrons in the bond), the **stronger** the attraction between the atoms, the higher the **bond enthalpy** and the **shorter** the bond length.
   It makes sense really. If there's more attraction, the nuclei are pulled **closer** together.

A C=C bond has a **greater bond enthalpy** and is **shorter** than a C–C bond. Four electrons are shared in C=C and only two in C–C, so the **electron density** between the two carbon atoms is greater and the **bond** is **shorter**.

C≡C has an even **higher** bond enthalpy and is **shorter** than C=C — six electrons are shared here.

Bond	C–C	C=C	C≡C
Average Bond Enthalpy (kJ mol^{-1})	+347	+612	+838
Bond length (nm)	0.154	0.134	0.120

Covalent Bonding

Dative Covalent Bonding is Where Both Electrons Come From One Atom

1) In the molecules on the last page, the atoms are acting in a bit of an "I'll lend you mine if you lend me yours" way — each atom puts an electron into the bond and, in return, they get use of the electron put in by the other atom.
2) But there's another kind of covalent bond as well — a **dative covalent** (or **coordinate**) bond. This is where one atom donates **both electrons** to a bond. You've already seen an example of this in CO.
3) The **ammonium ion** (NH_4^+) is formed by dative covalent (or coordinate) bonding. It forms when the nitrogen atom in an ammonia molecule **donates a pair of electrons** to a proton (H^+).

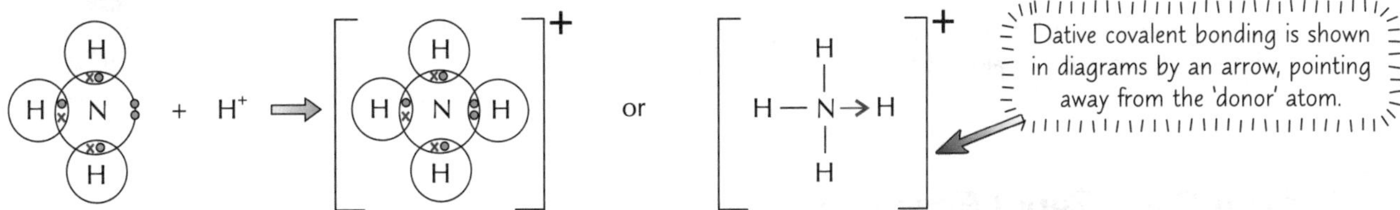

H
H N
+ H+
H
+
or
H — N → H
Dative covalent bonding is shown in diagrams by an arrow, pointing away from the 'donor' atom.

4) The ammonium ion can go on to form ionic bonds with other ions (see pages 19-21 for more on ionic bonding).

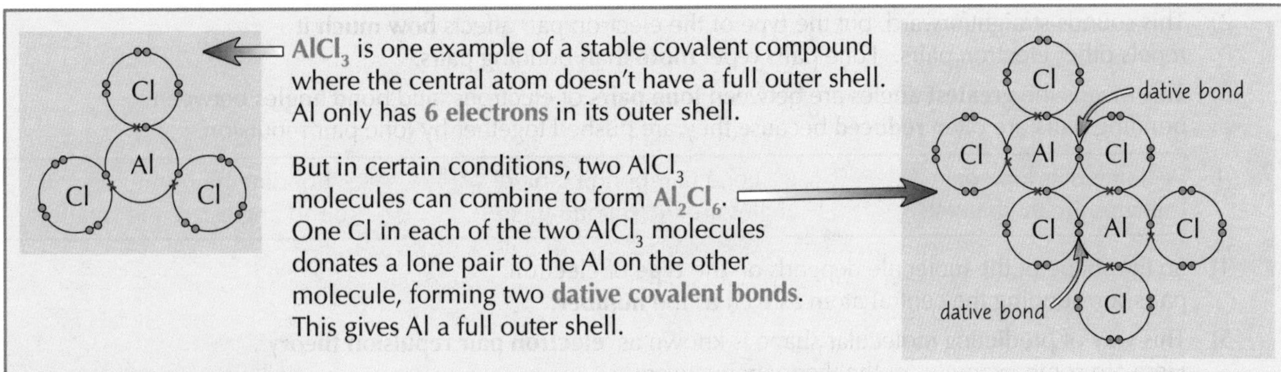

$AlCl_3$ is one example of a stable covalent compound where the central atom doesn't have a full outer shell. Al only has **6 electrons** in its outer shell.

But in certain conditions, two $AlCl_3$ molecules can combine to form **Al_2Cl_6**. One Cl in each of the two $AlCl_3$ molecules donates a lone pair to the Al on the other molecule, forming two **dative covalent bonds**. This gives Al a full outer shell.

Practice Questions

Q1 What happens during covalent bonding?

Q2 Put the following three bonds in order from shortest to longest: C–C, C=C, C≡C.

Q3 What is a dative covalent bond?

Q4 Draw a dot-and-cross diagram to show the arrangement of the outer electrons in a molecule of Al_2Cl_6.

Exam Questions

Q1 Draw a dot-and-cross diagram (showing outer shell electrons only) to represent the bonding in the molecule silicon hydride (SiH_4). [1 mark]

Q2 a) Draw a dot-and-cross diagram of the ammonia molecule (NH_3) showing the outer shell electrons only. [1 mark]

b) Draw a dot-and-cross diagram of the hydrogen chloride molecule (HCl) showing the outer shell electrons only. [1 mark]

c) Ammonia reacts with hydrogen chloride to form ammonium chloride. Draw a dot-and-cross diagram to show the bonding in ammonium chloride. [2 marks]

Q3 a) Would you expect an N–N single bond to be shorter or longer than an N=N bond? Explain your answer. [3 marks]

b) Draw a dot-and-cross diagram to show the bonding a molecule of nitrogen gas (N_2). [1 mark]

c) How would you expect the bond enthalpy of the bond(s) in a molecule of N_2 to compare to those in a)? Explain your answer. [3 marks]

Dative covalent bonds — an act of charity on an atomic scale...

More pretty diagrams to learn. If you're asked to draw dot-and-cross diagrams in the exam, don't panic. It's a bit of trial and error really. Just sort the outer electrons until every atom has a full outer shell (that's 8 electrons for most atoms, except hydrogen which only has 2 in its outer shell). Watch out for double, triple and dative covalent bonds too...

Shapes of Molecules

Chemistry would be heaps more simple if all molecules were flat. But they're not.

Molecular Shape Depends on Electron Pairs Around the Central Atom

Molecules and molecular ions come in loads of **different shapes**.
The shape depends on the **number** of pairs of electrons in the outer shell of the central atom.

In ammonia, the outermost shell of nitrogen has four pairs of electrons.

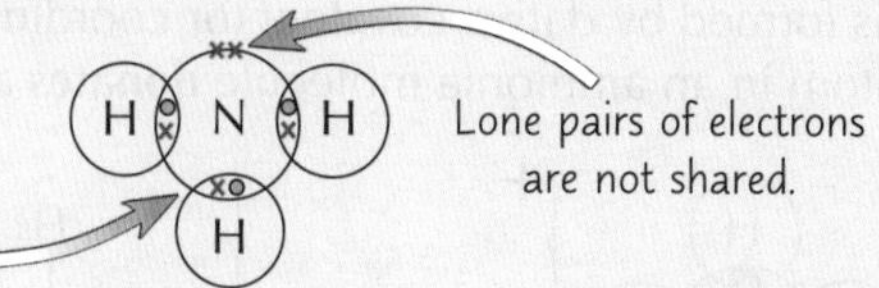

A lone pear.

Electron Pairs Repel Each Other

1) Electrons are all **negatively charged**, so electron pairs will **repel** each other as much as they can.
2) This sounds straightforward, but the **type** of the electron pair affects **how much** it repels other electron pairs. Lone pairs repel **more** than bonding pairs.
3) This means the **greatest** angles are between **lone pairs** of electrons, and bond angles between bonding pairs are often **reduced** because they are pushed together by lone pair repulsion.

Lone pair/lone pair angles are the biggest.	Lone pair/bonding pair angles are the second biggest.	Bonding pair/bonding pair bond angles are the smallest.

4) So the shape of the molecule depends on the **type** of electron pairs surrounding the central atom as well as the **number**.
5) This way of predicting molecular shape is known as '**electron pair repulsion theory**'. Here are some examples of the theory being used:

Learn the bond angles for these three examples.

The central atoms in these molecules all have **four pairs** of electrons in their outer shells, but they're all **different shapes**.

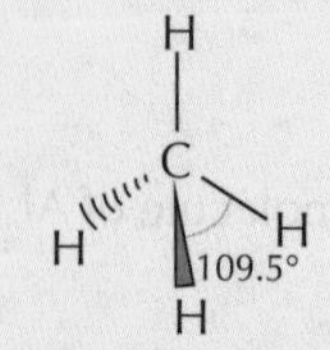

Methane — no lone pairs.
All the bond angles are 109.5°.

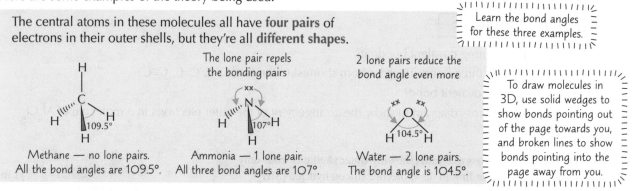

The lone pair repels the bonding pairs

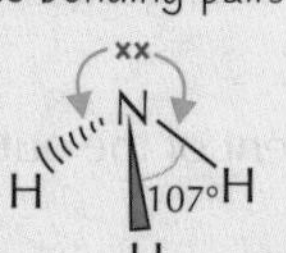

Ammonia — 1 lone pair.
All three bond angles are 107°.

2 lone pairs reduce the bond angle even more

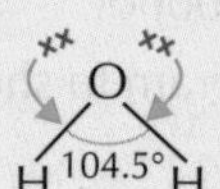

Water — 2 lone pairs.
The bond angle is 104.5°.

To draw molecules in 3D, use solid wedges to show bonds pointing out of the page towards you, and broken lines to show bonds pointing into the page away from you.

You Can Use Electron Pairs to Predict the Shapes of Molecules

To predict the shape of a molecule, you first have to know how many bonding and non-bonding electron pairs are on the central atom. Here's how:

1) Find the **central atom** (the one all the other atoms are bonded to).
2) Work out the number of **electrons** in the **outer shell** of the central atom. Use the periodic table to do this, or you could draw a dot-and-cross diagram.
3) The **molecular formula** tells you how many atoms the central atom is **bonded** to. From this you can work out how many electrons are **shared with** the central atom.
4) **Add up** the electrons and **divide by 2** to find the **number of electron pairs** on the central atom. If you have an ion remember to account for its **charge**.
5) **Compare** the number of **electron pairs** with the number of **bonds** to find the number of **lone pairs**.
6) You can then use the **number of electron pairs** and the number of **lone pairs** and **bonding centres** around the central atom to work out the **shape** of the molecule (see next page).

If there's a double bond, count it as two bonds.

Bonding centres are the atoms bonded to the central atom.

Shapes of Molecules

Practise **Drawing** these Molecules

Once you know how many electron pairs are on the central atom, you can use **electron pair repulsion theory** to work out the **shape** of the molecule. These are the common shapes that you need to be able to draw:

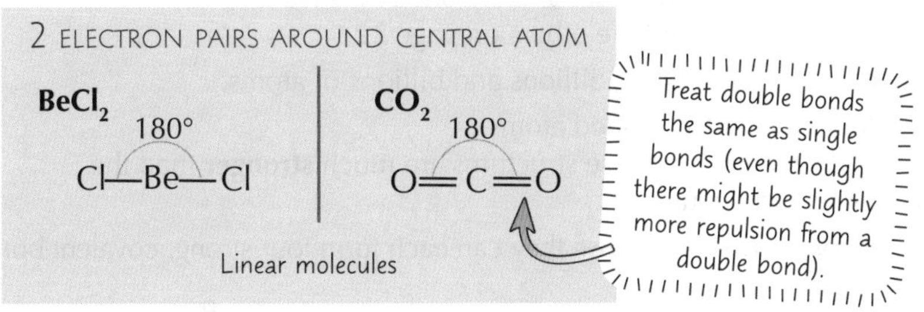

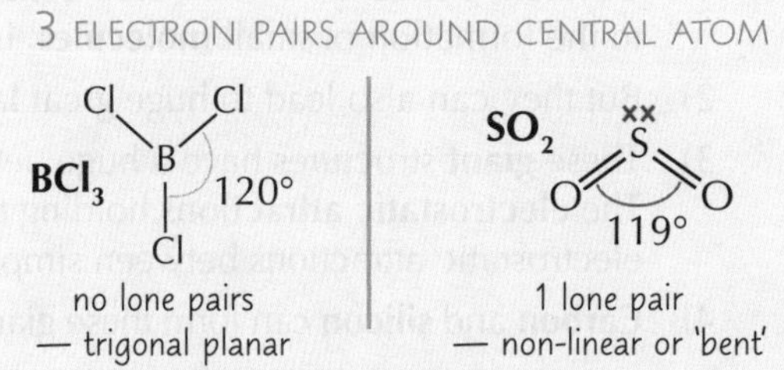

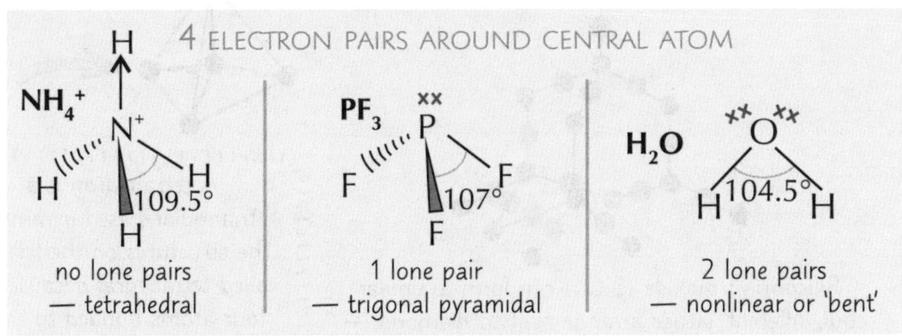

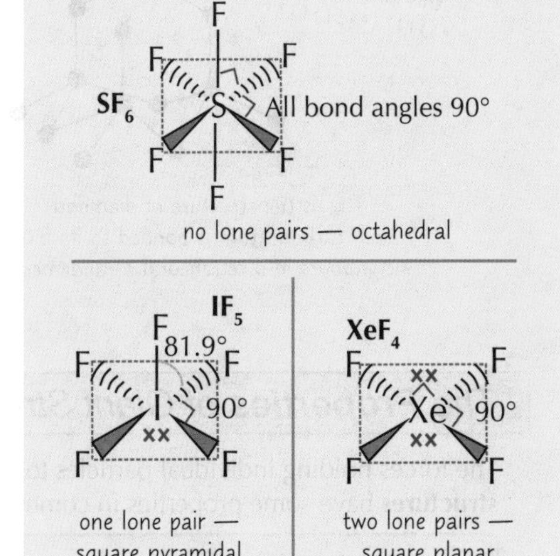

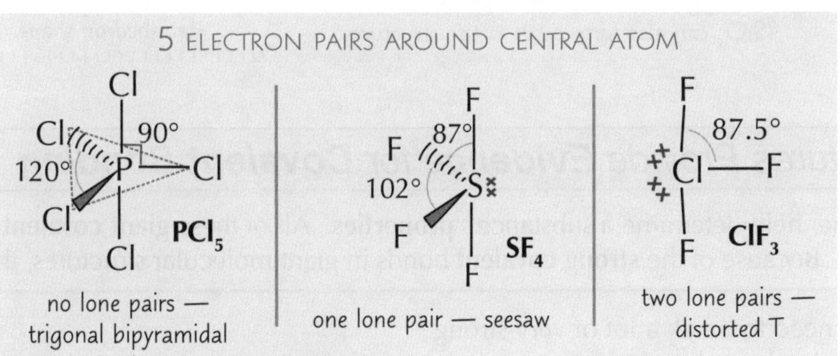

Practice Questions

Q1 What is a lone pair of electrons?

Q2 Write down the order of the strength of repulsion between different kinds of electron pair.

Q3 Explain why a water molecule is not linear.

Q4 Draw a tetrahedral molecule.

Exam Questions

Q1 a) Draw the shapes of the following molecules, showing the approximate values of the bond angles on the diagrams and naming each shape.

i) NCl_3 ii) BF_3 **[6 marks]**

b) Explain why the shapes of NCl_3 and BCl_3 are different. **[3 marks]**

Q2 The displayed formula of an organic compound is shown. Use electron pair repulsion theory to predict the shape and relevant bond angles of the bonds around atoms A, B and C. **[3 marks]**

O=C(H)–CH2–CH2–O–H (atom A: the C=O carbon; atom B: the middle carbon; atom C: the O of O–H)

atom A   atom B   atom C

These molecules ain't square...

In the exam, those evil examiners might try to throw you by asking you for the shape of an unfamiliar molecule. Don't panic — you can use the steps on page 24 to work out the shape of any covalent molecule. It often helps to draw a dot-and-cross diagram of the molecule you're working out the shape of — it'll help you see where all the electrons are.

Giant Covalent and Metallic Structures

Not all covalent structures are tiny molecules... some form vast structures (well... vast compared to simple molecules).

*Some **Covalently Bonded** Substances Have **Giant Structures***

1) **Covalent bonds** form when atoms **share** electrons with other atoms. Very often, this leads to the formation of small **molecules**, including CO_2, N_2 and the others on page 22.
2) But they can also lead to huge great **lattices** too — containing billions and billions of atoms.
3) These **giant** structures have a huge network of **covalently** bonded atoms. The **electrostatic attractions** holding the atoms together in these structures are much **stronger** than the electrostatic attractions between simple covalent molecules.
4) **Carbon** and **silicon** can form these giant networks. This is because they can each form four strong, covalent bonds.

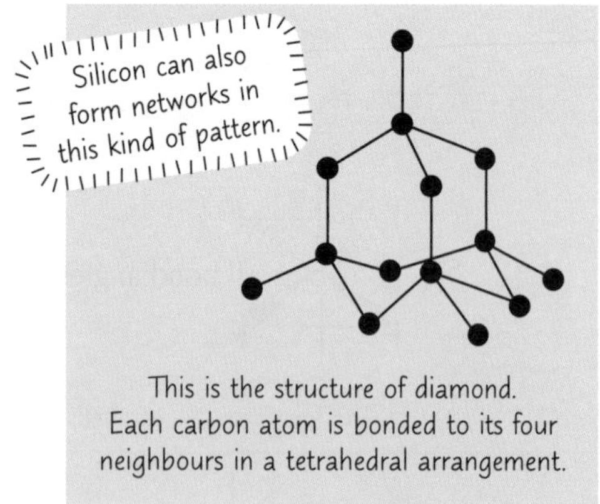

Silicon can also form networks in this kind of pattern.

This is the structure of diamond. Each carbon atom is bonded to its four neighbours in a tetrahedral arrangement.

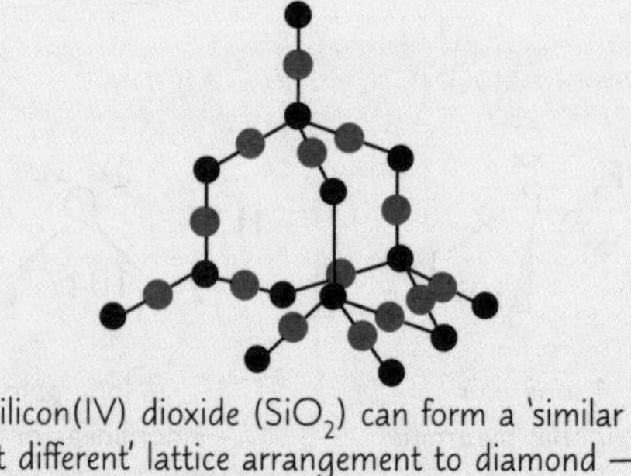

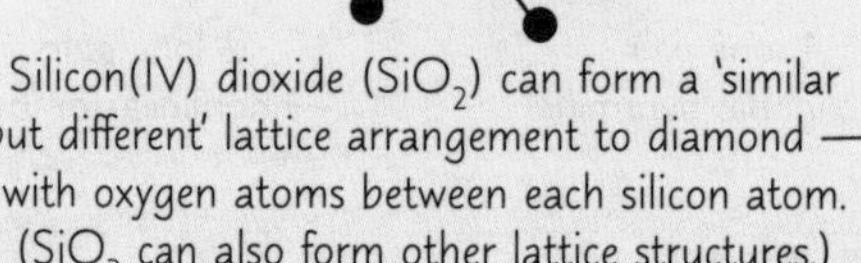

Silicon(IV) dioxide (SiO_2) can form a 'similar but different' lattice arrangement to diamond — with oxygen atoms between each silicon atom. (SiO_2 can also form other lattice structures.)

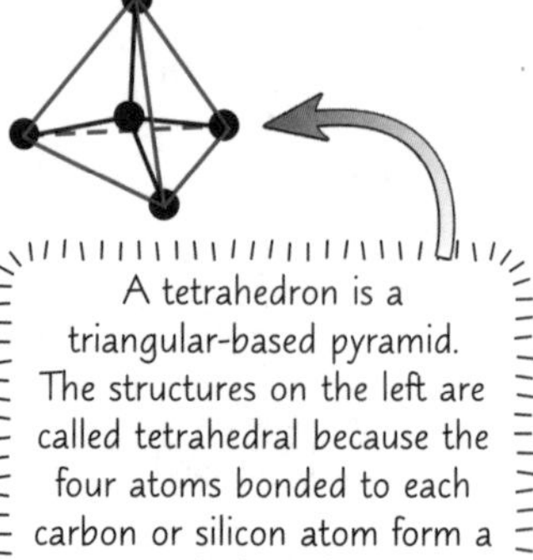

A tetrahedron is a triangular-based pyramid. The structures on the left are called tetrahedral because the four atoms bonded to each carbon or silicon atom form a tetrahedron shape.

*The **Properties** of Giant Structures Provide **Evidence** for **Covalent Bonding***

The forces holding individual particles together help determine a substance's **properties**. All of these **giant covalent structures** have some properties in common. Because of the **strong covalent** bonds in giant molecular structures, they:

1) Have very **high melting points** — you need to break a lot of very strong bonds before the substance melts, which takes a lot of energy.
2) Are often extremely **hard** — again, this is because of the very **strong bonds** all through the lattice arrangement.
3) Are **good thermal conductors** — since vibrations travel easily through the stiff lattices.
4) **Insoluble** — the covalent bonds mean atoms are more attracted to their neighbours in the lattice than to solvent molecules. The fact that they are all **insoluble** in polar solvents (like water) shows that they don't contain ions.
5) **Can't conduct electricity** — since there are (in most giant covalent lattice structures) **no charged ions** or **free electrons** (all the bonding electrons are held in localised covalent bonds).

Graphite** Can **Conduct Electricity

An **exception** to the "can't conduct electricity rule" above is **graphite** (a form of carbon). Carbon atoms form **sheets**, with each carbon atom sharing three of its **outer shell** electrons with three other carbon atoms. This leaves the fourth outer electron in each atom fairly **free** to move between the sheets, making graphite a **conductor**.

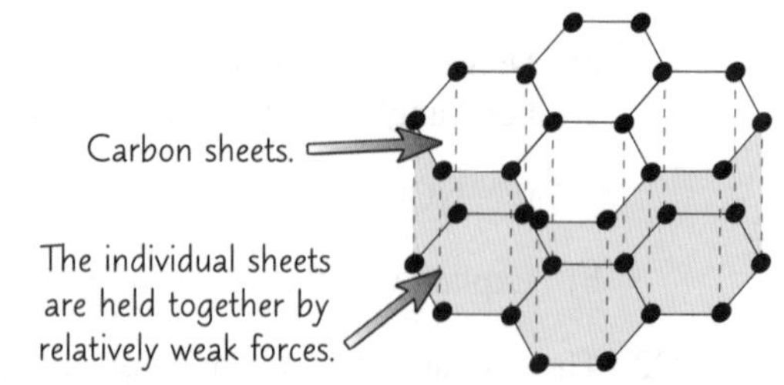

Carbon sheets.
The individual sheets are held together by relatively weak forces.

Graphene** is **One Layer** of **Graphite

Graphene is a **sheet** of carbon atoms joined together in **hexagons**. The sheet is just **one atom** thick, making it a **two-dimensional** compound.

Graphene's **structure** gives it some pretty **useful properties**. Like **graphite**, it can **conduct electricity** as the delocalised electrons are free to move along the sheet. It's also incredibly strong, transparent, and really light.

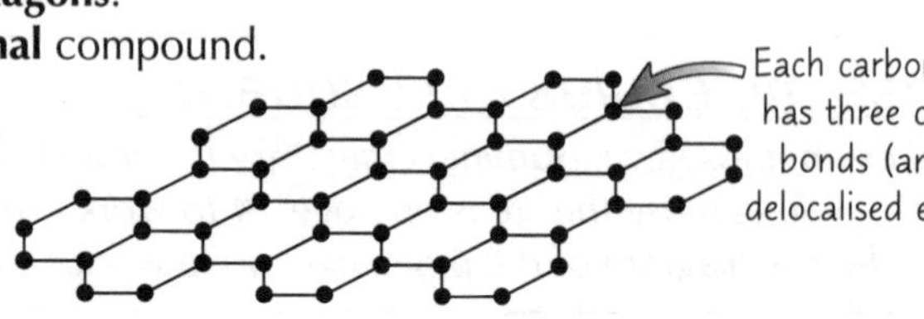

Giant Covalent and Metallic Structures

Metals have Giant Structures Too

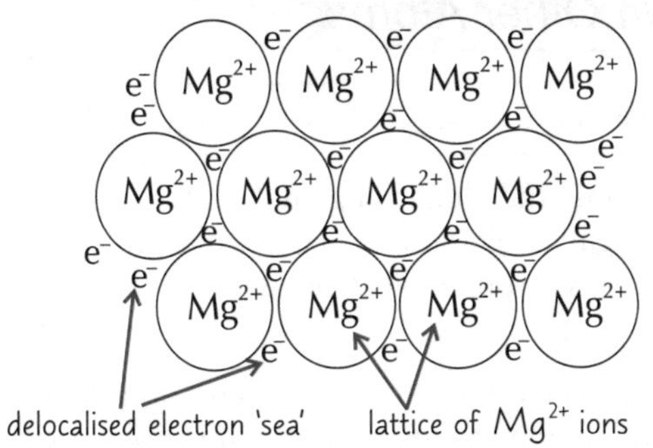

Metal elements exist as **giant metallic lattice structures.**

1) In metallic lattices, the electrons in the outermost shell of the metal atoms are **delocalised** — they're free to move. This leaves a **positive metal ion**, e.g. Na^+, Mg^{2+}, Al^{3+}.
2) The positive metal ions are **electrostatically attracted** to the delocalised negative electrons. They form a lattice of closely packed positive ions in a **sea** of delocalised electrons — this is **metallic bonding**.
3) The overall lattice structure is made up of **layers** of **positive** metal **ions, separated** by **layers** of **electrons.**

The **metallic bonding model** explains why metals do what they do —

1) The **melting points** of metals are generally **high** because of the strong metallic bonding, with the **number of delocalised electrons per atom** affecting the melting point. The **more** electrons there are, the **stronger** the bonding will be and the **higher** the melting point. Mg^{2+} has **two** delocalised electrons per atom, so it's got a **higher melting point** than Na^+, which only has **one**. The **size** of the metal ion and the **lattice structure** also affect the melting point.
2) As there are **no bonds** holding specific ions together, and the layers of positive metal ions are separated by layers of electrons, metals are **malleable** (can be **shaped**) and are **ductile** (can be drawn into a wire). The layers of metal ions can slide over each other without disrupting the attraction between the positive ions and electrons.
3) The delocalised electrons can pass **kinetic energy** to each other, making metals **good thermal conductors.**
4) Metals are **good electrical conductors** because the **delocalised electrons** are free to move and can carry a **charge.** Any **impurities** can dramatically **reduce** electrical conductivity by reducing the number of electrons that are free to move and carry charge — the electrons transfer to the impurities and form anions.
5) Metals are **insoluble**, except in **liquid metals**, because of the **strength** of the metallic bonds.

Practice Questions

Q1 Are the melting points of giant covalent lattices high or low? Explain why.

Q2 Why won't giant covalent structures dissolve?

Q3 Explain how the model of metallic bonding accounts for: i) the relatively high melting points of metals. ii) a metal's ability to conduct electricity.

Exam Questions

Q1 a) Explain what is meant by metallic bonding. Draw a diagram to illustrate your explanation. [2 marks]

b) Explain why calcium has a higher melting point than potassium. [1 mark]

Q2 Silicon dioxide is a covalent compound that melts at 1610 °C. Explain the high melting point of silicon in terms of its bonding. [2 marks]

Q3 Graphite is a giant covalent structure. However, unlike most giant covalent structures, it is able to conduct electricity. Explain why graphite is able to conduct electricity. [2 marks]

Q4 Electrical grade copper must be 99.99% pure. If sulfur and oxygen impurities react with the copper ions, its electrical conductivity is reduced. Use your knowledge of metallic and ionic bonding to explain this. [3 marks]

Q5 Carborundum (silicon carbide) has the formula SiC and is almost as hard as diamond.

a) What sort of structure would you expect carborundum to have as a solid? [1 mark]

b) Apart from hardness, give two other physical properties you would expect carborundum to have. [2 marks]

Tetrahedron — sounds like that monster from Greek mythology...

Close the book and write down a list of the typical properties of a giant covalent lattice — then look back at the page and see what you missed. Then do the same for the typical properties of giant metallic lattices. The fun never stops...

Electronegativity and Polarisation

I find electronegativity an incredibly attractive subject. It's all to do with how strongly an atom attracts electrons.

*Some Atoms **Attract** Bonding Electrons More than Other Atoms*

The ability of an atom to attract the bonding electrons in a covalent bond is called **electronegativity**.

1) Electronegativity is usually measured using the **Pauling scale**. The higher the electronegativity value, the more electronegative the element. **Fluorine** is the most electronegative element — it's given a value of **4.0** on the Pauling scale. Oxygen, chlorine and nitrogen are also very strongly electronegative.
2) The least electronegative elements have electronegativity values of around 0.7.
3) More electronegative elements have **higher nuclear charges** (there are more protons in the nucleus) and **smaller atomic radii**. Therefore, electronegativity **increases** across **periods** and **up** the **groups** (ignoring the noble gases).
4) There'll be a copy of the **periodic table** showing the **Pauling values** of different elements in your exam data book.

*Covalent Bonds may be **Polarised** by **Differences** in **Electronegativity***

1) In a covalent bond, the bonding electrons sit in orbitals between two nuclei. If both atoms have **similar** or **identical electronegativities**, the electrons will sit roughly **midway** between the two nuclei and the bond will be **non-polar**.
2) The covalent bonds in homonuclear, diatomic gases (e.g. H_2, Cl_2) are **non-polar** because the atoms have **equal** electronegativities and so the electrons are equally attracted to both nuclei. H–H
3) Some elements, like carbon and hydrogen, also have pretty **similar** electronegativities, so bonds between them are essentially **non-polar**.
4) If the bond is between two atoms with **different electronegativities**, the bonding electrons will be pulled towards the more electronegative atom. This causes the electrons to be spread unevenly, and so there will be a **charge** across the bond (each atom has a **partial charge** — one atom is slightly positive, and the other slightly negative). The bond is said to be **polar**.
5) In a **polar bond**, the difference in electronegativity between the two atoms causes a **dipole**. A dipole is a **difference in charge** between the two atoms caused by a shift in **electron density** in the bond.
6) So **remember** that the greater the **difference** in electronegativity, the greater the shift in electron density, and the **more polar** the bond.

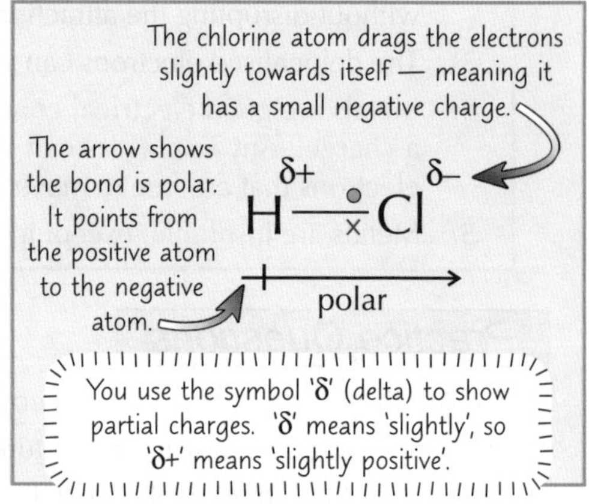

The chlorine atom drags the electrons slightly towards itself — meaning it has a small negative charge.
The arrow shows the bond is polar. It points from the positive atom to the negative atom.
δ+
δ–
H
Cl
polar
You use the symbol 'δ' (delta) to show partial charges. 'δ' means 'slightly', so 'δ+' means 'slightly positive'.

*Use the **Pauling Scale** to work out the **Percentage Ionic Character***

1) Only bonds between atoms of a **single** element, like diatomic gases, can be **purely covalent**. This is because the **electronegativity difference** between the atoms is **zero** and so the bonding electrons are arranged completely **evenly** within the bond. At the same time, very few compounds are completely ionic.
2) Really, most compounds come somewhere **in between** the two extremes — meaning they've often got ionic **and** covalent properties.
3) You can use electronegativity to **predict** what type of bonding will occur between two atoms. The higher the difference in electronegativity, the more ionic in character the bonding becomes.
4) In your data book, you'll be given a periodic table of all the Pauling values of the elements, and also see a table which tells you **how ionic** a bond is, given the electronegativity difference between the atoms. A copy is shown below:

Electronegativity difference	0.1	0.3	0.5	0.7	1.0	1.3	1.5	1.7	2.0	2.5	3.0
% ionic character	0.5	2	6	12	22	34	43	51	63	79	89

Example: Predict the % ionic character of a C–Cl bond, given that the Pauling electronegativity values of carbon and chlorine are C = 2.5 and Cl = 3.0.

The difference between the electronegativities of chlorine and carbon is:

3.0 – 2.5 = 0.5

So the bond will have a percentage ionic character of about **6%**.

Bonds are polar if the difference in electronegativity values is <u>more</u> than about 0.4.

Electronegativity and Polarisat

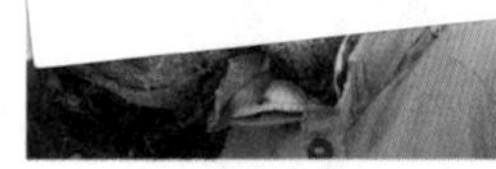

Polar Bonds **Don't** Always Make **Polar Molecules**

Whether a molecule is **polar** or not depends on its **shape** and the **polarity** of its bonds. A **polar molecule** has an **overall dipole**, which is just a dipole caused by the presence of a **permanent charge** across the molecule.

Permanent polar bonding

1) In a simple molecule, such as **hydrogen chloride**, the polar bond gives the whole molecule a permanent dipole — it's a **polar molecule**.

$\overset{\delta+}{H}$—$\overset{\delta-}{Cl}$ (polar)

You may see molecules with an overall dipole referred to as having 'overall polarity'. They're both just ways of saying the molecule is polar.

2) A more complicated molecule may have **several polar bonds**. If the polar bonds are arranged so they point in opposite directions, they'll **cancel each other out** — the molecule is **non-polar** overall.

No dipole overall.

$\overset{\delta-}{O}=\overset{\delta+}{C}=\overset{\delta-}{O}$

3) If the polar bonds all point in roughly the **same direction**, then the molecule will be **polar**.

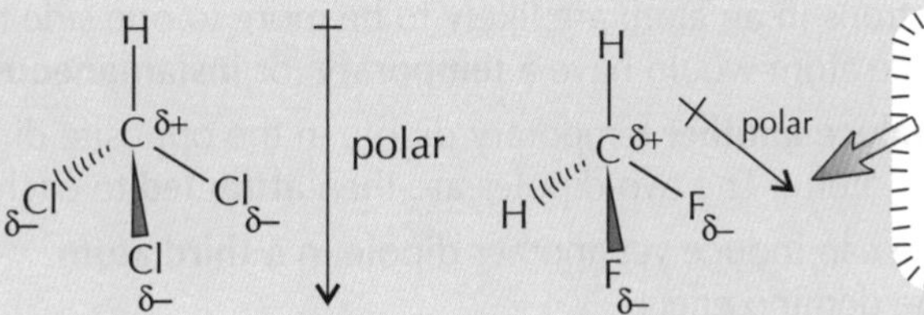

Be careful with examples like this — the tetrahedral shape means the two dipoles don't cancel out, so the molecule is polar.

Practice Questions

Q1 What scale is electronegativity measured on?

Q2 What is the most electronegative element?

Q3 What is a dipole?

Q4 Why isn't CO_2 a polar molecule, even though it has polar bonds?

Exam Questions

Q1 Many covalent molecules have a permanent dipole, due to differences in electronegativities.

a) Define the term electronegativity. [1 mark]

b) What are the trends in electronegativity as you go across a period and down a group in the periodic table? [1 mark]

c) Which of the following molecules is polar?

A H_2O **B** Br_2 **C** CCl_4 **D** SF_6 [1 mark]

Q2 a) Draw diagrams to show the shape of the covalently bonded molecules below. Mark any partial charges on your diagrams.

i) Boron trichloride (BCl_3) [2 marks]

ii) Dichloromethane (CH_2Cl_2) [2 marks]

b) Explain whether or not the molecules in part a) have an overall dipole. [2 marks]

I got my tongue stuck on an ice cube last week — it was a polar bond...

It's important to remember that just because a molecule has polar bonds, doesn't mean it will have a permanent dipole — you have to look carefully at the shape first to see if the polar bonds will cancel each other out or not. So if you're feeling a bit hazy on how to work out the shape of a molecule, have a read of pages 24-25, and all will be revealed.

Intermolecular Forces

Intermolecular forces hold molecules together. They're pretty important, cos we'd all be gassy clouds without them.

Intermolecular Forces are ***Very Weak***

Intermolecular forces are forces **between** molecules. They're much **weaker** than covalent, ionic or metallic bonds. There are three types you need to know about:

You might see intermolecular forces called intermolecular bonds — don't worry, they're exactly the same thing.

1) **London forces (instantaneous dipole-induced dipole bonds).**
2) **Permanent dipole-permanent dipole bonds.**
3) **Hydrogen bonding** (this is the strongest type of intermolecular forces — see pages 32-33).

All *Atoms and Molecules Form* ***London Forces***

London forces (also called instantaneous dipole-induced dipole bonds) cause **all** atoms and molecules to be **attracted** to each other.

1) **Electrons** in charge clouds are always **moving** really quickly. At any particular moment, the electrons in an atom are likely to be more to one side than the other. At this moment, the atom would have a **temporary** (or **instantaneous**) **dipole**.
2) This dipole can **induce another** temporary dipole in the opposite direction on a neighbouring atom. The two dipoles are then **attracted** to each other.
3) The second dipole can induce yet another dipole in a **third atom**. It's kind of like the domino effect.
4) Because the electrons are constantly moving, the dipoles are being **created** and **destroyed** all the time. Even though the dipoles keep changing, the **overall effect** is for the atoms to be **attracted** to each other.

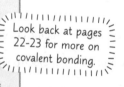

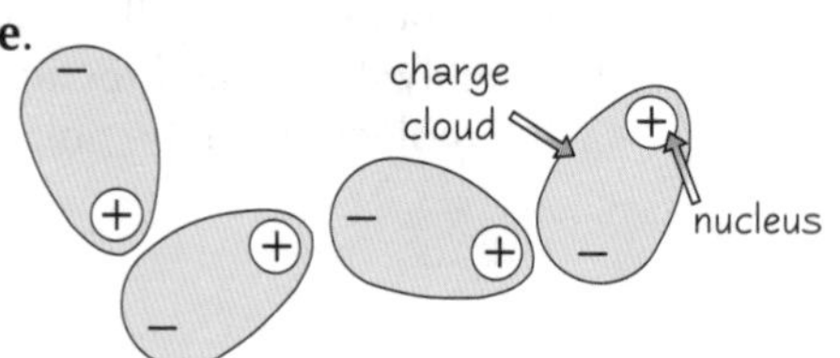

London Forces *Can Hold Molecules in a* ***Lattice***

London forces are responsible for holding **iodine** molecules together in a **lattice**.

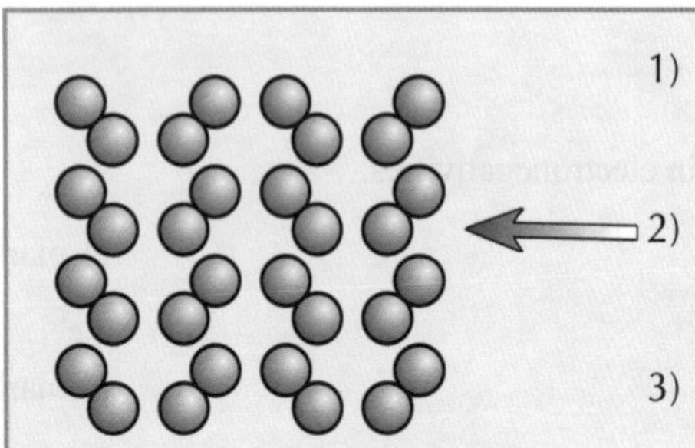

1) Iodine atoms are held together in pairs by **strong** covalent bonds to form molecules of I_2.
2) But the molecules are then held together in a **molecular lattice** arrangement by **weak London forces.**
3) This structure is known as a **simple molecular structure.**

Look back at pages 22-23 for more on covalent bonding.

Stronger ***London Forces*** *mean* ***Higher Melting and Boiling Points***

1) Not all London forces are the same strength — larger molecules have **larger electron clouds**, meaning **stronger** London forces.
2) Molecules with greater **surface areas** also have stronger London forces because they have a **bigger exposed electron cloud** (see next page).
3) When you **boil** a liquid, you need to **overcome** the intermolecular forces, so that the particles can **escape** from the liquid surface. It stands to reason that you need **more energy** to overcome **stronger** intermolecular forces, so liquids with stronger London forces will have **higher boiling points**.
4) Melting solids also involves **overcoming intermolecular forces**, so solids with stronger London forces will have **higher melting points** too.
5) Alkanes demonstrate this nicely...

London Forces.

Intermolecular Forces

Intermolecular Forces in Organic Molecules Depend on Their *Sh*

The **shape** of an organic compound's molecules affects the **strength** of the **intermolecular force**
Take alkanes, for example...

1) Alkanes have **covalent bonds** inside the molecules. **Between** the molecules there are **London forces**, which hold them all together.
2) The **longer** the carbon chain, the **stronger** the London forces — because there's **more molecular surface contact** and **more electrons** to interact.
3) So as the molecules get longer, it gets harder to separate them because it takes **more energy** to overcome the London forces.

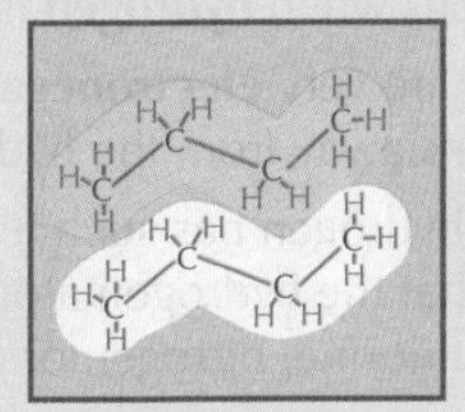

Smaller molecular surface contact, so weaker intermolecular forces.

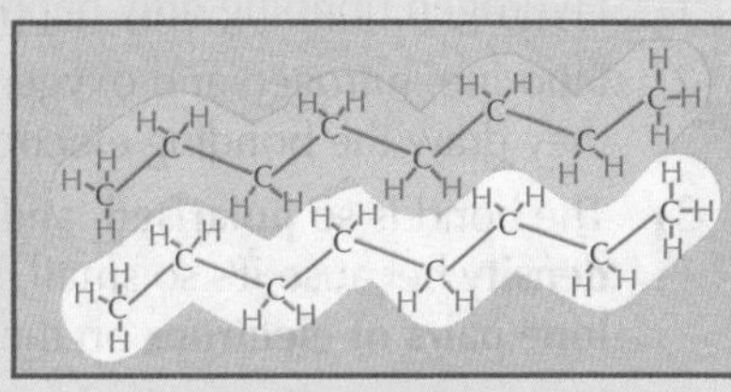

Greater molecular surface contact, so stronger intermolecular forces.

4) Branched-chain alkanes can't **pack closely** together and their **molecular surface contact** is **small** compared to straight chain alkanes of similar molecular mass.
So fewer London forces can form. Look at these **isomers** of $\mathbf{C_4H_{10}}$, for example...

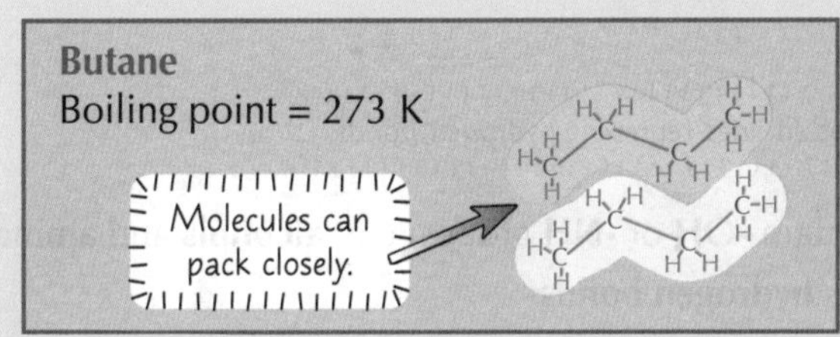

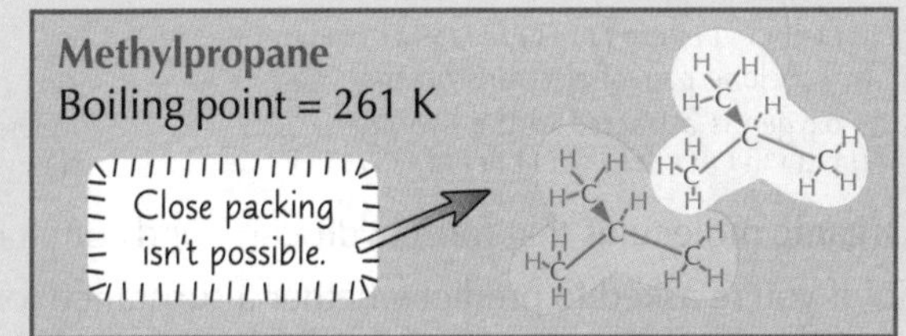

Methylpropane
Boiling point = 261 K
Close packing isn't possible.

Polar Molecules have *Permanent Dipole-Permanent Dipole* Bonds

The δ+ and δ– charges on polar molecules cause weak electrostatic forces of attraction between molecules.
These are known as **permanent dipole-permanent dipole bonds**. E.g., hydrogen chloride gas has polar molecules:

$$\overset{\delta+}{H}-\overset{\delta-}{Cl}\cdots\cdots\overset{\delta+}{H}-\overset{\delta-}{Cl}\cdots\cdots\overset{\delta+}{H}-\overset{\delta-}{Cl}$$

Permanent dipole-permanent dipole bonds happen **as well as** (not instead of) London forces. So, molecules that can form permanent dipole-permanent dipole bonds, in addition to their London forces, will generally have **higher boiling** and **melting points** than those with similar London forces that can't form permanent dipole-permanent dipole bonds.

Practice Questions

Q1 What's the strongest type of intermolecular force?

Q2 Explain what London forces are.

Q3 Explain what gives rise to permanent dipole-permanent dipole intermolecular forces.

Exam Questions

Q1 The molecules in the table on the right all have the molecular formula C_5H_{12}.

Explain the differences in the boiling points of these molecules.

Molecule	Boiling Point (°C)
Pentane	36.1
2-methylbutane	27.7
2,2-dimethylpropane	9.50

[3 marks]

Q2 What intermolecular forces are present in chloroethane (CH_3CH_2Cl)? [1 mark]

Q3 N_2 and NO are both gases at room temperature.
Predict, with reasoning, which gas has a higher boiling point. [2 marks]

London Forces — the irresistible pull of streets paved with gold...

You may well see London forces called instantaneous dipole-induced dipole bonds. But don't panic, they're the same thing. It's useful to remember both names though — especially since instantaneous dipole-induced dipole describes what's going on in this sort of intermolecular bonding. It's all to do with the attraction between temporary dipoles.

Hydrogen Bonding

Hydrogen bonds form between certain types of molecule. Water, alcohols, ammonia, hydrogen fluoride... Shall I go on?

***Hydrogen Bonding** is the **Strongest** Intermolecular Force*

1) Hydrogen bonding **only** happens when **hydrogen** is covalently bonded to **fluorine**, **nitrogen** or **oxygen**.
2) Fluorine, nitrogen and oxygen are very **electronegative**, so they draw the bonding electrons away from the hydrogen atom.
3) The bond is so **polarised**, and hydrogen has such a **high charge density** because it's so small, that the hydrogen atoms form weak bonds with **lone pairs of electrons** on the fluorine, nitrogen or oxygen atoms of **other molecules**.
4) **Water**, **ammonia** and **hydrogen fluoride** all have hydrogen bonding:

See page 28 for more about electronegativity.

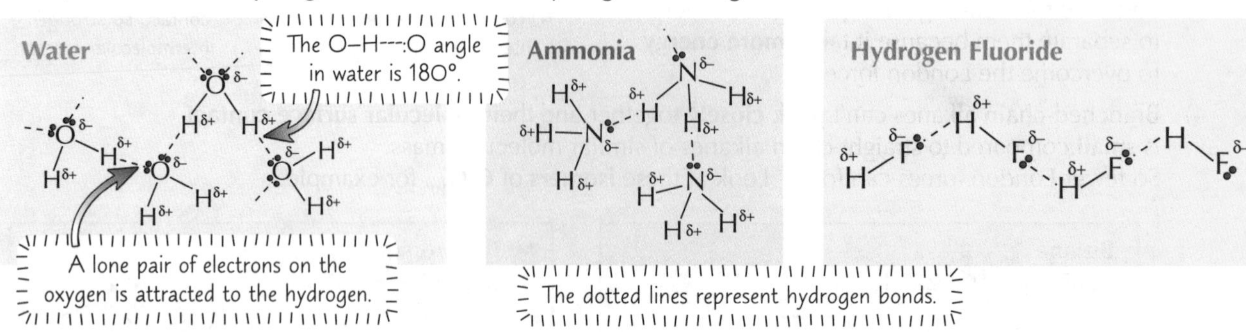

5) **Organic** molecules that form hydrogen bonds often contain **-OH** or **-NH** groups, e.g. **alcohols** and **amines**.
6) So, if you're asked to predict whether a substance forms **hydrogen bonds** or not, you need to watch out for these **groups** of **atoms**.

Hydrogen Bonds** Affect How a Substance **Behaves

Hydrogen bonds are the **strongest** type of intermolecular forces and have a huge effect on the properties of substances. Substances that form hydrogen bonds have **high melting and boiling points** because a lot of **energy** is required to overcome the intermolecular forces.

The graph on the right shows how the boiling points of **Group 7 hydrides** vary as you go down Group 7.

- Molecules of **hydrogen fluoride** form hydrogen bonds with each other (see above). Hydrogen bonding is the **strongest** intermolecular force, so the intermolecular bonding in HF is **very strong**. It requires a lot of **energy** to overcome these bonds, so HF has a **high boiling point**.
- From HCl to HI, although the permanent dipole-dipole interactions **decreases**, the **number of electrons** in the molecule increases, so the **strength** of the London forces also **increases**. This effect overrides the decrease in the strength of the permanent dipole-permanent dipole interactions, so the boiling points increase from **HCl** to **HI**.

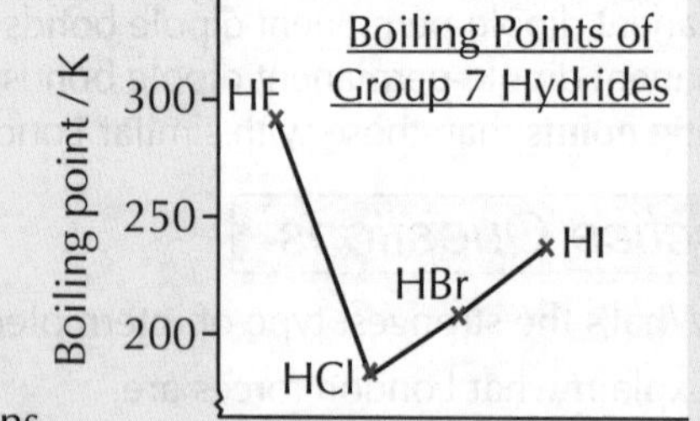

- **Water** has some pretty weird properties. Despite the fact that it's a pretty small molecule, it has a fairly **high boiling point** (373 K, or 100 °C).
- If you look at the trend in boiling points of **Group 6 hydrides**, you'll see they follow a **similar** trend to the boiling points of the **Group 7 hydrides** above.
- Water's ability to form **hydrogen bonds** with itself gives it a **high boiling point**, while the **increase** in the strength of the **London forces** from H_2S to H_2Te **overrides** the **decrease** in the strength of the **permanent dipole-permanent dipole forces**, causing the boiling point to increase from H_2S to H_2Te.

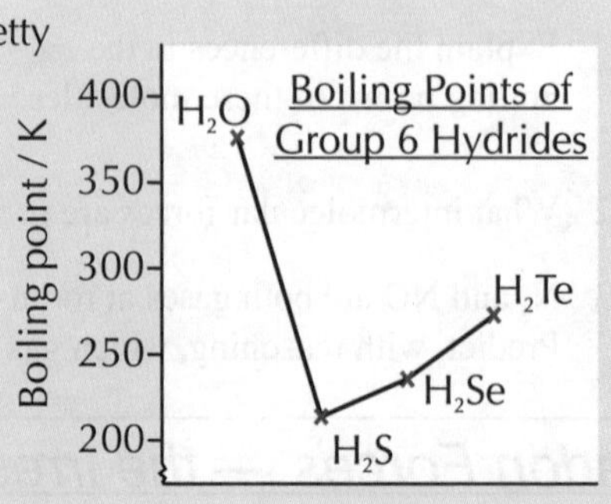

Substances that form hydrogen bonds are also **soluble** in water.
This is because they can form hydrogen bonds with the water molecules, allowing them to mix and dissolve.

Hydrogen Bonding

Hydrogen Bonds Explains Why Ice Floats on Water

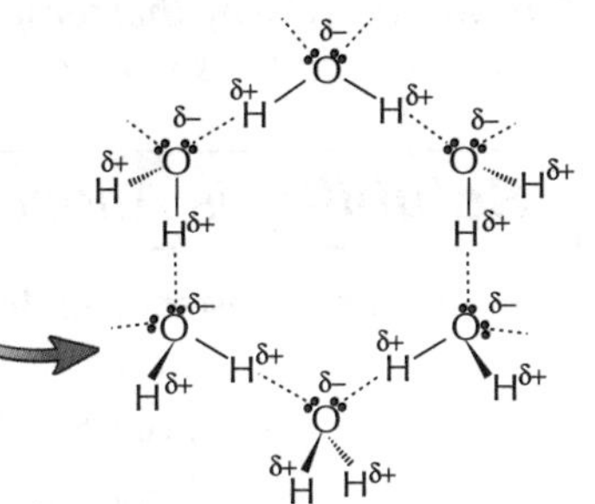

1) Ice is another example of a **simple molecular** structure.
2) In **ice**, the water molecules are arranged so that there is the maximum number of hydrogen bonds — the **lattice structure** formed in this way '**wastes**' lots of space.
3) As the ice **melts**, some of the hydrogen bonds are **broken** and the lattice **breaks down** — allowing molecules to 'fill' the spaces.
4) This effect means ice is much less dense than water — which is why **ice floats**.

Alcohols are Less Volatile than Similar Alkanes

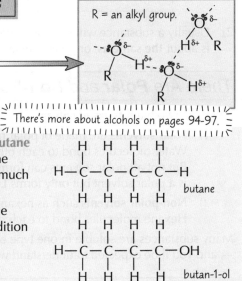

1) All alcohols contain a **polar hydroxyl group** (-OH) that has a δ– charge on the oxygen atom and a δ+ charge on the hydrogen atom. This polar group helps alcohols to form **hydrogen bonds**.
2) Hydrogen bonding gives alcohols **low volatilities** (i.e. they have **high boiling points**) compared to **non-polar compounds**, e.g. alkanes, of similar sizes, with similar numbers of electrons.

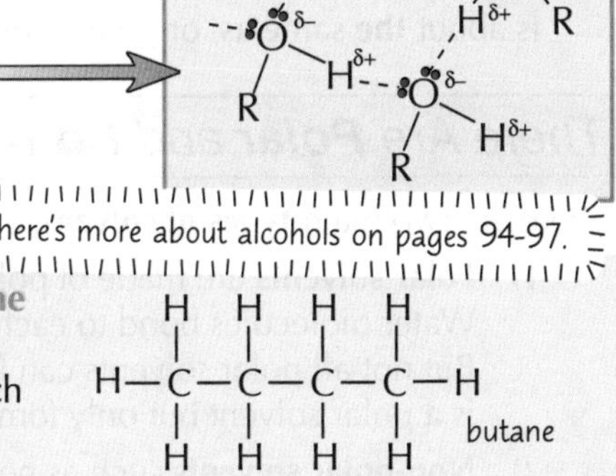

There's more about alcohols on pages 94-97.

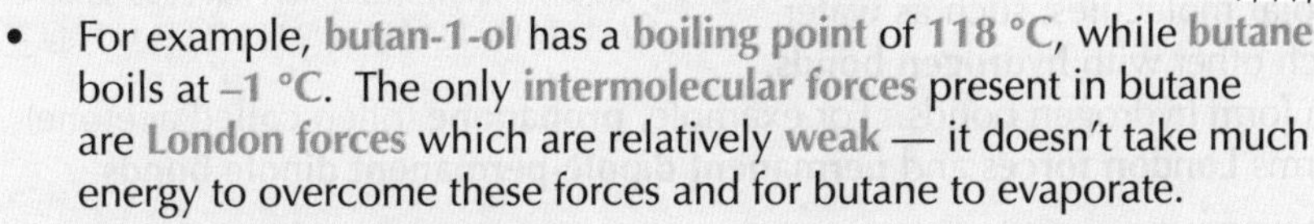

- For example, **butan-1-ol** has a **boiling point** of **118 °C**, while **butane** boils at **–1 °C**. The only **intermolecular forces** present in butane are **London forces** which are relatively **weak** — it doesn't take much energy to overcome these forces and for butane to evaporate.
- The strength of the London forces in both butan-1-ol and butane will be **similar**, but butan-1-ol can form **hydrogen bonds** in addition to London forces. Hydrogen bonds are the **strongest** type of intermolecular force and require much **more energy** to break. This gives butan-1-ol a much higher boiling point.

```
  H   H   H   H
  |   |   |   |
H—C———C———C———C—H
  |   |   |   |
  H   H   H   H      butane

  H   H   H   H
  |   |   |   |
H—C———C———C———C—OH
  |   |   |   |
  H   H   H   H      butan-1-ol
```

Practice Questions

Q1 What atoms need to be present for hydrogen bonding to occur?

Q2 Name three substances that undergo hydrogen bonding.

Q3 Why is ice less dense than water?

Exam Questions

Q1 a) Explain why water's boiling point is higher than expected in comparison to other similar molecules. [2 marks]

b) Draw a labelled diagram showing the intermolecular bonding that takes place in water. Your diagram should show at least 4 water molecules. [2 marks]

Q2 a) For each of the following pairs of compounds, state which will have the higher boiling point.

i) Ammonia (NH_3) and methane (CH_4). [1 mark]

ii) Water and hydrogen sulfide (H_2S). [1 mark]

iii) Butane and propan-1-ol. [1 mark]

b) Explain your choices in part a). [2 marks]

Q3 An organic compound used as antifreeze is ethane-1,2-diol. Its structure is shown on the right.

```
  OH OH
  |  |
H—C——C—H
  |  |
  H  H
```

The boiling point of ethane-1,2-diol is 197 °C, whereas the boiling point of ethanol is 78 °C. Suggest a reason for this difference. [1 mark]

I never used to like Chemistry, but after this, I feel we've truly bonded...

There you have it, hydrogen bonding. The king of intermolecular bonding in my opinion. If you need to draw a picture of hydrogen bonding in the exam, make sure you draw any lone pairs and all the partial charges (those are the δ– and δ+ signs). And show any hydrogen bonds with a dotted line (unless you're told otherwise). Don't go missing easy marks.

Solubility

Ever wondered why that teaspoon of sugar dissolves in your afternoon cuppa'? Or why all the salt doesn't just fall out of the sea onto the seabed? Well my friend, you're about to find out. It's all to do with solubility...

Solubility is Affected by *Bonding*

1) For one substance to **dissolve** in another, all these things have to happen:

   - bonds in the **substance** have to **break**,
   - bonds in the **solvent** have to **break**, and
   - **new bonds** have to form **between** the **substance** and the **solvent**.

2) Usually a substance will only dissolve if the strength of the new bonds **formed** is about **the same as**, or **greater than**, the strength of the bonds that are **broken**.

There Are Polar and Non-Polar Solvents

You may see water referred to as an aqueous solvent. Any solvent that isn't water is known as a non-aqueous solvent.

There are two main **types of solvent**:

1) **Polar solvents** are made of polar molecules, such as water. Water molecules bond to each other with **hydrogen bonds**. But not all polar solvents can form hydrogen bonds. For example, **propanone** (often called acetone) is a polar solvent but only forms **London forces** and **permanent dipole-permanent dipole bonds**.
2) **Non-polar solvents** such as hexane. Hexane molecules bond to each other by **London forces**.

Look back at pages 28-29 for more on polarity, and pages 30-33 for lots on intermolecular forces.

Many substances are soluble in one type of solvent but not the other — and you'll be expected to understand why...

Ionic Substances Dissolve in Polar Solvents such as Water

1) Water is a **polar solvent** — water molecules have a slightly positively-charged end (the δ+ hydrogens) and a slightly negatively-charged end (the δ– oxygen).
2) When an ionic substance is mixed with water, the ions in the ionic substance are attracted to the **oppositely charged ends** of the water molecules.
3) The ions are pulled away from the ionic lattice by the water molecules, which surround the ions. This process is called **hydration**.

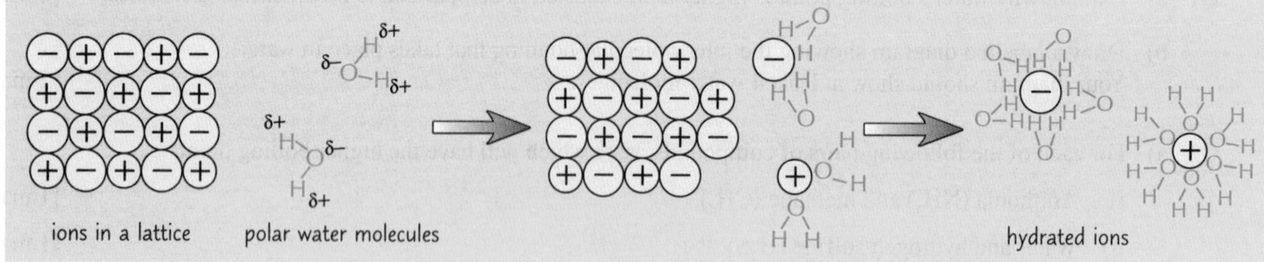

4) Some ionic substances **don't dissolve** because the bonding between their ions is **too strong**. For example, aluminium oxide (Al_2O_3) is insoluble in water because the bonds between the ions are stronger than the bonds they'd form with the water molecules. (Al^{3+} has a high charge density, so forms strong ionic bonds — see page 19.)

Alcohols also Dissolve in Polar Solvents such as Water

1) Alcohols are **covalent** but they dissolve in water...
2) ... because the polar O-H bond in an alcohol is attracted to the polar O-H bonds in water. **Hydrogen bonds** form between the lone pairs on the δ– oxygen atoms and the δ+ hydrogen atoms.
3) The **carbon chain** part of the alcohol isn't attracted to water, so the more carbon atoms there are, the **less soluble** the alcohol will be.

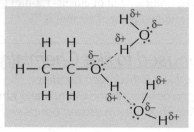

Solubility

Not All Molecules with Polar Bonds Dissolve in Water

1) **Halogenoalkanes** (see page 90) contain **polar bonds** but their dipoles aren't strong enough to form **hydrogen bonds** with water.
2) The hydrogen bonding **between** water molecules is **stronger** than the bonds that would be formed with halogenoalkanes, so halogenoalkanes don't dissolve.

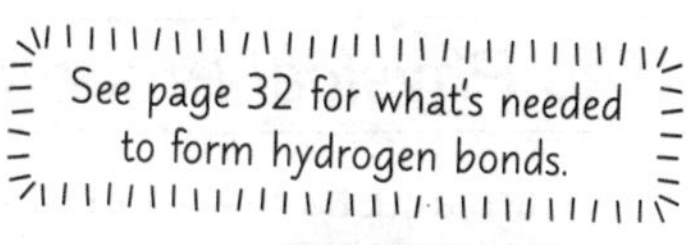
See page 32 for what's needed to form hydrogen bonds.

Example:
When the halogenoalkane chlorobutane is added to water, they don't mix, but separate into two layers.

chlorobutane layer

water layer

Henry couldn't understand why the champagne wouldn't dissolve.

3) But, halogenoalkanes can form **permanent dipole-permanent dipole bonds**. They happily dissolve in polar solvents that also form **permanent dipole-permanent dipole bonds** (not hydrogen bonds).

Non-Polar Substances Dissolve Best in Non-Polar Solvents

1) Non-polar substances such as **ethene** have **London forces** between their molecules. They form **similar bonds** with **non-polar solvents** such as hexane — so they tend to dissolve in them.
2) Water molecules are attracted to **each other** more strongly than they are to **non-polar molecules** such as iodine — so non-polar substances don't tend to dissolve easily in water.

Like dissolves like (usually) — substances usually dissolve best in solvents with similar **intermolecular forces.**

Practice Questions

Q1 Which type of solvent, polar or a non-polar, would you choose to dissolve: i) sodium chloride? ii) ethane?

Q2 Why do most ionic substances dissolve in water?

Q3 What is meant by 'hydration'?

Q4 Some ionic substances don't dissolve in water. Why not?

Q5 What type of bonding occurs between an alcohol and water?

Q6 Why are most non-polar substances insoluble in water?

Exam Questions

Q1 Hydrogen bonds are present between molecules of water.

a) i) Explain why alcohols often dissolve in water while halogenoalkanes do not. [4 marks]

ii) Draw a diagram to show the bonds that form when propan-1-ol dissolves in water. [2 marks]

b) Explain the process by which potassium iodide dissolves in water to form hydrated ions. Include a diagram of the hydrated ions. [5 marks]

Q2 a) An unknown substance, X is suspected to be a non-polar simple covalent molecule. Describe how you could confirm this by testing with two different solvents. Name the solvents chosen and give the expected results. [3 marks]

b) Explain these results in terms of the intermolecular bonding within X and the solvents. [4 marks]

When the ice-caps melt, where will all the polar solvents live?

I reckon it's logical enough, this business of what dissolves what. Remember, water is a polar molecule — so other polar molecules, as well as ions, are attracted to its δ+ and δ– ends. If that attraction's stronger than the existing bonds (which have to break), the substance will dissolve. It's worth remembering that rule of thumb about 'like dissolves like'.

Predicting Structures and Properties

By looking at certain properties that a substance has, such as its melting/boiling points, its solubility and whether it conducts electricity, you can predict what sort of bonding it has. If this doesn't excite you, then I don't know what will.

The Physical Properties of a Solid Depend on the Nature of its Particles

Here are a just a few examples of the ways in which the particles that make up a substance affect it properties:

1) The **melting** and **boiling points** of a substance are determined by the strength of the **attraction** between its particles (the **intermolecular forces**).
2) A substance will only **conduct electricity** if it contains **charged particles** that are **free to move**.
3) How **soluble** a substance is in **water** depends on the **type** of particles that it contains. Water is able to form **hydrogen bonds**, so substances that are also able to form hydrogen bonds, or are **charged** (i.e. ions) will dissolve in it well, whereas **non-polar** or **uncharged** substances won't.

Learn the Properties of the Main Substance Types

Make sure you know this stuff like the back of your hand:

Bonding	Examples	Melting and boiling points	Typical state at room temperature and pressure	Does solid conduct electricity?	Does liquid conduct electricity?	Is it soluble in water?
Ionic	NaCl $MgCl_2$	High	Solid	No (ions are held in place)	Yes (ions are free to move)	Yes
Simple covalent (molecular)	CO_2 I_2 H_2O	Low (involves breaking intermolecular forces but not covalent bonds)	May be solid (like I_2) but usually liquid or gas	No	No	Depends on whether it can form hydrogen bonds
Giant covalent	Diamond Graphite SiO_2	High	Solid	No (except graphite)	— (sublimes rather than melting)	No
Metallic	Fe Mg Al	High	Solid	Yes (delocalised electrons)	Yes (delocalised electrons)	No

You Can Use the Properties of a Material to Predict its Structure

You need to be able to predict the type of structure from a list of its properties. Here's a quick example.

Example: Substance X has a melting point of 1045 K. When solid, it is an insulator, but once melted it conducts electricity. Identify the type of structure present in substance X.

1) Substance X **doesn't** conduct electricity when it's **solid**, but **does** conduct electricity once **melted**. So it looks like it's **ionic** — that would fit with the fact that it has a **high melting point** too.
2) You can also tell that it definitely **isn't simple covalent** because it has a **high melting point**, it definitely **isn't metallic** because it **doesn't** conduct electricity when it's **solid**, and it definitely **isn't giant covalent** because it **does** conduct electricity when **melted**.

So substance X must be **ionic**.

Snowman building — family bonding with a melting point of 0 °C.

Predicting Structures and Prop

*You can make **Predictions** about a **Substance's Properties** fr*

1) You can also **predict** how a substance will behave depending on the **bonding** it has.
2) If you're dealing with **metallic**, **ionic** or **giant covalent substances**, you just need to consider the strong **ionic** or **covalent** bonds between the atoms.
3) If you're dealing with simple molecular compounds, you need to think about the **intermolecular forces** between the molecules, rather than the **covalent bonds** between the atoms.

Example: Aminomethane (CH_3NH_2) has a simple molecular structure. Predict the properties of aminomethane, including its solubility in water, its electrical conductivity, and its physical state at room temperature.

- Aminomethane contains an $-NH_2$ group, so is likely to form hydrogen bonds with water. This would make aminomethane **soluble in water**.
- Aminomethane has a simple molecular structure. In this type of structure, there are no free particles that can carry a charge, so aminomethane **doesn't conduct electricity**.
- To melt or boil a simple covalent compound you only have to overcome the intermolecular forces that hold the molecules together. You don't need to break the much stronger covalent bonds that hold the atoms together in the molecules. Aminomethane would have weak London forces between its molecules as well as stronger hydrogen bonds. However you would still expect aminomethane to have **low** boiling and melting points, and so be a **gas at room temperature**.

Practice Questions

Q1 If a substance has a low melting point, what type of structure is it most likely to have?

Q2 Out of the four main types of structure (ionic, simple covalent, giant covalent and metallic), which will conduct electricity when they are liquids?

Q3 Would you expect a substance with a giant covalent structure to be soluble or insoluble in water?

Exam Questions

Q1 The table below describes the properties of four compounds, A, B, C and D.

Substance	Melting point	Electrical conductivity of solid	Electrical conductivity of liquid	Solubility in water
A	high	poor	good	soluble
B	low	poor	poor	insoluble
C	high	good	good	insoluble
D	very high	poor	— (compound sublimes rather than melting)	insoluble

Identify the type of structure present in each substance. [4 marks]

Q2 Iodine, I_2, and graphite are both solid at r.t.p.. At 500 K, iodine exists as a gas, while graphite remains solid. Explain this difference in the properties of iodine and graphite in terms of their structures. [4 marks]

Q3 A substance, X, has a melting point of 650 °C and a boiling point of 1107 °C. It conducts electricity in both the solid and liquid states, but is insoluble in water. Which of the follow substances could be substance X?

A Carbon dioxide **B** Magnesium **C** Caesium chloride **D** Silicon dioxide [1 mark]

Mystic Molecular Meg — predicting fortunes and properties since 1995...

You need to learn the info in the table on page 36. With a quick glance in my crystal ball, I can almost guarantee you'll need a bit of it in your exam... let me look closer and tell you which bit.... hmm.... No, it's clouded over. You'll have to learn the lot. Sorry. Tell you what — close the book and see how much of the table you can scribble out from memory.

Oxidation Numbers

s double page has more occurrences of "oxidation" than the Beatles' "All You Need is Love" features the word "love".

Oxidation Numbers Tell You About the Movement of Electrons

When atoms **react** with or **bond** to other atoms, they can **lose** or **gain** electrons. The **oxidation number** (or oxidation state) tells you how many electrons an atom has donated or accepted to form an **ion**, or to form part of a **compound**. There are certain rules you need to remember to help you assign oxidation numbers. Here they are...

1) All uncombined elements have an oxidation number of **0**. This means they haven't accepted or donated any electrons. Elements that are bonded to identical atoms will also have an oxidation number of **0**.

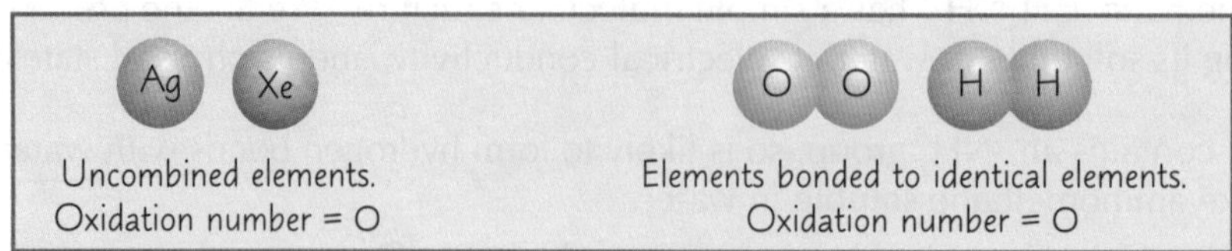

2) The oxidation number of a simple, monatomic ion (that's an ion consisting of just one atom) is the same as its **charge**.

Metals generally form ions with a charge that's equal to their Group number. Non-metals form ions with charges equal to their Group number minus 8.

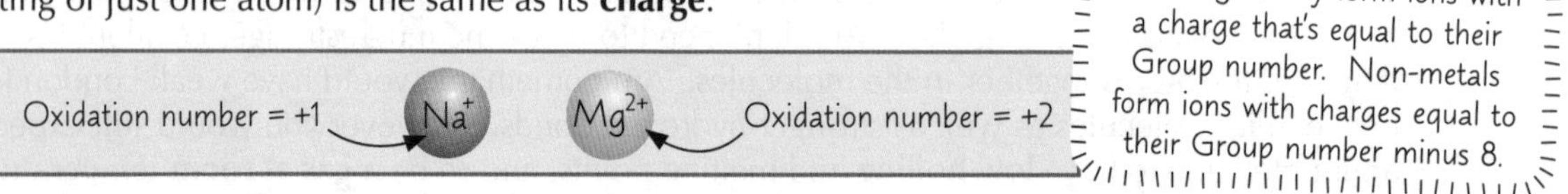

3) For **molecular ions** (ions that are made up of a group of atoms with an overall charge), the sum of the oxidation numbers is the same as the overall charge of the ion. Each of the constituent atoms will have an oxidation number of its own, and the **sum** of their oxidation numbers equals the **overall charge**.

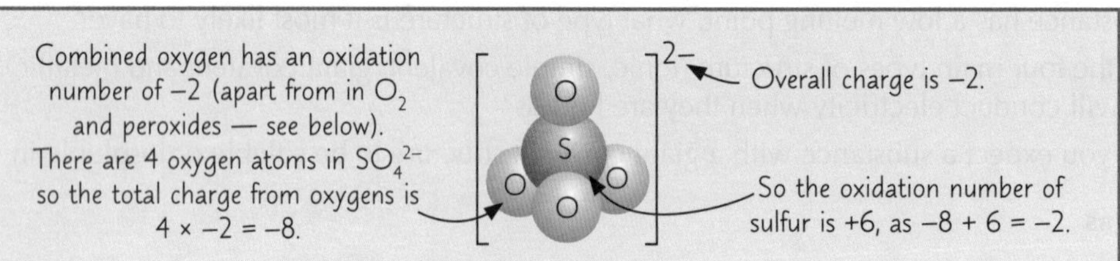

Combined oxygen has an oxidation number of −2 (apart from in O2 and peroxides — see below).
There are 4 oxygen atoms in SO4 2− so the total charge from oxygens is 4 × −2 = −8.
2−
Overall charge is −2.
O
S
O
O
O
So the oxidation number of sulfur is +6, as −8 + 6 = −2.

4) For a neutral compound, the overall charge is **0**, and each atom in the compound will have its own oxidation number. The **sum** of these oxidation numbers is 0.

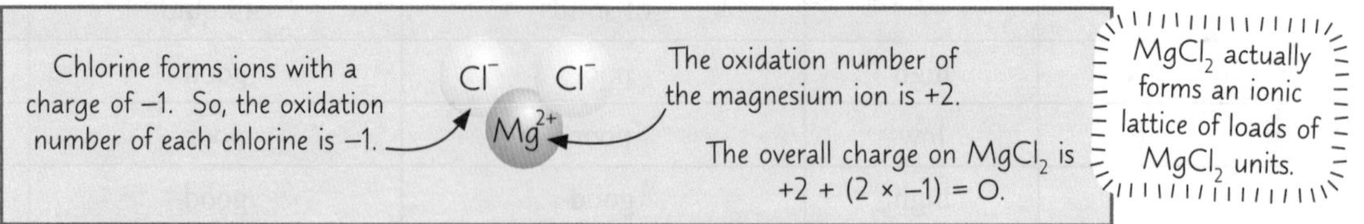

Chlorine forms ions with a charge of −1. So, the oxidation number of each chlorine is −1.
Cl−
Cl−
Mg2+
The oxidation number of the magnesium ion is +2.
The overall charge on MgCl2 is +2 + (2 × −1) = 0.

$MgCl_2$ actually forms an ionic lattice of loads of $MgCl_2$ units.

5) **Hydrogen** always has an oxidation number of **+1**, except in **metal hydrides** (MH_x, where M = metal) where it's **−1** and in **molecular hydrogen** (H_2) where it's **0**.

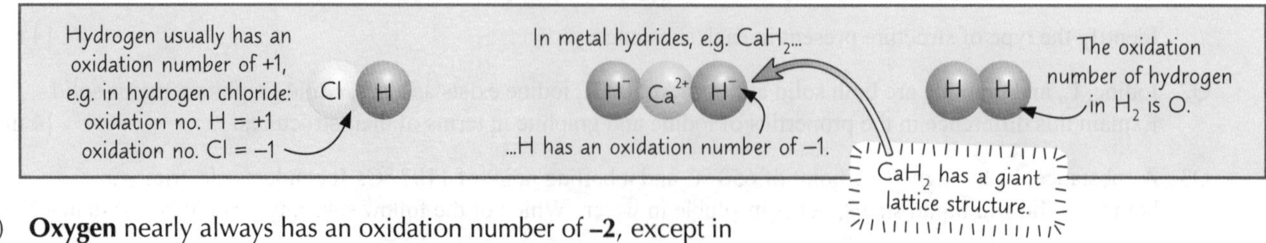

Hydrogen usually has an oxidation number of +1, e.g. in hydrogen chloride:
oxidation no. H = +1
oxidation no. Cl = −1
Cl
H
In metal hydrides, e.g. CaH2...
H−
Ca2+
H−
...H has an oxidation number of −1.
H H
The oxidation number of hydrogen in H2 is 0.

CaH_2 has a giant lattice structure.

6) **Oxygen** nearly always has an oxidation number of **−2**, except in **peroxides** (O_2^{2-}) where it's **−1**, and **molecular oxygen** (O_2) where it's **0**.

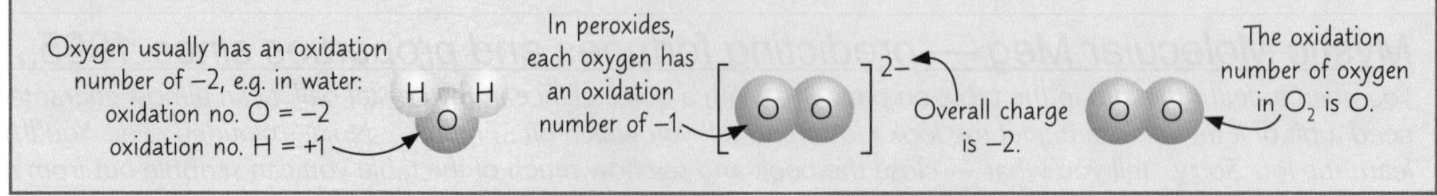

Oxidation Numbers

Roman Numerals tell you the *Oxidation Number*

1) If an element can have **multiple** oxidation numbers, or **isn't** in its 'normal' oxidation number, its oxidation number can be shown by using **Roman numerals**, e.g. (I) = +1, (II) = +2, (III) = +3 and so on. The Roman numerals are written after the name of the element they correspond to.

Example: In copper(I) oxide, copper has an oxidation number of **+1**. Formula = Cu_2O
In copper(II) sulfate, copper has an oxidation number of **+2**. Formula = $CuSO_4$

2) Ions with names ending in -ate (e.g. sulfate, nitrate, chlorate, carbonate) contain **oxygen** and another element. For example, sulfates contain sulfur and oxygen, nitrates contain nitrogen and oxygen... and so on.
3) Sometimes the 'other' element in the ion can exist with different oxidation numbers, and so form different '-ate ions'. In these cases, the oxidation number is attached as a Roman numeral **after** the name of the -ate compound. The Roman numerals correspond to the **non-oxygen** element in the -ate compound.

If there are no oxidation numbers shown, assume nitrate = NO_3^- and sulfate = SO_4^{2-}.

Example: In sulfate(VI) ions, the **sulfur** has oxidation number **+6** — this is the SO_4^{2-} ion.
In nitrate(III), **nitrogen** has an oxidation number of **+3** — this is the NO_2^- ion.

You can use *Oxidation Numbers* to Write *Chemical Formulae*

1) You might need to use oxidation numbers to work out the **chemical formula** of a certain compound.
2) Unless you're told otherwise, you can assume the overall charge on a **compound** is **0**.
3) To work out the chemical formula, you've just got to work out what ratio of **anions** (negatively charged ions) and **cations** (positively charged ions) gives an overall charge of 0.

Example: What is the formula of barium(II) nitrate?

From the systematic name, you can tell barium has an **oxidation number** of +2.
The formula of the nitrate ion is NO_3^- and it has an **overall charge** of –1.
The overall charge of the compound is 0, so you need to find a ratio of $Ba^{2+}:NO_3^-$ that will make the overall charge 0.

(+2) + (–1 × 2) = 2 + –2 = 0 The ratio of $Ba^{2+}:NO_3^-$ is **1:2**.

So the formula is $\mathbf{Ba(NO_3)_2}$.

Hands up if you like Roman numerals...

Practice Questions

Q1 What is the oxidation number of H in H_2?

Q2 What is the usual oxidation number for oxygen when it's combined with another element?

Exam Questions

Q1 Sulfur can exist in a variety of oxidation states.

Work out the oxidation state of sulfur in the following compounds:

a) S_8, b) SO_3^{2-}, c) H_2SO_4, d) H_2S. [4 marks]

Q2 Hydrogen peroxide (H_2O_2) is a commonly used component of bleach.

a) In hydrogen peroxide, what is the oxidation number of: i) hydrogen? ii) oxygen? [2 marks]

b) Hydrogen peroxide reacts with sodium sulfite (Na_2SO_3) to produce sodium sulfate and water. What is the oxidation number of sulfur in the sodium sulfite compound? [1 mark]

Sockidation number — a measure of how many odd socks are in my drawers...

There isn't any tricky maths involved with oxidation numbers, just a bit of adding, some subtracting... maybe a bit of multiplying if you're unlucky. The real trick is to learn all the rules about predicting oxidation numbers. So get cracking.

Redox Reactions

Oxidation numbers are great. They're darn useful for showing where electrons move from and to during redox reactions.

If Electrons are Transferred, it's a ***Redox Reaction***

1) A **loss** of electrons is called **oxidation**.
2) A **gain** in electrons is called **reduction**.
3) Reduction and oxidation happen **simultaneously** — hence the term "**redox**" reaction.
4) An **oxidising agent accepts** electrons and gets reduced.
5) A **reducing agent donates** electrons and gets oxidised.

Example: the formation of **sodium chloride** from sodium and chlorine is a **redox reaction**:

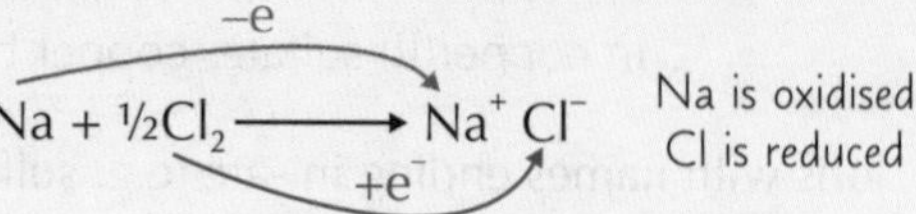

Oxidation Numbers go ***Up*** *or* ***Down*** *as Electrons are* ***Lost*** *or* ***Gained***

1) The oxidation number for an atom will **increase by 1** for each **electron lost**.
2) The oxidation number will **decrease by 1** for each **electron gained**.
3) To work out whether something has been **oxidised** or **reduced**, you need to assign each element an oxidation number **before** the reaction, and **after** the reaction.
4) If the oxidation number has increased, then the element has **lost** electrons and been **oxidised**.
5) If the oxidation number has decreased, then the element has **gained** electrons and been **reduced**.

Example: Identify the oxidising and reducing agents in this reaction: $4Fe + 3O_2 \rightarrow 2Fe_2O_3$

Iron has gone from having an oxidation number of 0 to having an oxidation number of +3. It's **lost electrons** and has been **oxidised**. This makes it the **reducing agent** in this reaction.

Oxygen has gone from having an oxidation number of 0 to having an oxidation number of –2. It's **gained electrons** and has been **reduced**. This means it's the **oxidising agent** in this reaction.

Check back at the rules for assigning oxidation numbers on page 38 if you're unsure about this.

6) When **metals** form compounds, they generally **donate** electrons to form **positive ions** and their oxidation numbers **increase** (they usually have **positive oxidation numbers**).
7) When **non-metals** form compounds, they generally **gain** electrons to form **negative ions** and their oxidation numbers **decrease** (they usually have **negative oxidation numbers**).
8) A **disproportionation reaction** is a special redox reaction. During a disproportionation reaction, an **element** in a **single species** is **simultaneously oxidised** and **reduced**. Oxidation numbers can show this happening.

Example:
Chlorine and its ions undergo disproportionation reactions:

$$Cl_2 + 2OH^- \rightarrow ClO^- + Cl^- + H_2O$$

Oxidation Number of Cl: 0 → +1 (oxidation), 0 → –1 (reduction)

You can Write ***Half-Equations*** *and Combine them into* ***Redox Equations***

1) **Ionic half-equations** show oxidation or reduction.
2) You show the **electrons** that are being lost or gained in a half-equation. For example, this is the half-equation for the **oxidation of sodium**: $Na \rightarrow Na^+ + e^-$
3) You can **combine** half-equations for different oxidising or reducing agents together to make **full equations** for redox reactions.

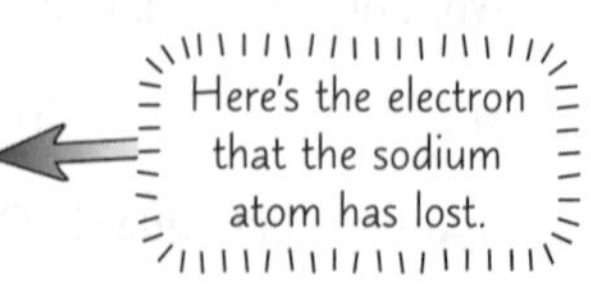

Here's the electron that the sodium atom has lost.

Example: Magnesium burns in oxygen to form magnesium oxide.

Oxygen is reduced to O^{2-}: $O_2 + 4e^- \rightarrow 2O^{2-}$ Magnesium is oxidised to Mg^{2+}: $Mg \rightarrow Mg^{2+} + 2e^-$

You need both equations to contain the same number of electrons. So double everything in the second half-equation: $2Mg \rightarrow 2Mg^{2+} + 4e^-$

Combining the half-equations makes: $2Mg + O_2 \rightarrow 2MgO$

The electrons aren't included in the full equation. You end up with four on each side — so they cancel.

Redox Reactions

Use e^-, H^+ and H_2O to Balance Half-Equations

1) For some redox equations, you'll find that you can't balance the equation by just multiplying up the reactants and products and adding a few electrons.
2) You might have to add some H^+ ions and H_2O to your half-equations to make them **balance**.

Example: Acidified manganate(VII) ions (MnO_4^-) can be reduced to Mn^{2+} by Fe^{2+} ions. Write the full redox equation for this reaction.

Iron is being oxidised. The half-equation for this is: $Fe^{2+}_{(aq)} \rightarrow Fe^{3+}_{(aq)} + e^-$

The second half-equation is a little bit trickier...

1) Manganate is being reduced. Start by writing this down: $MnO^-_{4\,(aq)} \rightarrow Mn^{2+}_{(aq)}$
2) To balance the **oxygens**, you need to add **water** to the right-hand side of the equation: $MnO^-_{4\,(aq)} + \rightarrow Mn^{2+}_{(aq)} + 4H_2O_{(l)}$
3) Now you need to add some **H^+ ions** to the left-hand side to balance the **hydrogens**: $MnO^-_{4\,(aq)} + 8H^+_{(aq)} \rightarrow Mn^{2+}_{(aq)} + 4H_2O_{(l)}$
4) Finally, balance the **charges** by adding some **electrons**: $MnO^-_{4\,(aq)} + 8H^+_{(aq)} + 5e^- \rightarrow Mn^{2+}_{(aq)} + 4H_2O_{(l)}$

There's an overall charge of +2 on each side of the equation.

Now you have to make sure the number of **electrons** produced in the **iron half-equation equal** the number of **electrons** used up in the **manganate half-equation.**

$Fe^{2+}_{(aq)} \rightarrow Fe^{3+}_{(aq)} + e^- \xrightarrow{\times 5} 5Fe^{2+}_{(aq)} \rightarrow 5Fe^{3+}_{(aq)} + 5e^-$

Now combine both half-equations to give a **full redox equation.**

$MnO^-_{4\,(aq)} + 8H^+_{(aq)} + 5Fe^{2+}_{(aq)} \rightarrow Mn^{2+}_{(aq)} + 5Fe^{3+}_{(aq)} + 4H_2O_{(l)}$

Practice Questions

Q1 What is a reducing agent?

Q2 What happens to the oxidation number of an element that loses electrons?

Q3 What happens during a disproportionation reaction?

Exam Questions

Q1 Lithium oxide forms when lithium is burned in air. Combustion is a redox reaction.
The equation for the combustion of lithium is: $4Li_{(s)} + O_{2(g)} \rightarrow 2Li_2O_{(s)}$

a) Define oxidation in terms of the movement of electrons. [1 mark]

b) State which reactant in this reaction is reduced. Write a half-equation for this reduction reaction. [2 marks]

Q2 The half-equation for chlorine acting as an oxidising agent is: $Cl_2 + 2e^- \rightarrow 2Cl^-$

a) Define the term oxidising agent in terms of electron movement. [1 mark]

b) Given that indium reacts with chlorine to form indium(III) ions, form a balanced equation for the reaction of indium with chlorine. [2 marks]

Q3 The following reaction is a disproportionation reaction: $2H_2O_2 \rightarrow 2H_2O + O_2$.
By using oxidation numbers, show why this reaction can be classified as a disproportionation reaction. [3 marks]

Q4 Vanadyl(IV) ions (VO^{2+}) react with tin(II) ions. During this reaction, the vanadyl(IV) ions are reduced to vanadium(III) ions, and tin is oxidised to tin(IV). Write a full redox equation for this reaction. [3 marks]

Oxidising agent SALE NOW ON — everything's reduced...

Half-equations look evil, with all those electrons flying about. But they're not too bad really. Just make sure you get lots of practice using them. (Oh, look, there are some handy questions up there.)

And while we're on the redox page, I suppose you ought to learn the most famous memory aid thingy in the world...

OIL RIG
— **O**xidation **I**s **L**oss
— **R**eduction **I**s **G**ain
(of electrons)

Group 2

...ready to learn about the elements magnesium, calcium, strontium and barium. They're lovely.

Ionisation Energy **Decreases** Down the Group

Mr Kelly has one final attempt at explaining electron shielding to his students...

1) Each element down Group 2 has an **extra electron shell** compared to the one above.
2) The extra inner shells **shield** the outer electrons from the attraction of the nucleus.
3) Also, the extra shell means that the outer electrons are **further away** from the nucleus, which greatly reduces the electrostatic attraction between the nucleus and the outer electrons.

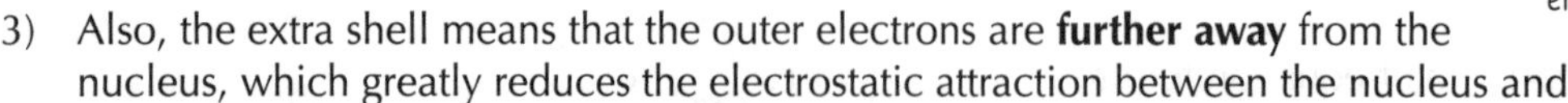

Both of these factors make it **easier** to remove outer electrons, meaning the **ionisation energy decreases** as you go down Group 2.

The positive charge of the nucleus does increase as you go down a group (due to the extra protons), but this effect is overridden by the effect of the extra shells.

4) This can explain the trend in **reactivity** of the Group 2 elements — most of these elements react by losing their **two outer electrons** (see below). So, the higher their first and second ionisation energies, the less likely they are to lose these electrons and the **less reactive** they will be. So, reactivity **increases** down the group.

Group 2 Elements React with **Water, Oxygen** and **Chlorine**

When Group 2 elements react, they form ions with a charge of **2+**. This is because Group 2 atoms contain **2 electrons** in their outer shell. They lose both of these electrons when they react.

Here, M stands for any Group 2 metal.

$$M \rightarrow M^{2+} + 2e^-$$

E.g. $$Ca \rightarrow Ca^{2+} + 2e^-$$

They react with WATER to produce HYDROXIDES.

The Group 2 metals react with water to give a **metal hydroxide and hydrogen.**

$$M_{(s)} + 2H_2O_{(l)} \rightarrow M(OH)_{2\,(aq)} + H_{2\,(g)}$$

e.g. $$Ca_{(s)} + 2H_2O_{(l)} \rightarrow Ca(OH)_{2\,(aq)} + H_{2\,(g)}$$

Be	doesn't react
Mg	VERY slowly
Ca	steadily
Sr	fairly quickly
Ba	rapidly

If you add water to some barium in a test tube, lots of bubbles are produced, showing barium reacts really easily. If you add water to some magnesium in a test tube, you won't see much happening.

They burn in OXYGEN to form OXIDES.

When Group 2 metals burn in oxygen, you get solid white **oxides.**

$$2M_{(s)} + O_{2\,(g)} \rightarrow 2MO_{(s)}$$

e.g. $$2Ca_{(s)} + O_{2\,(g)} \rightarrow 2CaO_{(s)}$$

They react with CHLORINE to form CHLORIDES.

When Group 2 metals react with chlorine, you get solid white **chlorides.**

$$M_{(s)} + Cl_{2\,(g)} \rightarrow MCl_{2\,(s)}$$

e.g. $$Ca_{(s)} + Cl_{2\,(g)} \rightarrow CaCl_{2\,(s)}$$

The Oxides and Hydroxides are **Bases...**

1) The **oxides** of the Group 2 metals react readily with **water** to form **metal hydroxides**, which dissolve. The **hydroxide ions, OH^-**, make these solutions **strongly alkaline**.
2) **Beryllium oxide** is an exception — it **doesn't react** with **water**, and **beryllium hydroxide** is **insoluble**.
3) **Magnesium oxide** is another exception — it only reacts **slowly** and the hydroxide isn't very soluble.
4) The oxides form **more strongly alkaline** solutions as you go down the group, because the hydroxides get more soluble.
5) Because they're **bases**, both the oxides and hydroxides will **neutralise** dilute acids, forming solutions of the corresponding salts. See the next page for examples of these reactions.

Group 2

...So They Form Alkaline Solutions and Neutralise Acids

	Reaction with Water	Reaction with Dilute Acid
Oxides	$MO_{(s)} + H_2O_{(l)} \rightarrow M(OH)_{2\,(aq)}$	$MO_{(s)} + 2HCl_{(aq)} \rightarrow MCl_{2\,(aq)} + H_2O_{(l)}$
Hydroxides	$M(OH)_{2\,(s)} \xrightarrow{+H_2O_{(l)}} M(OH)_{2\,(aq)}$	$M(OH)_{2\,(aq)} + 2HCl_{(aq)} \rightarrow MCl_{2\,(aq)} + 2H_2O_{(l)}$

Solubility Trends Depend on the Compound Anion

1) Generally, compounds of Group 2 elements that contain **singly charged** negative ions (e.g. OH^-) **increase** in solubility down the group...
2) ...whereas compounds that contain **doubly charged** negative ions (e.g. SO_4^{2-} and CO_3^{2-}) **decrease** in solubility down the group.
3) You need to know the solubility trends for the Group 2 **hydroxides** and the **sulfates**.

Group 2 element	hydroxide (OH^-)	sulfate (SO_4^{2-})
magnesium	least soluble	most soluble
calcium	↓	↑
strontium		
barium	most soluble	least soluble

4) Most sulfates are soluble in water, but **barium sulfate** is **insoluble**.
5) Compounds like magnesium hydroxide that have **very low** solubilities are said to be **sparingly soluble**.

Practice Questions

Q1 Which is the least reactive metal in Group 2?

Q2 Why does reactivity with water increase down Group 2?

Q3 Describe two reactions of a Group 2 oxide that show it to be a base.

Q4 Which is less soluble, barium hydroxide or magnesium hydroxide?

Q5 Which is more soluble, strontium sulfate or calcium sulfate?

Exam Questions

Q1 Barium and calcium are both Group 2 elements.

a) Which of the following would be more soluble than calcium hydroxide?

A magnesium hydroxide only
B strontium hydroxide and barium hydroxide
C strontium hydroxide only
D magnesium hydroxide and barium hydroxide [1 mark]

b) Which, out of barium and calcium, has the highest, combined first and second ionisation energy? Explain your answer. [4 marks]

c) Calcium can be burned in chlorine gas. Write an equation, including state symbols, for the reaction. [1 mark]

Q2 a) Write a balanced equation for the reaction of magnesium hydroxide with dilute hydrochloric acid. [2 marks]

b) Write a balanced equation for the reaction of calcium oxide with water. [2 marks]

I'm not gonna make it. You've gotta get me out of here, Doc...

We're deep in the dense jungle of Inorganic Chemistry now. Those carefree days of atomic structure are well behind us. It's now an endurance test and you've just got to keep going. It's tough, but you've got to stay awake and keep learning.

Group 1 and 2 Compounds

These pages are about Group 1 and 2 compounds, starting with the thermal stability of their carbonates and nitrates. So — quick, get your vest and long johns on before you topple over — we haven't even started yet.

Thermal Stability of Carbonates and Nitrates *Changes* Down the Group

Thermal decomposition is when a substance **breaks down** (decomposes) when **heated**.
The more thermally stable a substance is, the more heat it will take to break it down.

Thermal stability increases down a group

The carbonate and nitrate ions are **large negative ions (anions)** and can be made **unstable** by the presence of a **positively charged ion** (a cation). The cation **polarises** the anion, distorting it. The greater the distortion, the less stable the compound.

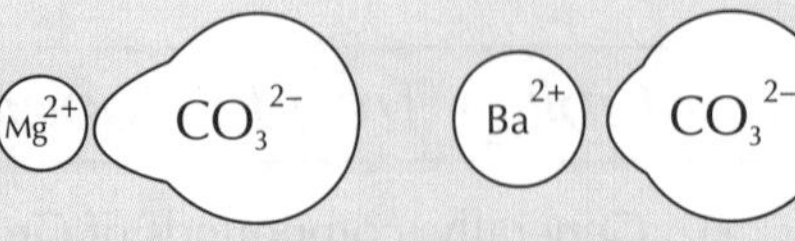

Magnesium ions polarise carbonate ions more than barium ions do, meaning magnesium carbonate is less stable.

Large cations cause **less distortion** than small cations as they have a lower charge density — the charge on the ion is spread out over a larger area. So the further down the group, the larger the cations, the lower the charge density so the less distortion caused and the **more stable** the carbonate/nitrate compound.

Group 2 compounds are less thermally stable than Group 1 compounds

The greater the **charge** on the cation, the greater the **distortion** and the **less stable** the carbonate/nitrate compound becomes. Group 2 cations have a **+2** charge, compared to a **+1** charge for Group 1 cations. So Group 2 carbonates and nitrates are less stable than those of Group 1.

Group 1	Group 2
Group 1 carbonates* are **thermally stable** — you can't heat them enough with a Bunsen to make them decompose (though they do decompose at higher temperatures). *except Li_2CO_3 which decomposes to Li_2O and CO_2 (there's always one...).	Group 2 carbonates decompose to form the **oxide** and **carbon dioxide**. $MCO_{3\,(s)} \rightarrow MO_{(s)} + CO_{2\,(g)}$ e.g. $CaCO_{3\,(s)} \rightarrow CaO_{(s)} + CO_{2\,(g)}$ calcium carbonate → calcium oxide
Group 1 nitrates** decompose to form the **nitrite** and **oxygen**. $2MNO_{3\,(s)} \rightarrow 2MNO_{2\,(s)} + O_{2\,(g)}$ e.g. $2KNO_{3\,(s)} \rightarrow 2KNO_{2\,(s)} + O_{2\,(g)}$ potassium nitrate → potassium nitrite **except $LiNO_3$ which decomposes to form Li_2O, NO_2 and O_2.	Group 2 nitrates decompose to form the **oxide**, **nitrogen dioxide** and **oxygen**. $2M(NO_3)_{2\,(s)} \rightarrow 2MO_{(s)} + 4NO_{2\,(g)} + O_{2\,(g)}$ e.g. $2Ca(NO_3)_{2\,(s)} \rightarrow 2CaO_{(s)} + 4NO_{2\,(g)} + O_{2\,(g)}$ calcium nitrate → calcium oxide, nitrogen dioxide

Here's How to Test *the* Thermal Stability of Nitrates and Carbonates

How easily nitrates decompose can be tested by measuring...

- how long it takes until a certain amount of **oxygen** is produced (i.e. enough to relight a glowing splint).
- how long it takes until an amount of **brown gas (NO_2)** is produced. This needs to be done in a fume cupboard because NO_2 is **toxic**.

Daisy the cow*

How easily carbonates decompose can be tested by measuring...

- how long it takes for an amount of **carbon dioxide** to be produced. You test for carbon dioxide using lime water — which is a saturated solution of calcium hydroxide. This turns cloudy with carbon dioxide.

You can collect gas using a gas syringe or a test tube upturned in a beaker of water.

* She wanted to be in the book. I said OK.

Group 1 and 2 Compoun

Group 1 and 2 Compounds Burn with Distinctive **Flame Col**

...not all of them, but quite a few. For compounds containing the ions below, flame te

Flame colours of Group 1 and 2 metals and their compounds

Li	red		
Na	orange/yellow	**Ca**	brick-red
K	lilac	**Sr**	crimson
Rb	red	**Ba**	green
Cs	blue		

Here's how to do a flame test:

1) Mix a small amount of the compound you're testing with a few drops of **hydrochloric acid.**
2) Heat a piece of **platinum or nichrome wire** in a hot Bunsen flame to clean it.
3) Dip the wire into the **compound/acid mixture.** Hold it in a very hot flame and note the **colour** produced.

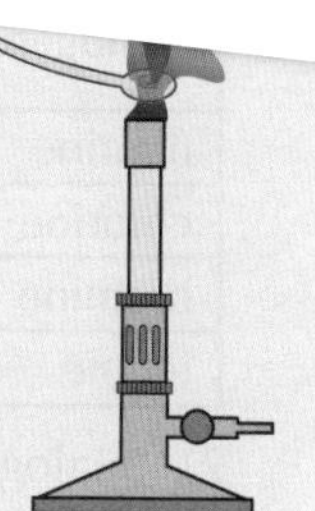

The explanation:
The **energy** absorbed from the flame causes electrons to move to **higher energy levels.** The colours are seen as the electrons fall back down to lower energy levels, releasing energy in the form of **light.** The difference in energy between the higher and lower levels determines the **wavelength** of the light released — which determines the **colour** of the light.

The movement of electrons between energy levels is called electron transition.

The principle is the same as for the formation of atomic emission spectra (see page 12).

Practice Questions

Q1 What is the trend in the thermal stability of the nitrates of Group 1 elements?

Q2 Write a general equation for the thermal decomposition of a Group 2 carbonate. Use M to represent the Group 2 metal.

Q3 Describe two ways that you could test how easily the nitrates of Group 2 decompose.

Q4 Which Group 1 or 2 metal ions are indicated by the following flame colours?
a) lilac b) brick-red c) orange/yellow

Exam Questions

Q1 Barium and calcium are both Group 2 elements. They both form carbonates.

a) Write a balanced equation for the thermal decomposition of calcium carbonate, including state symbols. [2 marks]

b) State whether barium carbonate or calcium carbonate is more thermally stable. Explain your answer. [3 marks]

Q2 a) Write a balanced equation, including state symbols, for the thermal decomposition of sodium nitrate. [1 mark]

b) How could you test for the gas produced in the thermal decomposition? [1 mark]

c) Place the following in order of ease of thermal decomposition (easiest first).

magnesium nitrate **potassium nitrate** **sodium nitrate**

Explain your answer. [3 marks]

Q3 a) When a substance is heated, what changes occur within the atom that give rise to a coloured flame? [2 marks]

b) A compound gives a blue colour in a flame test. What s-block metal ions might this compound contain? [1 mark]

Bored of Group 2? Me too. Let's play noughts and crosses...

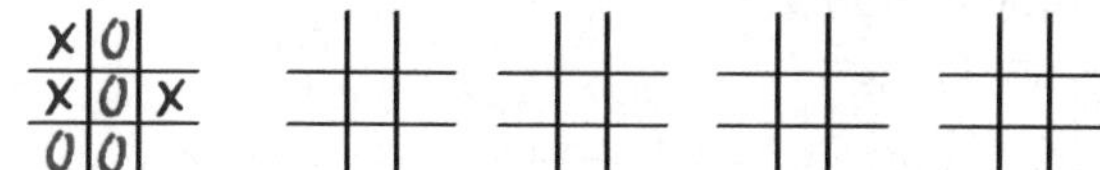

Noughts and crosses is pretty rubbish really, isn't it? It's always a draw. Ho hum. Back to Chemistry then, I guess...

Halogens

to your hats... here come the halogens...

*Halogens are the **Highly Reactive Non-Metals** of Group 7*

1) The table below gives some of the main properties of the first 4 halogens.

halogen	formula	colour	physical state (at room temp.)	electronic structure	electronegativity
fluorine	F_2	pale yellow	gas	$1s^2\ 2s^2\ 2p^5$	increases up the group ↑
chlorine	Cl_2	green	gas	$1s^2\ 2s^2\ 2p^6\ 3s^2\ 3p^5$	
bromine	Br_2	red-brown	liquid	$1s^2\ 2s^2\ 2p^6\ 3s^2\ 3p^6\ 3d^{10}\ 4s^2\ 4p^5$	
iodine	I_2	grey	solid	$1s^2\ 2s^2\ 2p^6\ 3s^2\ 3p^6\ 3d^{10}\ 4s^2\ 4p^6\ 4d^{10}\ 5s^2\ 5p^5$	

2) Halogens in their natural state exist as covalent diatomic molecules (e.g. Br_2, Cl_2). Because they're non-polar, they have **low solubility in water**.
3) But they do dissolve easily in **organic compounds** like hexane. Some of these resulting solutions have distinctive colours that can be used to identify them.

	colour in water	colour in hexane
chlorine	virtually colourless	virtually colourless
bromine	yellow/orange	orange/red
iodine	brown	pink/violet

*Halogens get **Less Reactive** Down the Group*

1) Halogen atoms usually react by **gaining an electron** in their outer p subshell — this means they're **reduced**. As they're reduced, they **oxidise** another substance (it's a redox reaction) — so they're **oxidising agents**.

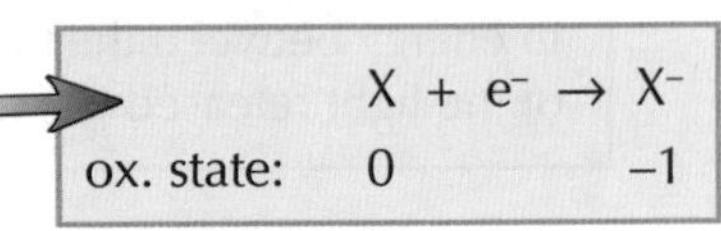

2) As you go down the group, the atoms become **larger**, so their outer electrons are **further** from the nucleus. The outer electrons are also **shielded** more from the attraction of the positive nucleus, because there are more inner electrons. This makes it harder for larger atoms to attract the electron needed to form an ion. So larger atoms are **less reactive** and reactivity **decreases** down the group.
3) This also explains the trend in **electronegativity**. Electronegativity is a measure of how well an atom attracts electrons in a covalent bond (see page 28). Electronegativity **decreases** down Group 7 due to the increase in the number of inner **electron shells** and the increase in **distance** between the nucleus and the bonding electrons.

***Melting** and **Boiling Points Increase** Down the Group*

1) As you go down Group 7, there's an increase in **electron shells** (and therefore electrons). This means the **London forces** (see pages 30-31) between the halogen molecules get stronger.
2) The increase in London forces makes it harder to overcome the intermolecular forces, and so **melting and boiling points** also **increase**.
3) The chemistry of **fluorine** and **astatine** is hard to study. Fluorine is a toxic gas and astatine is highly radioactive and decays quickly. But, you can **predict** how they will behave by looking at the trends in the behaviour of the other halogens. Generally, they **fit** with the trends seen down the other elements in Group 7.

Halogen	Melting Point / °C	Boiling Point / °C
F	−220	−188
Cl	−102	−34
Br	−7	59
I	114	184
At		

(Increasing Reactivity ↑ up the group)

*Halogens can **Displace** Halide Ions from Solution*

1) A displacement reaction is a type of reaction where one element **replaces** another element in a compound.

   For example, if you add **aqueous chlorine** to a **potassium bromide solution**, the chlorine kicks the bromine out and takes its place:

   $$Cl_{2(aq)} + 2KBr_{(aq)} \rightarrow 2KCl_{(aq)} + Br_{2(aq)}$$

   This is the full equation — the ionic equation is on the next page.

2) The halogens' **relative oxidising strengths** can be seen in their **displacement reactions** with halide ions.
3) In a **displacement reaction**, a **more reactive** halogen will replace a **less reactive** halide in a solution:

- **Chlorine** (Cl_2) will displace both **bromide** (Br^-) and **iodide** (I^-) ions.
- **Bromine** (Br_2) will displace **iodide** (I^-) but **not** chloride (Cl^-) ions.
- **Iodine** (I_2) will **not** displace chloride (Cl^-) or bromide (Br^-) ions.

'Halogen' should be used when describing the atom (X) or molecule (X_2), but 'halide' is used to describe the negative ion (X^-).

Halogens

Halogen-Halide Reactions are *Redox Reactions*

Ionic half-equations only show the reacting species. See page 58 for more.

1) A displacement reaction between halogens and halides is a **redox reaction**.
The thing that is **displaced** is **oxidised**, and the thing that does the **displacing** is **reduced**.

The half-equations for other halogen displacement reactions follow the same pattern.

Here are the **half-equations** for the reaction of chlorine with potassium bromide:

$Cl_2 + 2e^- \rightarrow 2Cl^-$ Chlorine **displaces** bromine and is **reduced**.

$2Br^- \rightarrow Br_2 + 2e^-$ Bromine **is displaced** by chlorine and gets **oxidised**.

2) This table shows the **ionic equations** for the reactions that happen if you add **aqueous halogen solutions** to solutions containing **halide ions.** (Remember, halogens only displace halides that are below them in the periodic table.)

	Potassium chloride solution $KCl_{(aq)}$ (colourless)	Potassium bromide solution $KBr_{(aq)}$ (colourless)	Potassium iodide solution $KI_{(aq)}$ (colourless)
Chlorine water $Cl_{2(aq)}$ (colourless)	no reaction	$Cl_{2\,(aq)} + 2Br^-_{(aq)} \rightarrow 2Cl^-_{(aq)} + Br_{2\,(aq)}$	$Cl_{2\,(aq)} + 2I^-_{(aq)} \rightarrow 2Cl^-_{(aq)} + I_{2\,(aq)}$
Bromine water $Br_{2(aq)}$ (orange)	no reaction	no reaction	$Br_{2\,(aq)} + 2I^-_{(aq)} \rightarrow 2Br^-_{(aq)} + I_{2\,(aq)}$
Iodine solution $I_{2(aq)}$ (brown)	no reaction	no reaction	no reaction

3) If a reaction takes place, you will see a **colour change**:
   - If bromide is displaced and bromine (Br_2) is formed, the reaction mixture will turn **orange**.
   - If iodide is displaced and iodine (I_2) is formed, the reaction mixture will turn **brown**.

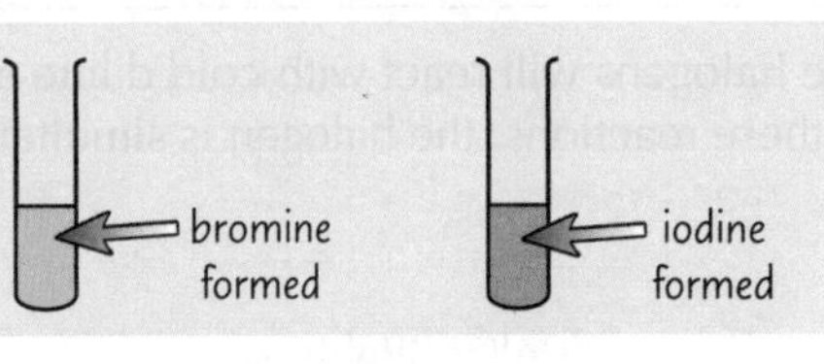

4) You can make these changes easier to see by shaking the reaction mixture with an **organic solvent** like hexane. The halogen that's present will dissolve in the organic solvent, which settles out as a distinct layer above the aqueous solution.

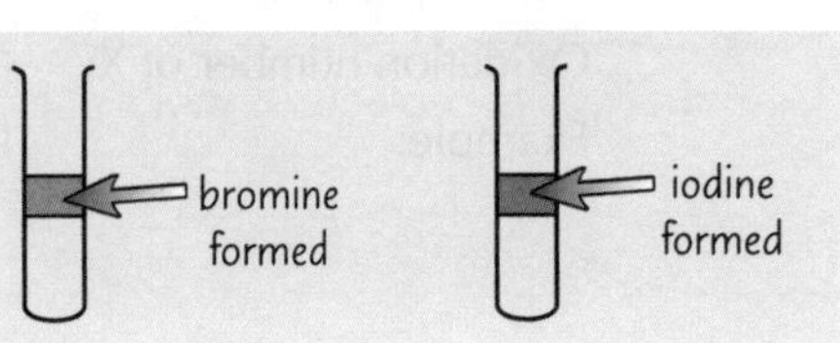

Practice Questions

Q1 What colour is a solution of bromine in water? And in hexane?

Q2 Going down the group, the halogens become less reactive. Explain why.

Q3 Write an ionic equation for the reaction that occurs when potassium iodide is added to bromine water.

Exam Questions

Q1 The halogens can be found in Group 7 of the periodic table.

a) Write an ionic equation for the reaction between chlorine solution and sodium bromide (NaBr). [1 mark]

b) Describe and explain the trend in the boiling points of the halogens. [3 marks]

Q2 A student has a sample of an aqueous potassium halide solution. She knows it contains either chloride, bromide or iodide ions. The student adds a few drops of aqueous bromine solution to the test tube and a reaction takes place.

a) Which halide ion is present in the potassium halide solution? [1 mark]

b) What colour will the aqueous solution in the test tube be after the reaction has finished? [1 mark]

Bromine molecules — Chemistry's greatest Bromance...

This looks like a lot of tricky stuff, but really it all boils down to just spending a bit of time learning it. Make sure you can remember the Group 7 trends, and that you're able to explain them too. But it's not all bad — you get a periodic table in the exam, so you don't have to remember what order the halogens come in. Sounds like you're being spoilt, to me...

Reactions of Halogens

Here comes another page jam-packed with golden nuggets of halogen fun. Oh yes, I kid you not. This page is the roller coaster of Chemistry... white-knuckle excitement all the way...

Halogens are toxic, so make sure you carry out any reactions with them in a fume cupboard.

Halogens Can React with **Group 1** and **Group 2 Metals**

Remember, when halogens react they're **reduced** — and they **oxidise** other substances.
For example, they oxidise Group 1 and Group 2 metals in reactions that produce **halide salts**.

Group 1 Metals...

E.g. $2Li_{(s)} + F_{2\,(g)} \rightarrow 2LiF_{(s)}$

ox. state of Li: **0** → **+1** oxidation **Lithium is oxidised:** $Li \rightarrow Li^+ + e^-$

ox. state of F: **0** → **–1** reduction **Fluorine is reduced:** $F_2 + 2e^- \rightarrow 2F^-$

Group 2 Metals...

E.g. $Mg_{(s)} + Cl_{2\,(g)} \rightarrow MgCl_{2(s)}$

ox. state of Mg: **0** → **+2** oxidation **Magnesium is oxidised:** $Mg \rightarrow Mg^{2+} + 2e^-$

ox. state of Cl: **0** → **–1** reduction **Chlorine is reduced:** $Cl_2 + 2e^- \rightarrow 2Cl^-$

Halogens Undergo **Disproportionation** with Cold Alkalis

The halogens will react with cold dilute alkali solutions.
In these reactions, the halogen is simultaneously oxidised and reduced (called **disproportionation**)...

$$\mathbf{X_2 + 2NaOH \rightarrow NaOX + NaX + H_2O}$$

Ionic equation: $X_2 + 2OH^- \rightarrow OX^- + X^- + H_2O$

Oxidation number of X: 0, +1, –1

Example: $I_2 + 2NaOH \rightarrow NaOI + NaI + H_2O$ (NaOI: sodium iodate(I))

X represents any halogen.

The halogens (except fluorine) can exist in a wide range of **oxidation states**.
For example:

Fluorine can't form F^+ ions — its oxidation number is always either 0 or –1.

Oxidation state	–1	0	+1	+1	+3	+5	+7
Ion	Cl^-	Cl	ClO^-	BrO^-	BrO_2^-	IO_3^-	IO_4^-
Name	chloride	chlorine	chlorate(I)	bromate(I)	bromate(III)	iodate(V)	iodate(VII)

Chlorine and **Sodium Hydroxide** make Bleach

If you mix chlorine gas with cold, dilute aqueous sodium hydroxide, the above reaction takes place and you get **sodium chlorate(I) solution**, $NaClO_{(aq)}$, which just happens to be **bleach**.

$$2NaOH_{(aq)} + Cl_{2\,(g)} \rightarrow NaClO_{(aq)} + NaCl_{(aq)} + H_2O_{(l)}$$

Oxidation number of Cl: **0** (in Cl_2), **+1** (in NaClO), **–1** (in NaCl)

The oxidation number of Cl goes up and down so, you guessed it, it's disproportionation. Hurray.

The sodium chlorite(I) solution (bleach) has loads of uses — it's used in **water treatment**, to bleach **paper** and **textiles**... and it's good for **cleaning toilets**, too. Handy...

Reactions of Halogens

Halogens Also Undergo **Disproportionation** with Hot Alkalis

In reactions with **hot alkalis**, halogens are also simultaneously oxidised and reduced (disproportionation).

	$3X_2 + 6NaOH \rightarrow NaXO_3 + 5NaX + 3H_2O$
Ionic equation:	$3X_2 + 6OH^- \rightarrow XO_3^- + 5X^- + 3H_2O$
Oxidation number of X:	0 +5 −1
Example:	$3Cl_2 + 6NaOH \rightarrow NaClO_3 + 5NaCl + 3H_2O$
	sodium chlorate(V)

You can use other alkalis too, e.g. KOH.

Reactions using chlorine need to be carried out in a fume cupboard because it's toxic.

Chlorine is used to Kill Bacteria in Water

When you mix chlorine with water, it undergoes disproportionation.
You end up with a mixture of hydrochloric acid and **hypochlorous acid.**

	$Cl_{2\,(g)} + H_2O_{(l)}$ ⇌	$HCl_{(aq)}$ +	$HClO_{(aq)}$
Oxidation number of Cl:	**0**	**−1**	**+1**
		hydrochloric acid	hypochlorous acid

Bromine and iodine also undergo disproportionation when mixed with water.

Hypochlorous acid **ionises** to make **chlorate(I) ions** (also called hypochlorite ions).

$$HClO_{(aq)} + H_2O_{(l)} \rightleftharpoons ClO^-_{(aq)} + H_3O^+_{(aq)}$$

Chlorate(I) ions **kill bacteria**.

So, **adding chlorine** (or a compound containing hypochlorite ions) to water can make it safe to **drink** or **swim** in.

Talia was thrilled to hear that the water was safe to swim in.

Practice Questions

Q1 What is formed when a halogen reacts with a Group 1 metal?

Q2 How is common household bleach formed?

Q3 Write the equation for the reaction of chlorine with water. State underneath the oxidation numbers of the chlorine.

Exam Question

Q1 If liquid bromine is mixed with cold, dilute potassium hydroxide, potassium bromate(I) is formed.

a) Give the ionic equation for the reaction. [1 mark]

b) What type of reaction is this? [1 mark]

If liquid bromine is reacted with hot, dilute potassium hydroxide, a reaction, different to that outlined in a), occurs.

c) Write the equation for the reaction that occurs when liquid bromine is mixed with hot, dilute potassium hydroxide [2 marks]

Remain seated until the page comes to a halt. Please exit to the right...

Oooh, what a lovely page, if I do say so myself. I bet the question of how bleach is made and how chlorine reacts with sodium hydroxide has plagued your mind since childhood. Well now you know. And remember... anything that chlorine can do, bromine and iodine can generally do as well. Eeee... it's just fun, fun, fun all the way.

Reactions of Halides

Ah, halides. Personally, I can never get enough of them.

*The **Reducing Power** of Halides **Increases** Down the Group...*

A halide ion can act as a **reducing agent** by losing an electron from its outer shell (see the reaction with halogens on page 47). How easy this is depends on the **attraction** between the halide's **nucleus** and the outer **electrons**. As you go down the group, the attraction gets **weaker** because...

1) ... the ions get bigger, so the electrons are **further** away from the positive nucleus,
2) ... there are extra inner electron shells, so there's a greater **shielding** effect.

*...which Explains their Reactions with **Sulfuric Acid***

All the halides react with concentrated sulfuric acid to give a **hydrogen halide** as a product to start with. But what happens next depends on which halide you've got. Here are the reactions of the Group 1 halides.

Reaction of KF or KCl with H_2SO_4

$$KF_{(s)} + H_2SO_{4(l)} \rightarrow KHSO_{4(s)} + HF_{(g)}$$

$$KCl_{(s)} + H_2SO_{4(l)} \rightarrow KHSO_{4(s)} + HCl_{(g)}$$

1) Hydrogen fluoride (HF) or hydrogen chloride gas (HCl) is formed. You'll see misty fumes as the gas comes into contact with moisture in the air.
2) But fluoride ions (F^-) and chloride ions (Cl^-) aren't strong enough reducing agents to reduce the sulfuric acid, so the **reaction stops** there.
3) It's **not a redox reaction** — the oxidation numbers of the halide and sulfur stay the same (–1 and +6).

Reaction of KBr with H_2SO_4

$$KBr_{(s)} + H_2SO_{4(l)} \rightarrow KHSO_{4(s)} + HBr_{(g)}$$

$$2HBr_{(aq)} + H_2SO_{4(l)} \rightarrow Br_{2(g)} + SO_{2(g)} + 2H_2O_{(l)}$$

ox. state of S:	+6	→	+4	reduction
ox. state of Br:	–1	→	0	oxidation

1) The first reaction gives misty fumes of hydrogen bromide gas (HBr).
2) But bromide ions (Br^-) are a stronger reducing agent than chloride ions (Cl^-) and react with the H_2SO_4 in a **redox reaction.**
3) The reaction produces choking fumes of sulfur dioxide (SO_2) and orange fumes of bromine (Br_2).

Reaction of KI with H_2SO_4

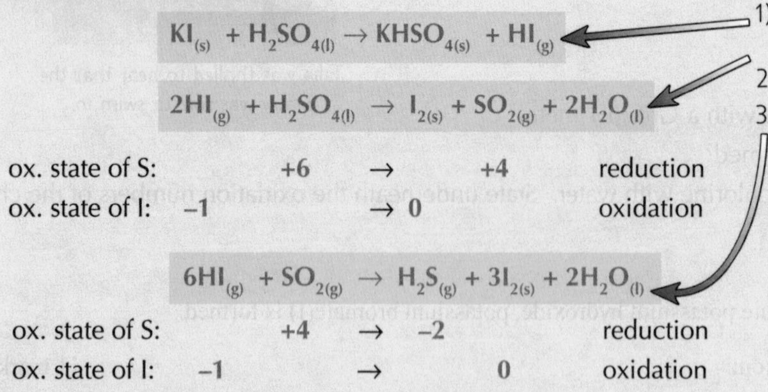

$$KI_{(s)} + H_2SO_{4(l)} \rightarrow KHSO_{4(s)} + HI_{(g)}$$

$$2HI_{(g)} + H_2SO_{4(l)} \rightarrow I_{2(s)} + SO_{2(g)} + 2H_2O_{(l)}$$

ox. state of S:	+6	→	+4	reduction
ox. state of I:	–1	→	0	oxidation

$$6HI_{(g)} + SO_{2(g)} \rightarrow H_2S_{(g)} + 3I_{2(s)} + 2H_2O_{(l)}$$

ox. state of S:	+4	→	–2	reduction
ox. state of I:	–1	→	0	oxidation

1) Same initial reaction giving hydrogen iodide (HI) gas.
2) Iodide ions (I^-) then reduce H_2SO_4 as above.
3) But I^- (being well 'ard as far as reducing agents go) keeps going and reduces the SO_2 to H_2S.

H_2S gas is toxic and smells of bad eggs. A bit like my mate Andy at times...

*Hydrogen Halides are **Acidic Gases***

The **hydrogen halides** are **colourless gases**, but you can't forget about them just cos you can't see 'em.

1) The **hydrogen halides** can dissolve in **water** (and moisture in the air) to produce misty fumes of acidic gas. (They'll happily turn damp, blue litmus paper red.)
2) Hydrogen chloride forms **hydrochloric** acid, hydrogen bromide forms **hydrobromic** acid and hydrogen iodide gives **hydroiodic** acid.
3) The hydrogen halides also react with **ammonia gas** to give **white fumes.** E.g. hydrogen chloride gives ammonium chloride.

E.g. $HCl_{(g)} \rightarrow H^+_{(aq)} + Cl^-_{(aq)}$

$HCl_{(g)} + H_2O \rightarrow H_3O^+_{(aq)} + Cl^-_{(aq)}$

E.g. $NH_{3(g)} + HCl_{(g)} \rightarrow NH_4Cl_{(s)}$

(It's an acid-base reaction.)

Reactions of Halides

Silver Ions React with Halide Ions to Form a Precipitate

Silver nitrate solution is corrosive, so be careful when handling it.

This can be used as a **test** for halides. First you add **dilute nitric acid** to remove ions which might interfere with the reaction. Then you just add **silver nitrate solution** ($AgNO_{3(aq)}$). A **precipitate** of the silver halide is formed.

$$Ag^{+}_{(aq)} + X^{-}_{(aq)} \rightarrow AgX_{(s)}$$ ...where X is Cl, Br or I

For example, if you add silver nitrate to **sodium chloride**:

$$Ag^{+}_{(aq)} + Cl^{-}_{(aq)} \rightarrow AgCl_{(s)}$$

The **colour** of the precipitate identifies the halide present in the original solution.

Halide	Precipitate formed
Fluoride, F^-	no precipitate (AgF is soluble)
Chloride, Cl^-	white precipitate
Bromide, Br^-	cream precipitate
Iodide, I^-	yellow precipitate

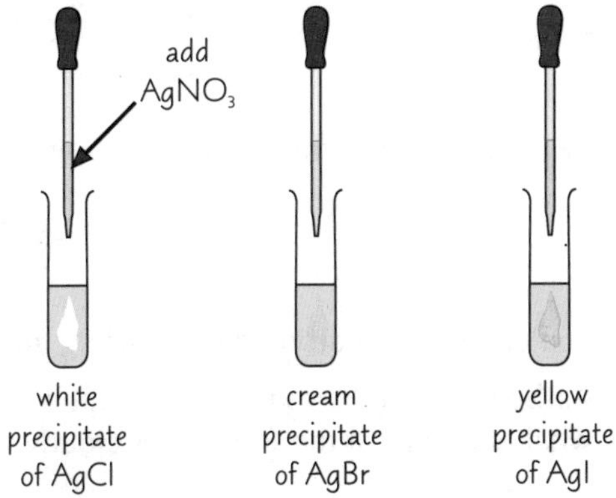

These precipitates can look quite similar, so it can be difficult to identify a halide based on just this test. Thankfully, you can tell them apart by watching what happens when you add some **ammonia solution**.

Original Precipitate	Observation
AgCl	precipitate dissolves in dilute ammonia solution to give a colourless solution
AgBr	precipitate remains unchanged if dilute ammonia solution is added, but will dissolve in concentrated ammonia solution to give a colourless solution
AgI	precipitate does not dissolve, even in concentrated ammonia solution

Practice Questions

Q1 Give two reasons why a bromide ion is a more powerful reducing agent than a chloride ion.

Q2 Name the gaseous products formed when potassium bromide reacts with concentrated sulfuric acid.

Q3 What type of substance is formed when a hydrogen halide is passed through water?

Q4 What would you see if you mixed hydrogen iodide with ammonia?

Q5 What colour precipitate forms during the reaction between silver ions and bromide ions?

Exam Questions

Q1 What colour precipitate would be produced from the reaction of sodium iodide with silver ions?

A yellow **B** white **C** blue **D** cream [1 mark]

Q2 A student carried out chemical tests using concentrated sulfuric acid in order to distinguish between solid samples of sodium chloride and sodium bromide. For each test, state what she would have observed and write an equation for the reaction which occurred. [6 marks]

Q3 Potassium iodide and potassium bromide both react with sulfuric acid. Compare the reactions of these two potassium halides with sulfuric acid. You should include suitable chemical equations in your answer. [6 marks]

Get your umbrella — there's silver halide precipitation heading this way...

Having to learn the reactions of the halides with silver nitrate can be a bore, but they're on the specification so you really do need to know 'em. You can't ignore the reactions of the halides with sulfuric acid either, or the reactions of hydrogen halides with ammonia and water. Sorry. Best thing for it is to just crack on I guess. Get yourself a cuppa first.

Tests for Ions

If you've got some unknown ions, there are some nifty little experiments you can do to identify them. There are tests for both positive ions and for negative ions. And that's what the next couple of pages are all about.

Hydrochloric Acid Can Help Detect **Carbonates**

The first of the negative ion tests is for **carbonate ions (CO_3^{2-})** and **hydrogencarbonate (HCO_3^-) ions**:

With dilute **hydrochloric acid**, **carbonates** will fizz because they give off **carbon dioxide**.

$$CO_3^{2-}{}_{(s)} + 2H^+_{(aq)} \rightarrow CO_{2\,(g)} + H_2O_{(l)}$$

With dilute **hydrochloric acid**, **hydrogencarbonates** will also fizz because they give off **carbon dioxide**.

$$HCO_3^-{}_{(s)} + H^+_{(aq)} \rightarrow CO_{2\,(g)} + H_2O_{(l)}$$

You can test for carbon dioxide using **limewater**.

Carbon dioxide **turns limewater cloudy** — just bubble the gas through a test tube of limewater and watch what happens. If the water goes cloudy you've identified a **carbonate ion** or a **hydrogencarbonate**.

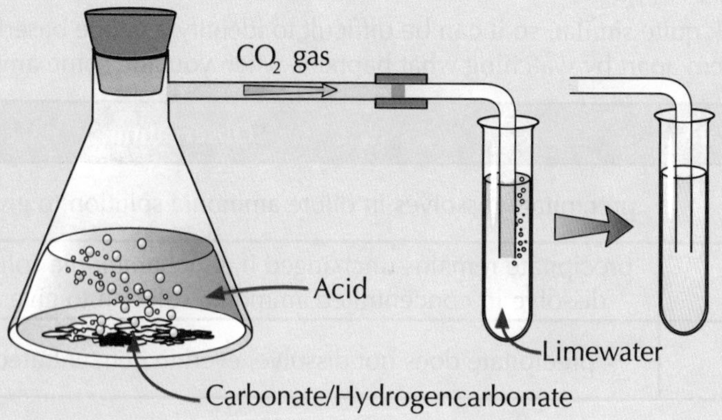

Test for **Sulfates** with **Hydrochloric Acid** and **Barium Chloride**

To identify a **sulfate** ion (SO_4^{2-}), add dilute HCl, followed by **barium chloride solution**, $BaCl_{2(aq)}$.

$$Ba^{2+}_{(aq)} + SO_4^{2-}{}_{(aq)} \rightarrow BaSO_{4\,(s)}$$

The hydrochloric acid is added to get rid of any traces of carbonate ions before you do the test. These would also produce a precipitate, so they'd confuse the results.

If a **white precipitate** of **barium sulfate** forms, it means the original compound contained a sulfate.

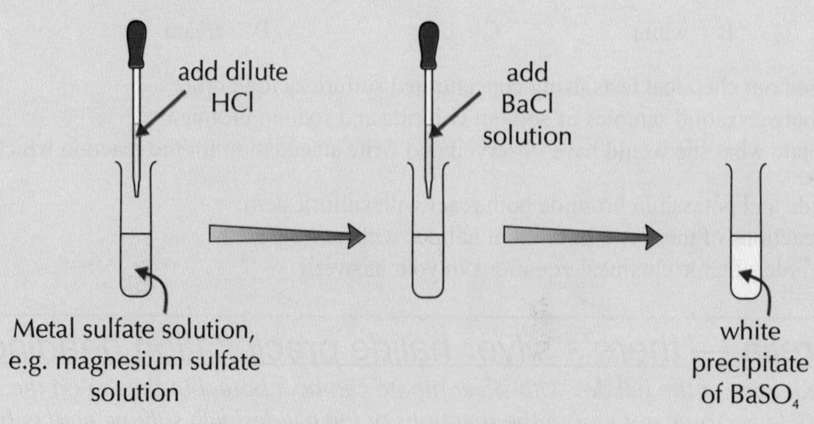

Tests for Ions

Use Litmus Paper and NaOH to Test for Ammonium Compounds

1) Ammonia gas (NH_3) is alkaline, so you can check for it using a damp piece of **red litmus paper**. If there's ammonia present, it'll dissolve in the water on the damp litmus paper, turning it **blue**.
2) You can use this to **test** whether a substance contains **ammonium ions** (NH_4^+). Add some **sodium hydroxide** to your mystery substance in a test tube and **gently heat** the mixture. If there's ammonia given off this means there are ammonium ions in your mystery substance.

$$NH_4^+{}_{(aq)} + OH^-{}_{(aq)} \rightarrow NH_{3(g)} + H_2O_{(l)}$$

You should do this experiment in a fume cupboard as it produces an irritant gas.

Example: $NH_4Cl_{(aq)} + NaOH_{(aq)} \rightarrow NH_{3(g)} + H_2O_{(l)} + NaCl_{(aq)}$

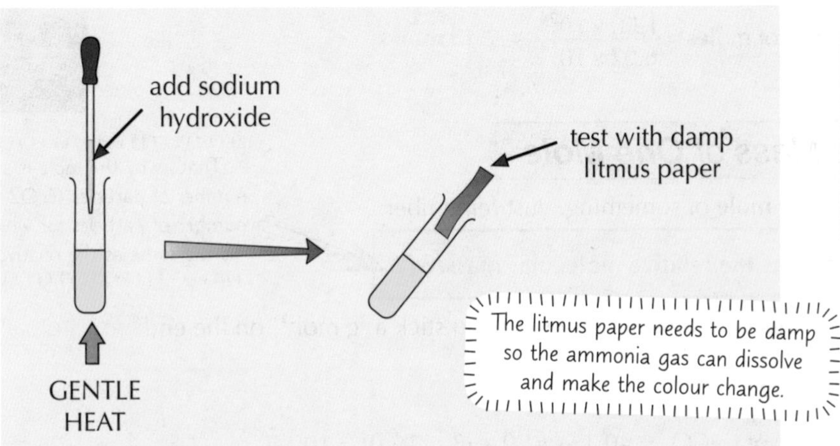
add sodium hydroxide
test with damp litmus paper
GENTLE HEAT
The litmus paper needs to be damp so the ammonia gas can dissolve and make the colour change.

Geoff's iron test had gone well.

Practice Questions

Q1 What substance do you need to add to a sample to test for hydrogencarbonate ions?

Q2 a) Why is dilute HCl added to a compound as the first step in a test for sulfates?

b) Name the second substance you need to add to a sample to test for sulfates.

Q3 a) In which ion test would you use damp red litmus paper?

b) Why does the litmus paper need to be damp?

Exam Questions

Q1 Describe a test that can be used to test for carbonates in a solution. [2 marks]

Q2 a) What colour precipitate would be produced from the reaction of calcium sulfate and barium chloride solution?

A yellow
B brick red
C white
D pale blue
[1 mark]

b) Write an ionic equation to show the formation of the precipitate in the reaction between magnesium sulfate and barium chloride solution, including state symbols. [2 marks]

Q3 A student is given a solution of ammonium bromide.
Describe how the student could prove that the solution contains ammonium ions. [2 marks]

I've got my ion you...

Remember, you know some other ways to identify ions too. You learnt about flame tests on p.45, which help to identify Group 1 and 2 metals. You also learnt about identifying halide ions using the colour of the precipitate formed when silver nitrate solution is added (p.51). Armed with this handful of tests, you're ready to do some fine detective work.

The Mole

It'd be handy to be able to count out atoms — but they're way too tiny. You'd never be able to pick them up with tweezers to count them. But never mind — by using the idea of relative mass, you can figure out how many you've got.

A Mole is Just a (Very Large) Certain Number of Particles

Chemists often talk about 'amount of substance'. Basically, all they mean is 'number of particles'.

1) Amount of substance is measured using a unit called the **mole** (or **mol**). The number of moles is given the symbol n.
2) The number of **particles** in one mole is 6.02×10^{23}. This number is **the Avogadro constant**, L. It's given to you in your data booklet in the exam, so don't worry about learning its value, just what it means.
3) It **doesn't matter** what the particles are. They can be atoms, molecules, penguins — **anything**.
4) Here's a nice simple formula for finding the number of moles from the number of atoms or molecules:

$$\text{Number of moles} = \frac{\text{Number of particles you have}}{\text{Number of particles in a mole}}$$

Example: I have 1.50×10^{24} carbon atoms. How many moles of carbon is this?

$$\text{Number of moles} = \frac{1.50 \times 10^{24}}{6.02 \times 10^{23}} \approx \mathbf{2.49\ moles}$$

Molar Mass is the Mass of One Mole

Molar mass, *M*, is the mass **per mole** of something. Just remember:

Molar mass is just the same as the relative molecular mass, M_r.

That's why the mole is such a ridiculous number of particles (6.02×10^{23}) — it's the number of particles for which the weight in g is the same as the relative molecular mass.

The only difference is it has units of 'grams per mole', so you stick a 'g mol^{-1}' on the end.

Example: Find the molar mass of $CaCO_3$.

Relative formula mass, M_r, of $CaCO_3$ = 40.1 + 12.0 + (3 × 16.0) = 100.1
So the molar mass, M, is **100.1 g mol^{-1}**. — i.e. 1 mole of $CaCO_3$ weighs 100.1 g.

Here's another formula.
This one's really important — you need it **all the time**:

$$\text{Number of moles} = \frac{\text{mass of substance}}{\text{molar mass}}$$

You can re-arrange this equation using this formula triangle: mass / moles | molar mass

Example: How many moles of aluminium oxide are present in 5.1 g of Al_2O_3?

Molar mass, M, of Al_2O_3 = (2 × 27.0) + (3 × 16.0) = 102.0 g mol^{-1}

Number of moles of $Al_2O_3 = \frac{5.1}{102.0}$ = **0.050 moles**

Example: How many moles of chlorine molecules are present in 71.0 g of chlorine gas?

We're talking chlorine **molecules** (not chlorine atoms), so it's Cl_2 we're interested in.
Molar mass, M, of Cl_2 = (2 × 35.5) = 71.0 g mol^{-1}

Number of moles of $Cl_2 = \frac{71.0}{71.0}$ = **1.00 mole**

But note that it would be 2 moles of chlorine atoms, since chlorine atoms have a molar mass of 35.5 g mol^{-1}.

You Need to be Able to Work Out the Number of Atoms in Something

Example: How many atoms are in 8.5 g of H_2S?

Molar mass, M, of H_2S = 1.0 + 1.0 + 32.1 = 34.1 g mol^{-1}
Number of moles of $H_2S = \frac{8.5}{34.1}$ = 0.249... moles
Number of molecules of H_2S = 0.249... × 6.02×10^{23} = $1.50... \times 10^{23}$
There are 3 atoms in 1 molecule of H_2S so, total no. atoms = $1.50... \times 10^{23} \times 3$ = **4.5×10^{23}** (2 s.f.)

Multiplying moles by the Avogadro constant gives you the number of molecules/particles.

The Mole

The **Concentration** of a Solution Can be Measured in **mol dm^{-3}**...

1) The **concentration** of a solution is how many **moles** are dissolved per **1 dm^3** (that's 1 litre) of solution. The units are **mol dm^{-3}**.
2) Here's the formula to find the **number of moles**:

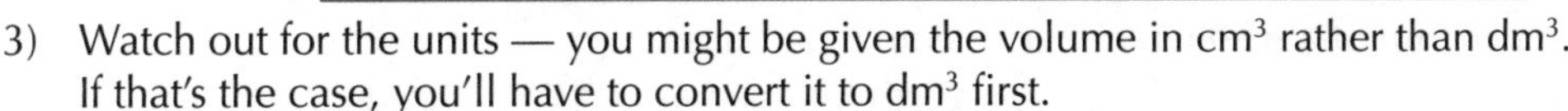

Number of moles = Concentration (mol dm^{-3}) × Volume (dm^3)

This one can go in a handy formula triangle too:

moles / conc. | vol.

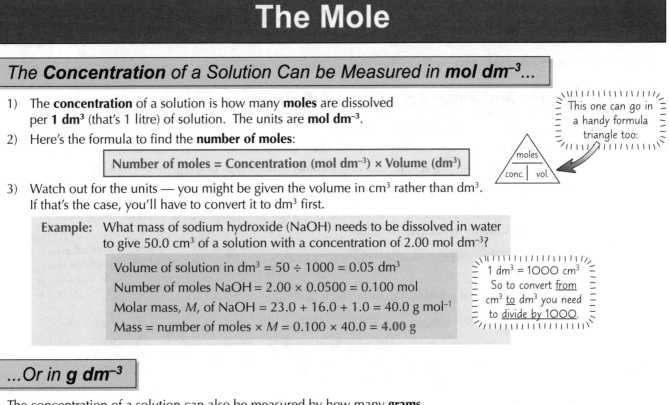

3) Watch out for the units — you might be given the volume in cm^3 rather than dm^3. If that's the case, you'll have to convert it to dm^3 first.

Example: What mass of sodium hydroxide (NaOH) needs to be dissolved in water to give 50.0 cm^3 of a solution with a concentration of 2.00 mol dm^{-3}?

Volume of solution in dm^3 = 50 ÷ 1000 = 0.05 dm^3
Number of moles NaOH = 2.00 × 0.0500 = 0.100 mol
Molar mass, *M*, of NaOH = 23.0 + 16.0 + 1.0 = 40.0 g mol^{-1}
Mass = number of moles × *M* = 0.100 × 40.0 = **4.00 g**

1 dm^3 = 1000 cm^3. So to convert from cm^3 to dm^3 you need to divide by 1000.

...Or in **g dm^{-3}**

The concentration of a solution can also be measured by how many **grams** of a substance are dissolved per **1 dm^3** of the solution. The units are **g dm^{-3}**.

Here's the formula to find the mass of the substance dissolved in a given volume of solution:

Mass of substance = Concentration (g dm^{-3}) × Volume (dm^3)

Example: What is the concentration, in g dm^{-3}, of a solution of sodium chloride (NaCl) that was made by dissolving 0.0210 mol NaCl in 16.0 cm^3 of water?

Volume of solution in dm^3 = 16.0 ÷ 1000 = 0.0160 dm^3
Molar mass, *M*, of NaCl = 23.0 + 35.5 = 58.5 g mol^{-1}
Mass of NaCl = 0.0210 mol × 58.5 = 1.2285 g

$$\text{Concentration} = \frac{\text{Mass of substance}}{\text{Volume}} = \frac{1.2285}{0.016} = 76.8 \text{ g dm}^{-3} \text{ (3 s.f.)}$$

Practice Questions

Q1 How many particles are there in one mole?

Q2 What are the units of molar mass?

Q3 What formula links the concentration in mol dm^{-3} to the number of moles and the volume of a solution?

Exam Questions

Q1 How many moles of calcium sulfate are there in 34.05 g of $CaSO_4$? [1 mark]

Q2 Calculate the mass of 0.360 moles of ethanoic acid (CH_3COOH). [1 mark]

Q3 Calculate the concentration, in g dm^{-3}, of 0.100 moles of HCl dissolved in 100 cm^3 of water. [2 marks]

Q4 What mass of H_2SO_4 is needed to produce 60.0 cm^3 of 0.250 mol dm^{-3} solution? [2 marks]

Q5 A 0.500 g sample of sterling silver is dissolved in 15.0 cm^3 concentrated nitric acid, and then an excess of potassium iodide is added. All the silver in the solution precipitates out as solid silver iodide ($AgI_{(s)}$). The total mass of the dry silver iodide precipitate formed is 1.01 g. What was the concentration, in mol dm^{-3}, of the silver ions in the solution before the addition of potassium iodide? [2 marks]

Put your back teeth on the scale and find out your molar mass...

You need this stuff for loads of the calculation questions you might get, so learn it inside out. Before you start plugging numbers into formulae, make sure they're in the right units. If they're not, you need to know how to convert them or you'll be tossing marks out the window. Learn all the definitions and formulae, then have a bash at the questions.

Empirical and Molecular Formulae

Here's another page piled high with numbers — it's all just glorified maths really.

Empirical and *Molecular* Formulae are *Ratios*

You have to know what's what with empirical and molecular formulae, so here goes...

1) The **empirical formula** gives the smallest whole number ratio of atoms of each element in a compound.
2) The **molecular formula** gives the **actual** numbers of atoms of each type of element in a molecule.
3) The molecular formula is made up of a **whole number** of empirical units.

Example: A molecule has an empirical formula of $C_4H_3O_2$, and a molecular mass of 166 g mol^{-1}. Work out its molecular formula.

First find the empirical mass: (4 × 12.0) + (3 × 1.0) + (2 × 16.0)
= 48.0 + 3.0 + 32.0 = 83.0 g mol^{-1}

But the molecular mass is 166 g mol^{-1},

so there are $\frac{166}{83.0} = 2$ empirical units in the molecule.

The molecular formula must be the empirical formula × 2,

so the molecular formula = $C_8H_6O_4$.

Compare the empirical and molecular masses.

Empirical mass is just like the relative formula mass... (if that helps at all...).

Empirical Formulae are Calculated from *Experiments*

You need to be able to work out empirical formulae from **experimental results**.

Example: When a hydrocarbon is burnt in excess oxygen, 4.4 g of carbon dioxide and 1.8 g of water are made. What is the empirical formula of the hydrocarbon?

First work out how many moles of the products you have.

$$\text{No. of moles of } CO_2 = \frac{\text{mass}}{M} = \frac{4.4}{12.0 + (2 \times 16.0)} = \frac{4.4}{44.0} = 0.10 \text{ moles}$$

1 mole of CO_2 contains 1 mole of carbon atoms, so you must have started with **0.10 moles of carbon atoms.**

$$\text{No. of moles of } H_2O = \frac{1.8}{(2 \times 1.0) + 16.0} = \frac{1.8}{18.0} = 0.10 \text{ moles}$$

1 mole of H_2O contains 2 moles of hydrogen atoms (H), so you must have started with **0.20 moles of hydrogen atoms.**

Ratio C:H = 0.10:0.20. Now you divide both numbers by the smallest — here it's 0.10.
So, the ratio C:H = 1:2. So the empirical formula must be CH_2.

This works because the only place the carbon in the carbon dioxide and the hydrogen in the water could have come from is the hydrocarbon.

You also need to know how to work out empirical formulae from the **percentages** of the different elements.

Example: A compound is found to have percentage composition 56.5% potassium, 8.70% carbon and 34.8% oxygen by mass. Calculate its empirical formula.

In 100 g of compound there are:

$\frac{56.5}{39.1} = 1.45$ moles of K $\quad \frac{8.70}{12.0} = 0.725$ moles of C $\quad \frac{34.8}{16.0} = 2.18$ moles of O

Use $n = \frac{\text{mass}}{M}$

These answers are rounded to 3 significant figures.

Divide each number of moles by the smallest number — in this case it's 0.725.

K: $\frac{1.45}{0.725} = 2.00 \quad$ C: $\frac{0.725}{0.725} = 1.00 \quad$ O: $\frac{2.18}{0.725} = 3.01$

The ratio of K:C:O ≈ 2:1:3. So you know the empirical formula's got to be K_2CO_3.

The calculation above involves using percentage compositions. Sometimes you may have to calculate the **percentage composition** yourself, by working out the **proportions** of different elements in a given compound.

You use the formula: percentage composition of element X = $\frac{\text{total mass of element in compound}}{\text{total mass of compound}} \times 100\%$

Example: The percentage composition of H in CH_4 is $\frac{(4 \times 1.0)}{12.0 + (4 \times 1.0)} \times 100 = $ **25%**.

Empirical and Molecular Formulae

Molecular Formulae are Calculated from Experimental Data Too

Once you know the empirical formula, you just need a bit more info and you can work out the **molecular formula** too.

Example:
When 4.6 g of an alcohol, with molar mass 46 g mol^{-1}, is burnt in excess oxygen, it produces 8.8 g of carbon dioxide and 5.4 g of water.
Calculate the empirical formula for the alcohol and then its molecular formula.

Alcohols contain C, H and O.

The carbon in the CO_2 and the hydrogen in the H_2O must have come from the alcohol — work out the number of moles of each of these.

Number of moles of $CO_2 = \frac{\text{mass}}{M} = \frac{8.8}{44} = 0.20$ moles

1 mole of CO_2 contains 1 mole of C. So, 0.20 moles of CO_2 contains **0.20 moles of C.**

Number of moles $H_2O = \frac{\text{mass}}{M} = \frac{5.4}{18} = 0.30$ moles

1 mole of H_2O contains 2 moles of H. So, 0.30 moles of H_2O contains **0.60 moles of H.**

Mass of C = no. of moles × M = 0.20 × 12.0 = 2.4 g
Mass of H = no. of moles × M = 0.60 × 1.0 = 0.60 g
Mass of O = 4.6 − (2.4 + 0.60) = 1.6 g
Number of moles O = $\frac{\text{mass}}{M} = \frac{1.6}{16.0} =$ **0.10 moles**

Now work out the mass of carbon and hydrogen in the alcohol. The rest of the mass of the alcohol must be oxygen — so work out that too. Once you know the mass of O, you can work out how many moles there are of it.

Molar Ratio = C:H:O = 0.20:0.60:0.10 = 2:6:1
Empirical formula = C_2H_6O
Mass of empirical formula = (2 × 12.0) + (6 × 1.0) + 16.0 = 46.0 g
In this example, the mass of the empirical formula equals the molecular mass, so the empirical and molecular formulae are the same.
Molecular formula = C_2H_6O

When you know the number of moles of each element, you've got the molar ratio. Divide each number by the smallest.

Compare the empirical and molecular masses.

Practice Questions

Q1 What's the difference between a molecular formula and an empirical formula?

Q2 What's the formula to work out the percentage composition of an element in a substance?

Exam Questions

Q1 In an experiment to determine the formula of an oxide of copper, 2.80 g of the oxide was heated in a stream of hydrogen gas until there was no further mass change. 2.50 g of copper remained.

Calculate the empirical formula of the oxide. [A_r(Cu) = 63.5, A_r(O) = 16.0] [4 marks]

Q2 Hydrocarbon X has a molecular mass of 78.0 g. It is found to have 92.3% carbon and 7.70% hydrogen by mass. Calculate the empirical and molecular formulae of X. [3 marks]

Q3 When 1.20 g of magnesium ribbon is heated in air, it burns to form a white powder which has a mass of 2.00 g. What is the empirical formula of the powder? [2 marks]

Q4 When 19.8 g of an organic acid, A, is burnt in excess oxygen, 33.0 g of carbon dioxide and 10.8 g of water are produced.
Calculate the empirical formula for A and hence its molecular formula, if M_r(A) = 132. [4 marks]

The Empirical Strikes Back...

With this stuff, you can't just learn some facts parrot-fashion to regurgitate in the exam — you've gotta know how to use them. The only way to do that is to practise. Go through the examples on these two pages again, this time working the answers out for yourself. Then test yourself on the practice exam questions. It'll help you sleep at night — honest.

Chemical Equations

Balancing equations might cause you a few palpitations — as soon as you make one bit right, the rest goes pear-shaped.

Balanced Equations Have **Equal Numbers** of Each Atom on **Both Sides**

1) Balanced equations have the **same number** of each atom on **both** sides. They're... well... you know... balanced.
2) You can only add more atoms by adding **whole reactants** or **products**. You do this by putting a number **in front** of a substance or changing one that's already there. You **can't** mess with formulae — ever.

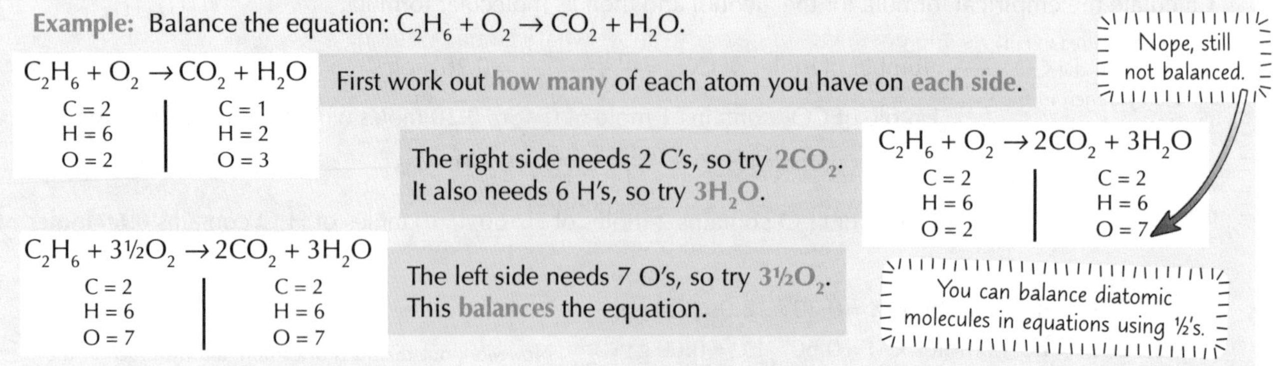

Example: Balance the equation: $C_2H_6 + O_2 \rightarrow CO_2 + H_2O$.
$C_2H_6 + O_2 \rightarrow CO_2 + H_2O$
C = 2 | C = 1
H = 6 | H = 2
O = 2 | O = 3
First work out how many of each atom you have on each side.
The right side needs 2 C's, so try $2CO_2$. It also needs 6 H's, so try $3H_2O$.
$C_2H_6 + O_2 \rightarrow 2CO_2 + 3H_2O$
C = 2 | C = 2
H = 6 | H = 6
O = 2 | O = 7
Nope, still not balanced.
$C_2H_6 + 3\frac{1}{2}O_2 \rightarrow 2CO_2 + 3H_2O$
C = 2 | C = 2
H = 6 | H = 6
O = 7 | O = 7
The left side needs 7 O's, so try $3\frac{1}{2}O_2$. This balances the equation.
You can balance diatomic molecules in equations using ½'s.

Ionic Equations Only Show the **Reacting Particles**

1) You can also write an **ionic equation** for any reaction involving **ions** that happens **in solution**.
2) In an ionic equation, only the **reacting particles** (and the **products** they form) are included.

Example: Here is the **full balanced equation** for the reaction of **nitric acid** with **sodium hydroxide**:

$$HNO_{3(aq)} + NaOH_{(aq)} \rightarrow NaNO_{3(aq)} + H_2O_{(l)}$$

These little symbols tell you what state each substance is in (see the next page).

The **ionic** substances in this equation will **dissolve**, breaking up into ions in solution. You can rewrite the equation to show all the **ions** that are in the reaction mixture:

$$H^+_{(aq)} + NO_3^-{}_{(aq)} + Na^+_{(aq)} + OH^-_{(aq)} \rightarrow Na^+_{(aq)} + NO_3^-{}_{(aq)} + H_2O_{(l)}$$

Leave anything that isn't an ion in solution (like the H_2O) as it is.

To get from this to the ionic equation, just cross out any ions that appear on **both sides** of the equation — in this case, that's the sodium ions (Na^+) and the nitrate ions (NO_3^-).

An ion that's present in the reaction mixture, but doesn't get involved in the reaction is called a spectator ion.

So the **ionic equation** for this reaction is:

$$\mathbf{H^+_{(aq)} + OH^-_{(aq)} \rightarrow H_2O_{(l)}}$$

3) When you've written an ionic equation, check that the **charges** are **balanced**, as well as the atoms — if the charges don't balance, the equation isn't right.

In the example above, the **net charge** on the left hand side is (+1 + −1) = **0** and the net charge on the right hand side is **0** — so the charges balance.

Balanced Equations Can Be Used to Work out **Masses**

Balanced equations show the **reaction stoichiometry**. The reaction stoichiometry tells you the ratios of reactants to products, i.e. how many moles of product are formed from a certain number of moles of reactants.

Example: Calculate the mass of iron oxide produced if 28 g of iron is burnt in air. $2Fe + \frac{3}{2}O_2 \rightarrow Fe_2O_3$

The molar mass, M, of Fe = 55.8 g mol^{-1}, so the number of moles in 28 g of Fe = $\frac{\text{mass}}{M} = \frac{28}{55.8} = 0.50$ moles.

From the equation: 2 moles of Fe produces 1 mole of Fe_2O_3, so 0.50 moles of Fe produce 0.25 moles of Fe_2O_3.

M of Fe_2O_3 = (2 × 55.8) + (3 × 16.0) = 159.6 g mol^{-1}

Mass of Fe_2O_3 = no. of moles × M = 0.25 × 159.6 = **40 g** (2 s.f.)

Once you know the number of moles and the molar mass (M) of Fe_2O_3, it's easy to work out the mass.

Chemical Equations

State Symbols Give a bit More Information about the Substances

State symbols are put after each reactant or product in an equation. They tell you what **state of matter** things are in.

s = solid	l = liquid
g = gas	aq = aqueous (solution in water)

To show you what I mean, here's an example —

$$CaCO_{3(s)} + 2HCl_{(aq)} \rightarrow CaCl_{2(aq)} + H_2O_{(l)} + CO_{2(g)}$$

solid, aqueous, aqueous, liquid, gas

You can use state symbols and chemical equations to show what's going on during a reaction...

In Displacement Reactions, One Element Replaces Another

Have a peek at pages 46-47 for more on the displacement reactions of halogens.

1) In displacement reactions, a **more reactive** element **reacts** to take the place of a less reactive element in a compound.
2) For example, **chlorine** reacts with **potassium bromide** to form **bromine** and **potassium chloride**.

Full equation: $Cl_{2(aq)} + 2KBr_{(aq)} \rightarrow Br_{2(aq)} + 2KCl_{(aq)}$

Ionic Equation: $Cl_{2(aq)} + 2Br^-_{(aq)} \rightarrow Br_{2(aq)} + 2Cl^-_{(aq)}$

In Reactions of Acids, a Salt and Water are Produced

When **bases** react with **acids**, a **salt** and **water** are always produced. Sometimes, other compounds such as **carbon dioxide gas** are also formed.

When acids react with bases, it's a neutralisation reaction.

Example: Sulfuric acid reacts with sodium hydroxide to form sodium sulfate and water:

$H_2SO_{4(aq)} + 2NaOH_{(aq)} \rightarrow Na_2SO_{4(aq)} + 2H_2O_{(l)}$

Ionic equation: $2H^+_{(aq)} + 2OH^-_{(aq)} \rightarrow 2H_2O_{(l)}$

Example: Nitric acid and sodium carbonate react to form sodium nitrate, water and carbon dioxide.

$2HNO_{3(aq)} + Na_2CO_{3(aq)} \rightarrow 2NaNO_{3(aq)} + H_2O_{(l)} + CO_{2(g)}$

Ionic equation: $2H^+_{(aq)} + CO_3^{2-}{}_{(aq)} \rightarrow H_2O_{(l)} + CO_{2(g)}$

In Precipitation Reactions, a Solid is Formed

If two **aqueous** compounds react together and one of the products forms as a **solid**, then a **precipitation reaction** has taken place.

E.g. barium chloride and potassium sulfate react to form potassium chloride and a **precipitate** of barium sulfate.

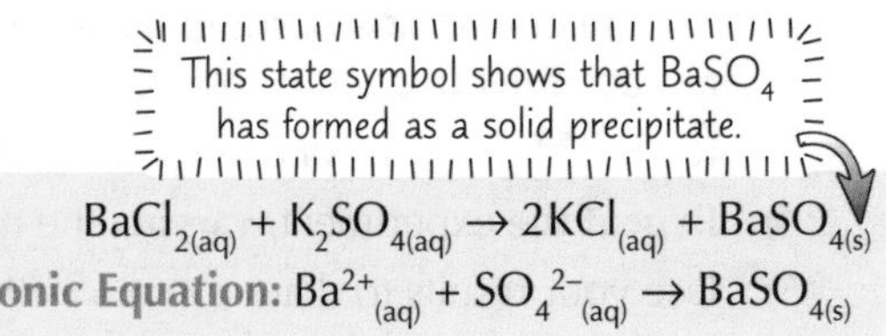

This state symbol shows that $BaSO_4$ has formed as a solid precipitate.

$BaCl_{2(aq)} + K_2SO_{4(aq)} \rightarrow 2KCl_{(aq)} + BaSO_{4(s)}$

Ionic Equation: $Ba^{2+}_{(aq)} + SO_4^{2-}{}_{(aq)} \rightarrow BaSO_{4(s)}$

Practice Questions

Q1 What is the difference between a full balanced equation and an ionic equation?

Q2 What is the state symbol for a solution of hydrochloric acid?

Exam Questions

Q1 Balance this equation: $KI_{(aq)} + Pb(NO_3)_{2\,(aq)} \rightarrow PbI_{2\,(s)} + KNO_{3\,(aq)}$ [1 mark]

Q2 Ethene (C_2H_4) reacts with hydrochloric acid (HCl) to produce chloroethane (C_2H_5Cl).
Calculate the mass of ethene required to produce 258 g of chloroethane. [4 marks]

Q3 A solution of magnesium chloride ($MgCl_2$) is mixed with a solution of silver nitrate ($AgNO_3$), resulting in a precipitation reaction to form silver chloride (AgCl) and a solution of magnesium nitrate ($Mg(NO_3)_2$).
Write a balanced ionic equation for this reaction, including state symbols. [2 marks]

Don't get in a state about equations...

Balancing equations is a really, really important skill in Chemistry, so make sure you can do it. You will ONLY be able to calculate reacting masses if you've got a balanced equation to work from. I've said it once, and I'll say it again — practise, practise, practise... It's the only road to salvation. (By the way, exactly where is salvation anyway?)

Calculations with Gases

You may think this page is full of hot air, but there are some important equations for calculating amounts of gases coming up.

All Gases Take Up the **Same Volume** under the Same Conditions

1) The space that one mole of a gas occupies at a certain temperature and pressure is known as the **molar gas volume**. It has units of **dm³ mol⁻¹**.
2) If temperature and pressure stay the same, **one mole** of **any** gas always has the **same volume**. At **room temperature and pressure** (r.t.p.), this happens to be **24 dm³ mol⁻¹** (r.t.p. is 293 K (20 °C) and 101.3 kPa). Meanwhile, at **standard temperature and pressure** (s.t.p.), it's **22.4 dm³ mol⁻¹** (s.t.p. is 273 K (0 °C) and 101.3 kPa).
3) Here's the formula for working out the number of moles in a volume of gas:

$$\text{Number of moles} = \frac{\text{Volume in dm}^3}{\text{Molar gas volume}}$$

At r.t.p., just substitute 24 dm³ mol⁻¹ into this equation as the molar gas volume. At s.t.p., substitute 22.4 dm³ mol⁻¹.

Example: How many moles are there in 6.0 dm³ of oxygen gas at r.t.p.?

Number of moles = $\frac{6.0}{24}$ = **0.25 moles of oxygen molecules**

You Can **Measure** the Molar Volume of a Gas

You can find the **volume** of gas evolved in a reaction by **collecting** the gas that is produced in a **gas syringe** or by **displacing water** from a **measuring cylinder**.

You can use **experiments** to work out the molar volume of a gas.

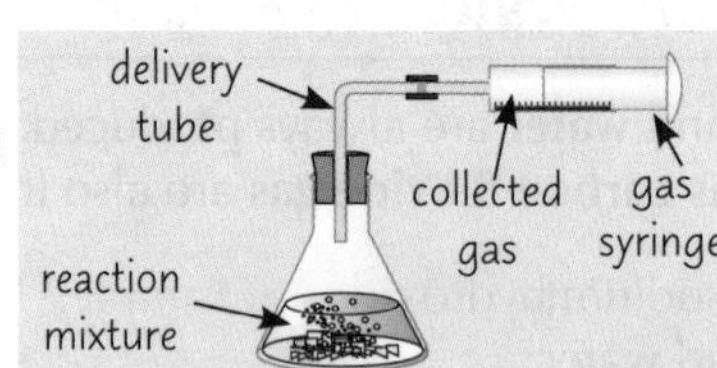

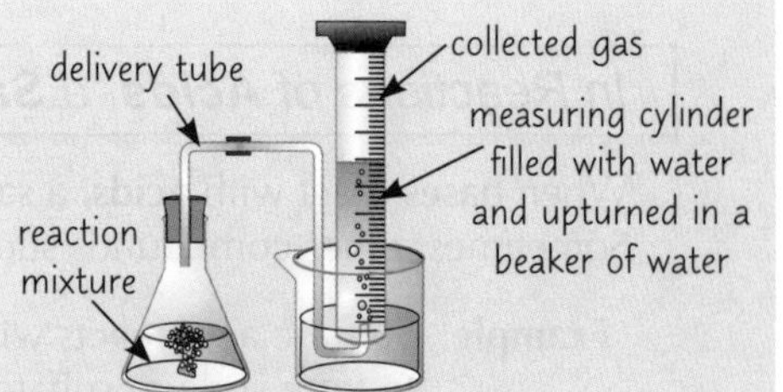

Example: Explain how you could measure the molar volume of carbon dioxide, in dm³, at room temperature using this reaction: $Na_2CO_{3\,(aq)} + 2HCl_{(aq)} \rightarrow NaCl_{(aq)} + H_2O_{(l)} + CO_{2\,(g)}$

1 dm³ = 1000 cm³

1) Measure out a set volume of hydrochloric acid into a conical flask connected to a **gas syringe**.
2) Add a **known mass** of sodium carbonate to the conical flask, replace the bung and allow the reaction to go to **completion**.
3) Record the **volume** of carbon dioxide gas collected in the gas syringe.
4) **Repeat** the experiment, **varying** the **mass** of sodium carbonate each time.
5) Use your results to draw a **graph** with the **mass** of sodium carbonate on the ***x*-axis** and the **volume** of gas produced on the ***y*-axis**.

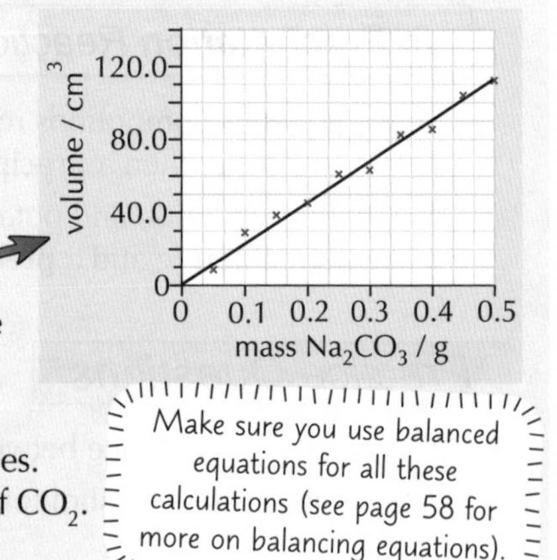

6) Read off the volume of gas produced for a sensible mass of sodium carbonate (e.g. **0.20 g** of **sodium carbonate** produces **45 cm³** of **carbon dioxide**).
7) From the reaction equation, **1 mole** of Na_2CO_3 reacts to form **1 mole** of CO_2. M_r Na_2CO_3 = 106, so 0.20 g of Na_2CO_3 contain 0.20 ÷ 106 = 0.00188... moles. Therefore, 1 mole of Na_2CO_3 will produce 0.045 ÷ 0.00188... = 23.85 dm³ of CO_2. So the molar volume of a gas under the conditions of this reaction is **24 dm³**.

Make sure you use balanced equations for all these calculations (see page 58 for more on balancing equations).

You Can Work Out Gas Volumes Using **Molar Calculations**...

It's handy to be able to work out **how much gas** a reaction will produce, so that you can use **large enough apparatus**.

Example: How much gas is produced when 15 g of sodium is reacted with excess water at r.t.p.?

$$2Na_{(s)} + 2H_2O_{(l)} \rightarrow 2NaOH_{(aq)} + H_{2\,(g)}$$

Excess water means you know all the sodium will react.

M of Na = 23.0 g mol⁻¹, so number of moles in 15 g of Na = $\frac{15}{23.0}$ = 0.652... moles

From the equation, 2 moles of Na produce 1 mole of H_2,

so you know 0.652... moles Na produces $\frac{0.652...}{2}$ = 0.326... moles H_2.

So the volume of H_2 = 0.326... × 24 = **7.8 dm³** (2 s.f.)

The reaction happens at room temperature and pressure, so you know 1 mole takes up 24 dm³.

Calculations with Gases

...Or Using Volume Calculations

If you have a reaction involving **gases**, you can use the **volumes** of **reactant** gases, along with the **reaction equation**, to work out the **volume** of gaseous products that will be produced.

Example: Calculate the total volume of gas produced when 8.25 dm³ of dinitrogen pentoxide decomposes:

$$2N_2O_{5(g)} \rightarrow O_{2(g)} + 4NO_{2(g)}$$

From the equation, 2 moles N_2O_5 produces 1 mole O_2 and 4 moles NO_2, which is 5 moles of gas in total.
So 8.25 dm³ N_2O_5 decomposes to produce $\frac{5}{2} \times 8.25 =$ **20.6 dm³** gas.

If you're given the volumes of gas that react and are produced, you can use the ratio of these volumes to work out the reaction equation.

Ideal Gas Equation — pV = nRT

The **ideal gas equation** lets you find the **number of moles** in a certain volume at **any temperature and pressure**.

$pV = nRT$ Where: p = pressure (Pa) V = volume (m³) n = number of moles
R = 8.31 J K⁻¹ mol⁻¹ T = temperature (K)

R is the gas constant.

K = °C + 273

Example: At a temperature of 60 °C and a pressure of 250 kPa, a gaseous hydrocarbon occupied a volume of 1100 cm³ and had a mass of 1.60 g. Find the molecular formula of the hydrocarbon.

1 kPa = 1000 Pa

$$n = \frac{pV}{RT} = \frac{(250 \times 10^3) \times (1.1 \times 10^{-3})}{8.31 \times 333} = 0.0993... \text{ moles}$$

1100 cm³ = 1.1 × 10⁻³ m³

If 0.0993... moles is 1.60 g, then 1 mole $= \frac{1.60}{0.0993...} = 16.1...$ g. So the molar mass (M) is **16 g mol⁻¹** (2 s.f.)

Hydrocarbons contain only carbon and hydrogen atoms.
The only hydrocarbon with a molecular mass of 16 g mol⁻¹ is **methane, CH_4**.

You can use the ideal gas equation to work out the **molar mass** of an unknown, **volatile** liquid:

Volatile liquids evaporate easily.

- Put a **known mass** of the liquid in a flask, then attach it to a sealed **gas syringe**. Gently **warm** the apparatus in a water bath, until the liquid completely **evaporates**.
- Record the **volume** of gas in the syringe and the **temperature** of the water bath.
- Use the ideal gas equation to work out how many **moles** of the liquid were in your sample, and the equation **molar mass = mass ÷ moles** to calculate the molar mass.

Practice Questions

Q1 What volume does 1 mole of gas occupy at r.t.p.?

Q2 Describe two methods you could use to measure the amount of gas produced over the course of a reaction.

Q3 State the ideal gas equation.

Exam Questions

Q1 At what temperature will 1.28 g of chlorine gas occupy 98.6 dm³, at a pressure of 175 Pa? [2 marks]

Q2 What volume will be occupied by 88 g of propane gas (C_3H_8) at r.t.p.? [2 marks]

Q3 What volume of oxygen is required, at room temperature and pressure for the complete combustion of 3.50×10^{-2} mol of butane (C_4H_{10})? [2 marks]

Q4 Magnesium carbonate ($MgCO_3$) thermally decomposes to produce magnesium oxide (MgO) and carbon dioxide. What mass of magnesium carbonate is needed to produce 6.00 dm³ of carbon dioxide at r.t.p.? [2 marks]

I can't carry on — I've run out of gas...

The ideal gas equation is really important, so make sure you know it. To make life a bit easier, the gas constant is in your exam data booklet along with the molar gas volumes at r.t.p. and s.t.p. and conversions between m³, dm³ and cm³.

Acid-Base Titrations

*Titrations are used to find out the **concentrations** of acid or alkali solutions.*

*Experiments Involve **Risks** and **Hazards***

1) A **hazard** is anything that has the potential to cause **harm** or **damage**. The **risk** associated with that hazard is the **probability** of someone (or something) being **harmed** if they are exposed to the hazard.
2) Many chemistry experiments have **risks** associated with them. These can include risks associated with the **equipment** you're using (e.g. the risk of burning from an electric heater) as well as risks associated with **chemicals**.
3) When you **plan** an experiment, you need to identify all the hazards and what the risk is from each hazard. This includes working out how **likely** it is that something could go wrong, and how **serious** it would be if it did. You then need to think of ways to **reduce** these risks. This procedure is called **a risk assessment**.

Example: A student is going to find the concentration of a solution of sodium hydroxide by titrating it with hydrochloric acid. Identify any hazards in this experiment, and suggest how you could reduce the risk.

Sodium hydroxide and hydrochloric acid are irritants at low concentrations and corrosive at high concentrations. Irritants cause inflammation, and corrosive substances cause **chemical burns** if they come into contact with your skin or eyes. To **reduce** the risks posed by these hazards, the student should try to use **low** concentrations of the substances if possible, and wear **gloves**, a **lab coat** and **goggles** when handling the chemicals.

*A **Standard Solution** Has a **Known** Concentration*

Before you start a titration, you have to make up a **standard solution**. A **standard solution** is any solution that you **know** the concentration of. Making a standard solution needs **careful** measuring and a hint of maths:

Example: Make 250 cm³ of a solution of benzoic acid (C_6H_5COOH) with a concentration of about 0.200 mol dm^{-3}.

1) First work out roughly how many **moles** of **solute** you need by using the formula:

$$\text{moles} = \frac{\text{concentration} \times \text{volume (cm}^3)}{1000} = \frac{0.200 \times 250}{1000} = 0.0500 \text{ mol}$$

The solute is the substance being dissolved into the solution — here it's the solid benzoic acid.

2) Now work out roughly how many **grams** of solute is needed using the formula **mass = moles × molar mass** = 0.0500 mol × 122.0 = 6.10 g

3) Carefully **weigh out** this mass of solute using a balance with a precision of at least 2 d.p. — first weigh the **weighing vessel**, note the weight, then **add** the correct mass.

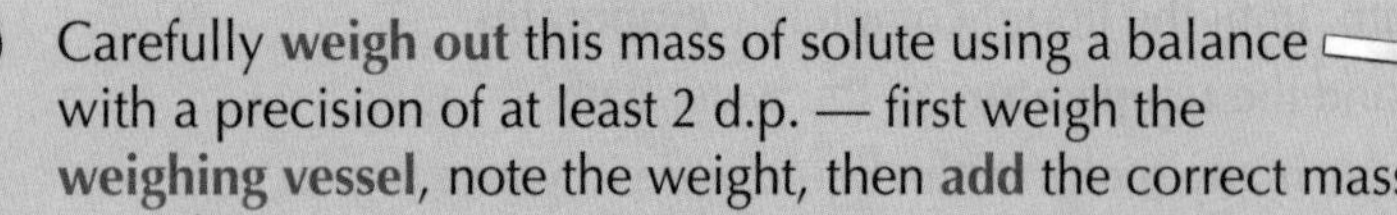

4) Add the solid acid to a beaker containing about 100 cm³ of **distilled water** and **stir** until all the solute has **dissolved.**

Dissolving an acid can release a lot of heat. To stay safe, always add the acid to the water.

4) **Reweigh** the weighing vessel, and use this value along with the combined mass of the vessel and the acid to calculate the **exact mass** of acid that has been added to the beaker. Use this **exact mass** to calculate what the **concentration** of your standard solution will be:

   Mass of acid added to beaker: 24.78 – 18.72 = 6.06 g

   Moles of acid added to beaker = 6.06 ÷ 122.0 = 0.0496... moles

   Exact concentration of standard solution = (0.0496... × 1000) ÷ 250 = **0.199 mol dm^{-3}**

18.72 grams

5) Tip the solution into a **volumetric flask** — make sure it's the right size for the volume you're making. Use a **funnel** to make sure it all goes in.
6) **Rinse** the beaker and stirring rod with distilled water and add that to the **flask** too. This makes sure there's no solute clinging to the beaker or rod.
7) Now top the flask up to the **correct volume** (250 cm³) with more distilled water. Make sure the **bottom** of the **meniscus** reaches the **line** — when you get close to the line use a **pipette** to add water drop by drop. If you go **over** the line you'll have to start all over again.
8) **Stopper** the bottle and turn it upside down a few times to make sure it's all **mixed.**

Volumetric flask

Acid-Base Titrations

Titrations Need to Be Done *Accurately*

1) **Titrations** allow you to find out **exactly** how much acid is needed to **neutralise** a quantity of alkali.
2) You measure out some **alkali** of unknown concentration (the analyte), e.g. NaOH using a pipette and put it in a flask, along with some **indicator**, e.g. **phenolphthalein**.
3) **Rinse** the burette with some of your **standard solution** of acid. Then **fill** it with your standard solution.
4) First of all, do a rough titration to get an idea where the **end point** is (the point where the alkali is **exactly neutralised** and the indicator changes colour). To do this, take an initial reading to see how much acid is in the burette to start off with. Then, add the **acid** to the alkali — giving the flask a regular **swirl**. Stop when your indicator shows a permanent colour change (the end point). Record the final reading from your burette.
5) Now do an **accurate** titration. Run the acid in to within 2 cm³ of the end point, then add the acid **dropwise**. If you don't notice exactly when the solution changed colour you've **overshot** and your result won't be accurate.
6) **Work out** the amount of acid used to **neutralise** the alkali. This is just the **final reading minus the initial reading**. This volume is known as the **titre**.
7) It's best to **repeat** the titration a few times, until you get answers that are **concordant** (similar) — your readings should be within 0.1 cm³ of each other. Then calculate a **mean titre** (see page 246), using only your **concordant results**. Also, remember to wash out the conical flask between each titration to remove any acid or alkali left in it.

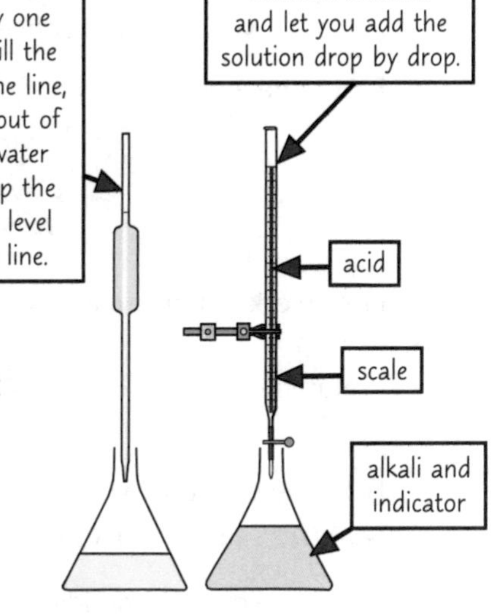

Pipette:
Pipettes measure only one volume of solution. Fill the pipette to just above the line, then take the pipette out of the solution (or the water pressure will hold up the level). Now drop the level down carefully to the line.
Burette:
Burettes measure different volumes and let you add the solution drop by drop.
acid
scale
alkali and indicator

You can also do titrations the other way round — adding alkali to acid.

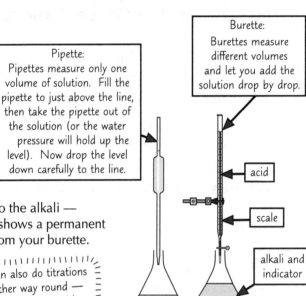

Indicators Show You When the Reaction's *Just Finished*

Universal indicator is no good here — its colour change is too gradual.

Indicators change **colour**, as if by magic. In titrations, indicators that change colour quickly over a **very small pH range** are used so you know **exactly** when the reaction has ended.

The main two indicators for **acid/alkali reactions** are —

> **methyl orange** — turns **yellow** to **red** when adding acid to alkali.
> **phenolphthalein** — turns **red** to **colourless** when adding acid to alkali.

It's best to place the flask containing the indicator and the acid or alkali solution on a **white surface**, so the colour change is easy to see.

Car indicators are no good here — they're not always right (because sometimes they're left).

Practice Questions

Q1 Describe the steps needed to make a standard solution from a solid.

Q2 Describe the procedure for doing a titration.

Exam Questions

Q1 Calculate the mass of sulfamic acid (H_3NSO_3) needed to make 200 cm³ of 0.500 mol dm^{-3} sulfamic acid solution. [2 marks]

Q2* Describe how indicators are used and explain the importance of selecting an appropriate indicator when carrying out a titration. Include examples of indicators that would and would not be suitable for use in titrations. [6 marks]

Burettes and pipettes — big glass things, just waiting to be dropped...

Titrations work best if the concentration of the standard solution is similar to what you think the concentration of the solution that you're titrating it against is. If the standard solution is too dilute it'll take ages to reach the end point of the titration. If it's too concentrated then tiny amounts will cause large pH changes and your results may be inaccurate.

* The quality of your extended response will be assessed for this question.

Titration Calculations

There's far more to a titration than just simply carrying it out. There are a whole load of calculations to carry out... Gulp.

You can Calculate **Concentrations** from Titrations

Example: 25.0 cm^3 of 0.500 mol dm^{-3} HCl was used to neutralise 35.0 cm^3 of NaOH solution. Calculate the concentration of the sodium hydroxide solution.

The method for carrying out this titration was shown on page 63.

First write a **balanced equation** and decide **what you know** and what you **need to know**:

$$HCl + NaOH \rightarrow NaCl + H_2O$$

25.0 cm^3 **35.0 cm^3**

0.500 mol dm^{-3} **?**

Now work out how many **moles of HCl** you have:

It's just the formula from page 55, but with volume in cm^3 rather than dm^3.

$$\text{Number of moles HCl} = \frac{\text{concentration} \times \text{volume (cm}^3\text{)}}{1000} = \frac{0.500 \times 25.0}{1000} = 0.0125 \text{ moles}$$

From the equation, you know 1 mole of HCl neutralises 1 mole of NaOH.
So 0.0125 moles of HCl must neutralise **0.0125** moles of NaOH.

Now it's a doddle to work out the **concentration of NaOH**.

If you're asked for the concentration in g dm^{-3}, you need to multiply the concentration by the molar mass.

$$\text{Concentration of NaOH(aq)} = \frac{\text{moles of NaOH} \times 1000}{\text{volume (cm}^3\text{)}} = \frac{0.0125 \times 1000}{35.0} = \mathbf{0.360 \text{ mol dm}^{-3}}$$

You Can **Also** Use Titrations to Find the **Concentration** of an **Acid**

If you carry out a titration like the one on page 63, but use a standard solution of a **base** and an **acid** of unknown concentration, then your results can be used to find the concentration of the acid.

Example: A student carried out an experiment to find the concentration of a solution of hydrochloric acid (HCl). He first dissolved 0.987 g of sodium hydroxide (NaOH) in 250 cm^3 of distilled water to make a standard solution. He then titrated this standard solution against 15.0 cm^3 of the hydrochloric acid solution of unknown concentration. Given that the mean titre of NaOH required to neutralise this volume of HCl solution was 21.7 cm^3, calculate the concentration of the solution of HCl.

First calculate the concentration of the standard solution of NaOH:

There's more about the techniques for making a standard solution on page 62.

Moles of NaOH dissolved = 0.987 ÷ 40.0 = 0.024675 moles
Concentration of standard solution = (0.024675 × 1000) ÷ 250 = **0.0987 mol dm^{-3}**

Now write out a **balanced equation** showing what **you do know**, and what you're **trying to find out**.

$$HCl + NaOH \rightarrow NaCl + H_2O$$

15.0 cm^3 **21.7 cm^3**

? **0.0987 mol dm^{-3}**

So, you can use the concentration of the standard solution (that you worked out above) to calculate the concentration of the HCl solution:

$$\text{Number of moles NaOH} = \frac{\text{concentration} \times \text{volume (cm}^3\text{)}}{1000} = \frac{0.0987 \times 21.7}{1000} = 0.00214... \text{moles}$$

Since the reaction equation shows that 1 mole of NaOH neutralises 1 mole of HCl, 0.00214... moles of NaOH will neutralise 0.00214... moles of HCl. So...

$$\text{Concentration of HCl} = \frac{\text{moles of HCl} \times 1000}{\text{volume (cm}^3\text{)}} = \frac{0.00214... \times 1000}{15.0} = \mathbf{0.143 \text{ mol dm}^{-3}}$$

Titration Calculations

You use a Pretty Similar Method to Calculate Volumes for Reactions

This is usually used for **planning experiments**.

You need to use your trusty old **concentration = moles ÷ volume** formula again, but this time you need to **rearrange** it to find the volume.

$$\text{volume (cm}^3) = \frac{\text{moles} \times 1000}{\text{concentration}}$$

Example: 20.4 cm³ of a 0.500 mol dm⁻³ solution of sodium carbonate reacts with 1.50 mol dm⁻³ nitric acid. Calculate the volume of nitric acid required to neutralise the sodium carbonate.

Like before, first write a **balanced equation** for the reaction and decide **what you know** and what you **want to know**:

$$Na_2CO_3 + 2HNO_3 \rightarrow 2NaNO_3 + H_2O + CO_2$$

Na_2CO_3	$2HNO_3$
20.4 cm³	**?**
0.500 mol dm⁻³	**1.50 mol dm⁻³**

Writing a balanced equation is really important because not all reactions happen as 1 : 1 molar reactions. This reaction is a 1 : 2 ratio of Na_2CO_3 : HNO_3.

Now work out how many **moles** of Na_2CO_3 you've got:

$$\text{No. of moles of } Na_2CO_3 = \frac{\text{concentration} \times \text{volume (cm}^3)}{1000} = \frac{0.500 \times 20.4}{1000} = 0.0102 \text{ moles}$$

1 mole of Na_2CO_3 neutralises 2 moles of HNO_3, so 0.0102 moles of Na_2CO_3 neutralises **0.0204 moles of HNO_3**.

Now you know the number of moles of HNO_3 and the concentration, you can work out the **volume**:

$$\text{Volume of } HNO_3 = \frac{\text{number of moles} \times 1000}{\text{concentration}} = \frac{0.0204 \times 1000}{1.50} = \mathbf{13.6\ cm^3}$$

If you're given a concentration in g dm⁻³, you should first divide by the molar mass, *M*, to convert it to mol dm⁻³.

You might also be asked to calculate the **volume** of a solution required to neutralise a known **mass** of a substance. The calculation is very similar to the one above, except that you start by working out the number of moles of the substance using your old friend '**moles = mass ÷ molar mass**'.

Practice Questions

Q1 What equation links the number of moles, concentration and volume (in cm³)?

Q2 What equation links the number of moles, the mass of a substance and its molar mass, *M*?

Exam Questions

Q1 Calculate the concentration (in mol dm⁻³) of a solution of ethanoic acid, CH_3COOH, if 25.4 cm³ of it is neutralised by 14.6 cm³ of 0.500 mol dm⁻³ sodium hydroxide solution.

$CH_3COOH + NaOH \rightarrow CH_3COONa + H_2O$ [3 marks]

Q2 You are supplied with 0.750 g of calcium carbonate and a solution of 0.250 mol dm⁻³ sulfuric acid. What volume of acid will be needed to neutralise the calcium carbonate?

$CaCO_3 + H_2SO_4 \rightarrow CaSO_4 + H_2O + CO_2$ [4 marks]

Q3 In a titration, 17.1 cm³ of 0.250 mol dm⁻³ hydrochloric acid neutralises 25.0 cm³ calcium hydroxide solution.

a) Write out a balanced equation for this reaction. [1 mark]

b) Work out the concentration of the calcium hydroxide solution. [3 marks]

DJs can't do titrations — they just keep on dropping the base...

This just looks like a horrible load of calculations, but it's not that bad. Just remember the equation linking volume, concentration and moles and the one that links moles, mass and molar mass, and you'll be able to work out pretty much everything. They're the only tools you need to become a whizz at titration calculations. And that's the dream.

Uncertainty and Errors

Even if you're a super duper Chemistry whizz, you're not error free. Time to meet errors and... errrmmm... uncertainty?

Uncertainty is the Amount of *Error* Your *Measurements* Might Have

1) Any measurements you make will have **uncertainty** in them due to the limits to the **sensitivity** of the equipment you used.
2) The **uncertainty** in your measurements **varies** for different equipment. For example, the scale on a 50 cm^3 **burette** has marks every **0.1 cm^3**. You should be able to tell which mark the level's closest to, so any reading you take won't be more than **0.05 cm^3** out (as long as you don't make a daft mistake). The **uncertainty** of a reading from the burette is the **maximum error** you could have — so that's **±0.05 cm^3**.
3) The ± sign tells you the **range** in which the true value could lie. This range can also be called the **margin of error**.
4) For any piece of equipment you use, the uncertainty will be **half** the **smallest increment** the equipment can measure, in either direction.
5) Equipment will also have an error based on how **accurately** it has been **made**. The manufacturers should give you these uncertainty values — often they'll be **written** on the equipment somewhere.
6) If you're **combining measurements** that have the same **units**, you'll need to combine their **uncertainties**.

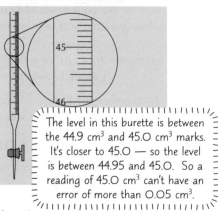

The level in this burette is between the 44.9 cm^3 and 45.0 cm^3 marks. It's closer to 45.0 — so the level is between 44.95 and 45.0. So a reading of 45.0 cm^3 can't have an error of more than 0.05 cm^3.

Example: A student is using a set of electronic scales that measures to the nearest 0.05 g. He zeros the scales and measures out 1.35 g of solid. Calculate the total uncertainty of the measurement.

There are two readings here — the initial reading is 0.00 g and the final reading is 1.35 g
The uncertainty of each reading is 0.05 ÷ 2 = 0.025 g, so the total uncertainty is 0.025 + 0.025 = **0.05 g**.

The *Percentage Uncertainty* in a Result Should be Calculated

You can calculate the **percentage uncertainty** of a measurement using this equation:

$$\text{percentage uncertainty} = \frac{\text{uncertainty}}{\text{reading}} \times 100$$

You might also see percentage uncertainty called 'percentage error'.

Example: A 250 cm^3 volumetric flask has a manufacturer's error of ±0.25 cm^3. Calculate the percentage uncertainty of the volumetric flask.

The standard volume of the volumetric flask has an uncertainty of 0.25 cm^3, so the percentage uncertainty is $\frac{0.25}{250} \times 100$ = **0.1%**

The percentage error of a combined uncertainty is $\frac{\text{total uncertainty}}{\text{difference in readings}} \times 100$. So the uncertainty of the mass reading above is $\frac{0.05}{1.35 - 0.00} \times 100 = 4\%$.

You Can *Minimise* the Percentage Uncertainty

1) One obvious way to **reduce errors** in your measurements is to use the most **precise equipment** you can.
2) **Planning** can also improve your results. If you measure out **5 cm^3** of liquid in a measuring cylinder that has increments of 0.1 cm^3 then the percentage uncertainty is (0.05 ÷ 5) × 100 = **1%**. But if you measure **10 cm^3** of liquid in the same measuring cylinder the percentage uncertainty is (0.05 ÷ 10) × 100 = **0.5%** — you've **halved** the percentage uncertainty. So the percentage uncertainty can be reduced by planning an experiment so you use a **larger volume** of liquid.

In general, the smaller the measurement, the larger the percentage uncertainty.

Errors Can Be *Systematic* or *Random*

1) **Systematic errors** are the same every time you repeat the experiment. They may be caused by the **set-up** or **equipment** you used. For example, if the 10.00 cm^3 pipette you used to measure out a sample for titration actually only measured 9.95 cm^3, your sample would have been about 0.05 cm^3 too small **every time** you repeated the experiment.
2) **Random errors** vary — they're what make the results a bit **different** each time you repeat an experiment. The errors when you make a reading from a burette are random. You have to estimate or round the level when it's between two marks — so sometimes your figure will be **above** the real one, and sometimes it will be **below**.
3) **Repeating an experiment** and finding the mean of your results helps to deal with **random errors**. The results that are a bit high will be **cancelled out** by the ones that are a bit low. But repeating your results won't get rid of any **systematic errors**, so your results won't get more **accurate**.

Uncertainty and Errors

The *Total Uncertainty* in a Result Should be Calculated

In **titrations**, here's how you find the **total uncertainty in the final result**:

- Find the **percentage uncertainty** for each bit of equipment.
- Add the individual percentage uncertainties together. This gives the **percentage uncertainty in the final result**.
- Use this to work out the **actual total uncertainty** in the final result.

Example: 10.00 cm³ of KOH solution is neutralised by 27.30 cm³ of HCl of known concentration.
The volume of KOH has an uncertainty of 0.060 cm³.
The volume of HCl has an uncertainty of 0.10 cm³.
The concentration of the KOH is calculated to be 1.365 mol dm⁻³.
What is the uncertainty in this concentration?

First work out the **percentage uncertainty** for each **volume measurement**:

The KOH volume of 10.00 cm³ has an uncertainty of 0.060 cm³:

percentage uncertainty = $\frac{0.060}{10.00} \times 100 = \mathbf{0.60\%}$

The HCl volume of 27.3 cm³ has an uncertainty of 0.1 cm³:

percentage uncertainty = $\frac{0.10}{27.30} \times 100 = \mathbf{0.36...\%}$

Find the **percentage uncertainty in the final result**:

Total percentage uncertainty = 0.60% + 0.36...% = **0.96...%**

You're not done yet — you still have to calculate the **uncertainty** in the final result.

Uncertainty in the final answer is 0.96...% of 1.365 mol dm⁻³ = **0.013 mol dm⁻³**

So the actual concentration may be 0.013 mol dm⁻³ bigger or smaller than 1.365 mol dm⁻³.

Practice Questions

Q1 If the uncertainty of a reading from a burette is 0.05 cm³, why is the uncertainty of a titre quoted as being 0.1 cm³?

Q2 Write down the equation for the percentage uncertainty of a measurement.

Q3 Other than using more precise equipment, describe one way in which you could minimise the percentage uncertainty of a measurement using a mass balance that reads to the nearest 0.05 g.

Exam Questions

Q1 The table shows the data recorded from a titration experiment.

Run	Initial volume (cm³)	Final volume (cm³)	Titre (cm³)
Rough	1.1	5.2	4.1
1	1.2	4.3	3.1

a) Each reading recorded in the experiment has an uncertainty of ±0.05 cm³. Calculate the percentage uncertainty in the **titre** in Run 1. [2 marks]

b) Explain how you could reduce the percentage error in these titre values by changing the concentration of the solution in the burette. [2 marks]

Q2 The concentration of a solution of NaOH is measured by titration against 0.100 mol dm⁻³ HCl. 25.00 cm³ of NaOH solution requires 19.25 cm³ of HCl for neutralisation, so the concentration of NaOH is 0.0770 mol dm⁻³.
The volume of NaOH was measured using a pipette with an uncertainty of 0.06 cm³.
The titre reading from the burette has an uncertainty of 0.1 cm³.

By combining percentage uncertainties calculate the uncertainty in the concentration of the NaOH. [4 marks]

Random error is human, systematic, divine...

Working out errors and uncertainty is important in every experiment you do. So important, in fact, that this topic is covered again in the Practical Skills section on page 248. Remember — if a question asks for the uncertainty of a result, find the uncertainty in the same units as the result. If you work out the total percentage uncertainty, you'll miss out.

Atom Economy and Percentage Yield

How to make a subject like Chemistry even more exciting — introduce the word 'economy'...

The Theoretical Yield of a Product is the Maximum You Could Get

1) The **theoretical yield** is the **mass of product** that **should** be made in a reaction if **no** chemicals are '**lost**' in the process. You can use the **masses of reactants** and a **balanced equation** to calculate the theoretical yield for a reaction.
2) The **actual** mass of product (the **actual yield**) is always **less** than the theoretical yield. Some chemicals are always 'lost', e.g. some solution gets left on filter paper, or is lost during transfers between containers.
3) The **percentage yield** is the **actual** amount of product you collect, written as a percentage of the theoretical yield. You can work out the percentage yield with this formula:

$$\text{percentage yield} = \frac{\text{actual yield}}{\text{theoretical yield}} \times 100\%$$

Example: Ethanol can be oxidised to form ethanal: $C_2H_5OH + [O] \rightarrow CH_3CHO + H_2O$
9.2 g of ethanol was reacted with an oxidising agent in excess and 2.1 g of ethanal was produced. Calculate the theoretical yield and the percentage yield.

[O] is just the symbol for any oxidising agent.

Number of moles = mass of substance ÷ molar mass

Moles of C_2H_5OH = 9.2 ÷ [(2 × 12.0) + (5 × 1.0) + 16.0 + 1.0] = 9.2 ÷ 46.0 = 0.20 moles

1 mole of C_2H_5OH produces 1 mole of CH_3CHO, so 0.2 moles of C_2H_5OH will produce 0.20 moles of CH_3CHO.

M of CH_3CHO = (2 × 12.0) + (4 × 1.0) + 16.0 = 44.0 g mol^{-1}

Theoretical yield (mass of CH_3CHO) = number of moles × M = 0.20 × 44.0 = **8.8 g**

So, if the actual yield was 2.1 g, the percentage yield = $\frac{\text{actual yield}}{\text{theoretical yield}} \times 100\% = \frac{2.1}{8.8} \times 100\% \approx$ **24%**

Atom Economy is a Measure of the Efficiency of a Reaction

1) The **percentage yield** tells you how wasteful the **process** is — it's based on how much of the product is lost because of things like reactions not completing or losses during collection and purification.
2) But percentage yield doesn't measure how wasteful the **reaction** itself is. A reaction that has a 100% yield could still be very wasteful if a lot of the atoms from the **reactants** wind up in **by-products** rather than the **desired product**.
3) **Atom economy** is a measure of the proportion of reactant **atoms** that become part of the desired product (rather than by-products) in the **balanced** chemical equation. It's calculated using this formula:

$$\%\ \text{atom economy} = \frac{\text{molar mass of desired product}}{\text{sum of molar masses of all products}} \times 100\%$$

4) In an **addition reaction**, the reactants **combine** to form a **single product**. The atom economy for addition reactions is **always 100%** since no atoms are wasted.

E.g. ethene (C_2H_4) and hydrogen react to form ethane (C_2H_6) in an addition reaction: $C_2H_4 + H_2 \rightarrow C_2H_6$
The **only product** is ethane (the desired product). No reactant atoms are wasted so the atom economy is **100%**.

5) In an ideal world, all reactions would have an atom economy of 100%. Unfortunately, this isn't the case, and reactions often have **unwanted by-products** which lead to a **lower** atom economy.

Example: Aluminium oxide is formed by heating aluminium hydroxide until it decomposes. Calculate the atom economy of the reaction.

$$2Al(OH)_3 \rightarrow Al_2O_3 + 3H_2O$$

$$\%\ \text{atom economy} = \frac{\text{molar mass of desired product}}{\text{sum of molar masses of all products}} \times 100\%$$

$$= \frac{M(Al_2O_3)}{M(Al_2O_3) + 3 \times M(H_2O)} \times 100\%$$

$$= \frac{(2 \times 27.0) + (3 \times 16.0)}{[(2 \times 27.0) + (3 \times 16.0)] + 3 \times [(2 \times 1.0) + 16.0]} \times 100\% = \frac{102}{102 + 54} \times 100\% = \mathbf{65.4\%}$$

Atom Economy and Percentage Yield

Reactions Can Have **High Percentage Yields** and **Low Atom Economies**

A **substitution reaction** is one where some atoms from one reactant are **swapped** with atoms from another reactant. This type of reaction **always** results in **at least two products** — the desired product and at least one by-product.

Example: 0.475 g of CH_3Br reacts with an excess of NaOH in this reaction: $CH_3Br + NaOH \rightarrow CH_3OH + NaBr$. 0.153 g of CH_3OH is produced.

a) Calculate the atom economy of this reaction.

$$\% \text{ atom economy} = \frac{\text{molar mass of desired product}}{\text{sum of molar masses of all products}} \times 100\%$$

$$= \frac{M(CH_3OH)}{M(CH_3OH) + M(NaBr)} \times 100\%$$

$$= \frac{12.0 + (3 \times 1.0) + 16.0 + 1.0}{[12.0 + (3 \times 1.0) + 16.0 + 1.0] + [23.0 + 79.9]} \times 100\%$$

$$= \frac{32.0}{32.0 + 102.9} \times 100\% = \mathbf{23.7\%}$$

Always make sure you're using a balanced equation.

b) Calculate the percentage yield of this reaction.

Number of moles = mass of substance ÷ molar mass

Moles of CH_3Br = 0.475 ÷ (12.0 + (3 × 1.0) + 79.9) = 0.475 ÷ 94.9 = **0.0050... moles**

The reactant : product ratio is 1 : 1, so the maximum number of moles of CH_3OH is **0.00500...**

Theoretical yield = 0.00500... × $M(CH_3OH)$
= 0.00500... × (12.0 + (3 × 1.0) + 16.0 + 1.0) = 0.00500... × 32 = **0.160... g**

$$\text{percentage yield} = \frac{\text{actual yield}}{\text{theoretical yield}} \times 100\% = \frac{0.153}{0.160...} \times 100\% = \mathbf{95.5\%}$$

So this reaction has a very high percentage yield, but the atom economy is low.

Practice Questions

Q1 Give the equation for calculating the % atom economy of a reaction.

Q2 How many products are there in an addition reaction?

Exam Questions

Q1 Reactions 1 and 2 below show two possible ways of preparing the compound chloroethane (C_2H_5Cl):

1 $C_2H_5OH + PCl_5 \rightarrow C_2H_5Cl + POCl_3 + HCl$
2 $C_2H_4 + HCl \rightarrow C_2H_5Cl$

a) **Which of these is an addition reaction?** **[1 mark]**

b) **Calculate the atom economy for reaction 1.** **[2 marks]**

c) **Reaction 2 has an atom economy of 100%. Explain why this is, in terms of the products of the reaction.** **[1 mark]**

Q2 Phosphorus trichloride (PCl_3) reacts with chlorine to give phosphorus pentachloride (PCl_5):

$PCl_3 + Cl_2 \rightarrow PCl_5$

a) **0.275 g of PCl_3 reacts with an excess of chlorine. What is the theoretical yield of PCl_5?** **[2 marks]**

b) **When this reaction is performed 0.198 g of PCl_5 is collected. Calculate the percentage yield.** **[1 mark]**

c) **Changing conditions such as temperature and pressure will alter the percentage yield of this reaction. Will changing these conditions affect the atom economy? Explain your answer.** **[2 marks]**

I knew a Tommy Conomy once — strange bloke...

These pages shouldn't be too much trouble — you've survived worse already. Make sure that you get plenty of practice using the percentage yield and atom economy formulae. And whatever you do, don't get mixed up between percentage yield (which is to do with the process) and atom economy (which is to do with the reaction).

The Basics

This topic's all about organic chemistry... carbon compounds, in other words. Read on...

There are **Loads of Ways** of **Representing** Organic Compounds

Type of formula	What it shows you	Formula for Butan-1-ol
General formula	An algebraic formula that can describe **any member** of a family of compounds.	$C_nH_{2n+1}OH$ (for all alcohols)
Empirical formula	The **simplest whole number ratio** of atoms of each element in a compound (cancel the numbers down if possible). (So ethane, C_2H_6, has the empirical formula CH_3.)	$C_4H_{10}O$
Molecular formula	The **actual** number of atoms of each element in a molecule.	$C_4H_{10}O$
Structural formula	Shows the arrangement of atoms **carbon by carbon**, with the attached hydrogens and functional groups.	$CH_3CH_2CH_2CH_2OH$
Skeletal formula	Shows the **bonds** of the carbon skeleton **only**, with any functional groups. The hydrogen and carbon atoms aren't shown. This is handy for drawing large complicated structures, like cyclic hydrocarbons.	 OH
Displayed formula	Shows how all the atoms are **arranged**, and all the bonds between them.	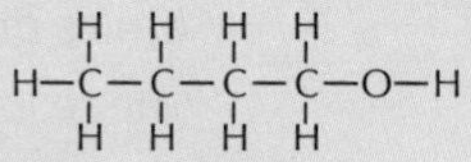 H H H H H–C–C–C–C–O–H H H H H

This could also be written as $CH_3(CH_2)_3OH$.

Nomenclature is a Fancy Word for the **Naming** of Organic Compounds

Organic compounds used to be given whatever names people fancied, but these names led to **confusion** between different countries.

The **IUPAC** system for naming organic compounds was invented as an **international language** for chemistry. It can be used to give any organic compound a **systematic name** using these **rules** of nomenclature...

1) Count the carbon atoms in the **longest continuous chain** — this gives you the stem.

No. of Carbons	1	2	3	4	5	6	7	8	9	10
Stem	meth-	eth-	prop-	but-	pent-	hex-	hept-	oct-	non-	dec-

2) The **main functional group** of the molecule usually tells you what **homologous series** the molecule is in, and so gives you the **prefix** or **suffix** — see the table on the next page.
3) Number the **longest** carbon chain so that the main functional group has the lowest possible number. If there's more than one longest chain, pick the one with the **most side-chains**.
4) Any side-chains or less important functional groups are added as prefixes at the start of the name. Put them in **alphabetical** order, after the **number** of the carbon atom each is attached to.
5) If there's more than one **identical** side-chain or functional group, use **di-** (2), **tri-** (3) or **tetra-** (4) before that part of the name — but ignore this when working out the alphabetical order.

Example: $CH_3CH(CH_3)CH(CH_2CH_3)C(CH_3)_2OH$

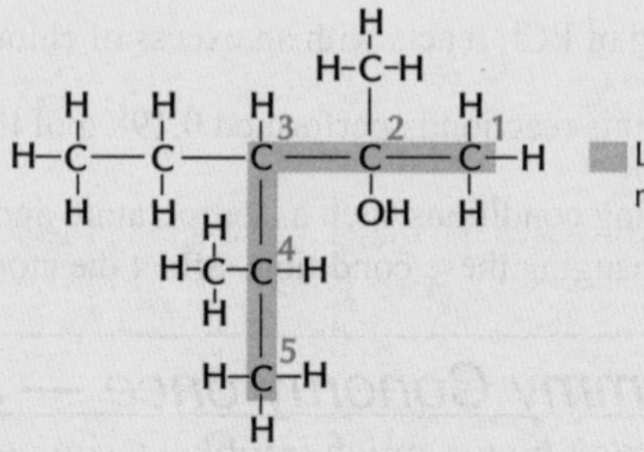

1) The longest chain is 5 carbons. So the stem is pent-.
2) The main functional group is -OH. So the name will be based on 'pentanol'.
3) Numbering the longest carbon chain so that -OH has the lowest possible number (and you have most side chains) puts -OH on carbon 2, so it's some sort of pentan-2-ol.
4) The side chains are an ethyl group on carbon-3, and methyl groups on carbon-2 and carbon-4, so the systematic name for this molecule is: **3-ethyl-2,4-dimethylpentan-2-ol.**

Longest chain with most side-chains

The Basics

Members of Homologous Series Have the Same General Formulae

1) Organic chemistry is more about **groups** of similar chemicals than individual compounds.
2) These groups are called **homologous series**. A homologous series is a bunch of organic compounds that have the same **functional group** and **general formula**. Consecutive members of a homologous series differ by **$-CH_2-$**.

A functional group is a group of atoms in a molecule responsible for the characteristic reactions of that compound.

Example:

1) The simplest homologous series is the **alkanes**. They're **straight chain** molecules that contain only **carbon** and **hydrogen** atoms. There's a lot more about the alkanes on pages 76-77.
2) The **general formula** for alkanes is **C_nH_{2n+2}**. So the first alkane in the series is $C_1H_{(2\times1)+2} = CH_4$ (you don't need to write the 1 in C_1), the second is $C_2H_{(2\times2)+2} = C_2H_6$, the seventeenth is $C_{17}H_{(2\times17)+2} = C_{17}H_{36}$, and so on...

3) Here are the homologous series you need to know about:

Homologous Series	Prefix or Suffix	Example
alkanes	–ane	propane — $CH_3CH_2CH_3$
branched alkanes	alkyl– (–yl)	methylpropane — $CH_3CH(CH_3)CH_3$
alkenes	–ene	propene — $CH_3CH{=}CH_2$
halogenoalkanes	chloro–/bromo–/iodo–	chloroethane — CH_3CH_2Cl
alcohols	–ol	ethanol — CH_3CH_2OH
aldehydes	–al	ethanal — CH_3CHO
ketones	–one	propanone — CH_3COCH_3
cycloalkanes	cyclo– ... –ane	cyclohexane C_6H_{12}
carboxylic acids	–oic acid	ethanoic acid — CH_3COOH

Don't worry if you don't recognise all these series yet — you'll meet them all by the end of the topic.

Practice Questions

Q1 Explain the difference between molecular formulae and structural formulae.

Q2 In what order should prefixes be listed in the name of an organic compound?

Q3 What is a homologous series? Give four examples of homologous series.

Exam Questions

Q1 1-bromobutane is prepared from butan-1-ol in this reaction: $C_4H_9OH + NaBr + H_2SO_4 \rightarrow C_4H_9Br + NaHSO_4 + H_2O$

a) Draw the displayed formulae for butan-1-ol and 1-bromobutane. [2 marks]

b) What does the '1' in the name butan-1-ol tell you, and why is it necessary to include it in the name? [2 marks]

Q2 a) Name the following molecules.

i)
```
         H
         |
      H—C—H
         |
   H     |     H
   |     |     |
H—C—— C —— C—H
   |     |     |
   H     H     Cl
```

ii)
```
         H
         |
      H—C—H
         |
   H     |
   |     |         H
H—C—— C —— C=C<
   |     |     |   H
   H     H     H
```

iii)
```
      Br  H
      |   |          H
H—C—C—C=C<
   |   |   |         H
   H   H   Br
```

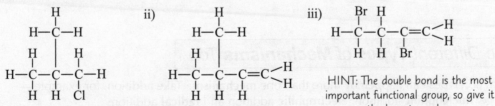

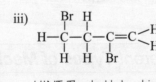

HINT: The double bond is the most important functional group, so give it the lowest number. [3 marks]

b) i) Write down the molecular formula for 3-ethylpentane. [1 mark]

ii) Write down the structural formula for this molecule. [1 mark]

It's as easy as 1,2,3-trichloropentan-2-ol...

The best thing to do now is find some organic compounds and work out their names. Then have a go at it the other way around — use the name to draw the compound. It might seem boring, but come the exam, you'll be thanking me.

Organic Reactions

This page is chock-full of really good words, like 'radical substitution'. And 'electrophilic addition'. It's well worth a read.

You Can **Classify** Reactions by Reaction **Type**...

There are lots of different **reaction types** that organic compounds can take part in.
Here's a run down of the ones that you'll meet in Topic 6:

Addition — joining two or more molecules together to **form** a larger molecule.
Polymerisation — joining together lots of simple molecules to **form** a **giant molecule**.
Elimination — when a **small group** of atoms **breaks away** from a larger molecule.
Substitution — when **one species** is **replaced by another**.
Hydrolysis — splitting a molecule into two new molecules by **adding H^+ and OH^-** derived from **water**.
Oxidation — any reaction in which a species **loses electrons**.
Reduction — any reaction in which a species **gains electrons**.

A species is an atom, an ion, a radical or a molecule.

A **Mechanism** Breaks Down a Reaction into Individual **Stages**

1) It's all very well knowing the outcome of a reaction, but it can also be useful to know **how** a reaction happens.
2) **Mechanisms** are diagrams that break reactions down into individual stages to show how substances react together. Some mechanisms use **curly arrows** to show how **electron pairs** move around when **bonds** are made or broken.

Curly Arrows Show How **Electron Pairs** Move Around

In order to make or break a bond in a reaction, **electrons** have to move around.
A **curly arrow** shows where a **pair** of electrons goes during a reaction. They look like this:

The arrow starts at the bond or lone pair where the electrons are at the beginning of the reaction.

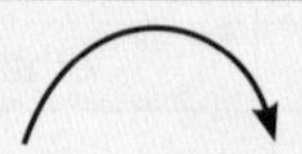

The arrow points to where the new bond is formed at the end of the reaction, or to the atom where the electrons go.

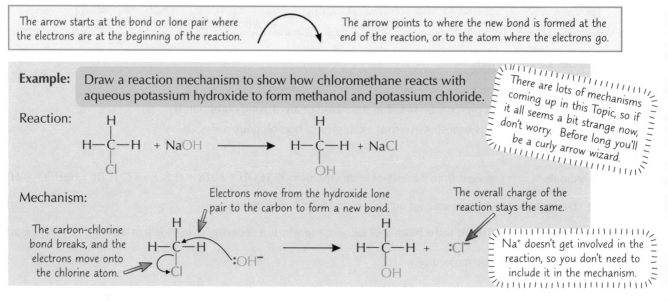

Example: Draw a reaction mechanism to show how chloromethane reacts with aqueous potassium hydroxide to form methanol and potassium chloride.

Reaction: $CH_3Cl + NaOH \longrightarrow CH_3OH + NaCl$

Mechanism: $H_3C{-}Cl + :OH^- \longrightarrow H_3C{-}OH + :Cl^-$

Electrons move from the hydroxide lone pair to the carbon to form a new bond.

The carbon-chlorine bond breaks, and the electrons move onto the chlorine atom.

The overall charge of the reaction stays the same.

There are lots of mechanisms coming up in this Topic, so if it all seems a bit strange now, don't worry. Before long you'll be a curly arrow wizard.

Na^+ doesn't get involved in the reaction, so you don't need to include it in the mechanism.

There are Different **Types** of **Mechanisms** Too

1) Some reaction types can happen by more than one **mechanism**. Take addition, for example — you can get **nucleophilic** addition, **electrophilic** addition and **radical** addition.
2) There are some mechanisms coming up in this Topic that you're expected to **remember**:

- **radical substitution** of halogens in alkanes, to make **halogenoalkanes** — see pages 76-77.
- **electrophilic addition** of halogens and hydrogen halides to alkenes, to make **halogenoalkanes** — see pages 86-87.
- **nucleophilic substitution** of primary halogenoalkanes with aqueous potassium hydroxide to make **alcohols** and with ammonia to make **amines** — see pages 92-93.

Organic Reactions

Classifying Reagents *Helps to Predict What Reactions Will Happen*

Knowing the **type of reagent** that you have helps you **predict** which chemicals will react together and what products you're likely to end up with.

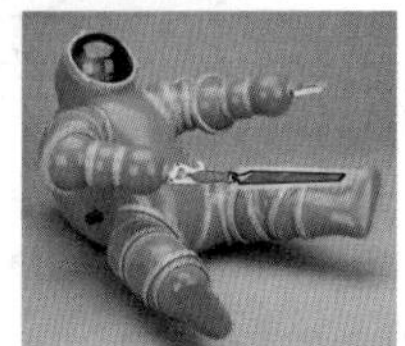

Frank put safety first when he tested his nuclear file...

1) **Nucleophiles** are **electron pair donors**. They're often **negatively charged ions** (e.g. halide ions) or species that contain a **lone pair of electrons** (e.g. the oxygen atoms in water). They're **electron rich**, so they're **attracted** to places that are electron poor. So they like to react with **positive** ions. Molecules with **polar bonds** are often attacked by nucleophiles too, as they have δ+ areas.

   Nucleophiles are attracted to the $C^{\delta+}$ atom in a **polar carbon-halogen bond**. The carbon-halogen bond breaks and the nucleophile takes the halogen's place — and that's **nucleophilic substitution** (see page 92).

   Remember that 'δ+' and 'δ–' show partial charges — see page 28.

2) **Electrophiles** are **electron pair acceptors**. They're often **positively charged ions** (e.g. H^+), or δ+ areas (e.g. $H^{\delta+}$ in a hydrogen halide H–X bond). They're **electron poor**, so they're **attracted** to places that are electron rich. They like to react with **negative** ions, atoms with **lone pairs** and the **electron-rich** area around a **C=C bond**.

   Alkene molecules undergo electrophilic addition. In a molecule with a polar bond, like HBr, the $H^{\delta+}$ acts as an **electrophile** and is strongly attracted to the C=C double bond (which **polarises** the H–Br bond even more, until it finally breaks). There's more about this reaction on page 87.

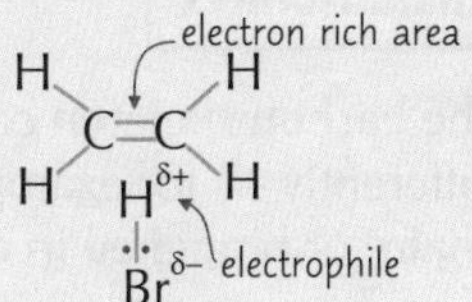

3) **Radicals** have an **unpaired electron**, e.g. the chlorine atoms produced when UV light splits a Cl_2 molecule. Because they have unpaired electrons, they're very, very **reactive**. Unlike electrophiles and nucleophiles, they'll react with anything, positive, negative or neutral.

   $$Cl{-}Cl \xrightarrow{UV} 2Cl\bullet$$

   Radicals will even attack stable non-polar bonds, like C–C and C–H (so they're one of the few things that will react with alkanes). There's loads about the reactions of radicals with alkanes on pages 76-77.

   Because a radical will react with anything in sight, you'll probably end up with a mixture of products. So radical reactions aren't much use if you're after a pure product.

Practice Questions

Q1 What is a hydrolysis reaction?

Q2 What do curly arrows show?

Q3 What type of reagent accepts a pair of electrons during a reaction?

Exam Questions

Q1 Which of the following species would you expect to act as a nucleophile?

A Bromine radicals, Br•.

B The non-polar alkane, methane, CH_4.

C Hydroxide ions, OH^-.

D The $C^{\delta+}$ atom in the polar C–OH bond in ethanol, CH_3CH_2OH. [1 mark]

Q2 Classify each of the following reactions according to its type:

a) A reaction in which lots of ethene molecules join together to form one long molecule, polyethene. [1 mark]

b) The reaction between chloroethane and water, in which a water molecule breaks chloroethane into ethanol and hydrogen chloride. [1 mark]

c) The reaction between chlorine radicals and ethane, in which a hydrogen atom in ethane is replaced by chlorine to form chloroethane. [1 mark]

My brother says I'm rubbish at archery, but I blame the curly arrows...

Scientists do love to classify everything, and have it neatly in order. I knew one who liked to alphabetise his socks. But that's a different issue. Just learn the definitions for the types of reactions and reagents — and what types of reagent undergo what types of reaction. Then you'll have this page sorted. Without having to alphabetise anything.

Isomerism

Isomerism is great fun. It's all about how many ways there are of making different molecules from the same molecular formula. They can be a bit sneaky, though, so best be on your guard...

Isomers Have the Same ***Molecular Formula***

1) Two molecules are isomers of one another if they have the same **molecular formula** but the atoms are **arranged differently**.
2) There are two types of isomers you need to know about — **structural isomers** and **stereoisomers**. Structural isomers are coming right up, and you'll meet stereoisomers on pages 83-85.

Structural Isomers *Have Different* ***Structural Arrangements*** *of Atoms*

In structural isomers, the atoms are **connected** in different ways.
So although the **molecular formula** is the same, the **structural formula** is different.
There are **three** different types of structural isomer:

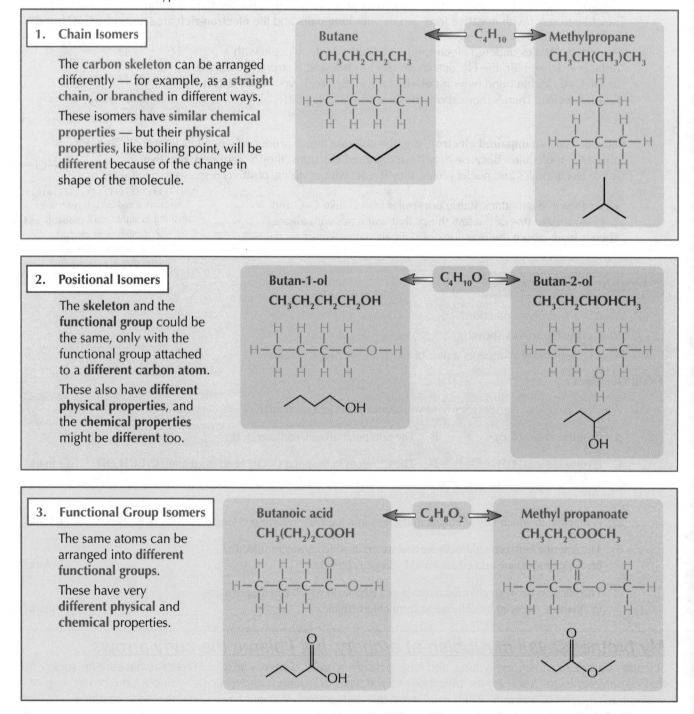

1. Chain Isomers

The **carbon skeleton** can be arranged differently — for example, as a **straight chain**, or **branched** in different ways.

These isomers have **similar chemical properties** — but their **physical properties**, like boiling point, will be **different** because of the change in shape of the molecule.

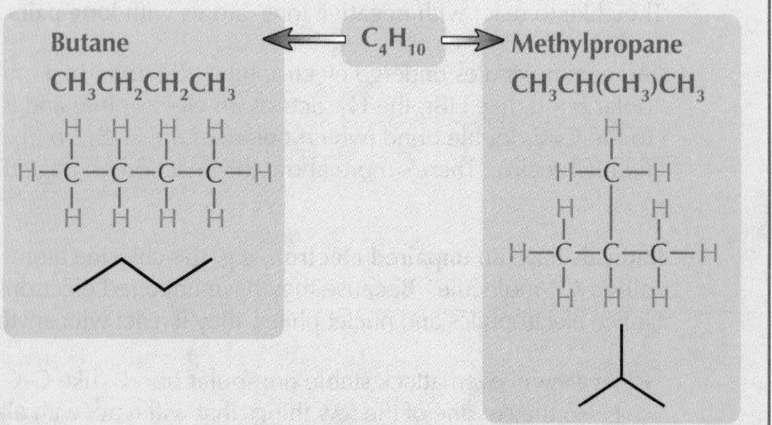

2. Positional Isomers

The **skeleton** and the **functional group** could be the same, only with the functional group attached to a **different carbon atom**.

These also have **different physical properties**, and the **chemical properties** might be **different** too.

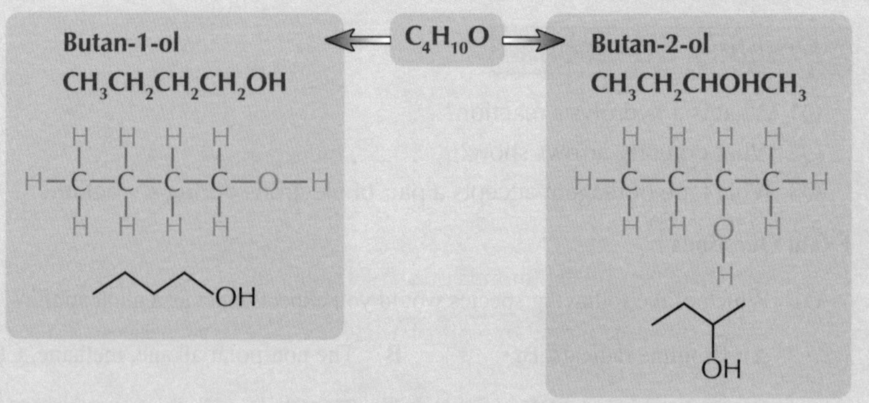

3. Functional Group Isomers

The same atoms can be arranged into **different functional groups**.

These have very **different physical** and **chemical** properties.

Butanoic acid
$CH_3(CH_2)_2COOH$

$C_4H_8O_2$

Methyl propanoate
$CH_3CH_2COOCH_3$

Isomerism

Don't be Fooled — What Looks Like an Isomer Might Not Be

Atoms can rotate as much as they like around single **C–C bonds**.

Remember this when you work out structural isomers — sometimes what looks like an isomer, isn't.

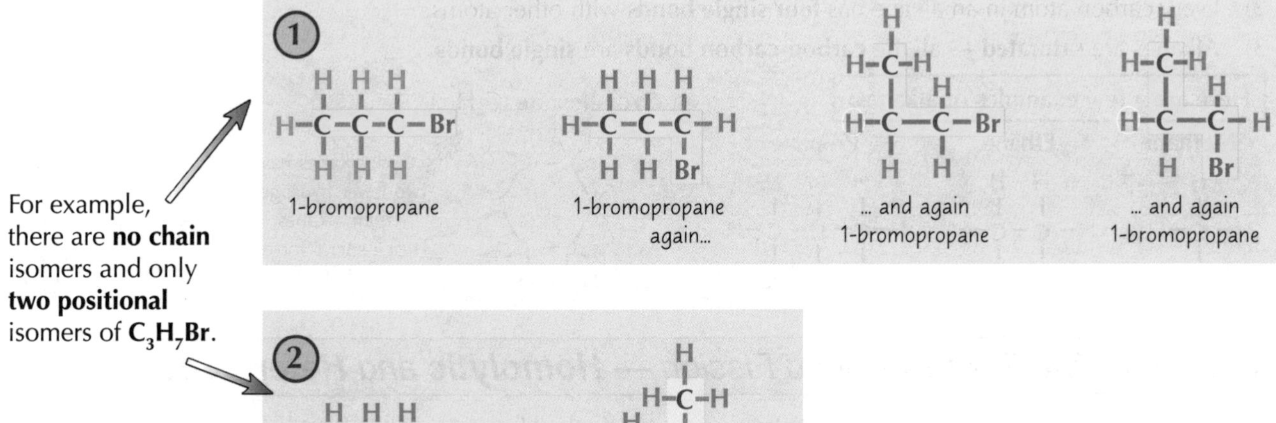

For example, there are **no chain** isomers and only **two positional** isomers of C_3H_7Br.

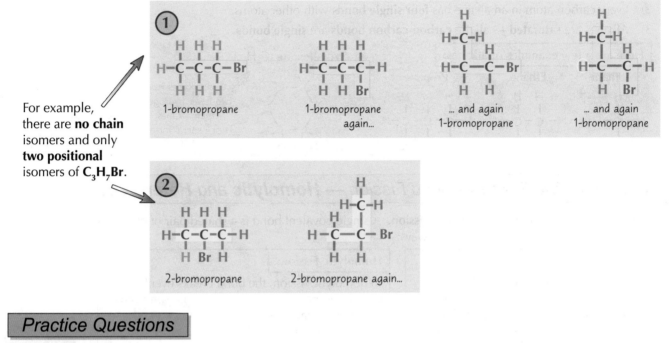

Practice Questions

Q1 What are isomers?

Q2 Name the three types of structural isomerism.

Q3 Draw the skeletal formulae of two isomers that both have the molecular formula C_4H_{10}.

Exam Questions

Q1 a) How many structural isomers are there of the alkane C_6H_{14}?

A 4 **B** 5 **C** 6 **D** 7 [1 mark]

b) Explain what is meant by the term 'structural isomerism'. [1 mark]

Q2 Pentane has the structural formula $CH_3CH_2CH_2CH_2CH_3$.

a) Draw the skeletal formula of a structural isomer of pentane. [1 mark]

b) Draw the displayed formula of an isomer of pentane that is not the molecule you drew in part a). [1 mark]

Q3 Two structural isomers, A and B, have the molecular formula C_3H_6O. They both contain a C=O double bond.

a) Draw the skeletal formulae of molecules A and B. [2 marks]

b) Give the structural formulae of isomers A and B. [2 marks]

Q4 Which of the following compounds is not an isomer of 1-buten-4-ol, $CH_2CHCH_2CH_2OH$?

A 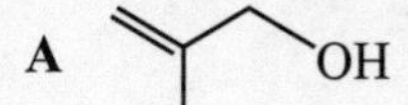

B OH **C** O **D** HO [1 mark]

Human structural isomers...

Alkanes

Alkanes are your basic hydrocarbons — like it says on the tin, they've got hydrogen and they've got carbon.

Alkanes are **Saturated Hydrocarbons**

1) Alkanes have the **general formula C_nH_{2n+2}**. They've only got **carbon** and **hydrogen** atoms, so they're **hydrocarbons**.
2) Every carbon atom in an alkane has **four single bonds** with other atoms.
3) Alkanes are **saturated** — all the **carbon-carbon bonds** are **single bonds**.

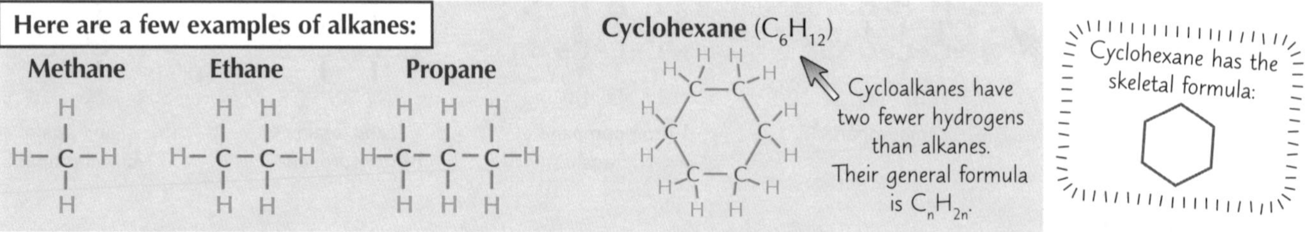
Here are a few examples of alkanes:
Methane
Ethane
Propane
Cyclohexane (C_6H_{12})
Cycloalkanes have two fewer hydrogens than alkanes. Their general formula is C_nH_{2n}.
Cyclohexane has the skeletal formula:

There are **Two Types** of Bond Fission — **Homolytic** and **Heterolytic**

Breaking a covalent bond is called **bond fission**. A single covalent bond is a shared pair of electrons between two atoms. It can break in two ways:

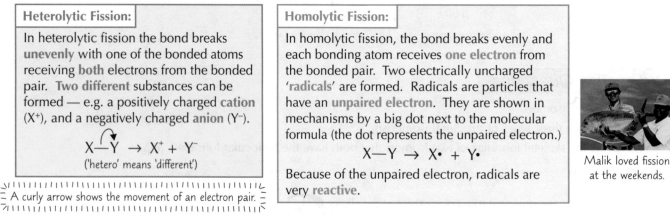

Heterolytic Fission:

In heterolytic fission the bond breaks **unevenly** with one of the bonded atoms receiving **both** electrons from the bonded pair. **Two different** substances can be formed — e.g. a positively charged **cation** (X^+), and a negatively charged **anion** (Y^-).

$$X—Y \rightarrow X^+ + Y^-$$

('hetero' means 'different')

A curly arrow shows the movement of an electron pair.

Homolytic Fission:

In homolytic fission, the bond breaks evenly and each bonding atom receives **one electron** from the bonded pair. Two electrically uncharged '**radicals**' are formed. Radicals are particles that have an **unpaired electron**. They are shown in mechanisms by a big dot next to the molecular formula (the dot represents the unpaired electron.)

X—Y → X• + Y•

Because of the unpaired electron, radicals are very **reactive**.

Malik loved fission at the weekends.

Halogens React with **Alkanes**, Forming **Halogenoalkanes**

1) Halogens react with alkanes in **photochemical** reactions. Photochemical reactions are started by **light** — this reaction requires **ultraviolet light** to get going.
2) A hydrogen atom is **substituted** (replaced) by chlorine or bromine. This is a **radical substitution reaction.**

Example: Chlorine and **methane** react with a bit of a bang to form **chloromethane**: $CH_4 + Cl_2 \xrightarrow{UV} CH_3Cl + HCl$

The **reaction mechanism** has three stages: **initiation**, **propagation** and **termination**.

The reaction between bromine and methane works the same way.
$CH_4 + Br_2 \xrightarrow{UV} CH_3Br + HBr$

Radicals are Produced by **Initiation** Reactions

In **initiation reactions**, radicals are **produced**.

1) Sunlight provides enough energy to break the Cl–Cl bond — this is **photodissociation**: $Cl_2 \xrightarrow{UV} 2Cl•$
2) The bond splits **equally** and each atom gets to keep one electron — **homolytic fission.** The atom becomes a highly reactive **radical**, Cl•, because of its **unpaired electron**.

Radicals are **Used Up** and **Created** in **Propagation** Reactions

During **propagation reactions**, radicals are **used up** and **created** in a **chain reaction**.

1) Cl• attacks a **methane** molecule: $Cl• + CH_4 \rightarrow •CH_3 + HCl$
2) The new **methyl radical**, $•CH_3$, can attack another Cl_2 molecule: $•CH_3 + Cl_2 \rightarrow CH_3Cl + Cl•$
3) The new Cl• can attack **another** CH_4 molecule, and so on, until all the Cl_2 or CH_4 molecules are wiped out.

Alkanes

Radicals are Destroyed in Termination Reactions

In **termination reactions**, radicals are mopped up by reacting together to form stable molecules.

1) If two free radicals join together, they make a **stable molecule**.
2) There are **heaps** of possible termination reactions. Here are a couple of them to give you the idea:

$Cl\bullet + \bullet CH_3 \rightarrow CH_3Cl$ $\quad$ $\bullet CH_3 + \bullet CH_3 \rightarrow C_2H_6$ ⇐ Some products formed will be trace impurities in the final sample.

The Problem is — You End Up With a Mixture of Products

1) The big problem with radical substitution if you're trying to make a **particular product** is that you **don't only get** the product you're after, but a **mixture of products**.
2) For example, if you're trying to make chloromethane and there's **too much chlorine** in the reaction mixture, some of the remaining **hydrogen atoms** on the **chloromethane molecule** will be swapped for chlorine atoms. The propagation reactions happen again, this time to make **dichloromethane**.

$Cl\bullet + CH_3Cl \rightarrow \bullet CH_2Cl + HCl$

$\bullet CH_2Cl + Cl_2 \rightarrow CH_2Cl_2 + Cl\bullet$

dichloromethane

3) It doesn't stop there. Another substitution reaction can take place to form **trichloromethane**.

$Cl\bullet + CH_2Cl_2 \rightarrow \bullet CHCl_2 + HCl$

$\bullet CHCl_2 + Cl_2 \rightarrow CHCl_3 + Cl\bullet$

trichloromethane

4) **Tetrachloromethane** (CCl_4) is formed in the last possible substitution. There are no more hydrogens attached to the carbon atom, so the substitution process has to stop.
5) So the end product is a mixture of CH_3Cl, CH_2Cl_2, $CHCl_3$ and CCl_4. This is a nuisance, because you have to **separate** the **chloromethane** from the other three unwanted by-products.
6) The best way of reducing the chance of these by-products forming is to have an **excess of methane**. This means there's a greater chance of a chlorine radical colliding only with a **methane molecule** and not a **chloromethane molecule**.
7) Another problem with radical substitution is that it can take place at any point along the **carbon chain**. So a mixture of **structural isomers** can be formed. For example, reacting **propane** with chlorine will produce a mixture of **1-chloropropane** and **2-chloropropane**.

Practice Questions

Q1 What's the general formula for alkanes?

Q2 What's homolytic fission?

Q3 What's a radical?

Q4 Write down the chemical equation for the radical substitution reaction between methane and chlorine.

Exam Question

Q1 When irradiated with UV light, methane gas will react with bromine to form a mixture of several organic compounds.

a) Name the type of mechanism involved in this reaction. [1 mark]

b) Write an overall equation to show the formation of bromomethane from methane and bromine. [1 mark]

c) Write down the two equations in the propagation step for the formation of CH_3Br. [2 marks]

d) i) Explain why a tiny amount of ethane is found in the product mixture. You should include the equation for the formation of this ethane in your answer. [2 marks]

ii) Name the mechanistic step that leads to the formation of ethane. [1 mark]

e) Name the major product formed when a large excess of bromine reacts with methane in the presence of UV light. [1 mark]

This page is like... totally radical, man...

Mechanisms can be a pain in the bum to learn, but unfortunately reactions are what Chemistry's all about. There's no easy trick — you've just got to sit down and learn the stuff. Keep hacking away at it, till you know it all off by heart.

Crude Oil

Crude oil is a big mixture of hydrocarbons. Some parts of the mixture are useful, like the hydrocarbons that make up petrol and diesel, but some aren't. Luckily, it's possible to convert the less useful parts into more usable compounds.

Crude Oil is Mainly *Alkanes*

1) **Petroleum** is just a fancy word for **crude oil** — the sticky black stuff they get out of the ground with oil wells.
2) Petroleum is a mixture of **hydrocarbons**. It's mostly made up of **alkanes**.
   They range from **small alkanes**, like pentane, to **massive alkanes** of more than 50 carbons.
3) Crude oil isn't very useful as it is, but you can **separate** it out into useful bits (**fractions**) by **fractional distillation**.

Here's how fractional distillation works — don't try this at home.

You might do fractional distillation in the lab, but if you do you'll use a safer crude oil substitute instead.

1) First, the crude oil is **vaporised** at about 350 °C.
2) The vaporised crude oil goes into a **fractionating column** and rises up through the trays. The largest hydrocarbons don't **vaporise** at all, because their boiling points are too high — they just run to the bottom and form a gooey **residue**.
3) As the crude oil vapour goes up the fractionating column, it gets **cooler**.
   Because the alkane molecules have different chain lengths, they have different **boiling points**, so each fraction **condenses** at a different temperature. The fractions are **drawn off** at different levels in the column.
4) The hydrocarbons with the **lowest boiling points** don't condense.
   They're drawn off as **gases** at the top of the column.

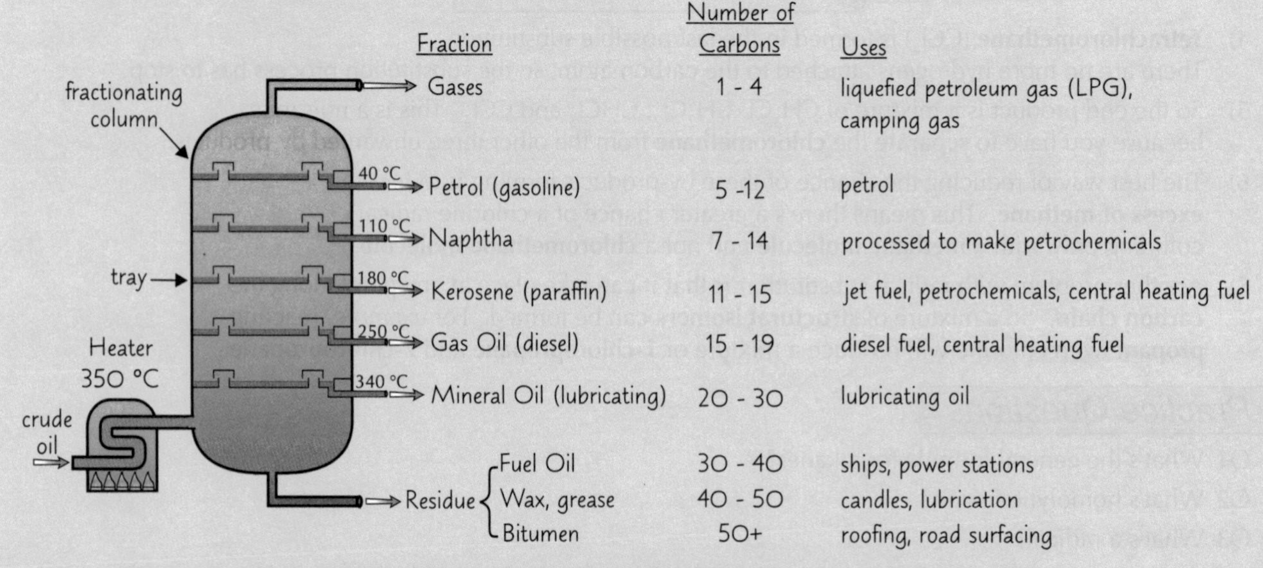

Fraction	Number of Carbons	Uses
Gases	1 - 4	liquefied petroleum gas (LPG), camping gas
Petrol (gasoline)	5 -12	petrol
Naphtha	7 - 14	processed to make petrochemicals
Kerosene (paraffin)	11 - 15	jet fuel, petrochemicals, central heating fuel
Gas Oil (diesel)	15 - 19	diesel fuel, central heating fuel
Mineral Oil (lubricating)	20 - 30	lubricating oil
Residue: Fuel Oil	30 - 40	ships, power stations
Residue: Wax, grease	40 - 50	candles, lubrication
Residue: Bitumen	50+	roofing, road surfacing

Heavy Fractions can be *'Cracked'* to Make *Smaller Molecules*

1) People want loads of the **light** fractions of crude oil, like petrol and naphtha. They don't want so much of the **heavier** stuff like bitumen though. Stuff that's in high demand is much more **valuable** than the stuff that isn't.
2) To meet this demand, the less popular heavier fractions are **cracked**. Cracking is **breaking** long-chain alkanes into **smaller** hydrocarbons (which can include alkenes). It involves breaking the **C–C bonds**.

   For example, **decane** could crack like this:

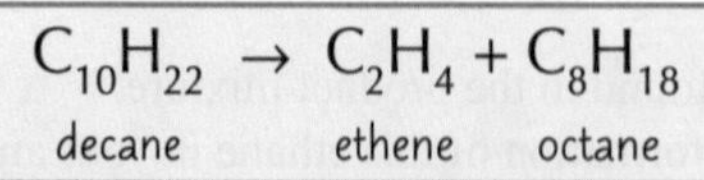

$$C_{10}H_{22} \rightarrow C_2H_4 + C_8H_{18}$$

decane → ethene + octane

Where the chain breaks is random, so you'll get a different mixture of products every time you crack a hydrocarbon.

Here are **two types** of **cracking** — **thermal cracking** and **catalytic cracking**.

Thermal Cracking Produces Lots of *Alkenes*

1) **Thermal cracking** takes place at **high temperature** (up to 1000 °C) and **high pressure** (up to 70 atm).
2) It produces a lot of **alkenes**.
3) These **alkenes** are used to make heaps of valuable products, like **polymers** (plastics). A good example is **poly(ethene)**, which is made from ethene.

Crude Oil

Catalytic Cracking Produces Lots of Aromatic Compounds

1) Catalytic cracking uses something called a **zeolite catalyst** (**hydrated aluminosilicate**), at a **slight pressure** and **high temperature** (about 450 °C).
2) It mostly produces **aromatic** hydrocarbons and **motor fuels**.
3) Using a catalyst **cuts costs**, because the reaction can be done at a **low** pressure and a **lower** temperature. The catalyst also **speeds** up the reaction, saving time (and time is money).

Aromatic compounds contain benzene rings. Benzene rings contain a ring of 6 carbon atoms with delocalised ring of electrons (see page 205).

Alkanes can be Reformed into Cycloalkanes and Aromatic Hydrocarbons

1) Most people's cars run on petrol or diesel, both of which contain a mixture of alkanes (as well as other hydrocarbons, impurities and additives).
2) Some of the alkanes in petrol are **straight-chain** alkanes, e.g. hexane — $CH_3CH_2CH_2CH_2CH_2CH_3$.
3) **Knocking** is where alkanes **explode** of their own accord when the fuel/air mixture in the engine is compressed. Straight chain alkanes are the **most likely** hydrocarbons to cause knocking. Adding branched chain and cyclic hydrocarbons to the petrol mixture makes knocking **less likely** to happen, so combustion is more **efficient**.
4) You can convert straight-chain alkanes into branched chain alkanes and cyclic hydrocarbons by **reforming**. This uses a catalyst (e.g. platinum stuck on aluminium oxide).

Don't worry too much about knocking. You shouldn't be asked about it in the exams, but you do have to know how alkanes are reformed.

Hexane can be reformed into cyclohexane and hydrogen gas, which can be reformed into benzene (C_6H_6) and hydrogen gas:

$$\underset{\text{hexane}}{CH_3CH_2CH_2CH_2CH_2CH_3} \xrightarrow{Pt} \text{cyclohexane} + H_2 \longrightarrow \text{benzene} + 3H_2$$

Octane can be reformed into 2,5-dimethylhexane:

$$\underset{\text{octane}}{CH_3CH_2CH_2CH_2CH_2CH_2CH_2CH_3} \xrightarrow{Pt} \underset{\text{2,5-dimethylhexane}}{CH_3CH(CH_3)CH_2CH_2CH(CH_3)CH_3}$$

Practice Questions

Q1 How does fractional distillation work?

Q2 What is cracking?

Q3 Why is reforming used?

Exam Question

Q1 Crude oil is a source of fuels and petrochemicals.
It's vaporised and separated into fractions using fractional distillation.

a) Some heavier fractions are processed using cracking.

i) Explain why cracking is carried out. [2 marks]

ii) Write a possible equation for the cracking of dodecane, $C_{12}H_{26}$. [1 mark]

b) Some hydrocarbons present in petrol are processed using reforming.

i) Name two types of compound that are produced by reforming. [2 marks]

ii) What effect do these compounds have on the petrol's performance? [1 mark]

Crude oil — not the kind of oil you could take home to meet your mother...

This isn't the most exciting topic in the history of the known universe. Although in a galaxy far, far away there may be lots of pages on more boring topics. But, that's neither here nor there, because you've got to learn this stuff anyway. Get fractional distillation and cracking straight in your brain and make sure you know why people bother to do it.

Fuels

If we didn't burn fuels to keep warm and power vehicles, we'd all wear lots of jumpers and use pogo sticks... maybe.

Alkanes are Useful as **Fuels...**

1) If you burn (**oxidise**) alkanes with **oxygen**, you get **carbon dioxide** and water — this is a **combustion reaction**.

   Here's the equation for the combustion of propane — $C_3H_{8(g)} + 5O_{2(g)} \rightarrow 3CO_{2(g)} + 4H_2O_{(g)}$

2) If there isn't much oxygen around, the alkane will still burn, but it will produce a mixture of mainly **carbon monoxide**, **carbon** and **water** (there could also be some carbon dioxide). This is **incomplete combustion**.

   For example, burning ethane with not much O_2 — $C_2H_{6(g)} + 2O_{2(g)} \rightarrow C_{(s)} + CO_{(g)} + 3H_2O_{(g)}$

3) Combustion reactions happen between **gases**, so liquid alkanes have to be **vaporised** first. Smaller alkanes turn into **gases** more easily (they're more **volatile**), so they'll **burn** more easily too.
4) Combustion reactions are **exothermic** reactions (they release **heat**).
5) Larger alkanes release heaps more **energy** per mole because they have more bonds to react.
6) Because they release so much energy when they burn, alkanes make excellent **fuels**. For example:

   1) Methane's used for **central heating** and **cooking** in homes.
   2) Alkanes with 5-12 carbon atoms are used in **petrol**.
   3) Kerosene is used as **jet fuel**. Its alkanes have 11-15 carbon atoms.
   4) **Diesel** is made of a mixture of alkanes with 15-19 carbon atoms.

...But They Produce **Harmful Emissions**

1) We generate most of our **electricity** by burning **fossil fuels** (coal, oil and natural gas) in **power stations**. We also use loads and loads of fossil fuels for **transport** and **heating**. Burning all these fossil fuels causes a lot of **pollution**.
2) Pollutants formed from burning fossil fuels include **carbon monoxide**, **unburnt hydrocarbons** and **carbon particulates** from the **incomplete combustion** of fuels, as well as **oxides** of **sulfur** (SO_x) and **nitrogen** (NO_x).
3) These pollutants can cause lots of **problems** for our **health** as well as for the **environment**.

Carbon Monoxide is Toxic

1) The **oxygen** in your bloodstream is carried around by **haemoglobin**.
2) **Carbon monoxide** is **better** at binding to haemoglobin than oxygen is, so it binds to the haemoglobin in your bloodstream **before** the oxygen can.
3) This means that **less oxygen** can be carried around your body, leading to **oxygen deprivation**. At very high concentrations, carbon monoxide can be fatal.

Sulfur Dioxide and Oxides of Nitrogen (NO_x) Lead to Acid Rain

1) **Acid rain** can be caused by burning fossil fuels that contain **sulfur**. The sulfur burns to produce **sulfur dioxide** gas which then enters the atmosphere, dissolves in the moisture, and is converted into **sulfuric acid**.
2) **Oxides of nitrogen** (NO_x) are produced when the high pressure and temperature in a car engine cause the nitrogen and oxygen in the air to react together. When oxides of nitrogen (NO_x) escape into the atmosphere, they dissolves in moisture and are converted into **nitric acid**, which can fall as **acid rain**.
3) Acid rain destroys trees and vegetation, as well as corroding buildings and statues and killing fish in lakes.

Catalytic Converters Remove Some Pollutants from **Car Emissions**

1) Catalytic converters sit quietly in a car **exhaust** and stop some **pollutants** from coming out.
2) Without catalytic converters, cars spew out **lots** of bad stuff, like **carbon monoxide**, **oxides of nitrogen** and **unburnt hydrocarbons**.
3) Catalytic converters **get rid** of theses pollutants by using a **platinum catalyst** to change them to **harmless gases**, like **water vapour** and **nitrogen**, or to **less harmful** ones like **carbon dioxide**.
4) For example, **nitrogen monoxide** and **carbon monoxide** can be converted to nitrogen and carbon dioxide: ⟹ $2NO_{(g)} + 2CO_{(g)} \rightarrow N_{2\,(g)} + 2CO_{2\,(g)}$

Fuels

Fossil Fuels are *Non-Renewable*

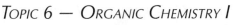

"Bruce... bring some more fossils — the barbie's going out."

The various kinds of pollution produced by burning fossil fuels aren't the only problems. They're also becoming more and more scarce as we use more and more of them.

1) The main fossil fuels (**coal**, **oil**, and **natural gas**) are relatively **easily extracted** and produce a **large amount** of energy when burnt. But, there's a finite amount of them and they're running out.
2) Oil will be the first to go — and as it gets really scarce, it'll become more **expensive**. It's not **sustainable** to keep using fossil fuels willy-nilly.

Biofuels Include *Biodiesel* and *Alcohols* Made from *Renewable Sources*

1) Fortunately, there are alternatives to fossil fuels which are renewable.
2) Biofuels are fuels made from **living matter** over a **short period** of time:
    - **bioethanol** is ethanol (an alcohol) made by the **fermentation of sugar** from crops such as maize,
    - **biodiesel** is made by **refining** renewable **fats** and **oils** such as vegetable oil,
    - **biogas** is produced by the breakdown of **organic waste matter**.
3) These fuels do produce CO_2 when they're burnt, but it's CO_2 that the plants **absorbed** while growing, so **biofuels** are usually still classed as **carbon neutral**. But CO_2 is still given out while refining and transporting the fuel, as well as making the fertilisers and powering agricultural machinery used to grow and harvest the crops.
4) Biodiesel and biogas can also be made from waste that would otherwise go to **landfill**.
5) But one problem with switching from fossil fuels to biofuels in transport is that **petrol car engines** would have to be **modified** to use fuels with high ethanol concentrations.
6) Also, the land used to grow crops for fuel can't be used to grow **food** — this could be a serious problem... **Developed** countries (like the UK) will create a huge demand as they try to find fossil fuel alternatives. Poorer **developing** countries (in South America, say) could use this as a way of **earning money**, and convert farming land to produce 'crops for fuels'. This may mean they won't grow enough food to eat.

Practice Questions

Q1 Name three products that form when an alkane burns in limited oxygen.

Q2 Why is the production of sulfur dioxide harmful for the environment?

Q3 Describe how bioethanol is produced.

Exam Questions

Q1 One of the components in petrol is the alkane pentane (C_5H_{12}).

a) Write a balanced equation for the complete combustion of pentane. [2 marks]

b) Explain how the incomplete combustion of pentane could cause serious health problems. [2 marks]

Q2 One problem caused by pollution is acid rain.

a) Name two pollutants which lead to acid rain. [1 mark]

b) Explain how one of these pollutants can be removed from car emissions. [1 mark]

Q3 Biodiesel is a fuel that can be used as an alternative to fossil fuels.
Give one advantage and one disadvantage of using biodiesel over fossil fuels. [2 marks]

Fixing the pollution problem — a fuels errand...

It's a dirty business, burning fossil fuels. You need to know about the various pollutants they release (such as sulfur oxides, nitrogen oxides, carbon monoxide, unburnt hydrocarbons, carbon particulates) and what damage they do. Then there are the alternatives. Biofuels may well be renewable, but they're not without their own drawbacks.

Alkenes

An alkene is like an alkane's wild younger brother. They look kinda similar, but alkenes are way more reactive.

*Alkenes are **Unsaturated Hydrocarbons***

1) Alkenes have the **general formula C_nH_{2n}**. They're made of carbon and hydrogen atoms, so they're **hydrocarbons**.
2) Alkene molecules **all** have at least one **C=C double covalent bond**. Molecules with C=C double bonds are **unsaturated** because they can make more bonds with extra atoms in **addition** reactions (see pages 86-87).

A cycloalkene has 2 H's fewer than an open-chain alkene.

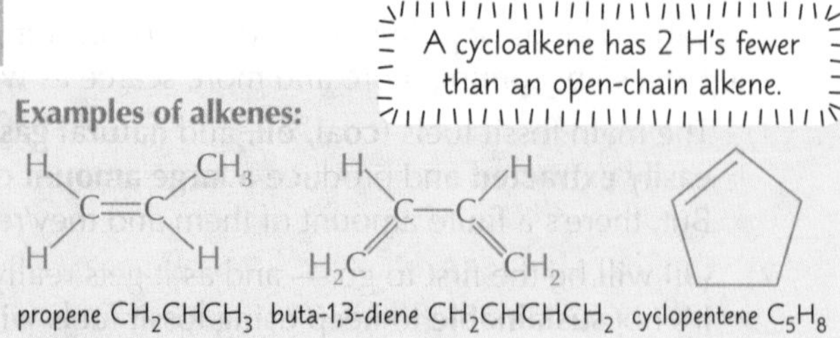

*Bonds in Organic Molecules can be **Sigma** or **Pi Bonds***

Covalent bonds form when **atomic orbitals** from different atoms, each containing a single electron, **overlap**, causing the electrons to become **shared**. A bond forms because the nuclei of the atoms are attracted by **electrostatic attraction** to the bonding electrons. The **way** that atomic orbitals overlap causes different **types** of bond to form.

1) Single covalent bonds in organic molecules are **sigma (σ-) bonds**. A σ-bond is formed when **two orbitals overlap**, in a straight line, in the space between two atoms. This gives the highest possible **electron density** between the two positive nuclei.

orbitals overlap in a straight line

atomic orbital

σ-bond

2) The **high electron density** between the nuclei means there is a strong **electrostatic attraction** between the nuclei and the shared pair of electrons. This means that σ-bonds have a high **bond enthalpy** — they're the **strongest** type of covalent bonds.
3) A double bond is made up of a **sigma (σ-) bond** and a **pi (π-) bond**. A **π-bond** is formed when **two lobes** of two orbitals **overlap sideways**. It's got two parts to it — one 'above' and one 'below' the molecular axis. For example, p-orbitals can form π-bonds.
4) In a π-bond, the electron density is **spread out** above and below the nuclei. This causes the **electrostatic attraction** between the nuclei and the shared pair of electrons to be **weaker** in π-bonds than in σ-bonds, so π-bonds have a **relatively low bond enthalpy**.
5) This means that a double bond (π-bond + σ-bond) is less than twice as strong as a single bond (just a σ-bond).
6) Although they're usually written as C=C, double bonds really look **more like this**:
7) In alkenes, the **C–C** and **C–H bonds** are all **σ-bonds**. The **C=C bonds** in **alkenes** contain both a σ- and a **π-bond**.

Any types of orbital can form a σ-bond, as long as they point towards the other atom. So you can get σ-bonds made from two s-orbitals, two p-orbitals, one s-orbital and one p-orbital as well as different types of orbitals.

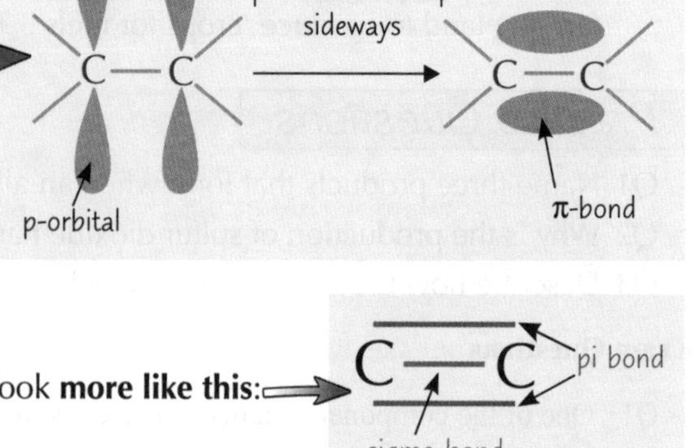

Practice Questions

Q1 What is the general formula of an alkene?

Q2 Describe how a sigma (σ–) bond forms.

Exam Question

Q1 The C=C bond in ethene is made up of two different types of bond.

a) Give one similarity between these bonds. [1 mark]

b) Give one difference between these bonds. [1 mark]

Double, double toil and trouble. Alkene burn and pi bond bubble...

Double bonds are always made up of a σ-bond and a π-bond. So even though π-bonds are weaker than σ-bonds, double bonds will be stronger than single bonds because they have the combined strength of a σ- and a π-bond.

Stereoisomerism

The chemistry on these pages isn't so bad. And don't be too worried when I tell you that a good working knowledge of both German and Latin would be useful. It's not absolutely essential... You'll be fine without.

Double Bonds Can't Rotate

1) Carbon atoms in a C=C double bond and the atoms bonded to these carbons all lie in the **same plane** (they're **planar**). Because of the way they're arranged, they're actually said to be **trigonal planar** — the atoms attached to each double-bonded carbon are at the corners of an imaginary equilateral triangle.

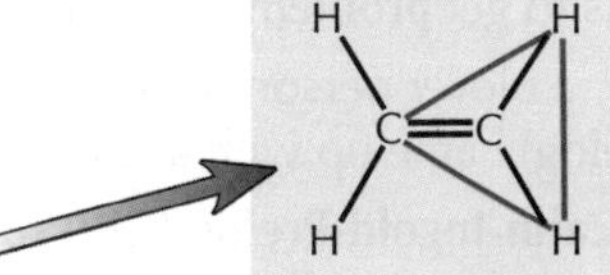

The H–C–H bond angles in the planar unit are all 120°.

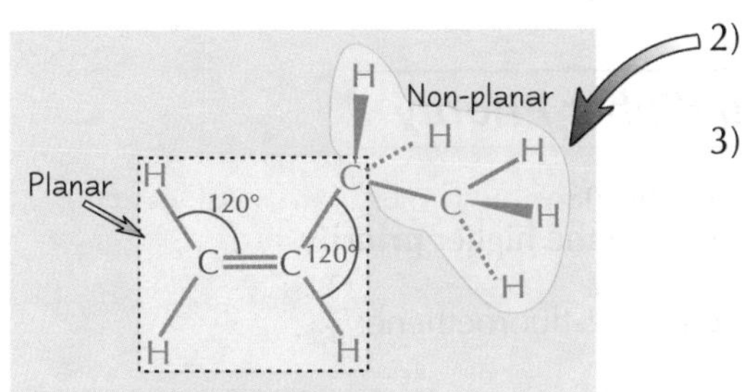

2) Ethene, C_2H_4 (like in the diagram above), is completely planar, but in larger alkenes, only the >C=C< unit is planar.
3) Another important thing about C=C double bonds is that atoms **can't rotate** around them like they can around single bonds (because of the way the p-orbitals **overlap** to form a **π-bond** — see previous page). In fact, double bonds are fairly **rigid** — they don't bend much either.
4) Even though atoms can't rotate about the **double bond**, things can still rotate about any **single bonds** in the molecule.
5) The **restricted rotation** around the C=C double bond is what causes **alkenes** to form **stereoisomers**.

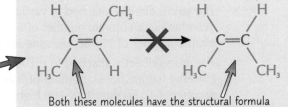

Both these molecules have the structural formula $CH_3CHCHCH_3$. The restricted rotation around the double bond means you can't turn one into the other so they are isomers.

E/Z isomerism is a Type of Stereoisomerism

1) **Stereoisomers** have the same structural formula but a **different arrangement** in space. (Just bear with me for a moment... that will become clearer, I promise.)
2) Because of the **lack of rotation** around the double bond, some **alkenes** can have stereoisomers.
3) Stereoisomers occur when the two double-bonded carbon atoms each have two **different atoms** or **groups** attached to them.
4) One of these isomers is called the **'E-isomer'** and the other is called the **'Z-isomer'** (hence the name E/Z isomerism).
5) The **Z-isomer** has the same groups either **both above** or **both below** the double bond, whilst the **E-isomer** has the same groups positioned **across** the double bond.

When you're naming stereoisomers, you need to put 'E' or 'Z' at the beginning of the name.

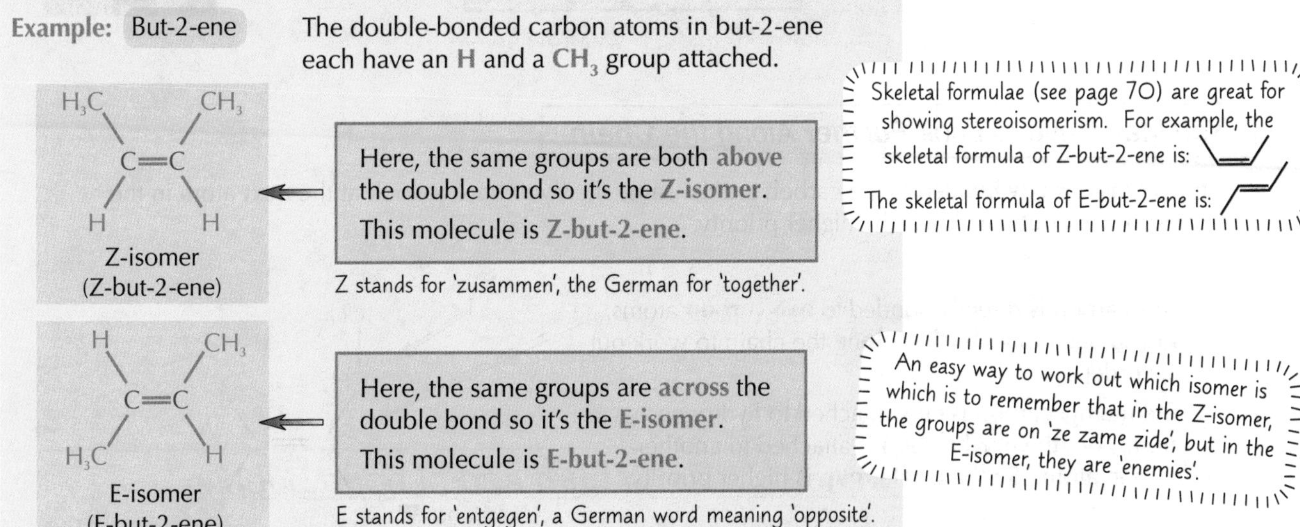

Example: But-2-ene — The double-bonded carbon atoms in but-2-ene each have an H and a CH_3 group attached.

Here, the same groups are both above the double bond so it's the Z-isomer. This molecule is **Z-but-2-ene**.

Z stands for 'zusammen', the German for 'together'.

Here, the same groups are across the double bond so it's the E-isomer. This molecule is **E-but-2-ene**.

E stands for 'entgegen', a German word meaning 'opposite'.

Skeletal formulae (see page 70) are great for showing stereoisomerism. For example, the skeletal formula of Z-but-2-ene is: — The skeletal formula of E-but-2-ene is:

An easy way to work out which isomer is which is to remember that in the Z-isomer, the groups are on 'ze zame zide', but in the E-isomer, they are 'enemies'.

Stereoisomerism

The E/Z System Works Even When All the Groups Are Different

1) When the carbons on either end of a double bond both have the **same groups** attached, then it's easy to work out which is the E-isomer and which is the Z-isomer (like in the example on the last page).
2) It only starts to get **problematic** if the carbon atoms both have **totally different groups** attached.
3) Fortunately, a clever person (well, three clever people — Mr Cahn, Mr Ingold and Mr Prelog) came up with a solution to this problem.
4) Using the **Cahn-Ingold-Prelog (CIP) rules** you can work out which is the E-isomer and which is the Z-isomer for any alkene. They're really simple, and they work every time.

Atoms With a Larger Atomic Number are Given a Higher Priority

1) Look at the atoms **directly bonded** to each of the C=C carbon atoms. The atom with the higher **atomic number** on each carbon is given the higher **priority**.

Example: Here's one of the stereoisomers of 1-bromo-1-chloro-2-fluoroethene:

- The atoms directly attached to **carbon-1** are bromine and chlorine. **Bromine** has an atomic number of **35** and **chlorine** has an atomic number of **17**. So **bromine** is the higher priority group.
- The atoms directly attached to **carbon-2** are fluorine and hydrogen. **Fluorine** has an atomic number of **9** and **hydrogen** has an atomic number of **1**. So **fluorine** is the higher priority group.

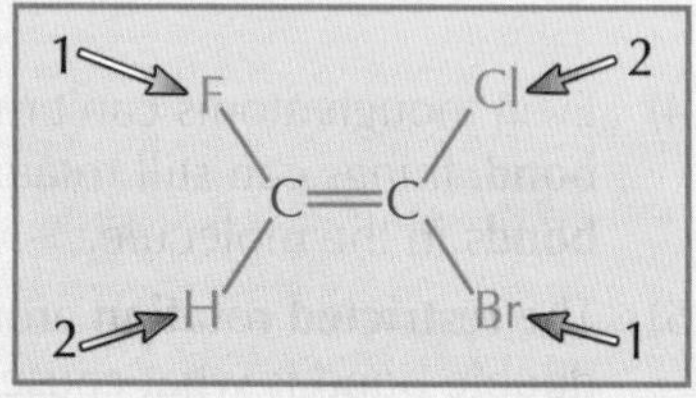

2) Now you can assign the isomers as E- and Z- as before, just by looking at how the groups of the **same priority** are arranged.

If you need to look up atomic numbers in the exams, you'll find them on the periodic table in your data booklet.

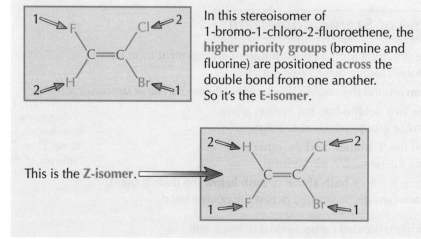

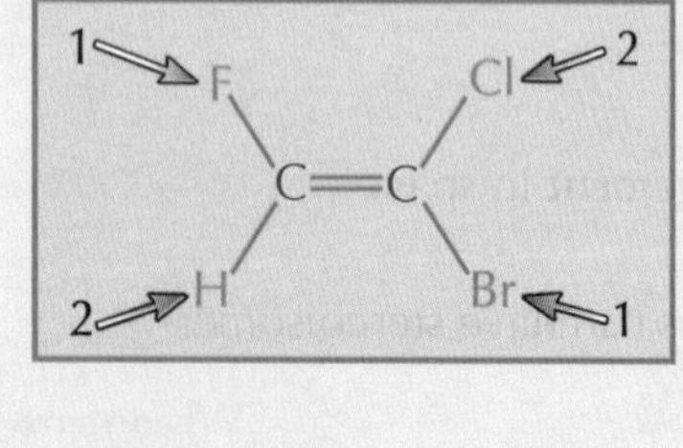

In this stereoisomer of 1-bromo-1-chloro-2-fluoroethene, the **higher priority groups** (bromine and fluorine) are positioned **across** the double bond from one another. So it's the **E-isomer**.

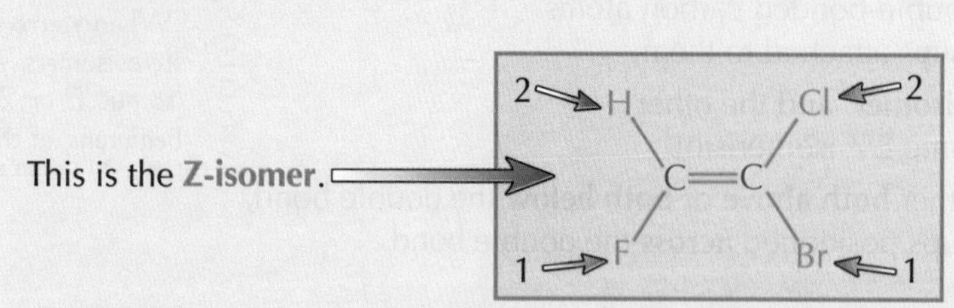

How come you always get to go first?
Because I'm bigger than you.

You May Have to Look Further Along the Chain

If the atoms **directly bonded** to the carbon are the **same** then you have to look at the **next** atom in the groups to work out which has the higher priority.

This carbon is directly bonded to **two carbon** atoms, so you need to go **further along** the chain to work out the ordering.

The methyl carbon is only attached to hydrogen atoms, but the ethyl carbon is attached to another carbon atom. So the **ethyl group** is higher priority.

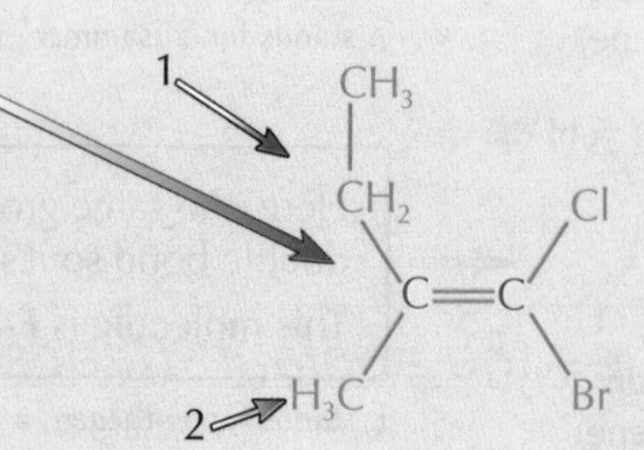

Stereoisomerism

Cis-Trans Isomerism is a Special Type of E/Z isomerism

1) If the carbon atoms have at least **one group in common** (like in but-2-ene), then you can call the isomers '**cis**' or '**trans**' (as well as E- or Z-) where...
   - '**cis**' means the same groups are on the **same side** of the double bond,
   - '**trans**' means the same groups are on **opposite sides** of the double bond.

   So E-but-2-ene can be called **trans-but-2-ene**, as it has methyl groups on **opposite sides** of the double bond, and Z-but-2-ene can be called **cis-but-2-ene**, as the methyl groups are on the **same side** of the double bond.

In cis-trans isomerism, you're looking at how identical groups are positioned, rather than the higher priority groups. This means there isn't a rule for whether the Z-isomer is the cis- or the trans-isomer (and the same for the E-isomer) — you just have to work it out.

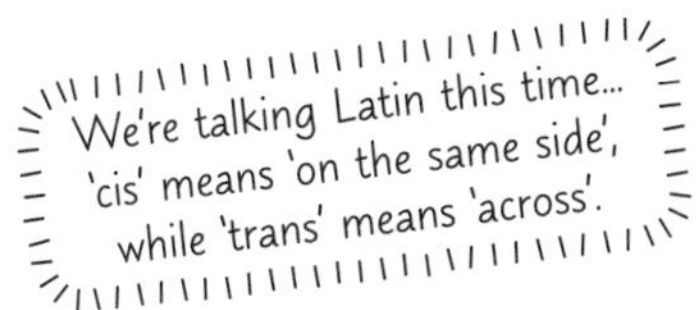

We're talking Latin this time...
'cis' means 'on the same side',
while 'trans' means 'across'.

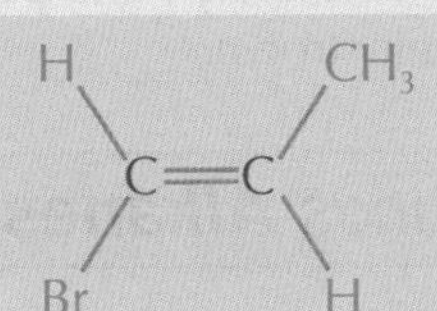

Here's an example:
The **H** atoms are on **opposite** sides of the double bond, so this is **trans-1-bromopropene**. No problems there.

2) If the carbon atoms both have totally **different** groups attached to them, the cis-trans naming system can't cope.

Here, the **cis/trans** naming system doesn't work because the carbon atoms have **different groups** attached so there's no way of deciding **which isomer** is cis and which isomer is trans.

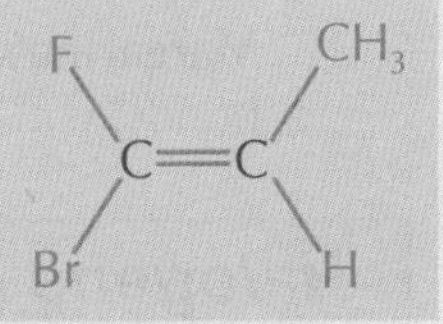

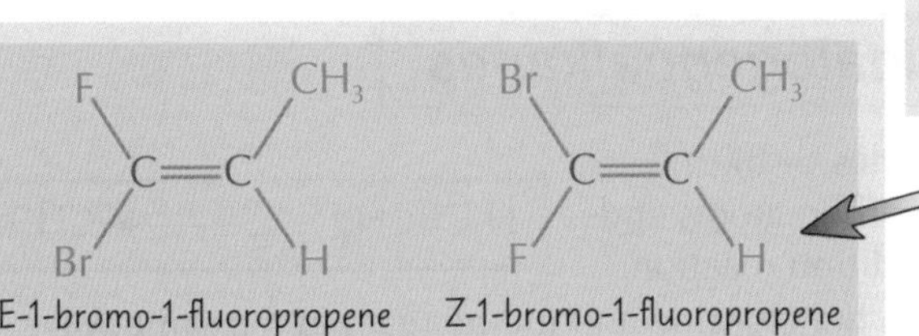

E-1-bromo-1-fluoropropene Z-1-bromo-1-fluoropropene

3) The E/Z system keeps on working though — in the E/Z system, Br has a **higher priority** than F, so the names depend on where the Br atom is in relation to the CH_3 group.

Practice Questions

Q1 Why is an ethene molecule said to be planar?

Q2 Define the term 'stereoisomers'.

Q3 Which of the following molecules, **A**, **B** or **C**, is the Z-isomer of but-2-ene?

A H_3C, H_3C / C=C / H, H

B 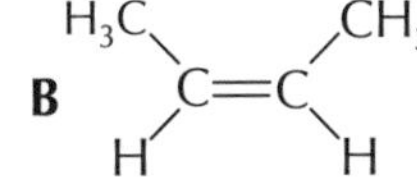

C 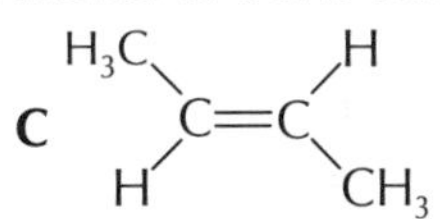

Q4 Is chlorine or bromine higher priority under the Cahn-Ingold-Prelog priority rules?

Q5 Which of the molecules in Question 3 (**A**, **B** or **C**) is the trans-isomer of but-2-ene?

Exam Questions

Q1 a) Draw and name the E/Z isomers of pent-2-ene, using full systematic names. [2 marks]

b) Explain why alkenes can have E/Z isomers but alkanes cannot. [2 marks]

Q2 How many stereoisomers are there of the molecule $CH_3CH{=}CHCH_2CH{=}C(CH_3)_2$?

A 1 **B** 2 **C** 3 **D** 4 [1 mark]

Q3 a) Draw and name the E/Z isomers of:

i) 1-bromo-2-chloroethene, ii) 1-bromo-2-chloroprop-1-ene. [4 marks]

b) i) Which of the molecules in part a) exhibits cis-trans isomerism? Explain your answer. [2 marks]

ii) Draw and name the cis-trans isomers of the molecule identified in part b) i). [2 marks]

You've reached the ausfahrt (that's German for exit)...

IMPORTANT FACT: If the two groups connected to one of the double-bonded carbons in an alkene are the same, then it won't have E/Z isomers. So neither propene nor but-1-ene have E/Z isomers. Try drawing them out if you're not sure.

Reactions of Alkenes

I'll warn you now — some of this stuff gets a bit heavy — but stick with it, as it's pretty important.

Electrophilic Addition Reactions *Happen to Alkenes*

In an **electrophilic addition** reaction, the alkene **double bond** opens up and atoms are **added** to the carbon atoms.

1) Electrophilic addition reactions happen because the double bond has got plenty of **electrons** and is easily attacked by **electrophiles**.
2) **Electrophiles** are **electron-pair acceptors** — they're usually a bit short of electrons, so they're **attracted** to areas where there are lots of electrons about.
3) Electrophiles include **positively charged ions**, like H^+ and NO_2^+, and **polar molecules** (since the δ+ atom is attracted to places with lots of electrons).

Adding ***Hydrogen*** *to C=C Bonds Produces* ***Alkanes***

1) Ethene will react with **hydrogen** gas in an addition reaction to produce ethane. It needs a **nickel catalyst** and a temperature of **150 °C** though.

$$H_2C{=}CH_2 + H_2 \xrightarrow[150\,°C]{Ni} CH_3CH_3$$

2) **Margarine's** made by **'hydrogenating' unsaturated** vegetable **oils**. By removing some double bonds, you **raise** the **melting point** of the oil so that it becomes **solid** at room temperature.

Halogens *React With Alkenes to Form* ***Dihalogenoalkanes***

1) **Halogens** will react with alkenes to form **dihalogenoalkanes** — the halogens add **across** the **double bond**, and each of the carbon atoms ends up bonded to one halogen atom. It's an **electrophilic addition** reaction.

$$H_2C{=}CH_2 + X_2 \longrightarrow CH_2XCH_2X$$

2) Here's the mechanism — bromine is used as an example, but chlorine and iodine react in the same way.

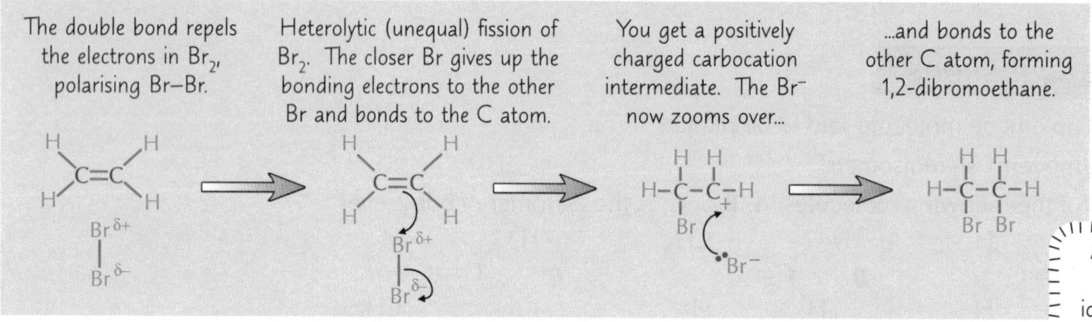

The double bond repels the electrons in Br_2, polarising Br–Br.

Heterolytic (unequal) fission of Br_2. The closer Br gives up the bonding electrons to the other Br and bonds to the C atom.

You get a positively charged carbocation intermediate. The Br^- now zooms over...

...and bonds to the other C atom, forming 1,2-dibromoethane.

A carbocation is an organic ion containing a positively charged carbon atom.

3) When you shake an alkene with **brown bromine water**, the solution quickly **decolourises**. This is because bromine is added across the double bond to form a colourless **dibromoalkane**. So **bromine water** is used to test for the presence of **carbon-carbon double bonds**.

bromine water + cyclohexene — SHAKE — solution goes colourless

Alcohols *Can be Made by* ***Steam Hydration***

1) Alkenes can be **hydrated** by **steam** at 300 °C and a pressure of 60-70 atm. The reaction needs a solid **phosphoric(V) acid catalyst**.
2) The reaction is used to manufacture **ethanol** from **ethene**:

$$H_2C{=}CH_{2\,(g)} + H_2O_{(g)} \underset{300\,°C,\ 60\,atm}{\overset{H_3PO_4}{\rightleftharpoons}} CH_3CH_2OH_{(g)}$$

Alkenes are ***Oxidised*** *by* ***Acidified Potassium Manganate(VII)***

1) If you shake an alkene with **acidified potassium manganate(VII)**, the **purple** solution is **decolourised**. You've **oxidised** the alkene and made a diol (an alcohol with two -OH groups).
2) For example, here's how **ethene** reacts with acidified potassium manganate(VII):

$$H_2C{=}CH_2 \xrightarrow{H^+/MnO_4^-} HOCH_2CH_2OH$$

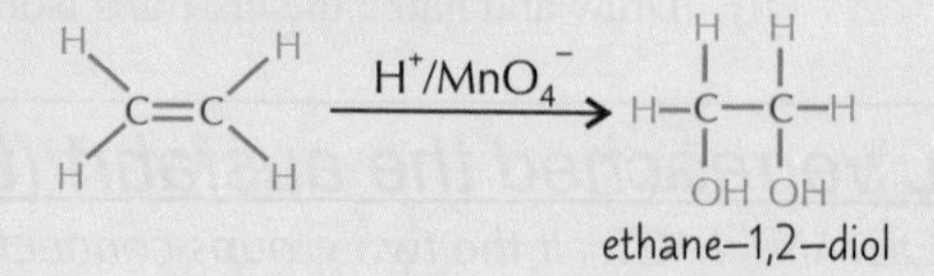

ethane–1,2–diol

Reactions of Alkenes

Alkenes also Undergo **Addition** with **Hydrogen Halides**

Alkenes also undergo **addition** reactions with hydrogen halides — to form **halogenoalkanes**.
For example, this is the reaction between **ethene** and HBr:

$$H_2C{=}CH_2 + HBr \rightarrow CH_2BrCH_3$$

Adding **Hydrogen Halides** to **Unsymmetrical Alkenes** Forms **Two Products**

1) If the hydrogen halide adds to an **unsymmetrical** alkene, there are two possible products.
2) The amount of each product depends on how **stable** the **carbocation** formed in the middle of the reaction is.
3) Carbocations with more **alkyl groups** are more stable because the alkyl groups feed **electrons** towards the positive charge. The **more stable carbocation** is much more likely to form.

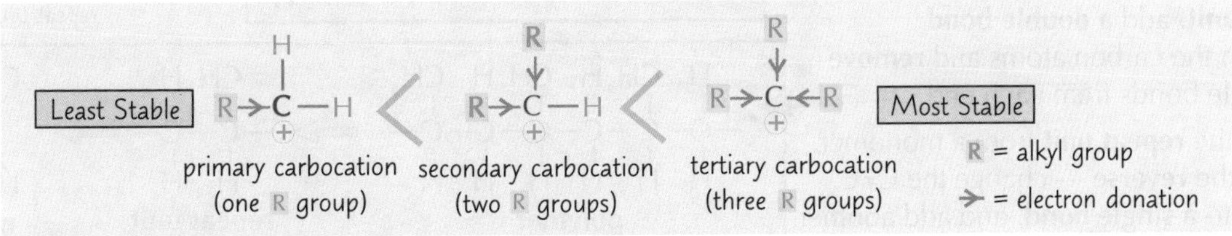

Least Stable — primary carbocation (one R group) < secondary carbocation (two R groups) < tertiary carbocation (three R groups) — Most Stable

R = alkyl group

→ = electron donation

4) Here's how hydrogen bromide reacts with propene:

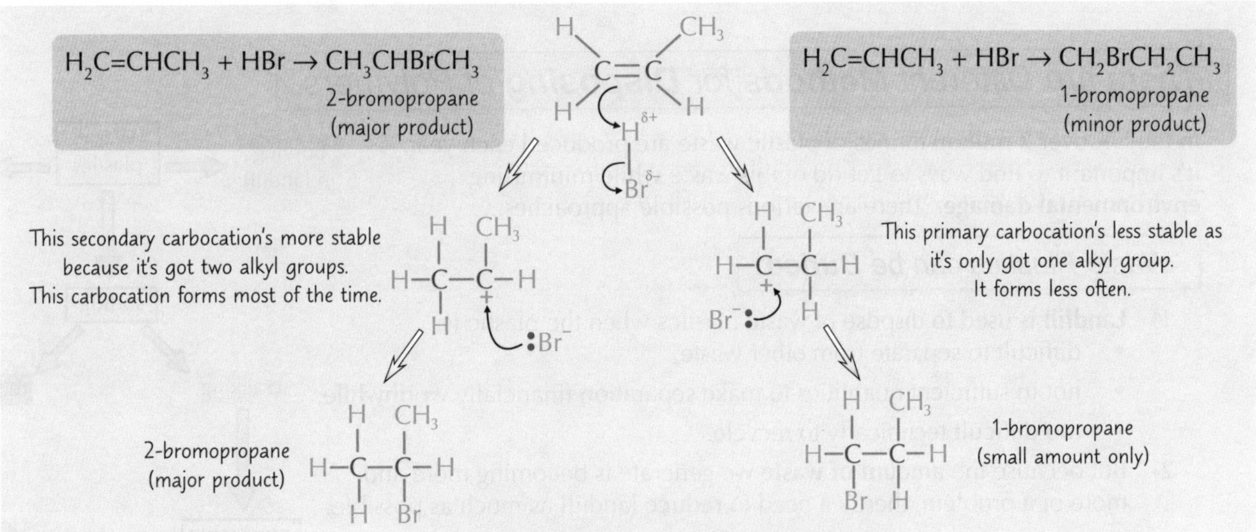

$H_2C{=}CHCH_3 + HBr \rightarrow CH_3CHBrCH_3$ 2-bromopropane (major product)

$H_2C{=}CHCH_3 + HBr \rightarrow CH_2BrCH_2CH_3$ 1-bromopropane (minor product)

This secondary carbocation's more stable because it's got two alkyl groups. This carbocation forms most of the time.

This primary carbocation's less stable as it's only got one alkyl group. It forms less often.

2-bromopropane (major product)

1-bromopropane (small amount only)

5) This can be summed up by **Markownikoff's rule** which says:

> The **major product** from addition of a hydrogen halide (HX) to an unsymmetrical alkene is the one where **hydrogen** adds to the carbon with the **most hydrogens** already attached.

Practice Questions

Q1 What is an electrophile?

Q2 Write an equation for the reaction of ethene with hydrogen.

Q3 Give the reagents and conditions needed to convert an alkene into a diol.

Exam Question

Q1 But-1-ene is an alkene. Alkenes contain at least one C=C double bond.

a) Describe how bromine water can be used to test for C=C double bonds. [1 mark]

b) Name and show the reaction mechanism involved in the above test. [5 marks]

c) Hydrogen bromide reacts with but-1-ene, producing two isomeric products.
Draw the displayed formulae of these two isomers and explain which will be the major product. [4 marks]

Electrophiles — they all want a piece of the pi...

Mechanisms are a classic that examiners just love. You need to know the electrophilic addition examples on these pages, so shut the book and scribble them out. And remember that sometimes the product has more than one isomer.

Polymers

Polymers are long, stringy molecules made by joining lots of alkenes together. They're made up of one unit repeated over and over and over and over and over and over and over and over again. Get the idea? OK, let's get started.

Alkenes ***Join Up*** *to form* ***Addition Polymers***

1) The **double bonds** in alkenes can open up and join together to make long chains called **polymers**. It's kind of like they're holding hands in a big line. The individual, small alkenes are called **monomers**.
2) This is called **addition polymerisation**. For example, **poly(ethene)** is made by the **addition polymerisation** of **ethene**.
3) To find the **monomer** used to form an addition polymer, take the **repeat unit**, add a **double bond** between the carbon atoms and **remove** the single bonds from each end.
4) To find the **repeat unit** from a monomer, just do the **reverse** — change the C=C bond into a **single bond**, and add another single bond to each of the **C=C** carbons.

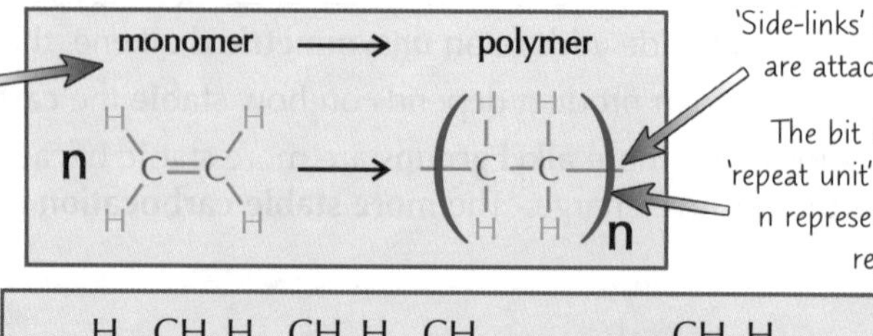

'Side-links' show that both sides are attached to other units.

The bit in brackets is the 'repeat unit' (or 'repeating unit'). n represents the number of repeat units.

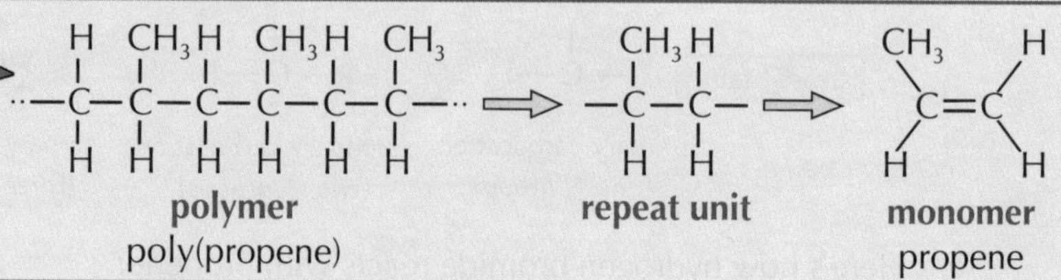

There are Different ***Methods*** *for* ***Disposing*** *of Polymers*

In the UK over **2 million** tonnes of plastic waste are produced each year. It's important to find ways to get rid of this waste while minimising **environmental damage**. There are various possible approaches...

Waste plastics → burying in landfill; Waste plastics → burning as fuel; Waste plastics → sorting → cracking → processing → other chemicals / new plastics; sorting → remoulding → new objects

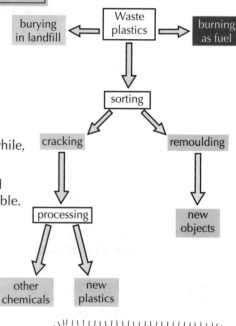

Waste Plastics can be ***Buried***

1) **Landfill** is used to dispose of waste plastics when the plastic is:
   - difficult to separate from other waste,
   - not in sufficient quantities to make separation financially worthwhile,
   - too difficult technically to recycle.
2) But because the **amount of waste** we generate is becoming more and more of a problem, there's a need to **reduce** landfill as much as possible.

Waste Plastics can be ***Reused***

1) Many plastics are made from non-renewable **oil-fractions**, so it makes sense to reuse plastics as much as possible.
2) There's more than one way to reuse plastics. After **sorting** into different types:
   - some plastics (poly(propene), for example) can be **recycled** by **melting** and **remoulding** them,
   - some plastics can be **cracked** into **monomers**, and these can be used as an **organic feedstock** to make more plastics or other chemicals.

Infrared spectroscopy (pages 102-103) can be used to help sort plastics into different types before they're recycled.

Waste Plastics can be ***Burned***

1) If recycling isn't possible for whatever reason, waste plastics can be burned — and the heat can be used to generate **electricity**.
2) This process needs to be carefully **controlled** to reduce **toxic** gases. For example, polymers that contain **chlorine** (such as **PVC**) produce **HCl** when they're burned — this has to be removed.
3) Waste gases from the combustion are passed through **scrubbers** which can **neutralise** gases, such as HCl, by allowing them to react with a **base**.
4) Plastics can also be **sorted** before they are burnt to separate out any materials that will produce **toxic gases**.

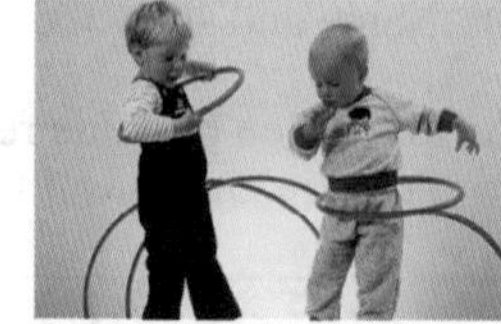

Rex and Dirk enjoy some waist plastic.

Polymers

Chemists Can Work to Make Polymers Sustainably

Lots of **chemicals** that are used in the manufacture of polymers are **pretty dangerous**.
The way that a polymer is made should be designed to **minimise** the **impact** on human **health** and the **environment**.
There are a set of principles that chemists follow when they design a **sustainable polymer manufacturing process**:

- Use **reactant** molecules that are as **safe** and **environmentally friendly** as possible.
- Use as few **other materials**, like **solvents**, as possible. If you have to use other chemicals, choose ones that **won't** harm the environment.
- **Renewable raw materials** should be used wherever possible.
- **Energy use** should be kept to a **minimum**. **Catalysts** are often utilised in polymer synthesis to lower energy use.
- Limit the **waste products** made, especially those which are **hazardous** to **human health** or the **environment**.
- Make sure the **lifespan** of the polymer is **appropriate** for its use. If you make a polymer that just keeps breaking, you'll end up having to make loads more than if you create a more enduring polymer.

Biodegradable Polymers Decompose in the Right Conditions

1) Scientists can now make **biodegradable** polymers (ones that naturally **decompose**). They decompose pretty quickly in certain conditions because organisms can digest them.
2) Biodegradable polymers can be made from **renewable** raw materials such as **starch** (from maize and other plants), or from **oil fractions** such as the hydrocarbon **isoprene**.

Being able to safely dispose of polymers in a way that doesn't harm the environment is part of making polymers sustainable.

Using **renewable** raw material has several **advantages**.

- Raw materials aren't going to **run out** like oil will.
- When polymers biodegrade, **carbon dioxide** (a greenhouse gas) is produced. If your polymer is **plant-based**, then the CO_2 released as it decomposes is the same CO_2 absorbed by the plant when it grew. But with an **oil-based** biodegradable polymer, you're effectively transferring carbon from the oil to the atmosphere.
- Over their 'lifetime' some plant-based polymers **save energy** compared to oil-based plastics.

3) Even though they're biodegradable, these polymers still need the right conditions before they'll decompose. This means that you still need to **collect** and **separate** the biodegradable polymers from non-biodegradable plastics. At the moment, they're also **more expensive** than non-biodegradable equivalents.

Practice Questions

Q1 Draw the displayed formulae for the monomer and repeat unit used to make poly(propene).

Q2 Describe three ways in which used polymers such as poly(propene) can be disposed of.

Q3 What is a biodegradable polymer?

Exam Questions

Q1 Part of the structure of a polymer is shown on the right.

```
   H    H     H    H     H
   |    |     |    |     |
...C----C-----C----C-----C...
   |    |     |    |     |
   H   C6H5   H   C6H5   H
```

a) Draw the repeating unit of the polymer. [1 mark]

b) Draw the monomer from which the polymer was formed. [1 mark]

Q2 Waste plastics can be disposed of by burning.

a) Describe one advantage of disposing of waste plastics by burning. [1 mark]

b) Describe a disadvantage of burning waste plastic that contains chlorine, and explain how the impact of this disadvantage could be reduced. [2 marks]

Q3* Outline and discuss some of the considerations an industrial chemist should make when designing a sustainable polymer manufacturing process. [6 marks]

Alkenes — join up today, your polymer needs YOU...

You may have noticed that all this recycling business is a hot topic these days. This suits examiners just fine — they like you to know how useful and important chemistry is. So learn this stuff, pass your exams, and do some recycling.

* The quality of your extended response will be assessed for this question.

Halogenoalkanes

*If you haven't had enough of organic chemistry yet, there's more. If you **have** had enough — there's still more.*

***Halogenoalkanes** are **Alkanes** with **Halogen** Atoms*

A **halogenoalkane** is an alkane with at least one **halogen atom** in place of a hydrogen atom.

E.g.

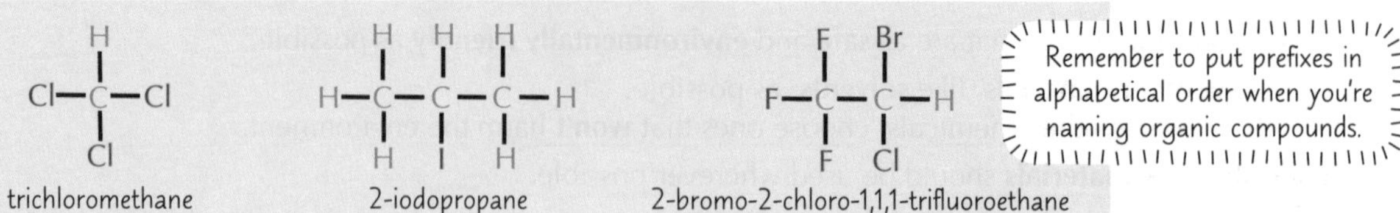

*Halogenoalkanes can be **Primary**, **Secondary** or **Tertiary***

Halogenoalkanes with just **one halogen atom** can be **primary**, **secondary** or **tertiary** halogenoalkanes.

On the **carbon** with the **halogen** attached:

1) A **primary** halogenoalkane has **two hydrogen atoms** and just **one alkyl group**.
2) A **secondary** halogenoalkane has **just one hydrogen atom** and **two alkyl groups**.
3) A **tertiary** halogenoalkane has **no hydrogen atoms** and **three alkyl groups**.

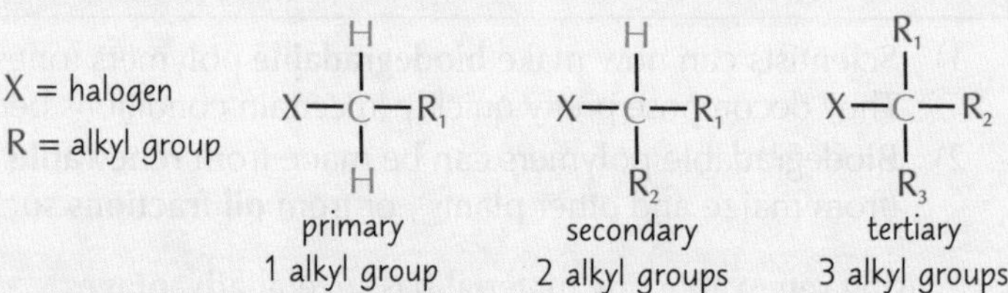

Halogenoalkanes** Can be **Hydrolysed** to Form **Alcohols

1) Halogenoalkanes can be hydrolysed to alcohols in a **nucleophilic substitution reaction** (see page 92). One way to do this is to use **water**.
2) The general equation is: $R\text{–}X + H_2O \rightarrow R\text{–}OH + H^+ + X^-$
3) Here's what would happen with bromoethane: $CH_3CH_2Br + H_2O \rightarrow C_2H_5OH + H^+ + Br^-$

Hydrolysis is when water breaks bonds.

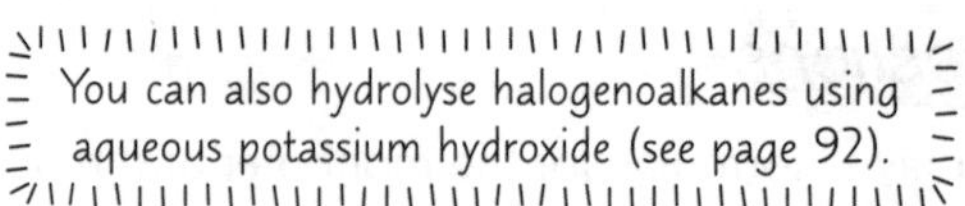

You can also hydrolyse halogenoalkanes using aqueous potassium hydroxide (see page 92).

*You Can **Compare** the **Reactivities** of **Halogenoalkanes** Using **Experiments***

1) When you mix a **halogenoalkane** with water, it reacts to form an **alcohol**. → $R\text{–}X + H_2O \rightarrow R\text{–}OH + H^+ + X^-$
2) If you put **silver nitrate solution** in the mixture too, the silver ions react with the **halide ions** as soon as they form, → $Ag^+_{(aq)} + X^-_{(aq)} \rightarrow AgX_{(s)}$ giving a **silver halide precipitate** (see page 51).
3) To **compare** the reactivities of different halogenoalkanes, set up three test tubes each containing a different halogenoalkane, ethanol (as a solvent) and silver nitrate solution (this contains the water).
4) **Time** how long it takes for a **precipitate** to form in each test tube. The **more quickly** a precipitate forms, the faster the **rate of hydrolysis** is for that halogenoalkane.

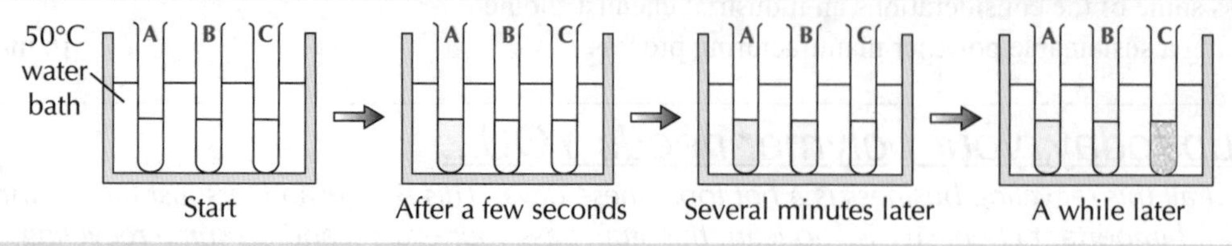

You can use the colours of the silver halide precipitates to distinguish between chloro, bromo and iodo alkanes (see page 51). Make sure you learn the colours for the exams.

Halogenoalkanes

Primary, Secondary and *Tertiary* Halogenoalkanes Have *Different* Reactivities

You can compare the reactivities of **primary**, **secondary** and **tertiary** halogenoalkanes using the reaction on the last page.

Example: A student sets up an experiment to compare the reactivities of a primary, a secondary and a tertiary bromoalkane. His results are shown below. Which is the most reactive halogenoalkane?

Halogenoalkane	Time taken for precipitate to form / s
1-bromobutane (primary)	112
2-bromobutane (secondary)	62
2-bromo-2-methylpropane (tertiary)	8

From the results, you can tell that the **tertiary halogenoalkane** is the most reactive, since it reacted **fastest** with the water. The **primary** halogenoalkane is the **least** reactive.

This example uses bromoalkanes, but the order of reactivity is the same whichever halogen you use.

Iodoalkanes are *Hydrolysed* the *Fastest*

1) In order to hydrolyse a halogenoalkane, you have to **break** the **carbon-halogen bond**.
2) How quickly different halogenoalkanes are hydrolysed depends on the carbon-halogen **bond enthalpy** — see page 110 for more on this.
3) **Weaker** carbon-halogen bonds **break** more easily — so they react **faster**.
4) Bond enthalpy depends on the **size** of the halogen — the **larger** the halogen, the **longer** the C–X bond, and the **lower** the bond enthalpy.
5) The **size** of the halogen **increases** down Group 7, so **iodoalkanes** have the **weakest bonds**, and are hydrolysed the **fastest**. **Fluoroalkanes** have the **strongest bonds**, so they're the **slowest** at hydrolysing.
6) You can **compare the reactivity** of chloroalkanes, bromoalkanes and iodoalkanes using an experiment like the one on the previous page.

bond	bond enthalpy / kJ mol^{-1}
C–F	467
C–Cl	346
C–Br	290
C–I	228

Faster hydrolysis as bond enthalpy decreases (the bonds get weaker).

Example: A student sets up an experiment to compare the reactivities of a chloroalkane, a bromoalkane and an iodoalkane. Her results are shown below. Which is the most reactive halogenoalkane?

Halogenoalkane	Time taken for precipitate to form / s
2-iodopropane	7
2-bromopropane	240
2-chloropropane	567

A pale yellow precipitate quickly forms with **2-iodopropane** — so iodoalkanes must be the **most reactive** of these halogenoalkanes. **Bromoalkanes** react slower than iodoalkanes to form a cream precipitate, and **chloroalkanes** form a white precipitate even more slowly.

The halogenoalkanes should have the same carbon skeleton so it's a fair test.

Practice Questions

Q1 What is a halogenoalkane?

Q2 What is a secondary halogenoalkane? Draw and name an example of one.

Q3 Put primary, secondary and tertiary halogenoalkanes in order of reactivity with water.

Exam Question

Q1 a) A tertiary halogenoalkane has the molecular formula C_4H_9I. Draw and name the halogenoalkane. [2 marks]

b) The halogenoalkane in part a) is mixed with water and silver nitrate solution. Give the formula of the precipitate that forms. [1 mark]

c) Predict, with reasoning, whether the tertiary chloroalkane with formula C_4H_9Cl will be hydrolysed faster or slower than the halogenoalkane in part a) if all the other reactant conditions are the same. [3 marks]

Hydra-lies — stories told by a many-headed monster...

You can only compare the effect of one variable on the rates of hydrolysis of different halogenoalkanes if you keep the other variables the same. If you're investigating the effect of the halogen, the carbon skeletons of the halogenoalkanes need to be the same, and for the effect of primary, secondary or tertiary, the molecular formulae need to be identical.

More on Halogenoalkanes

Two more pages all about halogenoalkanes. It must be your lucky day...

Halogenoalkanes May React by **Nucleophilic Substitution**

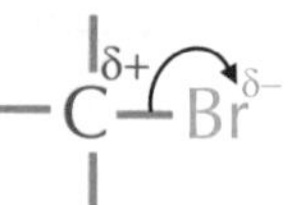

1) Halogens are generally more **electronegative** than carbon. So, the **carbon–halogen bond** is **polar**.
2) The **δ+ carbon** doesn't have enough electrons. This means it can be attacked by a **nucleophile**. A nucleophile's an **electron-pair donor**. It donates an electron pair to somewhere without enough electrons.
3) **OH^-**, **NH_3** and **CN^-** are examples of **nucleophiles** that react readily with halogenoalkanes. **Water** is also a weak nucleophile.
4) A nucleophile can bond with the δ+ carbon of a halogenoalkane, and be **substituted** for the halogen. This is called **nucleophilic substitution**:

Here's what happens. It's a nice simple **one-step mechanism**.

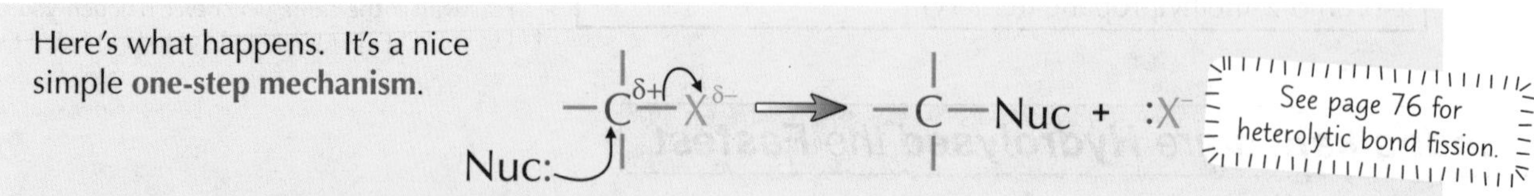

See page 76 for heterolytic bond fission.

- X is the halogen. **Nuc** is the **nucleophile**, which provides a **pair of electrons** for the $C^{\delta+}$.
- The C–X bond breaks **heterolytically** — **both** electrons from the bond are taken by the halogen.
- The halogen falls off as the nucleophile bonds to the carbon.

This reaction can actually happen via one of two mechanisms — see pages 190-191.

5) There are **three examples** of nucleophilic substitution you need to know. Read on.

Halogenoalkanes React with **Aqueous KOH** to form **Alcohols**

1) Halogenoalkanes react with **hydroxide ions** by **nucleophilic substitution** to form **alcohols**. You can use **warm aqueous potassium hydroxide** and do the reaction under reflux, otherwise it won't work.
2) Here's the general equation for the reaction:

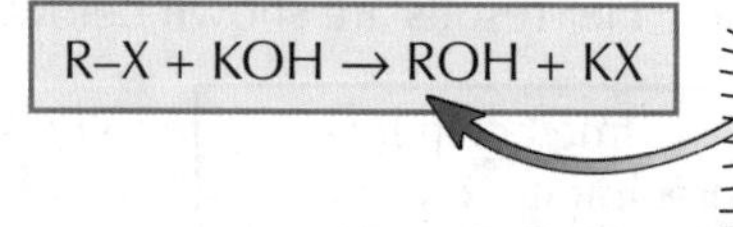

R represents an alkyl group. They're alkanes with one H removed, e.g. $-CH_3$, $-C_2H_5$. X stands for one of the halogens (F, Cl, Br or I).

3) And here's how the reaction happens:

The OH^- ion acts as a nucleophile, attacking the δ+ carbon atom.

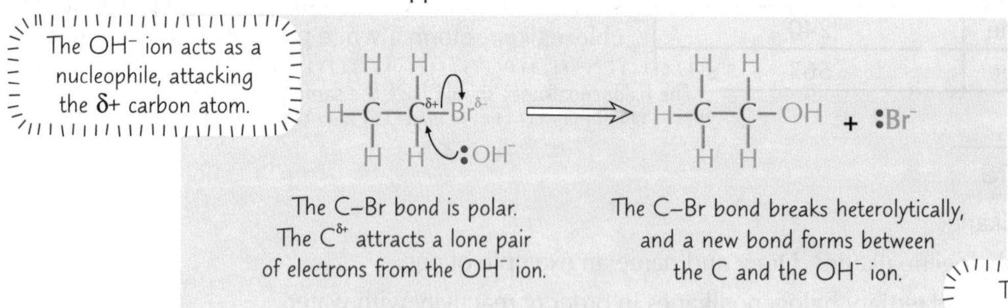

The C–Br bond is polar. The $C^{\delta+}$ attracts a lone pair of electrons from the OH^- ion.

The C–Br bond breaks heterolytically, and a new bond forms between the C and the OH^- ion.

The charges of each step in the mechanism have to balance — here, each step has an overall charge of –1.

4) As you saw on page 90, you can also use **water** to hydrolyse halogenoalkanes and form **alcohols**. Water is a **worse nucleophile** that hydroxide ions, so the reaction with water is **slower**.

Cyanide Ions React with Halogenoalkanes to form **Nitriles**

If you **reflux** a halogenoalkane with **potassium cyanide** in **ethanol**, then the cyanide ions will react with the halogenoalkane by **nucleophilic substitution** to form a **nitrile**.

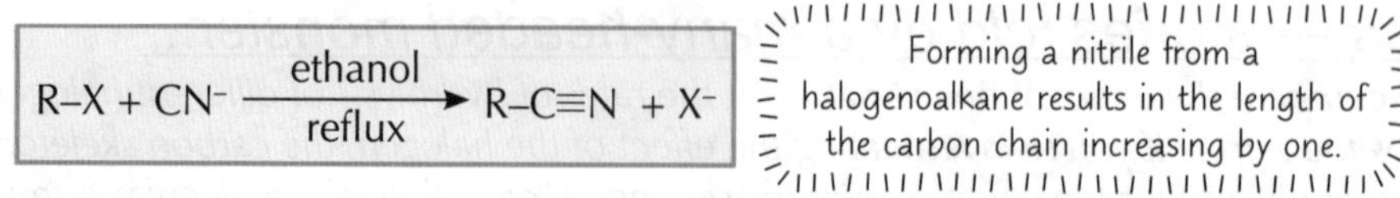

Forming a nitrile from a halogenoalkane results in the length of the carbon chain increasing by one.

More on Halogenoalkanes

Halogenoalkanes React With *Ammonia* to Form *Amines*

1) Amines are organic compounds. They're based on **ammonia** (NH_3), but one or more of the **hydrogen** atoms are **replaced** by **alkyl** groups.

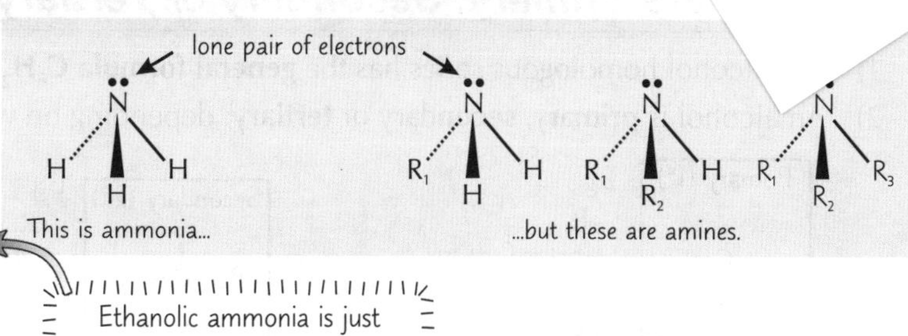

2) If you **warm** a halogenoalkane with excess **ethanolic** ammonia, the **ammonia** swaps places with the **halogen** to form a **primary amine** — yes, it's another one of those **nucleophilic substitution reactions**.

Ethanolic ammonia is just ammonia dissolved in ethanol.

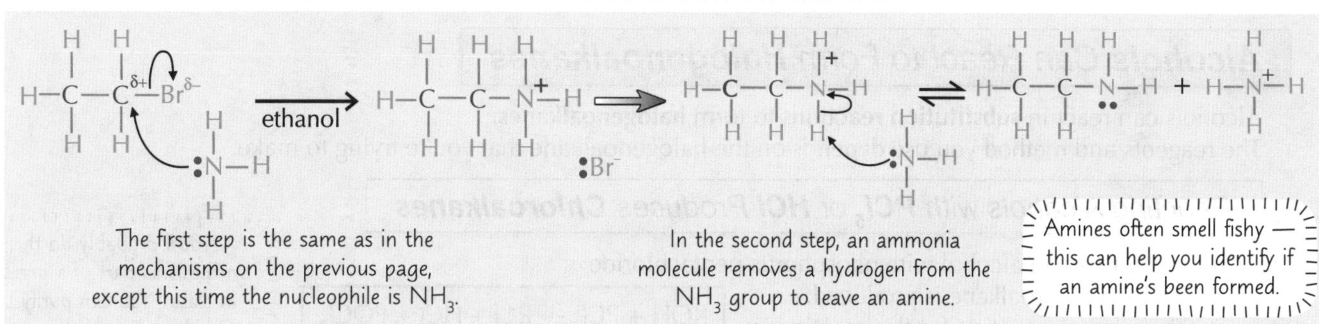

The first step is the same as in the mechanisms on the previous page, except this time the nucleophile is NH_3.

In the second step, an ammonia molecule removes a hydrogen from the NH_3 group to leave an amine.

Amines often smell fishy — this can help you identify if an amine's been formed.

Halogenoalkanes also Undergo *Elimination Reactions*

You know what happens when a halogenoalkane reacts with an aqueous alkali (yes, you do — it's on the opposite page). But nucleophilic substitution isn't the only game in town. Swap 'aqueous' for '**ethanolic**', and things change.

1) If you react a halogenoalkane with a warm alkali **dissolved in ethanol**, you get an **alkene**. The mixture must be **heated under reflux** or volatile stuff will be lost.
2) Here's bromoethane. Again.

It's possible that more than one isomer will form from elimination, just like with the elimination reaction of alcohols on page 95.

$$CH_3CH_2Br + KOH \xrightarrow[\text{reflux}]{\text{ethanol}} CH_2{=}CH_2 + H_2O + KBr$$

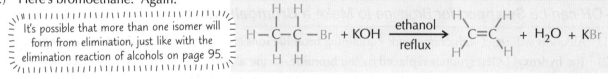

3) In elimination reactions, the hydroxide ions are acting as a **base** to remove an H^+ ion from the halogenoalkane.

Practice Questions

Q1 What is a nucleophile?

Q2 Sketch the mechanism, including curly arrows, for the reaction of bromoethane with warm aqueous KOH.

Q3 Write a general equation for the reaction under reflux of a halogenoalkane with potassium cyanide in ethanol.

Exam Question

Q1 Some reactions of 2-bromopropane, $CH_3CHBrCH_3$, are shown.

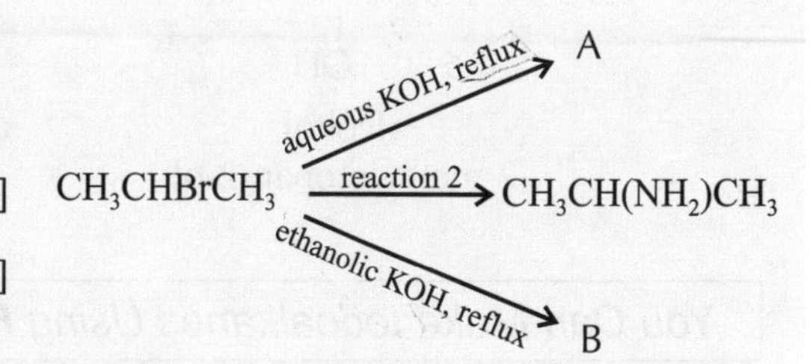

a) Give the structural formula of organic product, A. [1 mark]

b) i) Give the reagents and conditions for reaction 2. [2 marks]

ii) Draw a mechanism for reaction 2. [4 marks]

c) Give the structural formula of organic product, B. [1 mark]

If you don't learn this, you will be eliminated. Resistance is nitrile...

The nucleophilic substitution mechanisms on these pages are all quite similar. They start with the nucleophile attacking the δ+ carbon, causing the C–X bond to break. Then it's a case of getting rid of hydrogens from the substituted group, if necessary, to make the organic product neutral. Practise drawing the mechanisms — they may come up in the exams.

Alcohols

These two pages could well be enough to put you off alcohols for life...

Alcohols are **Primary**, **Secondary** or **Tertiary**

1) The alcohol homologous series has the **general formula $C_nH_{2n+1}OH$.**
2) An alcohol is **primary**, **secondary** or **tertiary**, depending on which carbon atom the **-OH** group is bonded to.

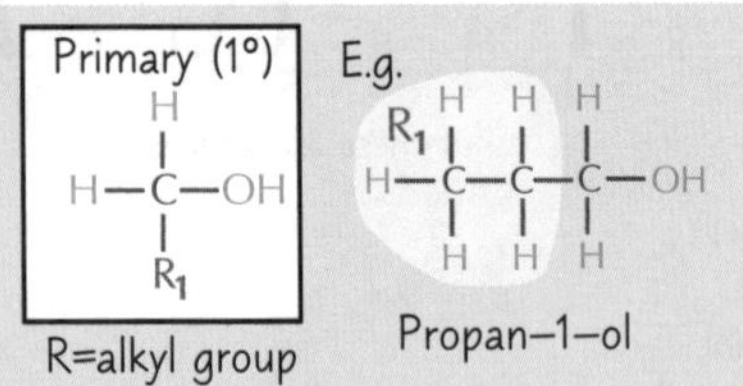

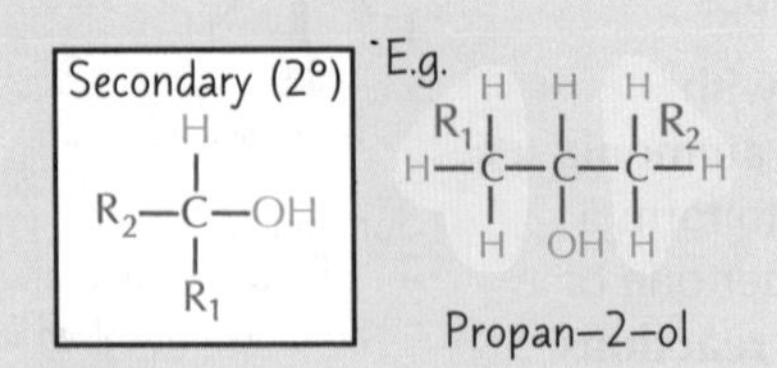

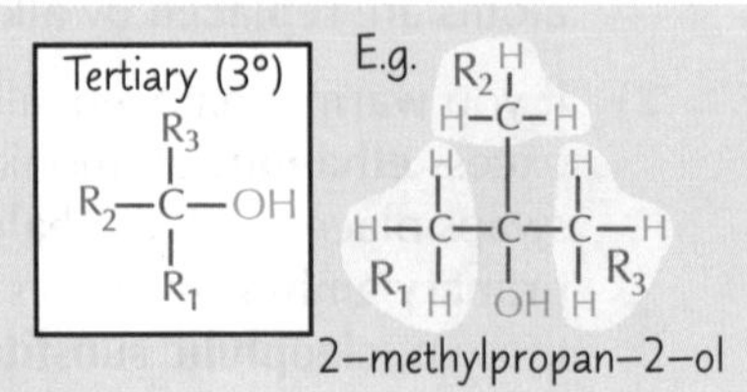

Alcohols Can React to Form **Halogenoalkanes**

Alcohols can react in **substitution reactions** to form **halogenoalkanes**.
The reagents and method you use depends on the halogenoalkane that you're trying to make.

Reacting Alcohols with PCl_5 or HCl Produces **Chloroalkanes**

1) If you react an alcohol with phosphorus pentachloride (PCl_5), a chloroalkane is produced. The general equation for this reaction is: $ROH + PCl_5 \rightarrow RCl + HCl + POCl_3$
2) You can also make chloroalkanes if you react an **alcohol** with **hydrochloric acid**. The general equation for this reaction is: $ROH + HCl \rightarrow RCl + H_2O$
3) For example, 2-methylpropan-2-ol reacts with hydrochloric acid at room temperature to form 2-chloro-2-methylpropane: $(CH_3)_3COH + HCl \rightarrow (CH_3)_3CCl + H_2O$
4) The reaction between alcohols and hydrochloric acid is **fastest** if the alcohol is a **tertiary alcohol**, and **slowest** if it is a **primary alcohol** (the rate for secondary alcohols is somewhere in between).

> You'll probably do this synthesis as part of a practical in class. You can purify the 2-chloro-2-methylpropane product by separation and then distillation (see page 98).

-OH can be **Swapped** for Bromine to Make a **Bromoalkane**

1) Alcohols will react with compounds containing **bromide ions** (such as KBr) in a **substitution reaction**.
2) The **hydroxyl** (-OH) group is **replaced** by the **bromide**, so the alcohol is transformed into a **bromoalkane**.
3) The reaction also requires an **acid catalyst**, such as **50% concentrated H_2SO_4**.

Example: To make 2-bromo-2-methylpropane you just need to shake 2-methylpropan-2-ol (a tertiary alcohol) with potassium bromide and 50% concentrated sulfuric acid at room temperature.

First, potassium bromide reacts with sulfuric acid to form hydrogen bromide: $2KBr + H_2SO_4 \rightarrow HBr + K_2SO_4$.

The hydrogen bromide then reacts with the alcohol to form a bromoalkane:

$$H_3C-C(CH_3)(OH)-CH_3 + HBr \longrightarrow H_3C-C(CH_3)(Br)-CH_3 + H_2O$$

alcohol (2-methylpropan-2-ol) → bromoalkane (2-bromo-2-methylpropane)

> 50% concentrated sulfuric acid is made up of 50% H_2SO_4 and 50% water.

You Can Make Iodoalkanes Using **Red Phosphorus** and **Iodine**

1) You can make an **iodoalkane** from an **alcohol** by reacting it with **phosphorus triiodide (PI_3)**.
2) **PI_3** is usually made **in situ** (within the reaction mixture) by refluxing the alcohol with 'red phosphorus' and iodine.
3) This is the general equation: $3ROH + PI_3 \rightarrow 3RI + H_3PO_3$

> There are different types of phosphorus, and red phosphorus is one of them (like how there are different types of carbon, e.g. graphite and diamond).

Alcohols

Alcohols can be Dehydrated to Form Alkenes

1) You can make alkenes by **eliminating** water from **alcohols** in an **elimination reaction**.
2) The alcohol is mixed with an **acid catalyst** such as **concentrated phosphoric acid** (H_3PO_4). The mixture is then **heated**.
3) When an alcohol dehydrates it eliminates **water**.

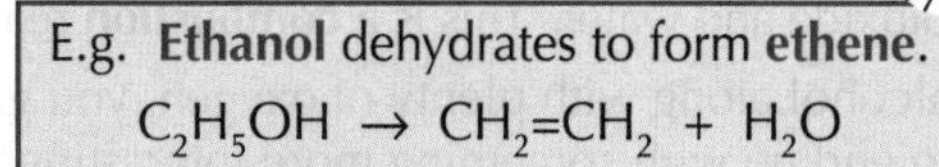
E.g. **Ethanol** dehydrates to form **ethene**.

$$C_2H_5OH \rightarrow CH_2{=}CH_2 + H_2O$$

An elimination reaction where water is eliminated is called a dehydration reaction.

4) The water molecule is made up from the hydroxyl group and a hydrogen atom that was bonded to a carbon atom adjacent to the hydroxyl carbon.
5) This means that often there are **two possible** alkene products from one elimination reaction depending on **which side** of the hydroxyl group the **hydrogen** is **eliminated** from.
6) Also, watch out for if any of the alkene products can form **E/Z isomers** (see pages 83-85) — if they can then a mixture of both isomers will form.

Example: When butan-2-ol is heated to 170 °C with concentrated phosphoric acid, it dehydrates to form a mixture of products. Give the names and structures of all the organic compounds in this mixture.

- Elimination can occur between the **hydroxyl group** and the hydrogen either on **carbon-1** or **carbon-3**. This results in **two** possible alkene products — **but-1-ene** and **but-2-ene.**
- In addition, **but-2-ene** can form **E/Z isomers.**
- So there are **3** possible products — but-1-ene, E-but-2-ene and Z-but-2-ene.

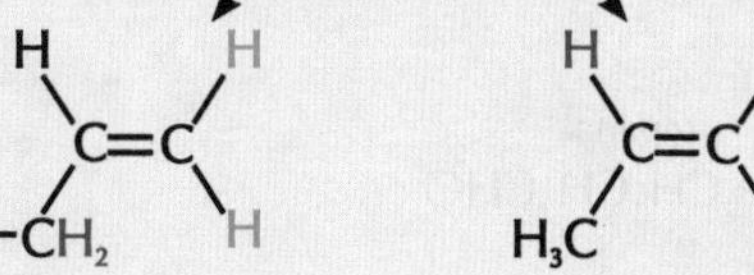

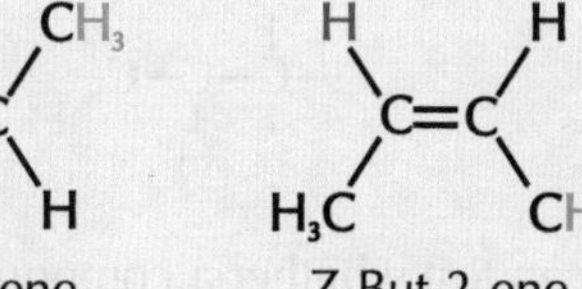

Practice Questions

Q1 What is the general formula for an alcohol?

Q2 Describe two different ways that propan-2-ol could be converted into 2-chloropropane.

Q3 What products are made when ethanol is refluxed with 'red phosphorus' and iodine?

Exam Questions

Q1 a) Draw and name a primary alcohol, a secondary alcohol and a tertiary alcohol, each with the formula $C_5H_{12}O$. [3 marks]

b) Describe how ethanol could be converted into bromoethane. [1 mark]

Q2 When 3-methyl-pentan-3-ol is heated with concentrated phosphoric acid, it reacts to form a mixture of organic products.

a) What is the name of this type of reaction? [1 mark]

b) How many organic compounds will be produced?

A 4 **B** 3 **C** 2 **D** 1 [1 mark]

Euuurghh, what a page... I think I need a drink...

Not too much to learn here — a few basic definitions, two different ways to make a chloroalkane, a reaction to make a bromoalkane and another to make an iodoalkane, a tricky little dehydration reaction...
As I was saying, not much here at all... Think I'm going to faint. *[THWACK]*

Oxidation of Alcohols

Another two pages of alcohol reactions. Probably not what you wanted for Christmas...

*The Simplest way to Oxidise Alcohols is to **Burn Them***

It doesn't take much to set ethanol alight and it burns with a **pale blue flame**. The C–C and C–H bonds break and ethanol is **completely oxidised** to make carbon dioxide and water. This is a **combustion** reaction.

$$C_2H_5OH_{(l)} + 3O_{2(g)} \rightarrow 2CO_{2(g)} + 3H_2O_{(g)}$$

If you burn any alcohol along with plenty of oxygen, you get carbon dioxide and water as products. But if you want to end up with something more interesting, you need a more sophisticated way of oxidising...

*How Much an Alcohol can be **Oxidised** Depends on its **Structure***

You can use the **oxidising agent acidified dichromate(VI)** ($Cr_2O_7^{2-}/H^+$, e.g. $K_2Cr_2O_7/H_2SO_4$) to **mildly** oxidise alcohols.

- **Primary** alcohols are oxidised to **aldehydes** and then to **carboxylic acids**.
- **Secondary** alcohols are oxidised to **ketones** only.
- **Tertiary** alcohols won't be oxidised.

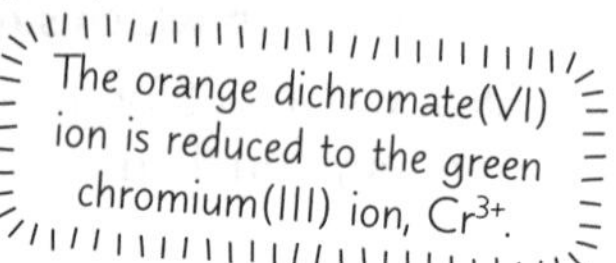

The orange dichromate(VI) ion is reduced to the green chromium(III) ion, Cr^{3+}.

***Aldehydes** and **Ketones** Contain **C=O** bonds*

Aldehydes and **ketones** are **carbonyl** compounds — they have the functional group C=O. Their general formula is $\mathbf{C_nH_{2n}O}$.

1) **Aldehydes** have a **hydrogen** and **one alkyl group** attached to the carbonyl carbon atom.
   E.g. propanal CH_3CH_2CHO

2) **Ketones** have **two alkyl groups** attached to the carbonyl carbon atom.
   E.g. propanone CH_3COCH_3

You can test whether a compound is an aldehyde or a ketone using Benedict's solution. This is a **blue** solution of complexed **copper(II) ions** dissolved in **sodium carbonate**.

If it's heated with an **aldehyde** the **blue** copper(II) ions are reduced to a **brick-red precipitate** of **copper(I) oxide**.

If it's heated with a ketone, nothing happens as ketones can't be easily oxidised.

This test can also be done using Fehling's solution, which contains copper(II) ions dissolved in sodium hydroxide. The colour change from blue to red in the presence of an aldehyde is the same. Again, nothing happens with a ketone.

Primary** Alcohols will Oxidise to **Aldehydes** and **Carboxylic Acids

Primary alcohols can be oxidised **twice** — first to form **aldehydes** which can then be oxidised to form **carboxylic acids**.

$$\underset{\text{primary alcohol}}{R{-}CH_2{-}OH} + [O] \xrightarrow{\text{distil}} \underset{\text{aldehyde}}{R{-}CHO + H_2O} + [O] \xrightarrow{\text{reflux}} \underset{\text{carboxylic acid}}{R{-}COOH}$$

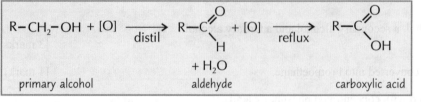

[O] = oxidising agent
e.g. potassium dichromate(VI)

Distil** for an **Aldehyde**, and **Reflux** for a **Carboxylic Acid

You can control how **far** the alcohol is oxidised by controlling the **reaction conditions**. For example...

1) Gently heating ethanol with potassium dichromate(VI) solution and sulfuric acid in a test tube should produce "apple" smelling **ethanal** (an aldehyde). However, it's **really tricky** to control the amount of heat and the aldehyde is usually oxidised to form "vinegar" smelling **ethanoic acid**.
2) To get just the **aldehyde**, you need to get it out of the oxidising solution **as soon** as it's formed. You can do this by gently heating excess alcohol with a **controlled** amount of oxidising agent in **distillation apparatus**, so the aldehyde (which boils at a lower temperature than the alcohol) is distilled off **immediately**.
3) To produce the **carboxylic acid**, the alcohol has to be **vigorously oxidised**. The alcohol is mixed with excess oxidising agent and heated under **reflux**.

There's loads more about distillation and reflux on page 98.

Oxidation of Alcohols

Secondary *Alcohols will Oxidise to* ***Ketones***

1) Refluxing a secondary alcohol, e.g. propan-2-ol, with acidified dichromate(VI) will produce a **ketone**.
2) Ketones can't be oxidised easily, so even prolonged refluxing won't produce anything more.

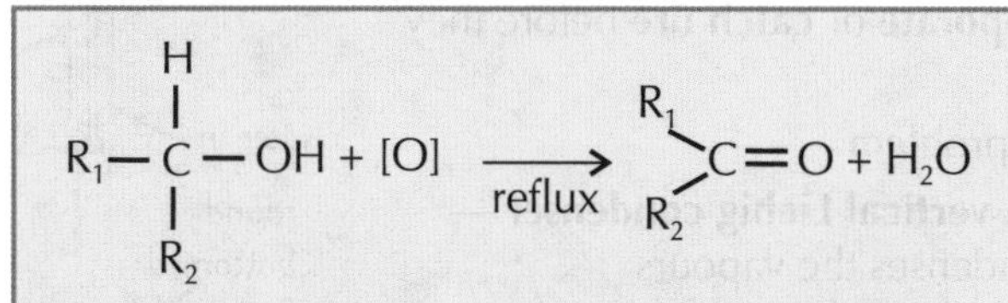

Monty and Bill were getting some much needed rest and refluxation.

Tertiary *Alcohols can't be Oxidised Easily*

1) Tertiary alcohols don't react with potassium dichromate(VI) at all — the solution stays orange.
2) The only way to oxidise tertiary alcohols is by **burning** them.

Practice Questions

Q1 Write an equation for the complete combustion of ethanol in oxygen.

Q2 What's the structural difference between an aldehyde and a ketone?

Q3 Why must you control the reaction conditions when oxidising a primary alcohol to an aldehyde?

Q4 How would you oxidise ethanol to ethanoic acid?

Q5 What will acidified potassium dichromate(VI) oxidise secondary alcohols to?

Q6 How would you oxidise a tertiary alcohol?

Exam Questions

Q1 A student wanted to produce the aldehyde propanal from propanol, and set up reflux apparatus using acidified potassium dichromate(VI) as the oxidising agent.

a) The student tested her product and found that she had not produced propanal.

i) What is the student's product? [1 mark]

ii) Write equations to show the two-stage reaction. You may use [O] to represent the oxidising agent. [2 marks]

iii) What technique should the student have used and why? [1 mark]

b) The student also tried to oxidise 2-methylpropan-2-ol, unsuccessfully.

i) Draw the full structural formula for 2-methylpropan-2-ol. [1 mark]

ii) Why is it not possible to oxidise 2-methylpropan-2-ol with an oxidising agent? [1 mark]

Q2 What will be produced if 2-methylbutan-2-ol is heated under reflux with acidified dichromate(VI)?

A an aldehyde **B** a carboxylic acid **C** a ketone **D** an unreacted alcohol [1 mark]

Q3 Plan an experiment to prepare 2-methylpropanal ($CH_3CH(CH_3)CHO$) from an appropriate alcohol. Your plan should include details of the chemicals (including an alcohol that could be used as a starting material) and procedure used for the reaction. [2 marks]

I've never been very good at singing — I'm always in the wrong key-tone...

These alcohols couldn't just all react in the same way, could they? Nope — it seems like they're out to make your life difficult. So close the book and write down all the different ways of oxidising primary, secondary and tertiary alcohols, and what the different products are. And don't get caught out by those pesky primary alcohols getting oxidised twice.

Organic Techniques

There are some practical techniques that get used a lot in organic chemistry. They may be used during the synthesis of a product, or to purify it from unwanted by-products or unreacted reagents once it's been made.

Refluxing *Makes Sure You Don't Lose Any* ***Volatile*** *Organic Substances*

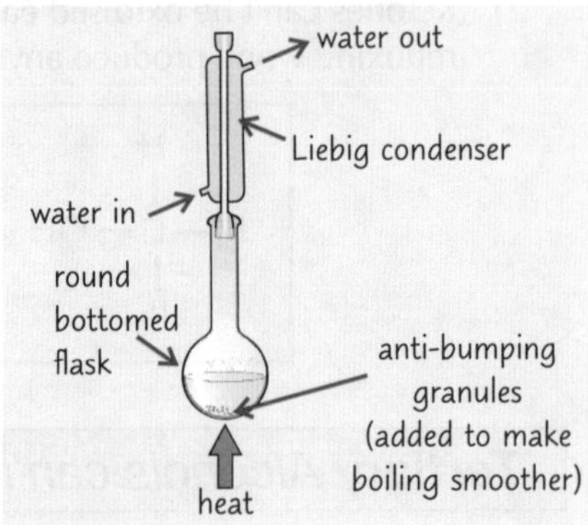

1) **Organic reactions** are **slow** and the substances are usually **flammable** and **volatile** (they've got **low boiling points**). If you stick them in a beaker and heat them with a Bunsen burner they'll **evaporate** or **catch fire** before they have **time to react.**
2) You can **reflux** a reaction to get round this problem.
3) The mixture's **heated in a flask** fitted with a **vertical Liebig condenser** — this continuously boils, evaporates and condenses the vapours and **recycles** them back into the flask, giving them **time to react**.
4) The **heating** is usually **electrical** — hot plates, heating mantles, or electrically controlled water baths are normally used. This **avoids naked flames** that might ignite the compounds.

Distillation *Separates Substances With Different* ***Boiling Points***

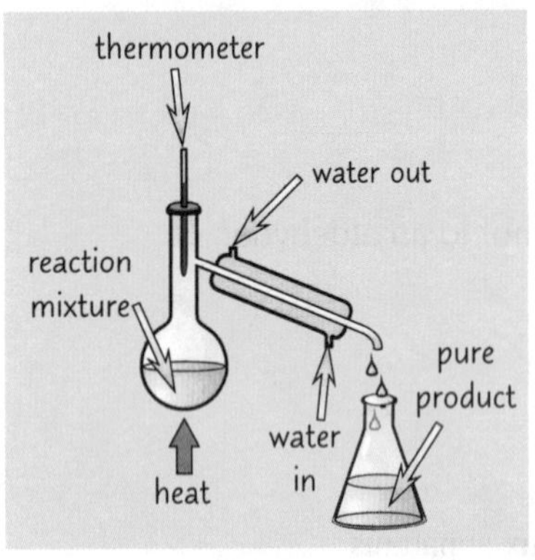

1) Distillation works by **gently heating** a mixture in a distillation apparatus. The substances will evaporate out of the mixture in order of **increasing boiling point**.
2) The thermometer shows the **boiling point** of the substance that is **evaporating** at any given time.
3) If you know the boiling point of your **pure product**, you can use the thermometer to tell you when it's evaporating and therefore when it's condensing.
4) If the **product** of a reaction has a **lower boiling point** than the **starting materials** then the reaction mixture can be **heated** so that the product **evaporates** from the reaction mixture as it forms.
5) If the starting material has a **higher boiling point** than the product, as long as the temperature is controlled, it won't evaporate out from the reaction mixture.

- Sometimes, a product is formed that will go on to **react further** if it's left in the reaction mixture.
- For example, when you oxidise a **primary alcohol**, it is first oxidised to an **aldehyde** and then oxidised to a **carboxylic acid**. If you want the **aldehyde product**, then you can do your reaction in the **distillation equipment**. The aldehyde product has a **lower boiling point** than the alcohol starting material, so will distil out of the reaction mixture **as soon** as it forms. It is then collected in a separate container.

6) If a product and its impurities have **different boiling points**, then distillation can be used to **separate** them. You use the distillation apparatus shown above, but this time you're heating an **impure product**, instead of the reaction mixture.
7) When the liquid you want **boils** (this is when the thermometer is at the boiling point of the liquid), you place a flask at the open end of the condenser ready to collect your product.
8) When the thermometer shows the temperature is changing, put another flask at the end of the condenser because a **different liquid** is about to be delivered.

Separation *Removes Any* ***Water Soluble Impurities*** *From the Product*

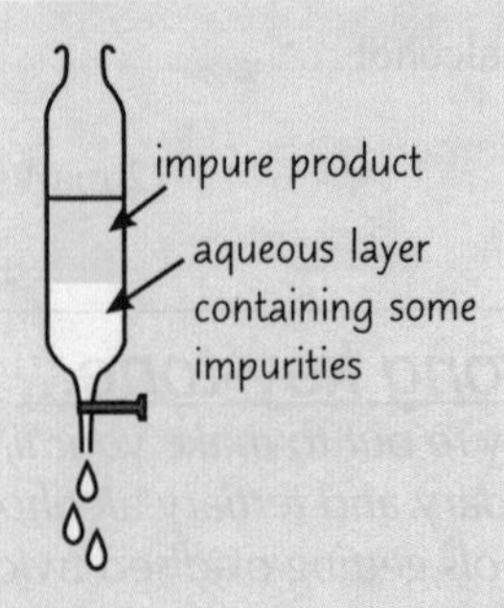

If a product is **insoluble** in water then you can use **separation** to remove any impurities that **do dissolve** in water such as **salts** or water soluble organic compounds (e.g. alcohols).

1) Once the reaction to form the product is completed, pour the mixture into a **separating funnel**, and add **water**.
2) Shake the funnel and then allow it to settle. The **organic layer** and the **aqueous layer** (which contains any water soluble impurities) are **immiscible**, (they don't mix), so separate out into two distinct layers.
3) You can then open the tap and run each layer off into a separate container. (In the example on the left, the impurities will be run off first, and the product collected second.)

Organic Techniques

You Can Remove Traces of Water From a Mixture Using an Anhydrous Salt

1) If you use separation to purify a product, the organic layer will end up containing **trace amounts** of **water**, so it has to be **dried**.
2) To do this you can add an **anhydrous salt** such as **magnesium sulfate** ($MgSO_4$) or **calcium chloride** ($CaCl_2$). The salt is used as a **drying agent** — it **binds** to any water present to become **hydrated**.
3) When you first add the salt to the organic layer it will be **lumpy**. This means you need to add more. You know that all the water has been removed when you can swirl the mixture and it looks like a snow globe.
4) You can **filter** the mixture to remove the solid **drying agent**.

Measuring Boiling Point is a Good way to Determine Purity

1) You can measure the purity of an organic, liquid product by looking at its boiling point.
2) If you've got a reasonable volume of liquid, you can determine its boiling point using a **distillation apparatus**, like the one shown on the previous page.
3) If you **gently heat** the liquid in the distillation apparatus, until it evaporates, you can read the temperature at which it is distilled, using the thermometer in the top of the apparatus. This temperature is the **boiling point**.
4) You can then look up the boiling point of the substance in **data books** and compare it to your measurement.
5) If the sample contains **impurities**, then your measured boiling point will be **higher** than the recorded value. You may also find your product boils over a range of temperatures, rather than all evaporating at a single temperature.

Be careful — different organic liquids can have similar boiling points, so you should use other analytical techniques (see topic 7) to help you determine your product's purity too.

Practice Questions

Q1 Draw a labelled diagram to show the apparatus used in a reflux reaction.

Q2 Why might you want to avoid naked flames when performing an experiment with organic substances?

Q3 Name two ways of purifying organic products.

Q4 Describe a technique you could use to assess the purity of an organic liquid.

Exam Question

Q1 a) A student carried out an experiment to make hex-1-ene from hexan-1-ol using the following procedure:

$$\text{HO-hexan-1-ol} \xrightarrow[\text{heat}]{H_3PO_4} \text{hex-1-ene}$$

1) Mix 1 cm^3 hexan-1-ol with concentrated phosphoric acid in a reflux apparatus, and reflux for 30 minutes.
2) Once the mixture has cooled, separate the alkene from any aqueous impurities.
3) Dry the organic layer with anhydrous magnesium sulfate.

i) What is meant by reflux and why is it a technique sometimes used in organic chemistry? [2 marks]

ii) What organic compound is removed in the separating step? [1 mark]

iii) Describe, in detail, how the student would carry out the separation in step 2). [3 marks]

b) In another experiment, the student decides to make 1-hexen-6-ol by carrying out a single dehydration reaction of the diol 1,6-hexanediol.

$$\text{HO-hexane-OH} \xrightarrow[\text{heat}]{H_3PO_4} \text{hexene-OH}$$

i) If the student follows the procedure in part a), why might he produce a mixture of products? [1 mark]

ii) How could the procedure in part a) be adapted to prevent a mixture of products being formed? [2 marks]

Thought this page couldn't get any drier? Try adding anhydrous $MgSO_4$...

Learning the fine details of how experiments are carried out may not be the most interesting thing in the world, but you should get to try out some of these methods in practicals, which is a lot more fun.

Mass Spectrometry

This topic's about some of the fancy techniques chemists use to work out what different unknown compounds are. Neat.

Mass Spectrometry Can Help to Identify Compounds

1) You saw on page 7 how you can use a mass spectrum showing the relative isotopic abundances of an element to work out its relative atomic mass. You can also get mass spectra for **molecular samples**.
2) A mass spectrum is produced by a **mass spectrometer**. The molecules in the sample are bombarded with electrons, which remove an electron from the molecule to form a **molecular ion**, $M^+_{(g)}$.
3) To find the relative molecular mass of a compound you look at the **molecular ion peak** (the **M peak**). This is the peak with the highest *m/z* value (ignoring any small M+1 peaks that occur due to the isotope carbon-13). The mass/charge value of the molecular ion peak is the **molecular mass**.

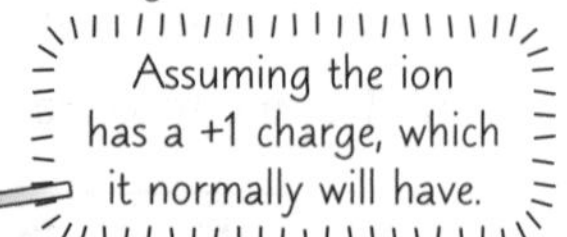

Assuming the ion has a +1 charge, which it normally will have.

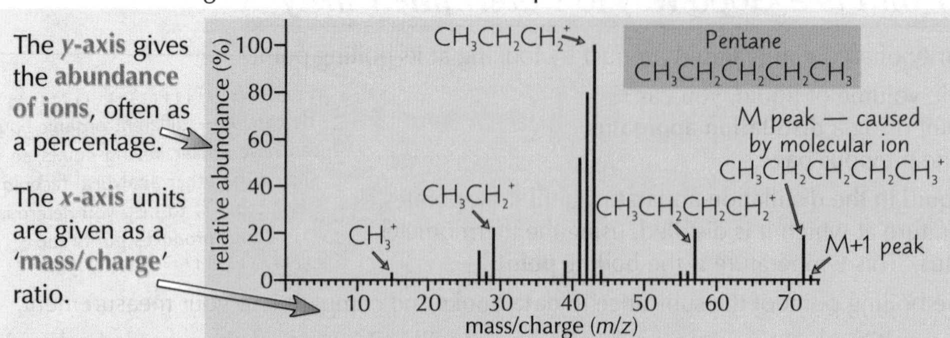

Here's the mass spectrum of pentane. Its M peak is at 72 — so the compound's M_r is 72. For most organic compounds the M peak is the one with the second highest mass/charge ratio. The smaller peak to the right of the M peak is called the M+1 peak — it's caused by the presence of the carbon isotope ^{13}C.

The Molecular Ion can be Broken into Smaller Fragments

1) The bombarding electrons make some of the molecular ions break up into **fragments**. The fragments that are ions show up on the mass spectrum, making a **fragmentation pattern**. Fragmentation patterns are actually pretty cool because you can use them to identify **molecules** and even their **structure**.

For propane, the molecular ion is $CH_3CH_2CH_3^+$, and the fragments it breaks into include CH_3^+ (M_r = 15) and $CH_3CH_2^+$ (M_r = 29).

Only the **ions** show up on the mass spectrum — the **free radicals** are 'lost'.

$CH_3CH_2CH_3^+ \rightarrow CH_3CH_2\bullet$ (free radical) $+ CH_3^+$ (ion)

$CH_3CH_2CH_3^+ \rightarrow CH_3CH_2^+$ (ion) $+ \bullet CH_3$ (free radical)

2) To work out the structural formula, you've got to work out what **ion** could have made each peak from its ***m/z* value**. (You assume that the *m/z* value of a peak matches the **mass** of the ion that made it.) Here are some common fragments:

Fragment	Molecular Mass
CH_3^+	15
$C_2H_5^+$	29
$CH_3CH_2CH_2^+$ or $CH_3CHCH_3^+$	43
OH^+	17

Example: Use this mass spectrum to work out the structure of the molecule:

It's only the *m/z* values you're interested in — ignore the heights of the bars.

relative abundance (%) / mass/charge (*m/z*)

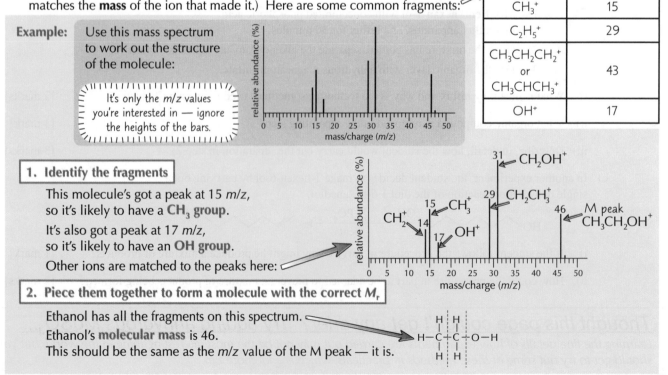

1. Identify the fragments

This molecule's got a peak at 15 *m/z*, so it's likely to have a **CH_3 group**.

It's also got a peak at 17 *m/z*, so it's likely to have an **OH group**.

Other ions are matched to the peaks here:

14: CH_2^+; 15: CH_3^+; 17: OH^+; 29: $CH_2CH_3^+$; 31: CH_2OH^+; 46: M peak $CH_3CH_2OH^+$

2. Piece them together to form a molecule with the correct M_r

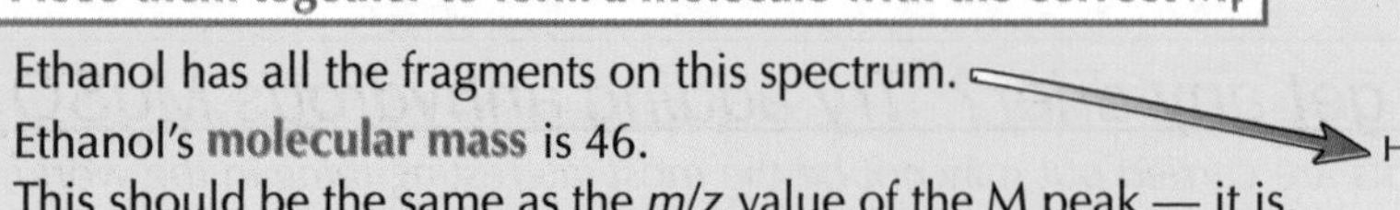

Ethanol has all the fragments on this spectrum.
Ethanol's **molecular mass** is 46.
This should be the same as the *m/z* value of the M peak — it is.

H–C(H)(H)–C(H)(H)–O–H

Mass Spectrometry

Mass Spectrometry is Used to Differentiate Between Similar Molecules

1) Even if two **different compounds** contain **the same atoms**, you can still tell them apart with mass spectrometry because they won't produce exactly the same set of fragments.
2) The formulae of **propanal** and **propanone** are shown below.

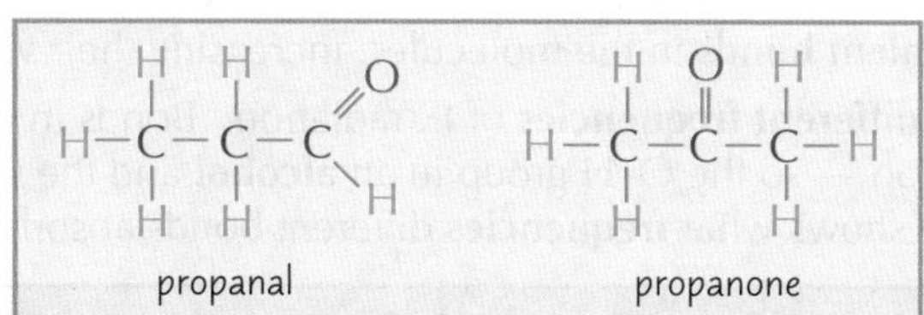

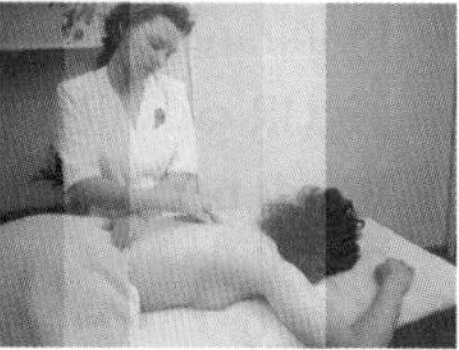
A massage spectrum

They've got the same M_r, but different structures, so they produce some **different fragments**. For example, propanal will have a $\mathbf{C_2H_5^+}$ fragment but propanone won't.

3) Every compound produces a different mass spectrum — so the spectrum's like a **fingerprint** for the compound. Large computer **databases** of mass spectra can be used to identify a compound from its spectrum.

Practice Questions

Q1 What is meant by the molecular ion?

Q2 What is the M peak?

Q3 What causes the presence of an M+1 peak on the mass spectra of most organic compounds?

Exam Questions

Q1 Below is the mass spectrum of an organic compound, Q.

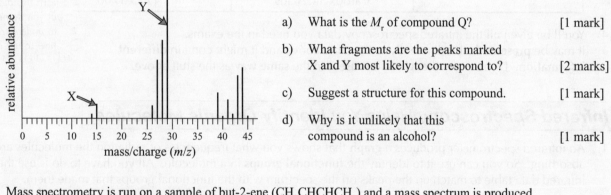

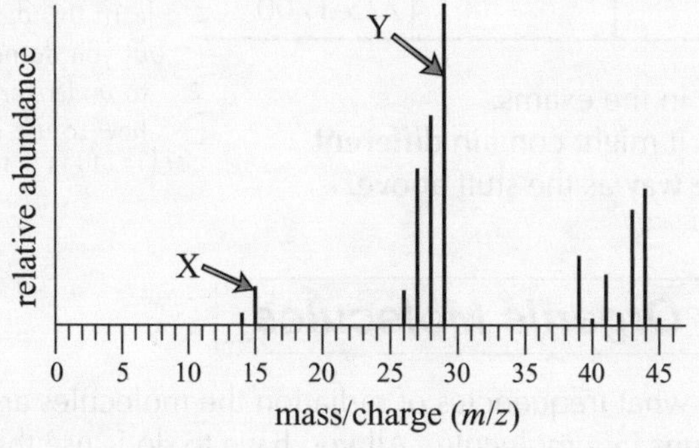

a) What is the M_r of compound Q? [1 mark]

b) What fragments are the peaks marked X and Y most likely to correspond to? [2 marks]

c) Suggest a structure for this compound. [1 mark]

d) Why is it unlikely that this compound is an alcohol? [1 mark]

Q2 Mass spectrometry is run on a sample of but-2-ene ($CH_3CHCHCH_3$) and a mass spectrum is produced. For the following questions, assume that all ions form with a +1 charge.

a) At what m/z value would you expect the M peak of but-2-ene to appear? [1 mark]

b) A peak appears on the spectrum at $m/z = 41$. Suggest which fragment is responsible for this peak. [1 mark]

c) Apart from the M peak and the peak at $m/z = 41$, suggest one other peak that you would expect to be present on the mass spectrum of but-2-ene. What fragment does it correspond to? [2 marks]

Q3 An unknown alcohol has the chemical formula C_3H_8O.
A sample of the compound was inserted into a mass spectrometer and a mass spectrum was produced.
A peak appears on the mass spectrum at $m/z = 31$.
Name the unknown alcohol and draw its structure. Explain your answer. [4 marks]

Use the clues, identify a molecule — mass spectrometry my dear Watson...

I hate break ups — even if it is to make some lovely ions and a fragmentation pattern. But remember — mass spectrometry only records fragments that have a charge. So, when drawing or writing the fragments that a peak could be responsible for, remember to put that little positive sign next to them — you'll lose marks in the exam if you don't show it.

Infrared Spectroscopy

If you've got some stuff and don't know what it is, don't taste it. You can stick it in an infrared spectrometer. You'll wind up with some scary looking graphs. But just learn the basics, and you'll be fine.

Infrared Radiation *Makes Some* ***Bonds Vibrate More***

1) In infrared (IR) spectroscopy, a beam of **IR radiation** is passed through a sample of a chemical.
2) The IR radiation is absorbed by the **covalent bonds** in the molecules, increasing their **vibrational** energy.
3) **Bonds between different atoms** absorb **different frequencies** of IR radiation. Bonds in different **places** in a molecule absorb different frequencies too — so the O–H group in an **alcohol** and the O–H in a **carboxylic acid** absorb different frequencies. This table shows what **frequencies** different bonds absorb:

Group	Where it's found	Wavenumber (cm^{-1})
C–H stretching	Alkanes	2962-2853
	Alkenes	3095-3010
	Aldehydes	2900-2820 and 2775-2700
C–H bending	Alkanes	1485-1365
N–H stretching	Amines	3500-3300
O–H stretching	Alcohols	3750-3200
	Carboxylic Acids	3300-2500 (broad)
C=C stretching	Alkenes	1669-1645
C=O stretching	Aldehydes	1740-1720
	Ketones	1720-1700
	Carboxylic Acids	1725-1700

Bending is just another sort of vibration.

You don't need to learn this data, but you do need to understand how to use it.

4) You'll be given all the infrared spectroscopy data you need in the exams. It may be **presented** a bit differently to the table above and it might contain **different information**. Don't worry though — just **use** it in the **same way** as the stuff above.

Infrared Spectroscopy *Helps You* ***Identify Organic Molecules***

1) An infrared spectrometer produces a **graph** that shows you what frequencies of radiation the molecules are absorbing. So you can use it to identify the **functional groups** in a molecule. All you have to do is use the infrared data table to match up the peaks on the spectrum with the functional groups that made them.
2) The peaks show you **where radiation** is being **absorbed** (the peaks on IR spectra are **upside-down** — they point **downwards**).
3) **Transmittance** is always plotted on the *y*-axis, and wavenumber on the *x*-axis. **Wavenumber** is the measure used for the frequency (it's just 1/wavelength in cm).

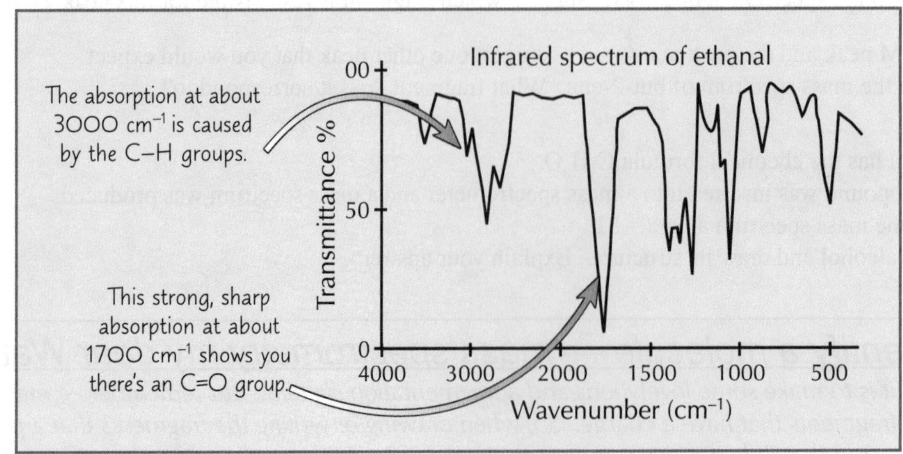
Infrared spectrum of ethanal
The absorption at about 3000 cm⁻¹ is caused by the C–H groups.
This strong, sharp absorption at about 1700 cm⁻¹ shows you there's an C=O group.
Transmittance %
100
50
0
4000
3000
2000
1500
1000
500
Wavenumber (cm⁻¹)

Alya was on wave number 1521. The smile was beginning to make her cheeks cramp.

Infrared Spectroscopy

Infrared Spectroscopy Can Show if a *Reaction's Happened*

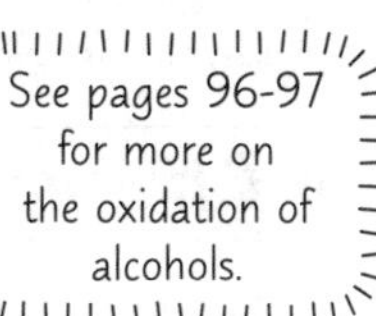

See pages 96-97
for more on
the oxidation of
alcohols.

Infrared spectroscopy is great for telling if a functional group has **changed** during a reaction. For example, if you **oxidise** an **alcohol** to an **aldehyde** you'll see the O–H absorption **disappear** from the spectrum, and a C=O absorption **appear**. If you then oxidise it further to a **carboxylic acid** an O–H peak at a slightly lower frequency than before will appear, alongside the C=O peak.

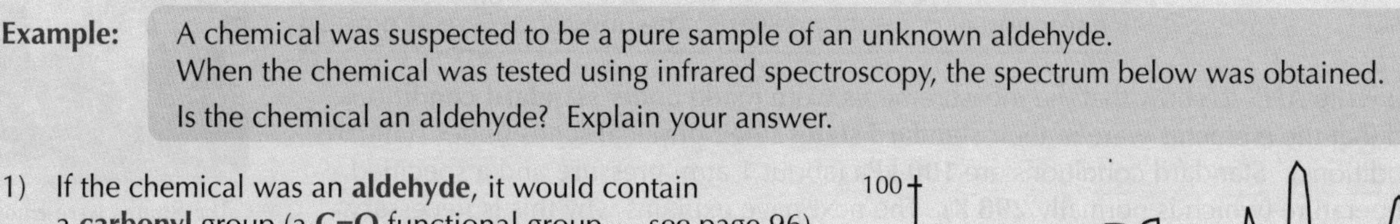

Example: A chemical was suspected to be a pure sample of an unknown aldehyde. When the chemical was tested using infrared spectroscopy, the spectrum below was obtained. Is the chemical an aldehyde? Explain your answer.

1) If the chemical was an **aldehyde**, it would contain a **carbonyl** group (a **C=O** functional group — see page 96).
2) In infrared spectroscopy, a carbonyl group would show a **strong, sharp peak** at about **1700-1750 cm^{-1}**.
3) The spectrum on the right doesn't have a strong peak at this frequency, and so is **not** an **aldehyde** (or a ketone, a carboxylic acid or an ester).

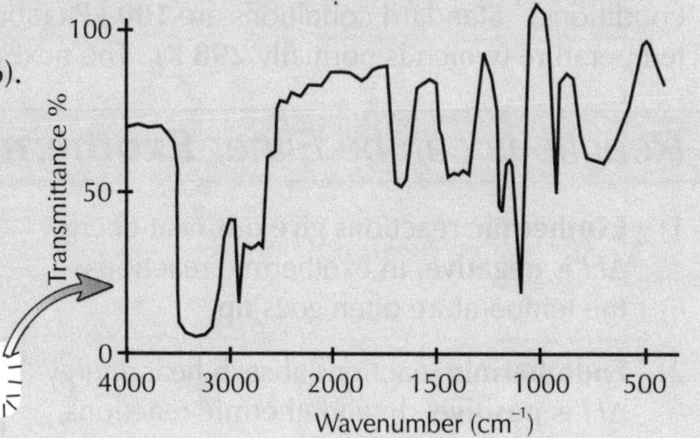

Actually, this is the infrared spectrum of ethanol.

Practice Questions

Q1 What happens to a covalent bond when it absorbs infrared radiation?

Q2 Why do most infrared spectra of organic molecules have a strong, sharp peak at around 3000 cm^{-1}?

Q3 What functional group would be responsible for a peak on an infrared spectrum at around 1740-1720 cm^{-1}?

Exam Questions

Q1 The IR spectrum of an organic molecule is shown on the right.

a) Which of the following compounds could be responsible for the spectrum? Use the infrared data on page 102.

A butanoic acid

B butanal

C 1-aminobutane

D butanol

[1 mark]

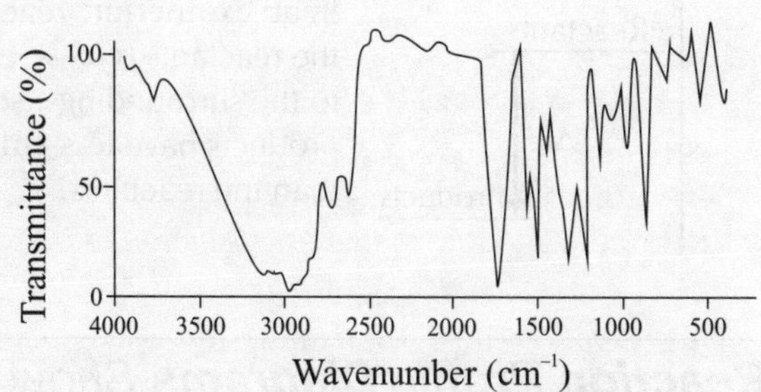

b) Explain your answer to a). [2 marks]

Q2 The molecule that produces the IR spectrum shown on the right has the molecular formula $C_3H_6O_2$.

Use the infrared data on page 102.

a) Which functional groups are responsible for peaks A and B? [2 marks]

b) Give the structural formula and name of this molecule. Explain your answer. [2 marks]

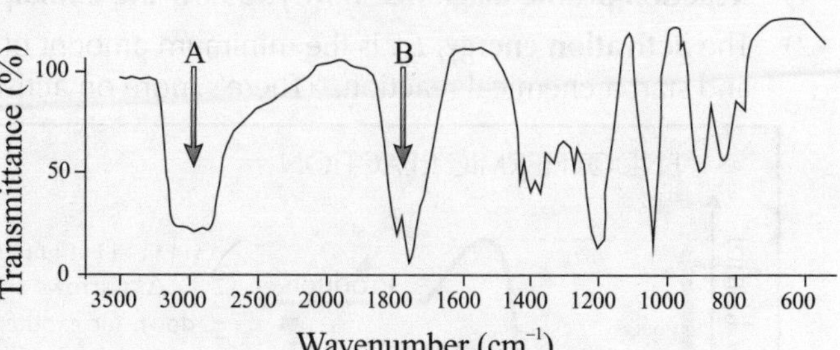

To analyse my sleep patterns, I use into-bed spectroscopy...

Infrared spectra may just appear to be big, squiggly messes — but they're actually dead handy at telling you what sort of molecule an unknown compound is. Luckily you don't have to remember where any of the infrared peaks are, but you do need to be able to identify them using your data sheet. So get some practice in now and do those exam questions above.

Enthalpy Changes

A whole new topic to enjoy — but don't forget, Big Brother is watching...

Chemical Reactions Often Have Enthalpy Changes

When chemical reactions happen, some bonds are **broken** and some bonds are **made**. More often than not, this'll cause a **change in energy**. The souped-up chemistry term for this is **enthalpy change**.

> **Enthalpy change**, ΔH (delta H), is the heat energy change in a reaction at **constant pressure**. The units of ΔH are **kJ mol^{-1}**.

You write ΔH° to show that the measurements were made under **standard conditions** and that the elements were in their **standard states** (their physical states under standard conditions). Standard conditions are **100 kPa** (about 1 atm) **pressure** and a specified temperature (which is normally **298 K**). The next page explains why this is necessary.

The Smiths were enjoying the standard conditions in British summertime.

Reactions can be Either Exothermic or Endothermic

1) **Exothermic** reactions **give out** heat energy. ΔH is **negative**. In exothermic reactions, the temperature often goes **up**.

The **combustion** of a fuel like methane is **exothermic**:
$CH_{4(g)} + 2O_{2(g)} \rightarrow CO_{2(g)} + 2H_2O_{(l)}$ $\quad \Delta_c H^{\circ} = -890$ kJ mol^{-1}

2) **Endothermic** reactions **absorb** heat energy. ΔH is **positive**. In endothermic reactions, the temperature often **falls**.

The **thermal decomposition** of calcium carbonate is **endothermic**:
$CaCO_{3(s)} \rightarrow CaO_{(s)} + CO_{2(g)}$ $\quad \Delta_r H^{\circ} = +178$ kJ mol^{-1}

The symbols $\Delta_c H^{\circ}$ and $\Delta_r H^{\circ}$ are explained on the next page.

Enthalpy Level Diagrams Show the Overall Change of a Reaction

1) Enthalpy (or energy) level diagrams show the **relative** energies of the reactants and products in a reaction. The **difference** in the enthalpies is the **enthalpy change** of the reaction.
2) The **less enthalpy** a substance has, the **more stable** it is.

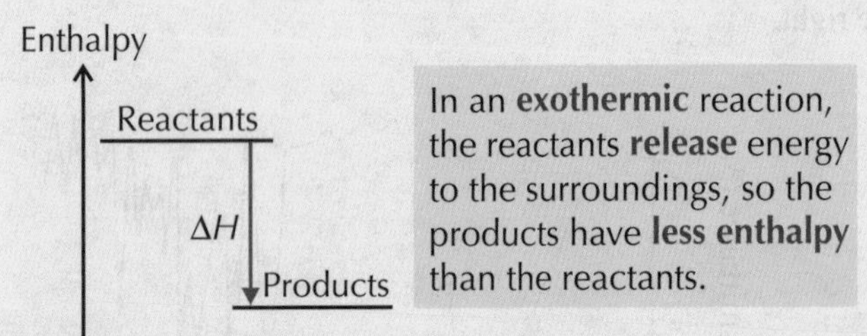

Enthalpy
Reactants
ΔH
Products
In an exothermic reaction, the reactants release energy to the surroundings, so the products have less enthalpy than the reactants.

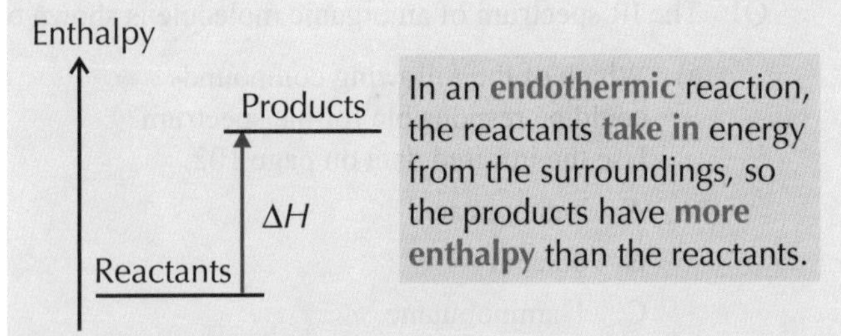

Enthalpy
Products
ΔH
Reactants
In an endothermic reaction, the reactants take in energy from the surroundings, so the products have more enthalpy than the reactants.

Reaction Profile Diagrams Show Enthalpy Changes During a Reaction

1) **Reaction profile diagrams** show you how the **enthalpy changes** during reactions.
2) The **activation energy**, E_a, is the minimum amount of energy needed to begin breaking reactant bonds and start a chemical reaction. (There's more on activation energy on page 112.)

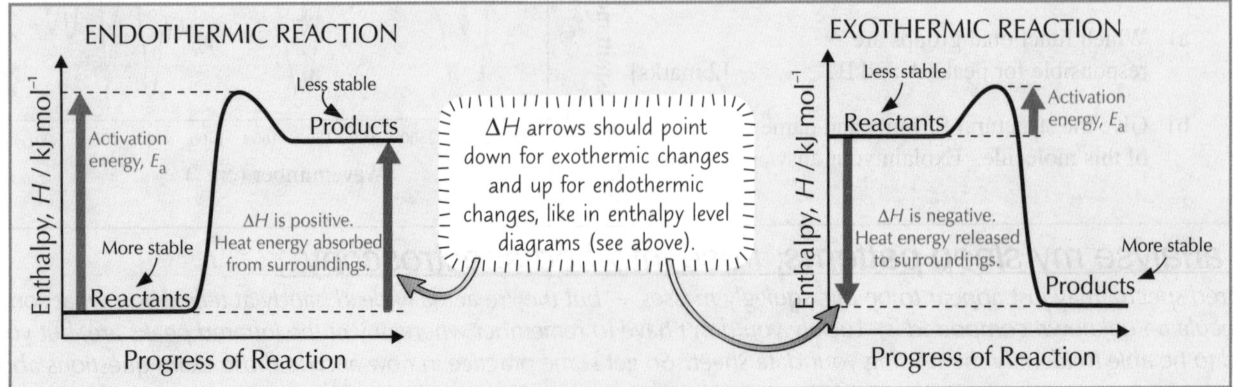

Enthalpy Changes

You Need to Specify the Conditions for Enthalpy Changes

1) You can't directly measure the **actual** enthalpy of a system. In practice, that doesn't matter, because it's only ever **enthalpy change** that matters. You can find enthalpy changes either by **experiment** or in **data books**.
2) Enthalpy changes you find in data books are usually **standard** enthalpy changes — enthalpy changes under **standard conditions** (**100 kPa** and a specified temperature, usually **298 K**).
3) This is important because changes in enthalpy are affected by **temperature** and **pressure** — using standard conditions means that everyone can know **exactly** what the enthalpy change is describing.

298 K is the same as 25 °C.

There are Different Types of ΔH Depending On the Reaction

1) **Standard enthalpy change of reaction**, $\Delta_r H^\circ$, is the enthalpy change when the reaction occurs in the **molar quantities** shown in the **chemical equation**, under standard conditions.
2) **Standard enthalpy change of formation**, $\Delta_f H^\circ$, is the enthalpy change when **1 mole** of a **compound** is formed from its **elements** in their standard states, under standard conditions, e.g. $2C_{(s)} + 3H_{2(g)} + \frac{1}{2}O_{2(g)} \rightarrow C_2H_5OH_{(l)}$.
3) **Standard enthalpy change of combustion**, $\Delta_c H^\circ$, is the enthalpy change when **1 mole** of a substance is completely **burned in oxygen**, under standard conditions.
4) **Standard enthalpy change of neutralisation**, $\Delta_{neut} H^\circ$, is the enthalpy change when an **acid** and an **alkali** react together, under standard conditions, to form **1 mole of water**.

Practice Questions

Q1 Explain the terms exothermic and endothermic, giving an example reaction in each case.

Q2 Draw and label enthalpy level diagrams for an exothermic and an endothermic reaction.

Q3 Define standard enthalpy change of formation and standard change enthalpy of combustion.

Exam Questions

Q1 Hydrogen peroxide, H_2O_2, can decompose into water and oxygen.

$$2H_2O_{2(l)} \rightarrow 2H_2O_{(l)} + O_{2(g)} \qquad \Delta H^\circ = -98 \text{ kJ mol}^{-1}$$

Draw a reaction profile diagram for this reaction. Mark on the activation energy, E_a, and ΔH. [3 marks]

Q2 Methanol, $CH_3OH_{(l)}$, when blended with petrol, can be used as a fuel. $\Delta_c H^\circ[CH_3OH] = -726$ kJ mol^{-1}

a) Write an equation, including state symbols, for the standard enthalpy change of combustion of methanol. [1 mark]

b) Write an equation, including state symbols, for the standard enthalpy change of formation of methanol. [1 mark]

c) Petroleum gas is a fuel that contains propane, C_3H_8.
Why does the following equation not represent a standard enthalpy change of combustion? [1 mark]

$$2C_3H_{8(g)} + 10O_{2(g)} \rightarrow 6CO_{2(g)} + 8H_2O_{(g)} \qquad \Delta_r H^\circ = -4113 \text{ kJ mol}^{-1}$$

Q3 Coal is mainly carbon. It is burned as a fuel. $\Delta_c H^\circ = -393.5$ kJ mol^{-1}

a) Write an equation, including state symbols, for the standard enthalpy change of combustion of carbon. [1 mark]

b) Explain why the standard enthalpy change of formation of carbon dioxide will also be –393.5 kJ mol^{-1}. [1 mark]

c) How much energy would be released when 1 tonne of carbon is burned? (1 tonne = 1000 kg) [2 marks]

Enthalpy changes — ethylpan, thenalpy, panthely, lanthepy, nyapleth...

Quite a few definitions here. And you need to know them all. If you're going to bother learning them, you might as well do it properly and learn all the pernickety details. They probably seem about as useful as a dead fly in your custard right now, but all will be revealed over the next few pages. Learn them now, so you've got a bit of a head start.

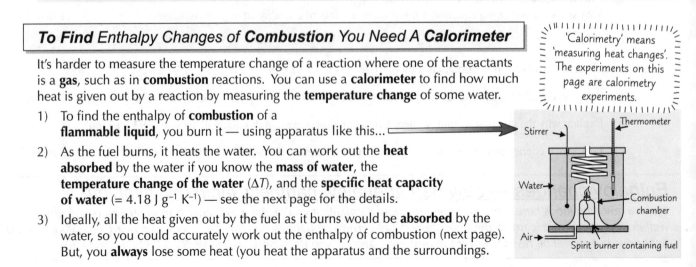

More on Enthalpy Changes

Now you know what enthalpy changes are, here's how to calculate them...

You Can Find **Enthalpy Changes** Using **Experiments**

To find the enthalpy change for a reaction, you only need to know two things:

- the **number of moles** of the stuff that's reacting,
- the change in **temperature** of the reaction.

Once you know these two things, you can work out the change in **heat energy** of the reaction using the equation on the next page. For reactions carried out at **constant pressure**, the heat change is the same as the enthalpy change.

Some enthalpy changes can't be found by measuring a single temperature change. Fear not — there's a way round this on page 109.

You Can **Directly Measure** the **Temperature Change** of Some **Reaction Mixtures**

For reactions where all the reactants are **solids** or **liquids**, you can just **mix** the reactants together, stick a thermometer in the reaction mixture and measure the **overall temperature change**. The **problem** with this method is that some heat will be **lost** to the surroundings (or gained if the reaction is endothermic), so the **temperature change** you measure will be **less** than the actual temperature change of the reaction. You can account for this problem by using the method below.

You should carry out the reaction in an insulated container, e.g. a polystyrene beaker, so that you don't lose or gain much heat through the sides.

Example: Describe an experiment that could be used to find the enthalpy change of the endothermic reaction between citric acid and sodium bicarbonate.

1) Add a set volume of citric acid of a known concentration to a polystyrene cup.
2) Put a lid on the beaker and measure the temperature of the solution every 30 seconds until it's stabilised.
3) Add a set mass of sodium bicarbonate to the beaker, and stir the mixture.
4) Measure the temperature of the reaction mixture every 30 seconds until the temperature has reached a minimum (or maximum for an exothermic reaction) and has been returning to the initial temperature for a couple of minutes.
5) Draw a graph of temperature against time.
6) To find the temperature change of the reaction, accounting for the fact the heat is gained from the surroundings, extrapolate the line from where the reaction is returning to its initial temperature back towards the time when the reaction started.
7) Read off the temperature from the extrapolated line at the time when the reaction started (when the sodium bicarbonate was added). Here, it's 2 minutes and the temperature is 1 °C.
8) Compare this with the initial reading to find the temperature change of the reaction — the initial temperature was 21 °C, so the temperature change is 1 – 21 = –20 °C.

Reaction mixture of citric acid and sodium bicarbonate; Thermometer; Lid; Polystyrene beaker

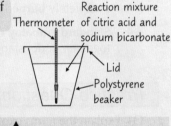

initial (maximum) temperature; extrapolated minimum temperature; temperature / °C; time / s

For an exothermic reaction, the temperature will rise to a maximum and then fall. To find the temperature change, extrapolate the line from the point where the temperature starts falling back to the time where the reaction started.

To Find Enthalpy Changes of **Combustion** You Need A **Calorimeter**

It's harder to measure the temperature change of a reaction where one of the reactants is a **gas**, such as in **combustion** reactions. You can use a **calorimeter** to find how much heat is given out by a reaction by measuring the **temperature change** of some water.

'Calorimetry' means 'measuring heat changes'. The experiments on this page are calorimetry experiments.

1) To find the enthalpy of **combustion** of a **flammable liquid**, you burn it — using apparatus like this...
2) As the fuel burns, it heats the water. You can work out the **heat absorbed** by the water if you know the **mass of water**, the **temperature change of the water** (ΔT), and the **specific heat capacity of water** (= 4.18 J g^{-1} K^{-1}) — see the next page for the details.
3) Ideally, all the heat given out by the fuel as it burns would be **absorbed** by the water, so you could accurately work out the enthalpy of combustion (next page). But, you **always** lose some heat (you heat the apparatus and the surroundings.

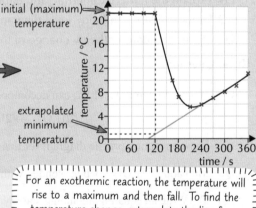

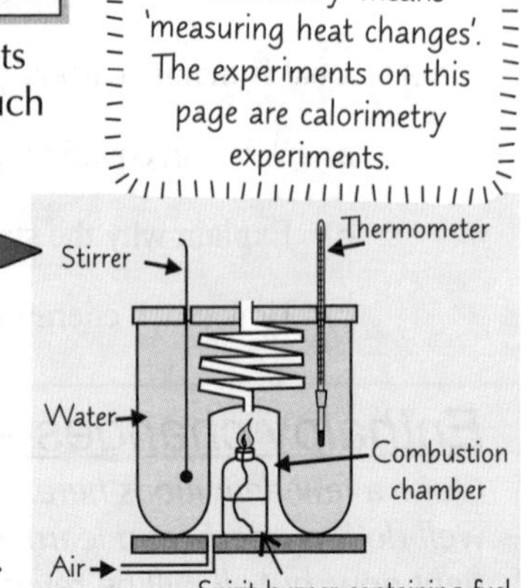

More on Enthalpy Changes

Calculate Enthalpy Changes Using the Equation $q = mc\Delta T$

It seems there's a snazzy equation for everything these days, and enthalpy change is no exception:

$q = mc\Delta T$ where, q = heat lost or gained (in joules). This is the same as the enthalpy change if the pressure is constant.

m = mass of water in the calorimeter, or solution in the insulated container (in grams).

c = specific heat capacity of water (4.18 J g^{-1} K^{-1}).

ΔT = the change in temperature of the water or solution (in K).

The specific heat capacity of water is the amount of heat energy it takes to raise the temperature of 1 g of water by 1 K.

This is the same as the change in °C.

Example: In a laboratory experiment, 1.16 g of an organic liquid fuel was completely burned in oxygen. The heat formed during this combustion raised the temperature of 100 g of water from 17.5 °C to 80.0 °C. Calculate the standard enthalpy of combustion, $\Delta_c H^\circ$, of the fuel. Its M_r is 58.0.

Remember — m is the mass of water, NOT the mass of fuel.

1. First, you need to calculate the **amount of heat** given out by the fuel, using $q = mc\Delta T$.

   $q = mc\Delta T$

   $q = 100 \times 4.18 \times (80.0 - 17.5) = 26\,125$ J

   $26\,125 \div 1000 = 26.125$ kJ

   If you're asked to calculate an enthalpy change, the answer should always be in kJ mol^{-1}. So change the amount of heat from J to kJ by dividing by 1000.

2. The standard enthalpy of combustion involves 1 mole of fuel. So next you need to find out **how many moles** of fuel produced this heat. It's back to the old n **= mass ÷** M_r equation.

   $n = 1.16 \div 58.0 = 0.0200$ mol of fuel

3. So, the heat produced by 1 mole of fuel = $26.125 \div 0.0200$

   ≈ **–1310 kJ mol^{-1}** (3 s.f.). This is the standard enthalpy change of combustion.

   It's negative because combustion is an exothermic reaction.

The actual $\Delta_c H^\circ$ of this compound is –1615 kJ mol^{-1} — lots of heat has been **lost** and not measured. For example, it's likely a bit escaped through the **calorimeter**, the fuel might not have **combusted completely**, or the **conditions** might not have been standard.

Practice Questions

Q1 Briefly describe an experiment that could be carried out to find the enthalpy of combustion of a reaction between a solid and a liquid.

Q2 What equation is used to calculate the enthalpy change in a calorimetry experiment?

Q3 Why might the enthalpy of combustion calculated from an experiment be different from the real value?

Exam Questions

Q1 The initial temperature of 25.0 cm^3 of 1.00 mol dm^{-3} hydrochloric acid in a polystyrene cup was measured as 19.0 °C. This acid was exactly neutralised by 25.0 cm^3 of 1.00 mol dm^{-3} sodium hydroxide solution. The maximum temperature of the resulting solution was measured as 25.8 °C.

Calculate the standard enthalpy change of neutralisation for the reaction. (You may assume the neutral solution formed has a specific heat capacity of 4.18 J g^{-1} K^{-1}, and a density of 1.00 g cm^{-3}.) [3 marks]

Q2 A 50.0 cm^3 sample of 0.200 mol dm^{-3} copper(II) sulfate solution placed in a polystyrene beaker gave a temperature increase of 2.00 K when excess zinc powder was added and stirred. (Ignore the increase in volume due to the zinc.) Calculate the enthalpy change when 1 mol of zinc reacts. Assume the solution's specific heat capacity is 4.18 J g^{-1} K^{-1}. The equation for the reaction is: $Zn_{(s)} + CuSO_{4(aq)} \rightarrow Cu_{(s)} + ZnSO_{4(aq)}$ [3 marks]

If you can't stand the heat, get out of the calorimeter...

There's quite a lot to wrap your noggin round on these pages. Not only are there some fiddly calorimetry experiments, but you need to know how to calculate enthalpy changes from your results. You need to know the limitations of the experiments, too. You'll often assume that no heat is lost (or gained) from the surroundings, but this isn't always true...

Hess's Law

You can't always work out an enthalpy change by measuring a single temperature change. But there are other ways...

Hess's Law — the Total Enthalpy Change is Independent of the Route Taken

Hess's Law says that: **The total enthalpy change of a reaction is always the same, no matter which route is taken.**

This law is handy for working out enthalpy changes that you **can't find directly** by doing an experiment.

Here's an example:
The **total enthalpy change** for route 1 is the **same as for route 2.**

So, $\Delta_r H^\circ = +114.4 + (-180.8) = \mathbf{-66.4\ kJ\ mol^{-1}}$.

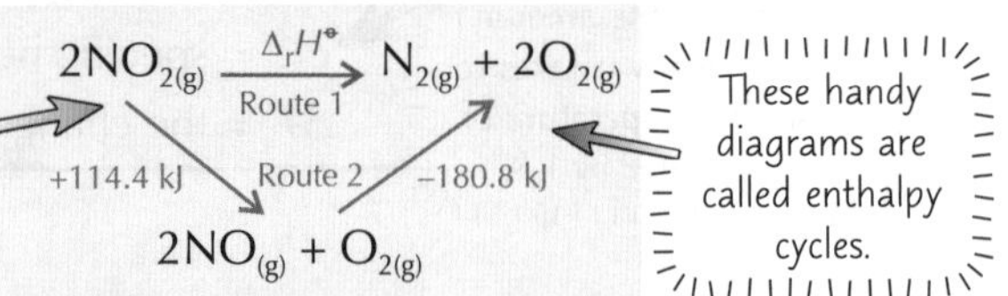

These handy diagrams are called enthalpy cycles.

Enthalpy Changes Can be Worked Out From Enthalpies of Formation

Enthalpy changes of formation are useful for calculating enthalpy changes you can't find directly.
You need to know $\Delta_f H^\circ$ for **all** the reactants and products that are **compounds** — $\Delta_f H^\circ$ for elements is **zero**.

Example: Use the enthalpy cycle on the right to calculate $\Delta_r H^\circ$ for the reaction: $SO_{2(g)} + 2H_2S_{(g)} \rightarrow 3S_{(s)} + 2H_2O_{(l)}$

REACTANTS $SO_{2(g)} + 2H_2S_{(g)} \xrightarrow{\Delta_r H^\circ}$ PRODUCTS $3S_{(s)} + 2H_2O_{(l)}$

Route 1 — $\Delta_f H^\circ_{(reactants)}$; Route 2 — $\Delta_f H^\circ_{(products)}$

$3S_{(s)} + 2H_{2(g)} + O_{2(g)}$ ELEMENTS

$\Delta_f H^\circ[SO_{2(g)}] = -297\ kJ\ mol^{-1}$
$\Delta_f H^\circ[H_2S_{(g)}] = -20.2\ kJ\ mol^{-1}$
$\Delta_f H^\circ[H_2O_{(l)}] = -286\ kJ\ mol^{-1}$

Using **Hess's Law**: Route 1 = Route 2

$\Delta_r H^\circ$ + the sum of $\Delta_f H^\circ$(reactants) = the sum of $\Delta_f H^\circ$(products)

So, $\Delta_r H^\circ$ = the sum of $\Delta_f H^\circ$(products) – the sum of $\Delta_f H^\circ$(reactants)

Just plug the numbers given on the right into the equation above:

$\Delta_r H^\circ = [0 + (2 \times -286)] - [-297 + (2 \times -20.2)] = \mathbf{-235\ kJ\ mol^{-1}}$

$\Delta_f H^\circ$ of sulfur is zero — it's an element.

There are 2 moles of H_2O and 2 moles of H_2S.

It **always** works, no matter how complicated the reaction...

Example: Use the enthalpy cycle on the right to calculate $\Delta_r H^\circ$ for the reaction: $2NH_4NO_{3(s)} + C_{(s)} \rightarrow 2N_{2(g)} + CO_{2(g)} + 4H_2O_{(l)}$

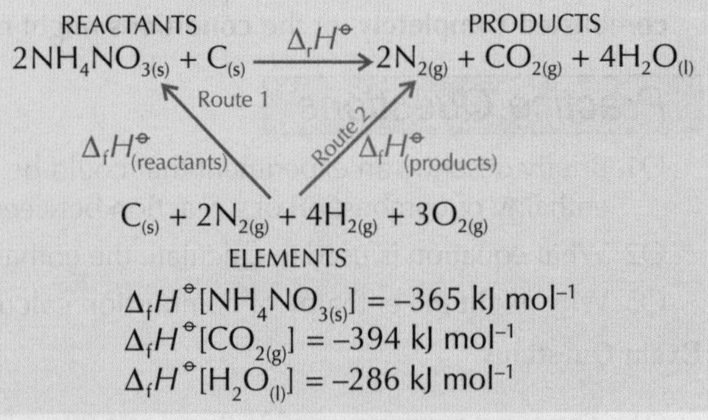

Using Hess's Law: Route 1 = Route 2

$\Delta_f H^\circ$(reactants) + $\Delta_r H^\circ$ = $\Delta_f H^\circ$(products)

$(2 \times -365) + 0 + \Delta_r H^\circ = 0 + -394 + (4 \times -286)$

$\Delta_r H^\circ = -394 + (-1144) - (-730)$

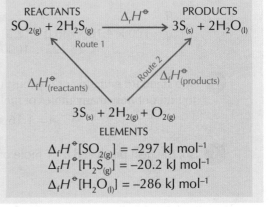

$= \mathbf{-808\ kJ\ mol^{-1}}$

Enthalpy Changes Can be Worked Out From Enthalpies of Combustion

You can use a similar method to find an enthalpy change from **enthalpy changes of combustion**.

Example: Use the enthalpy cycle on the right to calculate $\Delta_f H^\circ$ for C_2H_5OH.

You need to add enough oxygen to balance the equations.

REACTANTS $2C_{(s)} + 3H_{2(g)} + \frac{1}{2}O_{2(g)} \xrightarrow{\Delta_f H^\circ}$ PRODUCTS $C_2H_5OH_{(l)}$

Route 2 — $3O_{2(g)}$; Route 1 — $3O_{2(g)}$

$2CO_{2(g)} + 3H_2O_{(l)}$ COMBUSTION PRODUCTS

$\Delta_c H^\circ[C_{(s)}] = -394\ kJ\ mol^{-1}$
$\Delta_c H^\circ[H_{2(g)}] = -286\ kJ\ mol^{-1}$
$\Delta_c H^\circ[C_2H_5OH_{(l)}] = -1367\ kJ\ mol^{-1}$

Using Hess's Law: Route 1 = Route 2

$\Delta_f H^\circ[C_2H_5OH] + \Delta_c H^\circ[C_2H_5OH] = 2\Delta_c H^\circ[C] + 3\Delta_c H^\circ[H_2]$

$\Delta_f H^\circ[C_2H_5OH] + (-1367) = (2 \times -394) + (3 \times -286)$

$\Delta_f H^\circ[C_2H_5OH] = -788 + -858 - (-1367) = \mathbf{-279\ kJ\ mol^{-1}}$

Hess's Law

Hess's Law Lets You Find Enthalpy Changes **Indirectly** From Experiments

On pages 106-107 you saw how you could find the enthalpy change of a reaction using calorimetry. Sometimes you can **combine** the enthalpy change results from these experiments (neutralisation reactions, for example) to work out an enthalpy change that you **can't find directly**. It's clever stuff... read on.

You **can't** find the enthalpy change of the thermal decomposition of calcium carbonate by measuring a temperature change.

$CaCO_{3(s)} \rightarrow CaO_{(s)} + CO_{2(g)}$ Enthalpy change = ?

(It's an endothermic reaction, so you'd expect the temperature to fall. But you need to heat it up for the reaction to happen at all).

But you can find it in a more **indirect** way.

The aim is to make one of those **Hess cycles** (the technical name for a "Hess's Law triangle diagram thing").

1) Write the reaction you want to find the enthalpy change for at the top of the triangle — include your **reactants** and **products**:

$$CaCO_3 \xrightarrow{\Delta_r H^\ominus} CaO + CO_2$$

2) Next, you're going to carry out two **neutralisation** reactions involving **hydrochloric acid**, and use the results to complete your Hess cycle. You **can** find the enthalpy changes of these reactions (using calorimetry — see pages 106-107). Call them ΔH_1 and ΔH_2.

Reaction 1: $CaCO_3 + 2HCl \rightarrow CaCl_2 + CO_2 + H_2O$ $\quad \Delta H_1$

Reaction 2: $CaO + 2HCl \rightarrow CaCl_2 + H_2O$ $\quad \Delta H_2$

3) Now you can build the other two sides of your Hess cycle. Add **2 moles of HCl** to both sides of your triangle's top (representing the 2 moles of HCl in the above equations).

$$CaCO_3 + 2HCl \xrightarrow{\Delta_r H^\ominus} CaO + CO_2 + 2HCl$$

Add the **products** of the neutralisation reactions to the bottom of the triangle. Notice how all three corners 'balance'.

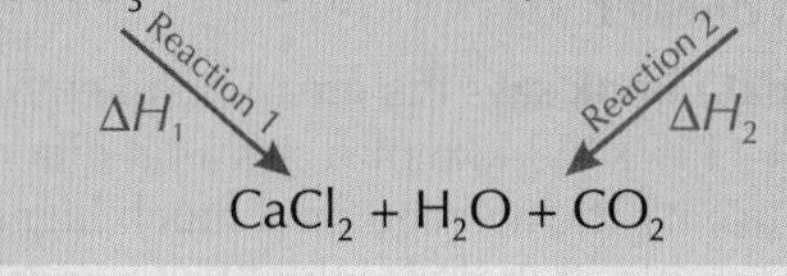

4) Add the enthalpy changes you found to your diagram.

5) And do the maths... the enthalpy change you want to find is just: $\Delta H_1 - \Delta H_2$

Practice Questions

Q1 What does Hess's Law state?

Q2 What is the standard enthalpy change of formation of any element?

Q3 Describe how you can make a Hess cycle to find the standard enthalpy change of a reaction using standard enthalpy changes of formation.

Exam Questions

Q1 Using the facts that the standard enthalpy change of formation of $Al_2O_{3(s)}$ is –1676 kJ mol^{-1} and the standard enthalpy change of formation of $MgO_{(s)}$ is –602 kJ mol^{-1}, calculate the enthalpy change of the following reaction.

$$Al_2O_{3(s)} + 3Mg_{(s)} \rightarrow 2Al_{(s)} + 3MgO_{(s)}$$ [2 marks]

Q2 Calculate the enthalpy change for the reaction below (the fermentation of glucose).

$$C_6H_{12}O_{6(s)} \rightarrow 2C_2H_5OH_{(l)} + 2CO_{2(g)}$$

Use the following standard enthalpies of combustion in your calculations:

$\Delta_c H^\ominus$(glucose) = –2820 kJ mol^{-1} $\quad$ $\Delta_c H^\ominus$(ethanol) = –1367 kJ mol^{-1} [2 marks]

Meet Hessie. She's the Lawch Hess Monster...

To get your head around those enthalpy cycles, you're going to have to do more than skim read them. It'll also help if you know the definitions for those standard enthalpy thingumabobs. I'd read those enthalpy cycle examples again and make sure you understand how the elements/compounds at each corner were chosen to be there.

Bond Enthalpy

During chemical reactions, some bonds are broken, whilst others are made. By working out the total energy needed to break all the bonds, and the energy given out as new bonds form, you can find the enthalpy change of a reaction.

*Reactions are all about **Breaking** and **Making** Bonds*

When reactions happen, **reactant bonds** are **broken** and **product bonds** are **formed**.

1) You **need** energy to break bonds, so bond breaking is **endothermic** (ΔH is **positive**).
2) Energy is **released** when bonds are formed, so this is **exothermic** (ΔH is **negative**).
3) The **enthalpy change** for a reaction is the **overall effect** of these two changes. If you need **more** energy to **break** bonds than is released when bonds are made, ΔH is **positive**. If it's **less**, ΔH is **negative**.

*You Need **Energy** to **Break** the **Attraction** Between **Atoms** or **Ions***

1) In ionic bonding, **positive** and **negative ions** are attracted to each other. In covalent molecules, the **positive nuclei** are attracted to the **negative** charge of the shared electrons in a covalent bond.
2) You need energy to **break** this attraction — **stronger** bonds take more energy to break.

Bond enthalpy is the amount of energy required to **break** **1 mole** of a type of bond in a molecule in the **gas phase**.

Breaking bonds is always an endothermic process, so bond enthalpies are always positive.

Mean Bond Enthalpies** are **Not Exact

1) Water (H_2O) has **two O–H bonds**. You'd think it'd take the same amount of energy to break them both... but it **doesn't**.

   The **first** bond, $H–OH_{(g)}$: $E(H–OH) = +492\ kJ\ mol^{-1}$
   The **second** bond, $H–O_{(g)}$: $E(H–O) = +428\ kJ\ mol^{-1}$
   (O–H is a bit easier to break apart because of the extra electron repulsion.)
   So the **mean** bond enthalpy is $(492 + 428) \div 2 = \mathbf{+460\ kJ\ mol^{-1}}$.

2) The **data book** says the mean bond enthalpy for O–H is $+463\ kJ\ mol^{-1}$. It's a bit different because it's the average for a **much bigger range** of molecules, not just water. For example, it includes the O–H bonds in alcohols and carboxylic acids too.
3) So when you look up a **mean bond enthalpy**, what you get is:

   The energy needed to break **one mole** of bonds in the **gas phase**, averaged over **many different** compounds.

Enthalpy Changes** Can Be Calculated Using **Mean Bond Enthalpies

In any chemical reaction, energy is **absorbed** to **break bonds** and **given out** during **bond formation**. The difference between the energy absorbed and released is the overall **enthalpy change of reaction**:

Enthalpy Change of Reaction = Sum of bond enthalpies of reactants − Sum of bond enthalpies of products

(Sum of bond enthalpies of reactants: This is the total energy absorbed to break bonds.)
(Sum of bond enthalpies of products: This is the total energy released in making bonds)

Example: Calculate the overall enthalpy change for this reaction: $N_{2(g)} + 3H_{2(g)} \rightarrow 2NH_{3(g)}$
Use the mean bond enthalpy values in the table.

Bond	Average Bond Enthalpy
N≡N	$945\ kJ\ mol^{-1}$
H–H	$436\ kJ\ mol^{-1}$
N–H	$391\ kJ\ mol^{-1}$

Bonds broken: 1 mole of N≡N bond broken $= 1 \times 945 = 945\ kJ\ mol^{-1}$
3 moles of H–H bonds broken $= 3 \times 436 = 1308\ kJ\ mol^{-1}$

Sum of bond enthalpies $= 945 + 1308 = \mathbf{2253\ kJ\ mol^{-1}}$

Bonds formed: 6 moles of N–H bonds formed $= 6 \times 391 = 2346\ kJ\ mol^{-1}$

Sum of bond enthalpies $= \mathbf{2346\ kJ\ mol^{-1}}$

Now you just subtract the bond enthalpies of the products from the bond enthalpies of the reactants.

Enthalpy Change of Reaction $= 2253 - 2346 = \mathbf{-93\ kJ\ mol^{-1}}$

There might be a small amount of **variation** between the enthalpy change of reaction calculated from **mean bond enthalpies** and the **true** enthalpy change of reaction. This is because the **specific** bond enthalpies of the molecules in the reaction will be **slightly different** from the **average** values.

Bond Enthalpy

You Can Calculate **Mean Bond Enthalpies** Using **Reaction Enthalpies**

If you're given the enthalpy change of a reaction along with all but **one** of the bond enthalpies of the reactants and products, you can **rearrange** the equation on the previous page to find the **remaining** mean bond enthalpy.

Example: The enthalpy change of the reaction between nitrogen and fluorine to form nitrogen trifluoride is –264.2 kJ mol⁻¹: $N_{2(g)} + 3F_{2(g)} \rightarrow 2NF_{3(g)}$
Find the mean N–F bond enthalpy in NF_3.

Bond	Mean Bond Enthalpy
N≡N	945 kJ mol^{-1}
F–F	158 kJ mol^{-1}

Bonds broken: 1 mole N≡N bonds broken = 1 × 945 = 945 kJ mol^{-1}
3 moles F–F bonds broken = 3 × 158 = 474 kJ mol^{-1}

Sum of bond enthalpies = 945 + 474 = **1419 kJ mol^{-1}**

Bonds formed: 6 N–F bonds formed = 6 × *E*(N–F) ⟸ 'E(X)' is just a quick way of writing the mean bond enthalpy of bond X.

Enthalpy change of reaction = –246.2 kJ mol^{-1}

You know that: Enthalpy Change of Reaction = Sum of bond enthalpies of reactants – Sum of bond enthalpies of products

Substituting in the values given in the question gives: –264.2 = (945 + 474) – (6 × *E*(N–F))
Rearranging this gives: *E*(N–F) = [945 + 474 – (–264.2)] ÷ 6 = **+281 kJ mol^{-1}**

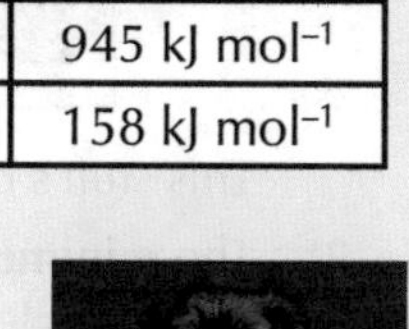
Jack preferred bones to bonds.

Practice Questions

Q1 Is energy taken in or released when bonds are broken?

Q2 Define bond enthalpy.

Q3 What state must compounds be in when bond dissociation enthalpies are measured?

Q4 Define mean bond enthalpy.

Exam Questions

Q1 The table below shows some mean bond enthalpy values.

Bond	C–H	C=O	O=O	O–H
Mean Bond Enthalpy (kJ mol^{-1})	435	805	498	464

The complete combustion of methane can be represented by the equation: $CH_{4(g)} + 2O_{2(g)} \rightarrow CO_{2(g)} + 2H_2O_{(l)}$

Use the table of bond enthalpies above to calculate the enthalpy change for the reaction. [2 marks]

Q2 Use the following bond enthalpy data to calculate the standard enthalpy change for the formation of water: $\frac{1}{2}O_{2(g)} + H_{2(g)} \rightarrow H_2O_{(l)}$

E(H–O) in water = +460 kJ mol^{-1}
E(O=O) in oxygen = +498 kJ mol^{-1}
E(H–H) in hydrogen = +436 kJ mol^{-1} [2 marks]

Q3 Methane and chlorine gas will react together under certain conditions to form chloromethane:

$$CH_{4(g)} + Cl_{2(g)} \rightarrow CH_3Cl_{(g)} + HCl_{(g)} \quad \Delta_r H = -101 \text{ kJ mol}^{-1}$$

E(C–H) in methane = +435 kJ mol^{-1} *E*(C–H) in chloromethane = +397 kJ mol^{-1}
E(Cl–Cl) = +243 kJ mol^{-1} *E*(H–Cl) = +432 kJ mol^{-1}

a) Calculate the C–Cl bond enthalpy in chloromethane. [2 marks]

b) The data book value for the mean bond enthalpy of C–Cl is +346 kJ mol^{-1}. Comment on this value with reference to your answer to part a). [1 mark]

Do you expect me to react? No, Mr Bond, I expect you to break...

Reactions are like pulling plastic building bricks apart and building something new. Sometimes bits get stuck together and you need lots of energy to pull 'em apart. Okay, so energy's not really released when you stick them together, but you can't have everything — it wasn't that bad an analogy up till now. Ah, well... You best get on and learn this stuff.

Collision Theory

The rate of a reaction is just how quickly it happens. Lots of things can make it go faster or slower.

Particles **Must** Collide to **React**

1) Particles in liquids and gases are **always moving** and **colliding** with **each other**. They **don't** react every time though — only when the **conditions** are right. A reaction **won't** take place between two particles **unless** —

- They collide in the **right direction**. They need to be **facing** each other the right way.
- They collide with at least a certain **minimum** amount of kinetic (movement) **energy**.

This stuff's called **Collision Theory**.

2) The **minimum amount of kinetic energy** particles need to react is called the **activation energy**. The particles need this much energy to **break the bonds** to start the reaction.
3) Reactions with **low activation energies** often happen **pretty easily**. But reactions with **high activation energies** don't. You need to give the particles extra energy by **heating** them.

To make this a bit clearer, here's a **reaction profile diagram**.

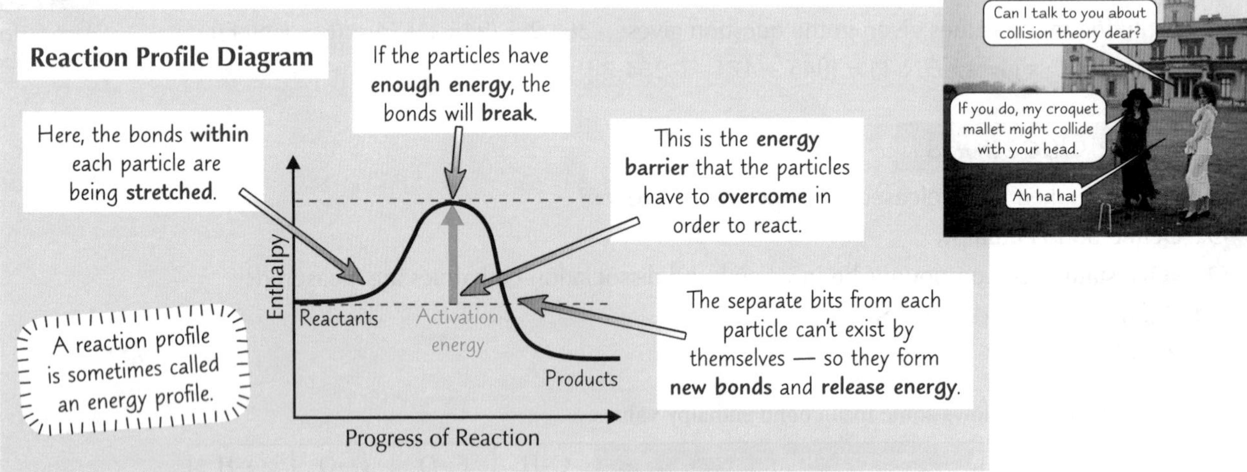
Reaction Profile Diagram
If the particles have enough energy, the bonds will break.
Here, the bonds within each particle are being stretched.
This is the energy barrier that the particles have to overcome in order to react.
Enthalpy
Reactants
Activation energy
Products
Progress of Reaction
The separate bits from each particle can't exist by themselves — so they form new bonds and release energy.
A reaction profile is sometimes called an energy profile.
Can I talk to you about collision theory dear?
If you do, my croquet mallet might collide with your head.
Ah ha ha!

Molecules **Don't** all have the **Same Amount of Energy**

Imagine looking down on Oxford Street when it's teeming with people. You'll see some people ambling along **slowly**, some hurrying **quickly**, but most of them will be walking with a **moderate speed**. It's the same with the **molecules** in a liquid or gas. Some **don't have much kinetic energy** and move **slowly**. Others have **loads** of **kinetic energy** and **whizz** along. But most molecules are somewhere **in between**.

If you plot a **graph** of the **numbers of molecules** in a substance with different **kinetic energies** you get a **Maxwell-Boltzmann distribution**. It looks like this —

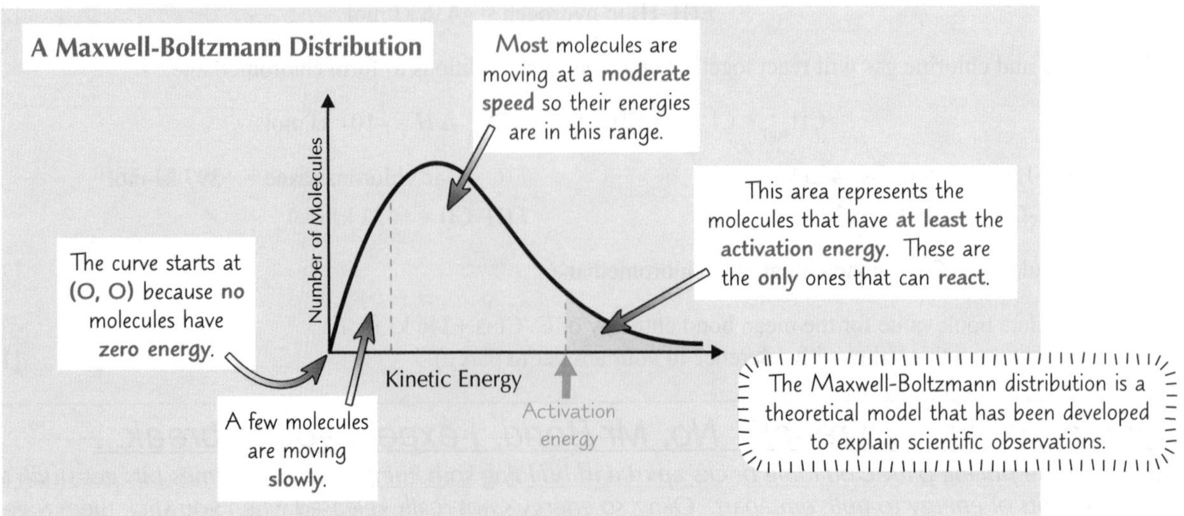
A Maxwell-Boltzmann Distribution
Most molecules are moving at a moderate speed so their energies are in this range.
Number of Molecules
This area represents the molecules that have at least the activation energy. These are the only ones that can react.
The curve starts at (0, 0) because no molecules have zero energy.
Kinetic Energy
Activation energy
A few molecules are moving slowly.
The Maxwell-Boltzmann distribution is a theoretical model that has been developed to explain scientific observations.

Collision Theory

Increasing the *Temperature* makes Reactions *Faster*

1) If you increase the **temperature**, the particles will, on average, have more **kinetic energy** and will move **faster**.
2) So, a **greater proportion** of molecules will have at least the **activation energy** and be able to **react**. This changes the **shape** of the **Maxwell-Boltzmann distribution curve** — it pushes it over to the **right**.

The total number of molecules is still the same, which means the area under each curve must be the same.

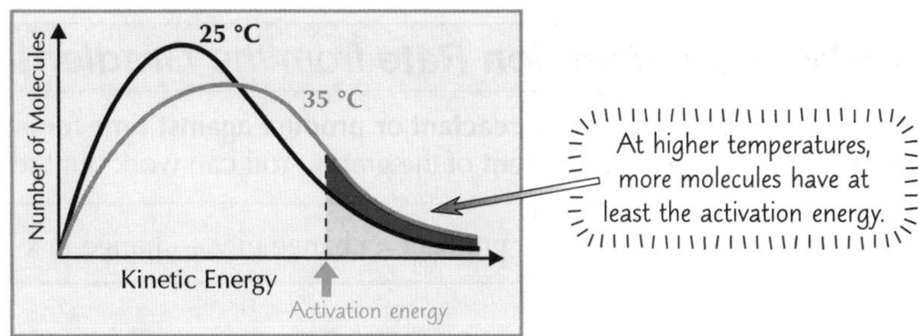

At higher temperatures, more molecules have at least the activation energy.

3) Because the molecules are flying about **faster**, they'll **collide more often**. This is **another reason** why increasing the temperature makes a reaction faster, i.e. the reaction rate increases (see the next page for more on reaction rates).

Concentration, *Pressure* and *Catalysts* also Affect the *Reaction Rate*

Increasing Concentration Speeds Up Reactions

If you increase the **concentration** of reactants in a **solution**, there'll be **more particles** in a **given volume** of the solution, so particles will **collide more frequently**. If there are **more collisions**, they'll have **more chances** to react.

Increasing Pressure Speeds Up Reactions

If any of your reactants are **gases**, increasing the **pressure** will increase the rate of reaction.
It's pretty much the same as increasing the **concentration** of a solution — at higher pressures, there are more particles in a **given volume** of gas, which increases the frequency of **successful collisions**.

Catalysts Can Speed Up Reactions

Catalysts are really useful. They **lower the activation energy** by providing a **different way** for the bonds to be broken and remade. If the activation energy's **lower**, more particles will have **enough energy** to react. There's heaps of information about catalysts on pages 116-117.

Increasing the surface area of a solid reactant(s) also makes the reaction faster as it increases the surface where collisions can happen.

Practice Questions

Q1 Explain the term 'activation energy'.

Q2 Name four factors that affect the rate of a reaction.

Exam Questions

Q1 Nitrogen oxide (NO) and ozone (O_3) sometimes react to produce nitrogen dioxide (NO_2) and oxygen (O_2). How would increasing the pressure affect the rate of this reaction? Explain your answer. [2 marks]

Q2 Use the collision theory to explain why the reaction between a solid and a liquid is generally faster than that between two solids. [2 marks]

Q3 On the right is a Maxwell-Boltzmann distribution curve for a sample of a gas at 25 °C.

a) Which of the curves, X or Y, shows the Maxwell-Boltzmann distribution curve for the same sample at 15 °C ? [1 mark]

b) Explain how this curve shows that the reaction rate will be lower at 15 °C than at 25 °C. [1 mark]

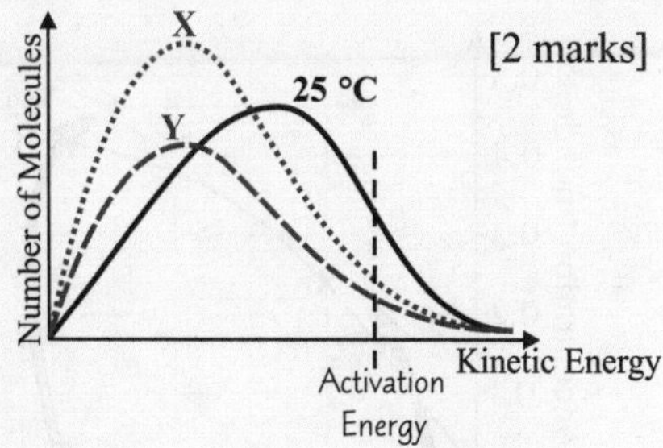

Will a collision between this book and my head increase my rate of revision?

No equations, no formulae... What more could you ask for. Remember, increasing concentration and pressure do exactly the same thing. The only difference is, you increase the concentration of a solution and the pressure of a gas.

Reaction Rates

Sorry — this section gets a bit mathsy. Just take a deep breath, dive in, and don't bash your head on the bottom.

Reaction Rate tells you How Fast Reactants are Converted to Products

Reaction rate is the **change in amount** of reactant or product **per unit time** (usually seconds).
E.g. if the reactants are in solution, the rate will be **change in concentration per second**. The units will be **mol dm^{-3} s^{-1}**.

You can Work out Reaction Rate from the Gradient of a Graph

If you draw a graph of the **amount of reactant or product against time** for a reaction (with time on the *x*-axis), then the reaction rate is just the **gradient** of the graph. You can work out the gradient using the equation...

gradient = change in y ÷ change in x

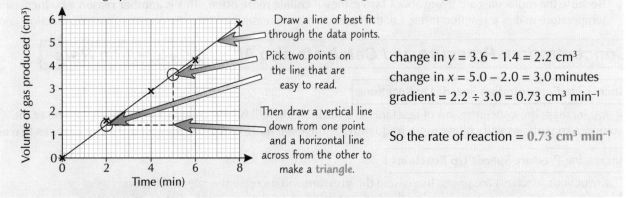

The data on the graph came from measuring the volume of gas given off during a chemical reaction.

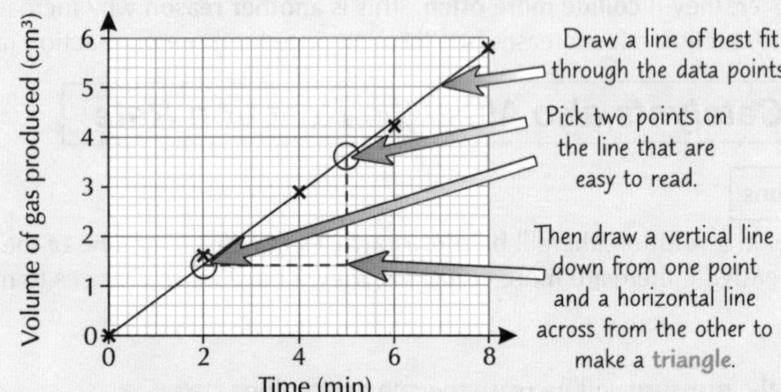

Then draw a vertical line down from one point and a horizontal line across from the other to make a triangle.

change in y = 3.6 – 1.4 = 2.2 cm^3
change in x = 5.0 – 2.0 = 3.0 minutes
gradient = 2.2 ÷ 3.0 = 0.73 cm^3 min^{-1}

So the rate of reaction = **0.73 cm^3 min^{-1}**

You May Need to Work Out the Gradient from a Curved Graph

When the points on a graph lie in a **curve**, you can't draw a straight line of best fit through them. But you can still work out the gradient, and so the rate, at a **particular point** in the reaction by working out the **gradient of a tangent**. The gradient at **time = 0** is called the **initial rate**.

A tangent is a line that just touches a curve and has the same gradient as the curve does at that point.

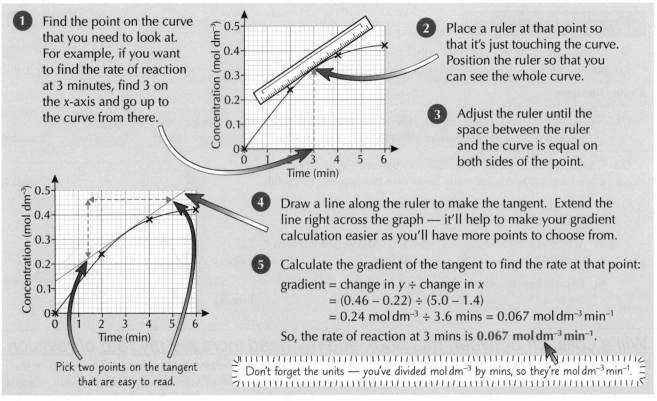

1. Find the point on the curve that you need to look at. For example, if you want to find the rate of reaction at 3 minutes, find 3 on the *x*-axis and go up to the curve from there.

2. Place a ruler at that point so that it's just touching the curve. Position the ruler so that you can see the whole curve.

3. Adjust the ruler until the space between the ruler and the curve is equal on both sides of the point.

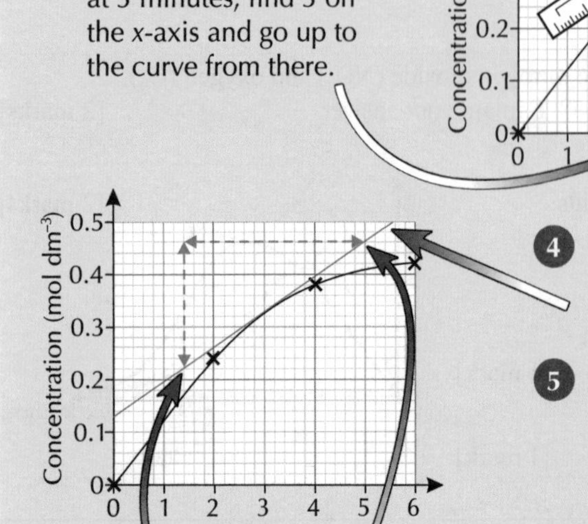

4. Draw a line along the ruler to make the tangent. Extend the line right across the graph — it'll help to make your gradient calculation easier as you'll have more points to choose from.

5. Calculate the gradient of the tangent to find the rate at that point:

gradient = change in y ÷ change in x
= (0.46 – 0.22) ÷ (5.0 – 1.4)
= 0.24 mol dm^{-3} ÷ 3.6 mins = 0.067 mol dm^{-3} min^{-1}

So, the rate of reaction at 3 mins is **0.067 mol dm^{-3} min^{-1}**.

Pick two points on the tangent that are easy to read.

Don't forget the units — you've divided mol dm^{-3} by mins, so they're mol dm^{-3} min^{-1}.

Reaction Rates

You Can Work out the Initial Rate of a Reaction

The **initial rate of a reaction** is the rate at the **start** of the reaction. You can find this from a **concentration-time** graph by calculating the **gradient** of the **tangent** at **time = 0**.

Example: The graph on the right shows the change in concentration of H^+ ions over time in a reaction. Calculate the initial rate of reaction.

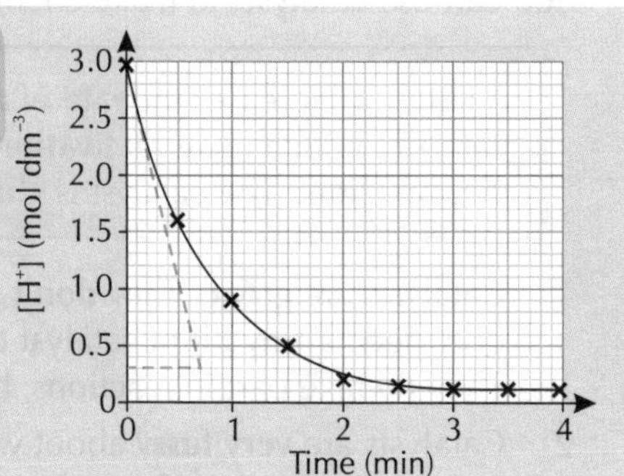

- Draw a **tangent** to the curve at **time = 0**.
- Work out the **gradient** of the tangent.
  gradient = change in y ÷ change in x
  = (0.3 – 3.0) ÷ (0.7 – 0.0) = –2.7 mol dm^{-3} ÷ 0.7 mins
  = –3.875... mol dm^{-3} min^{-1}
- So the initial rate of reaction was **3.9 mol dm^{-3} min^{-1}**.

You Can Work Out Rates From Experimental Data

1) In some reactions, you'll measure the time taken for something to happen, e.g. a **colour change** to occur.
2) If you're waiting for a set amount of **product to form**, or a set amount of **reactant to be used up**, you can use this equation to work out the rate:

$$\text{rate of reaction} = \frac{\text{amount of reactant used or amount of product formed}}{\text{time taken}}$$

So, for example, if during a reaction, it took **16 seconds** for **10 cm³** of a gas to form, the rate of reaction would be: 10 ÷ 16 = **0.625 cm^3 s^{-1}**

3) The rate of reaction is proportional to **1 ÷ time**, so you can use **1/time** as a measure of the relative **rate** of reaction.

Example: A student measures the time taken for a **colour change** to occur in a reaction as he varies the **concentration** of a reactant, A. His results are shown in the table. Calculate the relative rates of reaction.

[A] / mol dm^{-3}	Time taken until colour change (s)
0.10	124
0.15	62
0.20	25

1) First calculate the relative rate of **each reaction** in s^{-1}.
   When [A] = 0.10 mol dm^{-3}, 1 ÷ 124 = 0.00806... s^{-1}
   When [A] = 0.15 mol dm^{-3}, 1 ÷ 62 = 0.0161... s^{-1}
   When [A] = 0.20 mol dm^{-3}, 1 ÷ 25 = 0.0400 s^{-1}
2) You should report the relative rate as a **ratio**.
   Divide by the **smallest** relative rate to get the rates as the smallest whole number ratio possible.
   0.0081 : 0.016 : 0.040 = **1 : 2 : 5**

Practice Questions

Q1 What is meant by the term 'reaction rate'?

Q2 What is the formula to find the gradient of a line?

Exam Question

Q1 Compounds X and Y react as in the equation below.

$$X + Y \rightarrow Z$$

From the graph on the right, work out the rate of reaction at 3 minutes.

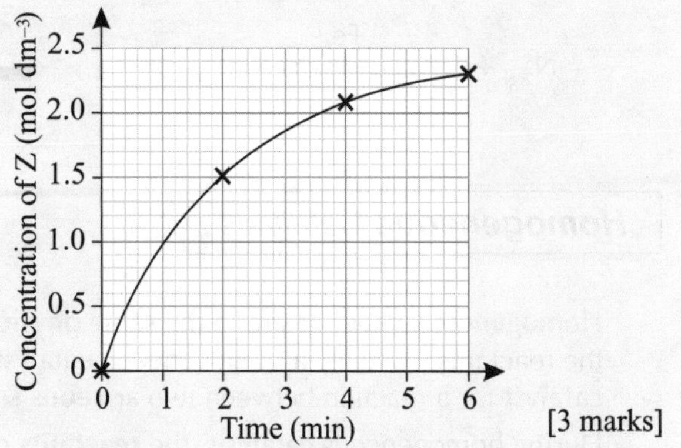

[3 marks]

Calculate your reaction to this page. Boredom? How dare you...

Plenty to learn on this page, but first things first — make sure you've got a ruler in the exam in case you need to draw a tangent to find the gradient from a curved graph. Then, make sure you know what you actually need to do with it. Finally, make sure you know how to deal with any calculations that might come your way, not forgetting any units.

Catalysts

Catalysts were tantalisingly mentioned a couple of pages ago — here's the full story...

Catalysts Increase the **Rate** of **Reactions**

You can use **catalysts** to make chemical reactions happen **faster**. Learn this definition:

> A **catalyst** increases the **rate** of a reaction by providing an **alternative reaction pathway** with a **lower activation energy**, so a greater proportion of **collisions** result in a **reaction**. The catalyst is **chemically unchanged** at the end of the reaction.

1) Catalysts are **great**. They **don't** get used up in reactions, so you only need a **tiny bit** of catalyst to catalyse a **huge** amount of stuff. They **do** take part in reactions, but they're **remade** at the end.
2) Catalysts are **very fussy** about which reactions they catalyse. Many will usually **only** work on a single reaction.

The 1985 Nobel Prize in Chemistry was awarded to Mr Tiddles for discovering catalysis.

Reaction Profiles Show Why **Catalysts** Work...

Heterogeneous Catalysis

A heterogeneous catalyst is one that is in a **different phase** from the reactants — i.e. in a different **physical state**. For example, in the Haber Process (see below), **gases** are passed over a **solid iron catalyst**.

The **reaction** happens on the **surface** of the **heterogeneous catalyst**. So, **increasing** the **surface area** of the catalyst increases the number of molecules that can **react** at the same time, **increasing the rate** of the reaction. The heterogeneous catalyst works by **lowering** the **activation energy** of the reaction — you can see this on a reaction profile diagram.

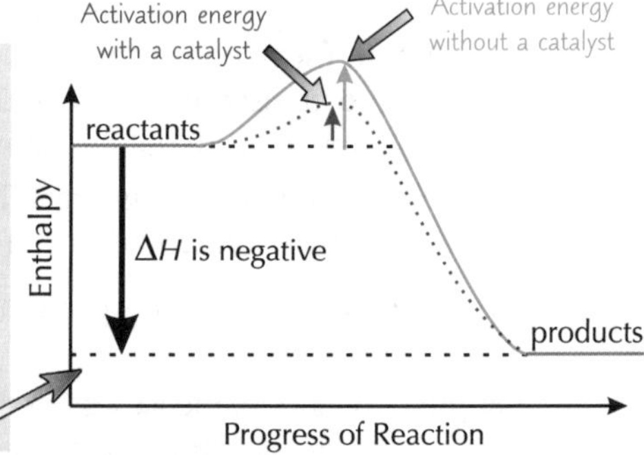

Solid heterogeneous catalysts can provide a **surface** for a reaction to take place on. Here's how it works —

1) **Reactant molecules** arrive at the **surface** and **bond** with the solid catalyst. This is called **adsorption**.
2) The bonds between the **reactant's** atoms are **weakened** and **break up**. This forms **radicals** — atoms or molecules with **unpaired** electrons. These radicals then **get together** and make **new molecules**.
3) The new molecules are then detached from the catalyst. This is called **desorption**.

This example shows you how an iron catalyst provides a surface for the atoms to react on in the **Haber Process** to produce ammonia.

$$N_{2(g)} + 3H_{2(g)} \xrightleftharpoons{Fe_{(s)}} NH_{3(g)}$$

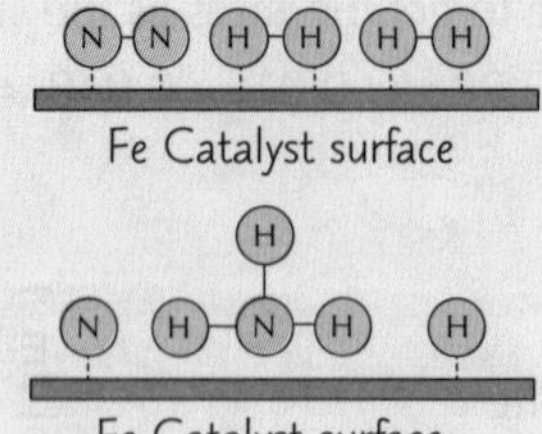

Adsorption of N_2 and H_2 to the catalyst.

Chemical reaction — NH_3 is formed.

Desorption of NH_3 from the catalyst.

Homogeneous Catalysis

Homogeneous catalysts are in the **same physical state** as the reactants. Usually a **homogeneous** catalyst is an **aqueous catalyst** for a reaction between two **aqueous solutions**.

During homogeneous catalysis, the **reactants** combine with the **catalyst** to make an **intermediate species**, which then reacts to form the **products** and **reform the catalyst**.

E' = the activation energy of the **first** step in the catalysed reaction.
E'' = the activation energy of the **second** step in the catalysed reaction.

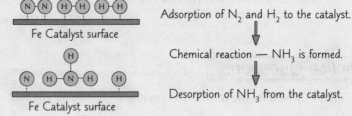

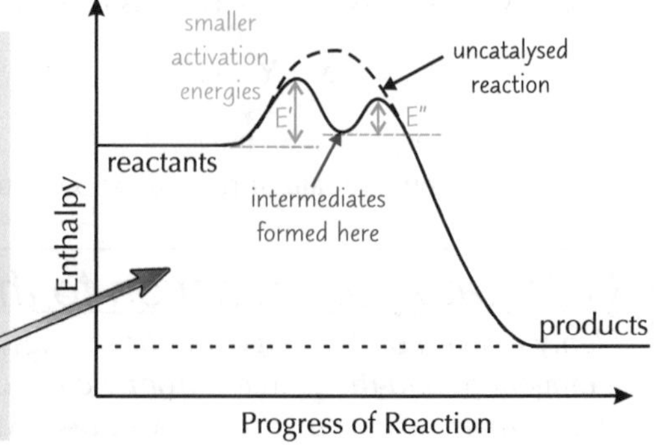

Catalysts

...as do **Maxwell-Boltzmann** Distributions

As you've seen in the graphs on the previous page, in both homogeneous and heterogeneous catalysis, the catalyst **lowers the activation energy**.
This means there are **more particles** with **enough energy** to react when they collide. This is shown by the Maxwell-Boltzmann distribution on the right.
So, in a certain amount of time, **more particles react**.

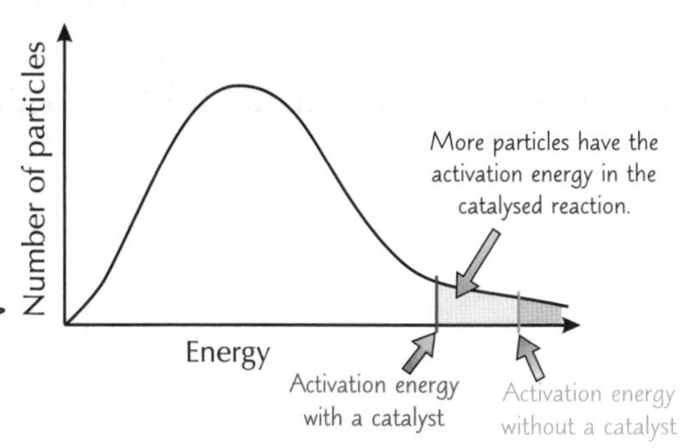

Catalysts *Have Economic Benefits*

Loads of industries rely on **catalysts**. They can dramatically lower production costs, give you more product in a shorter time and help make better products. Here are a few examples:

1) Iron is used as a catalyst in **ammonia** production. If it wasn't for the catalyst, the **temperature** would have to be raised loads to make the reaction happen **quick enough**. Not only would this be bad for the fuel bills, it'd **reduce the amount of ammonia** produced since the reaction is reversible, and exothermic in the direction of ammonia production.

See pages 120-121 for more on reversible reactions and changing conditions.

2) Using a catalyst can change the properties of a product to make it more useful, e.g. **poly(ethene)**.

	Made without a catalyst	Made with a catalyst (a Ziegler-Natta catalyst, to be precise)
Properties of poly(ethene)	less dense, less rigid	more dense, more rigid, higher melting point

Practice Questions

Q1 Explain what a catalyst is.

Q2 Explain what the difference between a heterogeneous and a homogeneous catalyst is.

Q3 Describe two reasons why catalysts are useful for industry.

Exam Question

Q1 Sulfuric acid is manufactured by the contact process. In one of the stages, sulfur dioxide gas is mixed with oxygen gas and converted into sulfur trioxide gas. A solid vanadium(V) oxide (V_2O_5) catalyst is used. The enthalpy change for the uncatalysed reaction is –197 kJ mol^{-1}.

a) Which of the following reaction profile diagrams is correct for the catalysed reaction? [1 mark]

A
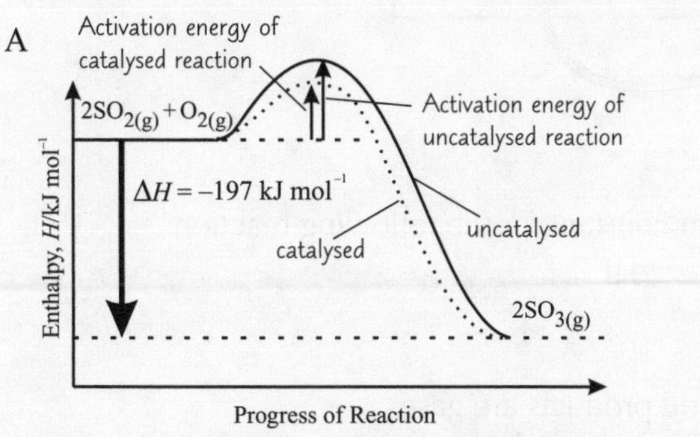

B
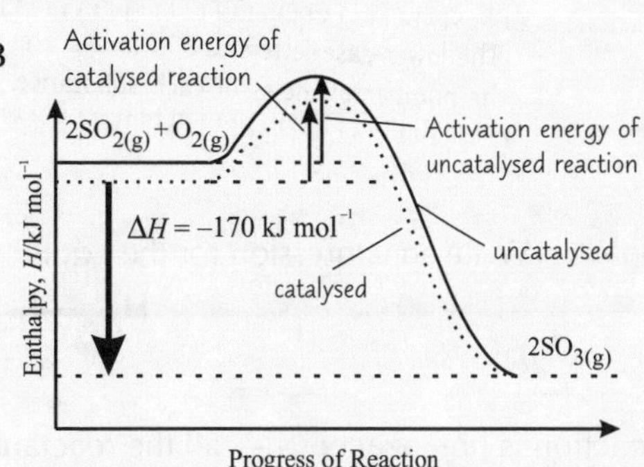

b) Describe how a catalyst works to increase the rate of the reaction. [3 marks]

c) Is the vanadium(V) oxide catalyst heterogeneous or homogeneous? Explain your answer. [1 mark]

Catalysts and walking past bad buskers — increased speed but no change...

Whatever you do, don't confuse the Maxwell-Boltzmann diagram for catalysts with the one for a temperature change. Catalysts lower the activation energy without changing the shape of the curve. BUT, the shape of the curve does change with temperature. Get these mixed up and you'll be the laughing stock of the Examiners' tea room.

Dynamic Equilibrium

There's a lot of to-ing and fro-ing on this page. Mind your head doesn't start spinning.

Reversible Reactions Can Reach *Dynamic Equilibrium*

1) Lots of chemical reactions are **reversible** — they go **both ways**. To show a reaction's reversible, you stick in a $\rightleftharpoons$. Here's an example:

$$H_{2(g)} + I_{2(g)} \rightleftharpoons 2HI_{(g)}$$

This reaction can go in **either direction** —

forwards $H_{2(g)} + I_{2(g)} \rightleftharpoons 2HI_{(g)}$ ...or **backwards** $2HI_{(g)} \rightleftharpoons H_{2(g)} + I_{2(g)}$

2) As the **reactants** get used up, the **forward** reaction **slows down** — and as more **product** is formed, the **reverse** reaction **speeds up**.
3) After a while, the forward reaction will be going at exactly the **same rate** as the backward reaction, so the amounts of reactants and products **won't be changing** any more — it'll seem like **nothing's happening**.
4) This is called **dynamic equilibrium**. At equilibrium the **concentrations** of **reactants** and **products** stay **constant**.
5) A **dynamic equilibrium** can only happen in a **closed system**. This just means nothing can get in or out.

Although it appeared that the Smiths were doing nothing, they were actually in a state of dynamic equilibrium.

K$_c$ is the *Equilibrium Constant*

The equilibrium constant, or K_c, gives you an idea of **how far** to the **left or right** the equilibrium is. It's calculated using the equilibrium concentrations of the reactants and products in a system.

In Chemistry, the word <u>system</u> is used to refer to a particular thing being studied.

Homogeneous Equilibria and *K*$_c$

1) A **homogeneous system** is a **system** in which everything is in the **same physical state**.
2) When you have a **homogeneous reaction** that's reached **dynamic equilibrium**, you can work out the **equilibrium constant**, K_c, using the concentrations of the products and reactants at equilibrium.
3) For homogeneous equilibria, all the products and reactants are included in the expression for K_c.

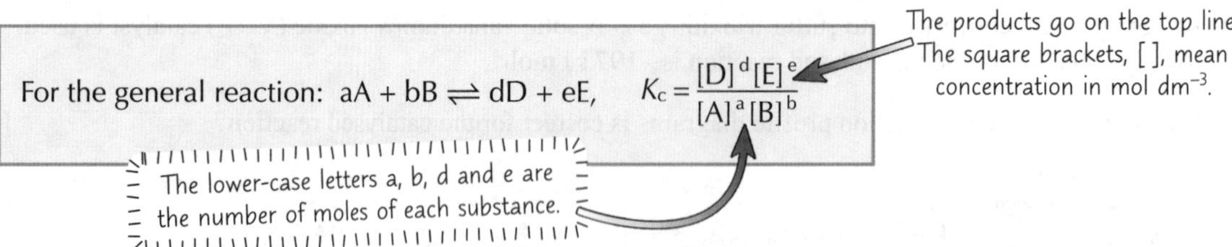

For the general reaction: $aA + bB \rightleftharpoons dD + eE$, $K_c = \frac{[D]^d[E]^e}{[A]^a[B]^b}$

The products go on the top line. The square brackets, [ ], mean concentration in mol dm^{-3}.

The lower-case letters a, b, d and e are the number of moles of each substance.

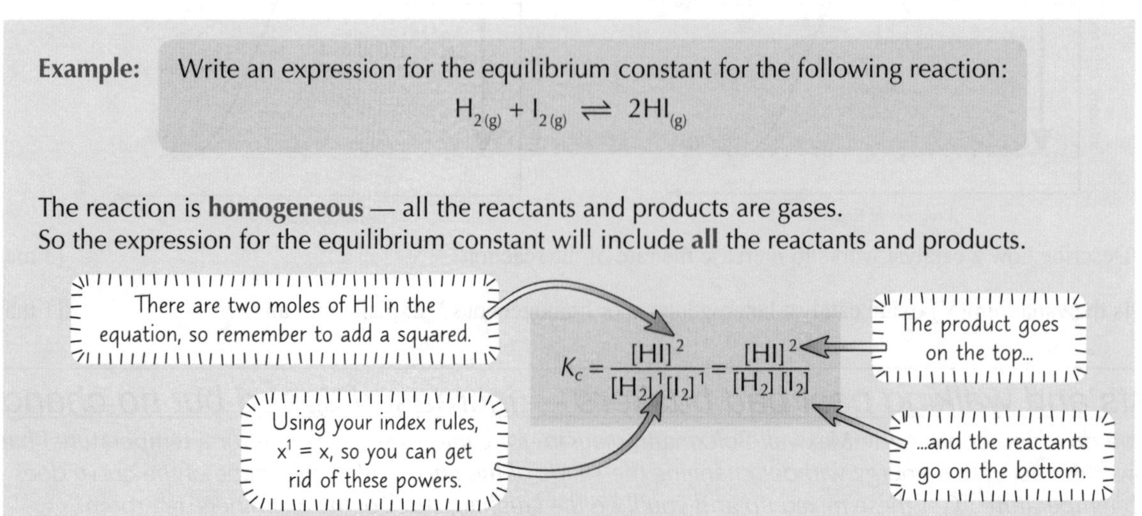

Example: Write an expression for the equilibrium constant for the following reaction:

$$H_{2(g)} + I_{2(g)} \rightleftharpoons 2HI_{(g)}$$

The reaction is **homogeneous** — all the reactants and products are gases.
So the expression for the equilibrium constant will include **all** the reactants and products.

$$K_c = \frac{[HI]^2}{[H_2]^1[I_2]^1} = \frac{[HI]^2}{[H_2][I_2]}$$

There are two moles of HI in the equation, so remember to add a squared.
Using your index rules, $x^1 = x$, so you can get rid of these powers.
The product goes on the top...
...and the reactants go on the bottom.

Dynamic Equilibrium

Heterogeneous Equilibria and K_c

1) In a **heterogeneous system**, **not everything's** in the same **physical state**.
2) Writing the expression for K_c for a **heterogeneous reaction** (a reaction where not all the reactants and products are in the same physical state) that's reached **dynamic equilibrium** can be a bit tricky.
3) Unlike with **homogeneous equilibria**, not everything is included in the expression for K_c.
4) You don't include **solids** or **pure liquids** in the expression for K_c when you're dealing with heterogeneous equilibria. This is because their concentrations **stay constant** throughout the reaction.

Example: Write an expression for the equilibrium constant for the following reaction:

$$H_2O_{(g)} + C_{(s)} \rightleftharpoons H_{2(g)} + CO_{(g)}$$

The reaction is **heterogeneous**, so don't include any solids or pure liquids in your expression for K_c.
In this reaction, carbon is a **solid** and everything else is a **gas**.
Therefore, **carbon** is the only thing you **exclude** from your expression for K_c.

$$K_c = \frac{[H_2]^1[CO]^1}{[H_2O]^1} = \frac{[H_2]\,[CO]}{[H_2O]}$$

Catalysts Don't Affect the Equilibrium Constant

You **don't** include **catalysts** in **expressions** for the **equilibrium constant**. Catalysts **don't affect** the equilibrium **concentrations** of the products or reactants — they just **speed up** the rate at which **dynamic equilibrium** is **reached**.

Practice Questions

Q1 Using an example, explain the term 'reversible reaction'.

Q2 What is a meant by a homogeneous system?

Q3 Write an expression for the equilibrium constant of the reaction, aA + bB $\rightleftharpoons$ dD + eE.

Q4 What shouldn't you include in the expression for K_c for a heterogeneous system at dynamic equilibrium?

Exam Questions

Q1 In the Haber Process, nitrogen and hydrogen gases react to form ammonia: $N_{2(g)} + 3H_{2(g)} \rightleftharpoons 2NH_{3(g)}$

a) At a certain point, the reaction reaches 'dynamic equilibrium'. Explain what is meant by this. [2 marks]

b) Write an expression for the equilibrium constant, K_c, for the Haber Process. [1 mark]

Q2 A student is investigating the equilibrium constant for the following reaction: $NH_{3(g)} + H_2O_{(l)} \rightleftharpoons NH_4^+{}_{(aq)} + OH^-{}_{(aq)}$

She states that the expression for the equilibrium constant, K_c, is: $K_c = \frac{[NH_3][H_2O]}{[NH_4^+][OH^-]}$.

Explain what mistakes the student has made in her expression for K_c. [2 marks]

Q3 Which of the reactions below can be represented by the following expression for the equilibrium constant? $K_c = [CO_2]$

A $C_{(s)} + O_{2(g)} \rightleftharpoons CO_{2(g)}$

B $CaCO_{3(s)} \rightleftharpoons CaO_{(s)} + CO_{2(g)}$

C $2NaOH_{(aq)} + CO_{2(g)} \rightleftharpoons Na_2CO_{3(aq)} + H_2O_{(l)}$

D $CH_{4(g)} + 2O_{2(g)} \rightleftharpoons CO_{2(g)} + 2H_2O_{(g)}$ [1 mark]

I'm constantly going on about equilibrium — that's what it feels like anyway...

Working out the expression for K_c for both homogeneous and heterogeneous systems is pretty straightforward once you've got the hang of it. If you've not quite got it yet go back through these two pages until it all makes perfect sense. Once you've done that, keep going. You're halfway through the topic already — just 2 pages to go. You lucky devil...

Le Chatelier's Principle

'Oh no, not another page on equilibria', I hear you cry... Fair enough really.

Le Chatelier's Principle Predicts what will Happen if Conditions are Changed

If you **change** the **concentration**, **pressure** or **temperature** of a reversible reaction, you tend to **alter** the **position of equilibrium**. This just means you'll end up with **different amounts** of reactants and products at equilibrium.

If the position of equilibrium moves to the **left**, you'll get more **reactants**.

$$H_{2(g)} + I_{2(g)} \rightleftharpoons 2HI_{(g)}$$

If the position of equilibrium moves to the **right**, you'll get more **products**.

$$H_{2(g)} + I_{2(g)} \rightleftharpoons 2HI_{(g)}$$

Le Chatelier's principle tells you how the **position of equilibrium** will change if a **condition changes**:

> If there's a change in **concentration**, **pressure** or **temperature**, the equilibrium will move to help **counteract** the change.

So, basically, if you **raise the temperature**, the position of equilibrium will shift to try to **cool things down**.
And, if you **raise the pressure or concentration**, the position of equilibrium will shift to try to **reduce it again**.

Here Are Some Handy Rules for Using Le Chatelier's Principle

You need to know how **temperature**, **concentration** and **pressure** affect equilibrium.
So, here goes...

Concentration

$$2SO_{2(g)} + O_{2(g)} \rightleftharpoons 2SO_{3(g)}$$

1) If you **increase** the **concentration** of a **reactant** (SO_2 or O_2), the equilibrium tries to **get rid** of the extra reactant. It does this by making **more product** (SO_3). So the equilibrium's shifted to the **right**.
2) If you **increase** the **concentration** of the **product** (SO_3), the equilibrium tries to remove the extra product. This makes the **reverse reaction** go faster. So the equilibrium shifts to the **left**.
3) **Decreasing** the concentrations has the **opposite effect**.

Pressure (this only affects gases)

$$2SO_{2(g)} + O_{2(g)} \rightleftharpoons 2SO_{3(g)}$$

There are 3 moles on the left, but only 2 on the right.
So, increasing the pressure shifts the equilibrium to the right.

1) **Increasing** the pressure shifts the equilibrium to the side with **fewer** gas molecules. This **reduces** the pressure.
2) **Decreasing** the pressure shifts the equilibrium to the side with **more** gas molecules. This **raises** the pressure again.

Temperature

1) **Increasing** the temperature means **adding heat**. The equilibrium shifts in the **endothermic (positive ΔH) direction** to absorb this heat.
2) **Decreasing** the temperature **removes heat**. The equilibrium shifts in the **exothermic (negative ΔH) direction** to try to replace the heat.
3) If the forward reaction's **endothermic**, the reverse reaction will be **exothermic**, and vice versa.

This reaction's exothermic in the forward direction (ΔH = –197 kJ mol^{-1}). If you increase the temperature, the equilibrium shifts to the left to absorb the extra heat.

Exothermic ⟹

$$2SO_{2(g)} + O_{2(g)} \rightleftharpoons 2SO_{3(g)}$$

⟸ Endothermic

Le Chatelier's Principle

*In **Industry**, the **Conditions** Chosen are a **Compromise***

In the exam, you may be asked to look at an **industrial process** and work out what **conditions** should be used to give the best **balance** between a **high rate** and a **high yield**. If you're asked to do this, you'll need to look at any **data** given, e.g. the **enthalpy change** of reaction, and use Le Chatelier's principle to work out what the **optimum conditions** are. Let's have a look at an example...

__Ethanol__ can be Formed From __Ethene__ and __Steam__

Mr and Mrs Le Chatelier celebrate another successful year in the principle business

1) The industrial production of **ethanol** is a good example of why Le Chatelier's principle is important in **real life**.
2) Ethanol is produced via a **reversible exothermic reaction** between **ethene** and **steam**:

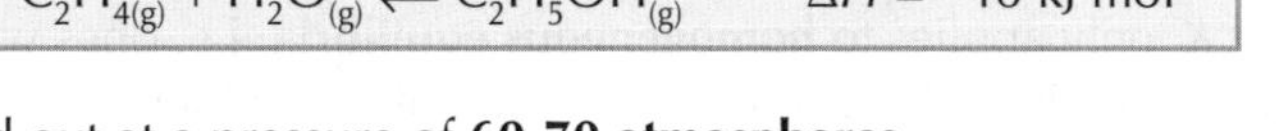

$$C_2H_{4(g)} + H_2O_{(g)} \rightleftharpoons C_2H_5OH_{(g)} \qquad \Delta H = -46\ \text{kJ mol}^{-1}$$

3) The reaction is carried out at a pressure of **60-70 atmospheres** and a temperature of **300 °C**, with a **phosphoric(V) acid** catalyst.

- Because it's an **exothermic reaction**, **lower** temperatures favour the forward reaction. This means **more** ethene and steam are converted to ethanol at lower temperatures — you get a better **yield**.
- But **lower temperatures** mean a **slower rate of reaction**. You'd be **daft** to try to get a **really high yield** of ethanol if it's going to take you 10 years. So the 300 °C is a **compromise** between **maximum yield** and **a faster reaction**.
- **Higher pressures** favour the **forward reaction,** so a pressure of **60-70 atmospheres** is used — **high pressure** moves the reaction to the side with **fewer molecules of gas. Increasing the pressure** also increases the **rate** of reaction.
- Cranking up the pressure as high as you can sounds like a great idea so far. But **high pressures** are **expensive** to produce. You need **stronger pipes** and **containers** to withstand high pressure. In this process, increasing the pressure can also cause **side reactions** to occur.
- So the **60-70 atmospheres** is a **compromise** between **maximum yield** and **expense**.

In the end, it all comes down to minimising costs.

Practice Questions

Q1 If the equilibrium moves to the right, do you get more products or reactants?

Q2 A reaction at equilibrium is endothermic in the forward direction.
What happens to the position of equilibrium as the temperature is increased?

Exam Questions

Q1 Nitrogen and oxygen gases were reacted together in a closed flask and allowed to reach equilibrium, with nitrogen monoxide being formed. The forward reaction is endothermic.

$$N_{2(g)} + O_{2(g)} \rightleftharpoons 2NO_{(g)}$$

a) Explain how the following changes would affect the position of equilibrium of the above reaction:

i) Pressure is increased. [1 mark]

ii) Temperature is reduced. [1 mark]

iii) Nitrogen monoxide is removed. [1 mark]

Q2 Explain why moderate reaction temperatures are a compromise for exothermic reactions. [2 marks]

If it looks like I'm not doing anything, I'm just being dynamic... honest...

Equilibria never do what you want them to do. They always oppose you. Be sure you know what happens to an equilibrium if you change the conditions. About pressure — if there's the same number of gas moles on each side of the equation, you can raise the pressure as high as you like and it won't make a difference to the position of equilibrium.

Calculations Involving K_c

The equilibrium constant is about to become a constant presence in your life — just you wait and see...

K_c is the Equilibrium Constant

You learnt on page 118 that K_c, the equilibrium constant, is calculated from the **ratio** of product concentration to reactant concentration. This means that if you know the **molar concentration** of each substance **at equilibrium**, you can work out K_c. A particular value of K_c will be constant for a given **temperature**.

For the general reaction $aA + bB \rightleftharpoons dD + eE$, $K_c = \frac{[D]^d[E]^e}{[A]^a[B]^b}$

The lower-case letters a, b, d and e are the relative mole ratios of each substance.

So for the reaction $H_{2(g)} + I_{2(g)} \rightleftharpoons 2HI_{(g)}$, $K_c = \frac{[HI]^2}{[H_2]^1[I_2]^1}$. This simplifies to $K_c = \frac{[HI]^2}{[H_2][I_2]}$.

1) Actually, this definition of K_c only applies to **homogeneous equilibria**, i.e. ones where all the products and reactants are in the **same phase**. If you've got more than one phase in there — a **heterogeneous equilibrium** — not everything is necessarily included in the expression for K_c.
2) You don't include **solids** or **pure liquids** in the expression for K_c when you're dealing with heterogeneous equilibria. This is because their concentrations **stay constant** throughout the reaction.

You Might Need to Work Out the Equilibrium Concentrations

You might have to figure out some of the **equilibrium concentrations** before you can find K_c:

Example: 0.20 moles of phosphorus(V) chloride decomposes at 600 K in a vessel of 5.00 dm³. The equilibrium mixture is found to contain 0.080 moles of chlorine. Write the expression for K_c and calculate its value, including units. $PCl_{5(g)} \rightleftharpoons PCl_{3(g)} + Cl_{2(g)}$

First find out how many moles of PCl_5 and PCl_3 there are at equilibrium:

The **equation** tells you that when **1 mole of PCl_5** decomposes, **1 mole of PCl_3** and **1 mole of Cl_2** are formed. So if 0.080 moles of chlorine are produced at equilibrium, then there will be **0.080 moles** of PCl_3 as well. 0.080 moles of PCl_5 must have decomposed, so there will be (0.20 – 0.080 =) **0.12 moles** left.

Divide each number of moles by the volume of the flask to give the molar concentrations:

$[PCl_3] = [Cl_2] = 0.08 \div 5.00 = \mathbf{0.016\ mol\ dm^{-3}}$ $[PCl_5] = 0.12 \div 5.00 = \mathbf{0.024\ mol\ dm^{-3}}$

Put the concentrations in the expression for K_c and calculate it:

$$K_c = \frac{[PCl_3][Cl_2]}{[PCl_5]} = \frac{[0.016][0.016]}{[0.024]} = \mathbf{0.011}$$

Now find the units of K_c: $K_c = \frac{\cancel{(mol\ dm^{-3})}(mol\ dm^{-3})}{\cancel{(mol\ dm^{-3})}} = \mathbf{mol\ dm^{-3}}$ So $K_c = \mathbf{0.011\ mol\ dm^{-3}}$

K_c can be used to Find Concentrations in an Equilibrium Mixture

Example: When the reaction between ethanoic acid and ethanol was allowed to reach equilibrium at 25 °C, it was found that the equilibrium mixture contained 2.0 mol dm⁻³ ethanoic acid and 3.5 mol dm⁻³ ethanol. K_c of the equilibrium is 4.0 at 25 °C. What are the concentrations of the other components?

$$CH_3COOH_{(l)} + C_2H_5OH_{(l)} \rightleftharpoons CH_3COOC_2H_{5(l)} + H_2O_{(l)}$$

Put all the values you know in the K_c expression: $K_c = \frac{[CH_3COOC_2H_5][H_2O]}{[CH_3COOH][C_2H_5OH]} \Rightarrow 4.0 = \frac{[CH_3COOC_2H_5][H_2O]}{2.0 \times 3.5}$

Rearranging this gives: $[CH_3COOC_2H_5][H_2O] = 4.0 \times 2.0 \times 3.5 = 28.0$

From the equation, you know that an equal number of moles of $CH_3COOC_2H_5$ and H_2O will form, so:

$$[CH_3COOC_2H_5] = [H_2O] = \sqrt{28} = \mathbf{5.3\ mol\ dm^{-3}}$$

Calculations Involving K_c

The Equilibrium Constant Can Be Calculated from Experimental Data

A simple experiment that can be carried out in the laboratory involves the following reaction: $Fe^{2+}_{(aq)} + Ag^{+}_{(aq)} \rightleftharpoons Fe^{3+}_{(aq)} + Ag_{(s)}$

1) If you leave a mixture of iron(II) sulfate solution and silver nitrate solution in a stoppered flask at 298 K, the reaction above will eventually reach **equilibrium**.

The silver nitrate provides the Ag^+ ions and the iron(II) sulfate provides the Fe^{2+} ions.

2) You can then take samples of the equilibrium mixture and **titrate** them — this will let you work out the **equilibrium concentration** of the **Fe^{2+} ions** (there's more on redox titrations on pages 162-167).
Normally, if you change the amounts involved in an equilibrium, the position of equilibrium changes (see page 120).
However, this reaction is really slow to reach equilibrium, so carrying out the titration doesn't affect the equilibrium enough to matter.
3) From this, you can work out the equilibrium concentrations of the other components, and so K_c.

Example: 500 cm³ of 0.100 mol dm⁻³ iron(II) sulfate solution and 500 cm³ of 0.100 mol dm⁻³ silver nitrate solution are placed in a stoppered flask and allowed to reach equilibrium. It's found that the equilibrium concentration of Fe^{2+} is 0.0439 mol dm⁻³ under s.t.p.. Calculate K_c for this reaction at s.t.p..

The reaction equation (see above) tells you 1 mole of Fe^{2+} reacts with 1 mole of Ag^+ to form 1 mole of Fe^{3+} and 1 mole of Ag. In this particular reaction, **solid** silver is formed. The concentration of a solid is **constant**, so you **don't** need to include it in the expression for K_c.

The **starting concentrations** of Ag^+ and Fe^{2+} are the same and equal to **0.0500 mol dm⁻³**.
The **equilibrium concentration** of **Ag^+** will be the same as Fe^{2+}, i.e. **0.0439 mol dm⁻³**.
The **equilibrium concentration** of **Fe^{3+}** will be 0.0500 – 0.0439 = **0.0061 mol dm⁻³**.

500 cm³ of each solution is used, so you have a total of 1000 cm³ of solution. The concentration of each reactant is therefore halved since you have the same number of moles of each reactant, but in double the volume.

$$\text{So } K_c = \frac{[Fe^{3+}]}{[Fe^{2+}][Ag^+]} = \frac{0.0061}{0.0439 \times 0.0439} = 3.17$$

$$\text{The units of } K_c \text{ are: } \frac{\cancel{\text{mol dm}^{-3}}}{(\cancel{\text{mol dm}^{-3}})(\text{mol dm}^{-3})} = \text{mol}^{-1}\,\text{dm}^3$$

At s.t.p., K_c = **3.17 mol⁻¹ dm³**

Practice Questions

Q1 What do the square brackets, [ ], represent in a K_c expression?

Q2 Write the expression for K_c for the following equilibrium: $Cl_{2(g)} + PCl_{3(g)} \rightleftharpoons PCl_{5(g)}$. What are the units of K_c?

Exam Questions

Q1 At 723 K, the equilibrium constant for the reaction $H_{2(g)} + Cl_{2(g)} \rightleftharpoons 2HCl_{(g)}$ is 60.
The equilibrium concentrations of H_2 and Cl_2 are 2.0 mol dm⁻³ and 0.30 mol dm⁻³ respectively.
What is the molar concentration of HCl at equilibrium?

A 0.10 mol dm⁻³ **B** 0.010 mol dm⁻³ **C** 6.0 mol dm⁻³ **D** 36 mol dm⁻³ [1 mark]

Q2 Copper is shaken with silver nitrate solution to form the following equilibrium. $Cu_{(s)} + 2Ag^{+}_{(aq)} \rightleftharpoons Cu^{2+}_{(aq)} + 2Ag_{(s)}$
At a certain temperature, there are 0.431 mol dm⁻³ Ag^+ and 0.193 mol dm⁻³ Cu^{2+} at equilibrium. Calculate K_c, giving its units. [3 marks]

Q3 Nitrogen dioxide dissociates according to the equation $2NO_{2(g)} \rightleftharpoons 2NO_{(g)} + O_{2(g)}$.
When 42.5 g of nitrogen dioxide were heated in a vessel of volume 22.8 dm³ at 500 °C, 14.1 g of oxygen were found in the equilibrium mixture.

a) Calculate: i) the number of moles of nitrogen dioxide originally. [1 mark]

ii) the number of moles of each gas in the equilibrium mixture. [3 marks]

b) Write an expression for K_c for this reaction. Calculate the value for K_c at 500 °C and give its units. [5 marks]

As far as I'm concerned, equilibria are a constant pain in the *@?!

K_c is there to be calculated, so calculate it you must — and the only way to get good at it is to practise. And then practise again, just to be on the safe side. Now now, don't start moaning — you'll thank me if it comes up in the exam.

Gas Equilibria

It's easier to talk about gases in terms of their pressures rather than their molar concentrations. If you want to do this, you need a slightly different equilibrium constant — it's called K_p (but I'm afraid it's got nothing to do with peanuts).

The ***Total Pressure*** *is* ***Equal*** *to the* ***Sum*** *of the* ***Partial Pressures***

In a mixture of gases, each individual gas exerts its own pressure — this is called its **partial pressure**.

The **total pressure** of a gas mixture is the **sum** of all the **partial pressures** of the individual gases.

You might have to put this fact to use in pressure calculations:

Example: When 3.0 moles of the gas PCl_5 is heated, it decomposes into PCl_3 and Cl_2: $PCl_{5(g)} \rightleftharpoons PCl_{3(g)} + Cl_{2(g)}$
In a sealed vessel at 500 K, the equilibrium mixture contains chlorine with a partial pressure of 2.6 atm. If the total pressure of the mixture is 7.0 atm, what is the partial pressure of PCl_5?

From the equation you know that PCl_3 and Cl_2 are produced in equal amounts, so the partial pressures of these two gases are the **same** at equilibrium — they're both 2.6 atm.

Total pressure = $p(PCl_5) + p(PCl_3) + p(Cl_2)$

$7.0 = p(PCl_5) + 2.6 + 2.6$

So the partial pressure of PCl_5 = 7.0 – 2.6 – 2.6 = **1.8 atm**

p(X) just means partial pressure of X. You might see this notation used without brackets, but it means the same thing.

Partial Pressures *can be Worked Out from* ***Mole Fractions***

A '**mole fraction**' is just the **proportion** of a gas mixture that is a particular gas. So if you've got four moles of gas in total, and two of them are gas A, the mole fraction of gas A is ½. There are **two formulae** you've got to know:

1) Mole fraction of a gas in a mixture = $\dfrac{\textbf{number of moles of gas}}{\textbf{total number of moles of gas in the mixture}}$
2) Partial pressure of a gas = **mole fraction of gas × total pressure of the mixture**

Example: When 3.00 mol of PCl_5 is heated in a sealed vessel, the equilibrium mixture contains 1.75 mol of chlorine. If the total pressure of the mixture is 7.0 atm, what is the partial pressure of PCl_5?

From the equation above, PCl_3 and Cl_2 are produced in equal amounts, so there'll be **1.75 moles** of PCl_3 too.
1.75 moles of PCl_5 must have decomposed so (3.00 – 1.75 =) **1.25 moles** of PCl_5 must be left at equilibrium.
This means that the total number of moles of gas at equilibrium = 1.75 + 1.75 + 1.25 = **4.75**

So the mole fraction of $PCl_5 = \dfrac{1.25}{4.75} = \mathbf{0.263...}$

The partial pressure of PCl_5 = mole fraction × total pressure = 0.263... × 7.0 = **1.8 atm**

The ***Equilibrium Constant K_p*** *is Calculated from* ***Partial Pressures***

K_p is an equilibrium constant that you can calculate dealing with equilibria involving **gases**.
The expression for K_p is just like the one for K_c — except you use partial pressures instead of concentrations.

For the equilibrium $aA_{(g)} + bB_{(g)} \rightleftharpoons dD_{(g)} + eE_{(g)}$: $K_p = \dfrac{p(D)^d p(E)^e}{p(A)^a p(B)^b}$

There are no square brackets because they're partial pressures, not molar concentrations.

To **calculate K_p**, you just have to put the partial pressures in the expression. You work out the **units** like you did for K_c.

Example: Calculate K_p for the decomposition of PCl_5 gas at 500 K: $PCl_{5(g)} \rightleftharpoons PCl_{3(g)} + Cl_{2(g)}$
The partial pressures of each gas are: $p(PCl_5)$ = 1.8 atm, $p(PCl_3)$ = 2.6 atm, $p(Cl_2)$ = 2.6 atm

$$K_p = \frac{p(Cl_2)p(PCl_3)}{p(PCl_5)} = \frac{2.6 \times 2.6}{1.8} = 3.755... = \mathbf{3.8} \text{ (2 s.f.)}$$

The units for K_p are worked out by putting the units into the expression instead of the numbers, and cancelling (like for K_c): $K_p = \dfrac{\cancel{atm} \times atm}{\cancel{atm}}$ = atm. So, K_p = **3.8 atm**

Gas Equilibria

K_p can be Used to Find **Partial Pressures**

You might be given the value of K_p and have to use it to calculate **equilibrium partial pressures.**

Example: An equilibrium exists between ethanoic acid monomers, CH_3COOH, and dimers, $(CH_3COOH)_2$. At 160 °C, K_p for the reaction $(CH_3COOH)_{2(g)} \rightleftharpoons 2CH_3COOH_{(g)}$ is 1.78 atm. At this temperature the partial pressure of the dimer, $(CH_3COOH)_2$, is 0.281 atm. Calculate the partial pressure of the monomer in this equilibrium and state the total pressure exerted by the equilibrium mixture.

First, use the chemical equilibrium to write an expression for K_p: $K_p = \frac{p(CH_3COOH)^2}{p((CH_3COOH)_2)}$

This rearranges to give: $p(CH_3COOH)^2 = K_p \times p((CH_3COOH)_2) = 1.78 \times 0.281 = 0.500...$

$p(CH_3COOH) = \sqrt{0.500...} = 0.707...$ atm

So the total pressure of the equilibrium mixture = 0.281 + 0.707... = **0.988 atm**

Add the two partial pressures together to get the total pressure.

K_p for **Heterogeneous** Equilibria Still **Only Includes Gases**

You met the idea of homogeneous and heterogeneous equilibria on pages 118 and 119. Up until now we've only thought about K_p expressions for **homogeneous equilibria.** If you're writing an expression for K_p for a **heterogeneous equilibrium**, only include **gases.**

Example: Write an expression for K_p for the following reaction: $NH_4HS_{(s)} \rightleftharpoons NH_{3(g)} + H_2S_{(g)}$.

The equilibrium is **heterogeneous** — a solid decomposes to form two gases. Solids don't get included in K_p, so $K_p = p(NH_3)\,p(H_2S)$.

There's no bottom line as the reactant is a solid.

Practice Questions

Q1 What is meant by partial pressure?

Q2 How do you work out the mole fraction of a gas?

Q3 Write the expression for K_p for the following equilibrium: $NH_4HS_{(g)} \rightleftharpoons NH_{3(g)} + H_2S_{(g)}$

Exam Questions

Q1 At high temperatures, SO_2Cl_2 dissociates according to the equation $SO_2Cl_{2(g)} \rightleftharpoons SO_{2(g)} + Cl_{2(g)}$. When 1.50 moles of SO_2Cl_2 dissociates at 700 K, the equilibrium mixture contains SO_2 with a partial pressure of 0.594 atm. The mixture has a total pressure of 1.39 atm.

a) Write an expression for K_p for this reaction. [1 mark]

b) Calculate the partial pressure of Cl_2 and the partial pressure of SO_2Cl_2 in the equilibrium mixture. [2 marks]

c) Calculate a value for K_p for this reaction and give its units. [2 marks]

Q2 When nitric oxide and oxygen were mixed in a 2:1 mole ratio at a constant temperature in a sealed flask, an equilibrium was set up according to the equation: $2NO_{(g)} + O_{2(g)} \rightleftharpoons 2NO_{2(g)}$. The partial pressure of the nitric oxide (NO) at equilibrium was 0.36 atm. The total pressure in the flask was 0.98 atm.

a) Deduce the partial pressure of oxygen in the equilibrium mixture. [1 mark]

b) Calculate the partial pressure of nitrogen dioxide in the equilibrium mixture. [1 mark]

c) Write an expression for the equilibrium constant, K_p, for this reaction and calculate its value at this temperature. State its units. [3 marks]

I'm rather partial to a few pressure calculations — and a chocolate biscuit...

Partial pressures are like concentrations for gases. The more of a substance you've got in a solution, the higher the concentration, and the more of a gas you've got in a container, the higher the partial pressure. It's all to do with how many molecules are crashing into the sides. With gases though, you've got to keep the lid on tight or they'll escape.

Le Chatelier's Principle and Equilibrium Constants

You should already know that changing conditions can change the position of the equilibrium. That's great, but you also need to be able to predict what will happen to the equilibrium constant when you change conditions.

If Conditions Change the Position of Equilibrium Will Move

1) You learnt on page 118 that when a reversible reaction reaches **dynamic equilibrium**, the forward reaction will be going at exactly the **same rate** as the backward reaction, so the amounts of reactants and products **won't be changing** any more. The **concentrations** of **reactants** and **products** stay **constant**.
2) If you **change** the **concentration**, **pressure** or **temperature** of a reversible reaction, you're going to **alter** the **position of equilibrium**. This just means you'll end up with **different amounts** of reactants and products at equilibrium.
3) If the change causes **more product** to form, then you say that the equilibrium shifts to the **right**. If **less product** forms, then the equilibrium has shifted to the **left**.
4) You also met Le Chatelier's principle on pages 120-121, which lets you predict how the **position of equilibrium** will change if a **condition changes**. Here it is again:

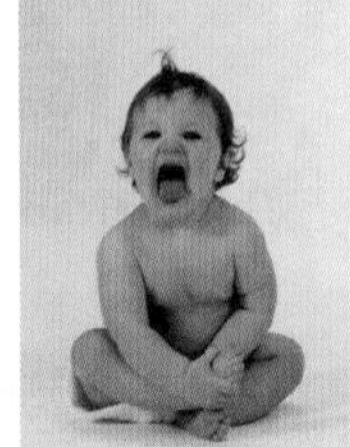

The removal of his dummy was a change that Maxwell always opposed.

> If there's a change in **concentration, pressure** or **temperature**, the equilibrium will move to help **counteract** the change.

5) So, basically, if you **raise the temperature**, the position of equilibrium will shift to try to **cool things down.** And if you **raise the pressure or concentration**, the position of equilibrium will shift to try to **reduce it again.**
6) The **size** of the equilibrium constant tells you where the equilibrium lies. The **greater** the value of K_c or K_p, the further to the **right** the equilibrium lies. **Smaller** values of K_c and K_p mean the equilibrium lies further to the **left.**

Temperature Changes Alter the Equilibrium Constant

1) From Le Chatelier's principle, you know that an **increase** in temperature causes more of the product of an **endothermic** reaction to form so that the extra heat is absorbed. Le Chatelier also states that a **decrease** in temperature causes more of the product of an **exothermic** reaction to form.
2) The equilibrium constant for a reaction depends on the **temperature**. Changing the temperature alters the position of equilibrium and the **value** of the equilibrium constant.

Example: The reaction below is exothermic in the forward direction. If you increase the temperature, the equilibrium shifts to the left to absorb the extra heat. What happens to K_p?

Exothermic ⟶

$$2SO_{2(g)} + O_{2(g)} \rightleftharpoons 2SO_{3(g)} \quad \Delta H = -197 \text{ kJ mol}^{-1}$$

⟵ Endothermic

An exothermic reaction releases heat and has a negative ΔH. An endothermic reaction absorbs heat and has a positive ΔH.

If the equilibrium shifts to the left, then less product will form. By looking at the expression for the equilibrium constant, you can see that if there's less product, the value of K_p will decrease.

$$K_p = \frac{p(SO_3)^2}{p(SO_2)^2 p(O_2)}$$

There's less product and more reactant, so the number on the top gets smaller and the number on the bottom gets bigger. This means K_p must have decreased.

This reaction is between gases, so it's easiest to use K_p, but it's exactly the same for K_c and the other equilibrium constants you'll meet in this course.

3) The general rule for what happens to an equilibrium constant when you change the **temperature** of a reaction is that:

> - If changing the temperature causes **less product** to form, the equilibrium moves to the **left**, and the equilibrium constant **decreases**.
> - If changing the temperature causes **more product** to form, the equilibrium moves to the **right**, and the equilibrium constant **increases**.

Le Chatelier's Principle and Equilibrium Constants

Concentration and **Pressure** Changes **Don't** Affect the Equilibrium Constant

Concentration

The value of the **equilibrium constant** is **fixed** at a given temperature. So if the concentration of one thing in the equilibrium mixture **changes** then the concentrations of the others must change to keep the value of K_c the same.

E.g. $CH_3COOH_{(l)} + C_2H_5OH_{(l)} \rightleftharpoons CH_3COOC_2H_{5(l)} + H_2O_{(l)}$

If you **increase** the concentration of **CH_3COOH** then the equilibrium will move to the **right** to get rid of the extra CH_3COOH — so more $CH_3COOC_2H_5$ and H_2O are produced. This keeps the **equilibrium constant** the same.

Pressure

Increasing the **total pressure** increases the **partial pressures** (or concentration) of each of the products and reactants. The equilibrium shifts to the side with **fewer moles** of gas to decrease the pressure. The overall effect is that K_p and K_c are **unchanged.**

E.g. $2SO_{2(g)} + O_{2(g)} \rightleftharpoons 2SO_{3(g)}$

There are 3 moles on the left, but only 2 on the right. So an **increase in pressure** would shift the equilibrium to the **right**. The equilibrium constant however doesn't change.

So, to summarise, concentration and pressure **don't** affect the **values** of K_c or K_p. Changes to concentration and pressure **do** change the **amounts** of products and reactants present at equilibrium, but the **ratio** of reactants to products stays the same (leaving K_c or K_p unchanged). Changes in **temperature** not only alter the **amounts** of products and reactants present at equilibrium, but also **change** the **value** of the equilibrium constants.

Catalysts have **NO EFFECT** on the **position of equilibrium**, so don't affect the value of K_c (or K_p). They **can't** increase **yield** — but they **do** mean equilibrium is approached **faster**.

Practice Questions

Q1 If you raise the temperature of a reversible reaction, in which direction will the reaction move?

Q2 Does temperature change affect the equilibrium constant?

Q3 Why doesn't concentration affect the equilibrium constant?

Exam Questions

Q1 At temperature T_1, the equilibrium constant K_c for the following reaction is 0.67 mol^{-1} dm^3.

$N_{2(g)} + 3H_{2(g)} \rightleftharpoons 2NH_{3(g)}$ $\Delta H = -92$ kJ mol^{-1}

a) When equilibrium was established at a different temperature, T_2, the value of K_c increased. State which of T_1 or T_2 is the lower temperature and explain why. [3 marks]

b) The experiment was repeated exactly the same in all respects at T_1, except a flask of smaller volume was used. How would this change affect the yield of ammonia and the value of K_c? [2 marks]

Q2 The reaction between methane and steam is used to produce hydrogen. The forward reaction is endothermic.

$CH_{4(g)} + H_2O_{(g)} \rightleftharpoons CO_{(g)} + 3H_{2(g)}$

a) Write an equation for K_p for this reaction. [1 mark]

b) Which of the following will cause the value of K_p to increase?

A Increasing the temperature. **B** Using a catalyst.

C Decreasing the pressure. **D** Decreasing the temperature. [1 mark]

The performers at the equilibrium concert were unaffected by pressure...

Predicting how the equilibrium position shifts if the conditions change isn't always simple. E.g. if you increase the pressure and temperature of the reaction between SO_2 and O_2 (see the last two pages), the increase in pressure would want to shift the equilibrium to the right but the increase in temperature would want to push it to the left. Tricky...

Acids and Bases

The scientific definition of an acid has changed over time — originally, the word acid just meant something that tasted sour. But, in 1923, Johannes Nicolaus Brønsted and Martin Lowry came along and refined the definition.

An Acid **Releases** Protons — a Base **Accepts** Protons

Brønsted-Lowry acids are **proton donors** — they release **hydrogen ions** (H^+) when they're mixed with water. You never get H^+ ions by themselves in water though — they're always combined with H_2O to form **hydroxonium ions,** H_3O^+.

$$HA_{(aq)} + H_2O_{(l)} \rightarrow H_3O^+_{(aq)} + A^-_{(aq)}$$

Brønsted-Lowry bases are **proton acceptors**. When they're in solution, they grab **hydrogen ions** from water molecules.

$$B_{(aq)} + H_2O_{(l)} \rightarrow BH^+_{(aq)} + OH^-_{(aq)}$$

HA is any old acid and B is just a random base.

Acids and Bases can be **Strong** or **Weak**

1) **Strong acids dissociate** (or ionise) **almost completely** in water — **nearly all** the H^+ ions will be released. **Hydrochloric acid** is a strong acid:

$$HCl \rightarrow H^+ + Cl^-$$

Strong bases (like sodium hydroxide) **dissociate almost completely** in water too:

$$NaOH \rightarrow Na^+ + OH^-$$

These are really both reversible reactions, but the equilibrium lies extremely far to the right.

2) **Weak acids** (e.g. ethanoic acid) dissociate only very **slightly** in water — so only small numbers of H^+ ions are formed. An **equilibrium** is set up which lies well over to the **left**:

$$CH_3COOH \rightleftharpoons CH_3COO^- + H^+$$

Weak bases (such as ammonia) **only slightly protonate** in water. Just like with weak acids, the equilibrium lies well over to the **left**:

$$NH_3 + H_2O \rightleftharpoons NH_4^+ + OH^-$$

Acids and Bases form **Conjugate Pairs**

1) Acids **can't** just throw away their protons — they can only get rid of them if there's a **base** to accept them. In this reaction the **acid**, HA, **transfers** a proton to the **base**, B:

$$HA_{(aq)} + B_{(aq)} \rightleftharpoons BH^+_{(aq)} + A^-_{(aq)}$$

2) It's an **equilibrium**, so if you add more **HA** or **B**, the position of equilibrium moves to the **right**. But if you add more BH^+ or A^-, the equilibrium will move to the **left**. This is all down to **Le Chatelier's principle** (see page 120).
3) Conjugate pairs are species that are linked by the **transfer** of a **proton**. They're always on opposite sides of the reaction equation.
4) The species that has **lost** a proton is the **conjugate base** and the species that has **gained** a proton is the **conjugate acid**. For example...

A species is just any type of chemical — it could be an atom, a molecule, an ion...

- When an acid's added to water, the equilibrium shown on the right is set up.
- In the **forward reaction**, HA acts as an **acid** as it **donates** a proton. In the **reverse reaction**, A^- acts as a **base** and **accepts** a proton from the H_3O^+ ion to form HA.
- HA and A^- are called a **conjugate pair** — HA is the **conjugate acid** of A^- and A^- is the **conjugate base** of the acid, HA. H_2O and H_3O^+ are a conjugate pair too.
- The acid and base of a conjugate pair are linked by an H^+, e.g. $HA \rightleftharpoons H^+ + A^-$ or this: $H^+ + H_2O \rightleftharpoons H_3O^+$

$$\underset{\text{acid}}{HA} + \underset{\text{base}}{H_2O} \rightleftharpoons \underset{\text{acid}}{H_3O^+} + \underset{\text{base}}{A^-}$$

(conjugate pair: H_2O / H_3O^+; conjugate pair: HA / A^-)

Here's the equilibrium for aqueous HCl. Cl^- is the conjugate base of $HCl_{(aq)}$.

$$\underset{\text{acid}}{HCl_{(aq)}} + \underset{\text{base}}{H_2O_{(l)}} \rightleftharpoons \underset{\text{acid}}{H_3O^+_{(aq)}} + \underset{\text{base}}{Cl^-_{(aq)}}$$

(conjugate pair: H_2O / H_3O^+; conjugate pair: HCl / Cl^-)

- An equilibrium with **conjugate pairs** is also set up when a **base** dissolves in water.
- The base, B, takes a proton from the water to form BH^+ — so B is the **conjugate base** of BH^+, and BH^+ is the **conjugate acid** of B. H_2O and OH^- also form a **conjugate pair**.

$$\underset{\text{base}}{B} + \underset{\text{acid}}{H_2O} \rightleftharpoons \underset{\text{base}}{OH^-} + \underset{\text{acid}}{BH^+}$$

(conjugate pair: H_2O / OH^-; conjugate pair: B / BH^+)

Acids and Bases

Acids and Bases React in **Neutralisation Reactions**

1) When **acids** and **bases** react together, a salt and water are produced:

Example: The reaction of hydrochloric acid and sodium hydroxide.

$$\underset{\text{acid}}{HCl_{(aq)}} + \underset{\text{base}}{NaOH_{(aq)}} \rightarrow \underset{\text{water}}{H_2O_{(l)}} + \underset{\text{salt}}{NaCl_{(aq)}}$$

2) If the concentration of H^+ ions from the acid is equal to the concentration of OH^- ions from the base, then a **neutral solution** is produced — this is one where $[H^+] = [OH^-]$. All of the H^+ ions from the acid and the OH^- ions from the base react to form water.

If $[H^+]$ is greater than $[OH^-]$ the solution is acidic, and if $[OH^-]$ is greater than $[H^+]$ the solution is basic (or alkaline).

3) There's a **change** in **enthalpy** when **neutralisation** reactions happen — the enthalpy change of **neutralisation**.

The **standard enthalpy change of neutralisation** is the enthalpy change when solutions of an **acid** and a **base** react together, under standard conditions, to produce **1 mole of water**.

Neutralisation reactions are always exothermic, so enthalpy changes of neutralisation are always negative.

4) As you saw on the last page, **weak acids** and **weak bases** only dissociate slightly in solution — it's a **reversible reaction**. When they're involved in neutralisation reactions, their H^+ ions (for acids) or OH^- ions (for bases) get used up quickly, as there are only a **few** of them in solution. The acid or base is therefore **constantly dissociating more** to replace the H^+/OH^- ions in solution and maintain the equilibrium (see page 120 for more on concentration and equilibrium). This requires enthalpy, so the standard enthalpy change of neutralisation for weak acids and weak bases includes **enthalpy** to do with the **reaction** between H^+ and OH^- **ions**, and enthalpy to do with **dissociation**. The enthalpy of dissociation varies, depending on the acid and base involved, so the standard enthalpy change of neutralisation for reactions involving weak acids or weak bases **varies**.

5) On the last page, you also saw that **strong acids** and **strong bases** fully dissociate in solution. When they react together in neutralisation reactions, there's **no dissociation enthalpy** for the acid or base — just **enthalpy** for the **reaction** of the H^+ and OH^- ions. Therefore, since this reaction is always the same, the standard enthalpy of neutralisation is **very similar** for all the reactions of strong acids with strong bases.

$$H^+_{(aq)} + OH^-_{(aq)} \rightarrow H_2O_{(l)}$$

Practice Questions

Q1 Give the Brønsted-Lowry definitions of an acid and a base.

Q2 Give the definition of: a) a strong acid, b) a weak acid.

Q3 Write the equilibrium for hydrochloric acid dissolving in water and identify the conjugate pairs.

Q4 What is a neutral substance?

Exam Questions

Q1 Hydrocyanic acid, $HCN_{(aq)}$, is a weak acid with a faint smell of bitter almonds. It is extremely poisonous.

a) Write the equation for the equilibrium set up when it dissolves in water. [1 mark]

b) What can you say about the position of this equilibrium? Explain your answer. [2 marks]

c) What is the conjugate base of this acid? [1 mark]

Q2 A student is investigating the standard enthalpy change of neutralisation of some acid/base reactions.

a) Define the standard enthalpy change of neutralisation. [2 marks]

b) The student knows that the standard enthalpy change of neutralisation for the reaction of potassium hydroxide and nitric acid (a strong acid) is $-57.1\ kJ\ mol^{-1}$. He predicts that the standard enthalpy change of neutralisation of the reaction of potassium hydroxide and ethanoic acid (a weak acid) will be the same. Is the student correct? Explain your answer. [3 marks]

I'm going to neutralise my hatred of acids and bases with a nice cup of tea...

Don't confuse strong acids with concentrated acids, or weak acids with dilute acids. Strong and weak are to do with how much an acid dissociates. Concentrated and dilute are to do with the number of moles of acid you've got per dm^3.

pH

Get those calculators warmed up — especially the log function key.

The **pH Scale** is a Measure of the **Hydrogen Ion Concentration**

The **concentration of hydrogen ions** can vary enormously, so some clever chemists decided to express the concentration on a **logarithmic scale**.

$$\mathbf{pH = -\log_{10}[H^+]}$$

The pH scale normally goes from **0** (very acidic) to **14** (very alkaline/basic). **pH 7** is regarded as being **neutral**.

For Strong **Monoprotic** Acids, **[H⁺] = Acid Concentration**

1) Hydrochloric acid and nitric acid ($HNO_{3(aq)}$) are **strong acids** so they dissociate fully. They're also **monoprotic**, so each mole of acid produces **one mole of hydrogen ions**. This means the H^+ concentration is the **same** as the acid concentration. Here's an example:

Example: Calculate the pH of 0.050 mol dm^{-3} nitric acid.

$[H^+] = 0.050 \Rightarrow pH = -\log_{10}(0.050) = \mathbf{1.30}$

2) You also need to be able to work out **[H⁺]** if you're given the **pH** of a solution. You do this by finding the **inverse log of –pH**, which is $\mathbf{10^{-pH}}$.

Example: An acid solution has a pH of 2.45. What is the hydrogen ion concentration, or [H⁺], of the acid?

$[H^+] = 10^{-2.45} = \mathbf{3.5 \times 10^{-3}\ mol\,dm^{-3}}$

Polyprotic Acids Can Lose **More Than One Proton**

1) You saw above that **monoprotic** acids only have **one proton** that they can release into solution.
2) But some acids, such as sulfuric acid (H_2SO_4), are **polyprotic** — this means they have **more than one proton** that they can release into solution.
3) Each molecule of a **strong diprotic acid** releases **two protons** when it dissociates.
4) Calculating the **[H⁺]**, and therefore the **pH** of **polyprotic acids** is a bit trickier, as more than one mole of hydrogen ions is released per mole of acid — you won't be asked to do this in the exam though, so don't panic.

To Find the **pH** of a **Weak Acid** You Use K_a (the **Acid Dissociation Constant**)

Weak acids (like CH_3COOH) **don't** dissociate fully in solution, so the [H⁺] **isn't** the same as the acid concentration. This makes it a **bit trickier** to find their pH. You have to use yet another **equilibrium constant**, K_a (the acid dissociation constant).

- For a weak aqueous acid, HA, you get the following equilibrium: $HA_{(aq)} \rightleftharpoons H^+_{(aq)} + A^-_{(aq)}$
- As only a **tiny amount** of HA dissociates, you can assume that $[HA_{(aq)}] >> [H^+_{(aq)}]$ so $[HA_{(aq)}]_{start} \approx [HA_{(aq)}]_{equilibrium}$.
- So if you apply the equilibrium law, you get: $K_a = \frac{[H^+][A^-]}{[HA]_{start}}$
- You can also assume that dissociation of the **acid** is much greater than dissociation of **water**. This means you can assume that all the H⁺ ions in solution come from the **acid**, so $[H^+_{(aq)}] \approx [A^-_{(aq)}]$.

See page 132 for more about the dissociation of water.

The units of K_a are mol dm^{-3}.

So $K_a = \frac{[H^+]^2}{[HA]}$

This expression is fine for calculations, but if you're asked for the expression of K_a, remember to give the one above ($K_a = [H^+][A^-]/[HA]$).

The assumptions made above to find K_a only work for **weak acids**. Strong acids **dissociate more** in solution, so the difference between $[HA]_{start}$ and $[HA]_{equilibrium}$ becomes **significant**, so the assumption that $[HA]_{start} = [HA]_{equilibrium}$ is no longer **valid**.

pH

To Find the pH of a Weak Acid, You Use K_a

K_a is an **equilibrium constant** just like K_c (see page 122). It applies to a particular acid at a **specific temperature** regardless of the **concentration**. You can use this fact to find the **pH** of a known concentration of a weak acid.

Example: Calculate the hydrogen ion concentration and the pH of a 0.02 mol dm^{-3} solution of propanoic acid (CH_3CH_2COOH). K_a for propanoic acid at this temperature is 1.30×10^{-5} mol dm^{-3}.

First, write down your expression for K_a and rearrange to find [H$^+$].

$$K_a = \frac{[H^+]^2}{[CH_3CH_2COOH]} \Rightarrow [H^+]^2 = K_a[CH_3CH_2COOH] = 1.30 \times 10^{-5} \times 0.02 = 2.60 \times 10^{-7}$$

$$\Rightarrow [H^+] = \sqrt{(2.60 \times 10^{-7})} = \mathbf{5.10 \times 10^{-4}\ mol\ dm^{-3}}$$

You can now use your value for [H$^+$] to find pH: $pH = -\log_{10} 5.10 \times 10^{-4} = \mathbf{3.29}$

You Might Have to Find the Concentration or K_a of a Weak Acid

You don't need to know anything new for this type of calculation. You usually just have to find **[H$^+$]** from the pH, then fiddle around with the **K_a expression** to find the missing bit of information.

This bunny may look cute, but he can't help Horace with his revision.

Example: The pH of an ethanoic acid (CH_3COOH) solution was 3.02 at 298 K. Calculate the molar concentration of this solution. K_a of ethanoic acid is 1.75×10^{-5} mol dm^{-3} at 298 K.

First, use the pH to find [H$^+$]: $[H^+] = 10^{-pH} = 10^{-3.02} = \mathbf{9.55 \times 10^{-4}\ mol\ dm^{-3}}$

Then rearrange the expression for K_a and plug in your values to find [CH_3COOH]:

$$K_a = \frac{[H^+]^2}{[CH_3COOH]} \Rightarrow CH_3COOH = \frac{[H^+]^2}{K_a} = \frac{(9.55 \times 10^{-4})^2}{1.75 \times 10^{-5}} = \mathbf{0.0521\ mol\ dm^{-3}}$$

Practice Questions

Q1 Explain what is meant by the term 'diprotic acid'?

Q2 Explain how to calculate the pH of a strong monoprotic acid from its concentration.

Q3 Explain how to calculate the pH of a weak acid from its concentration and K_a.

Exam Questions

Q1 a) What's the pH of a solution of the strong acid, hydrobromic acid (HBr), if it has a concentration of 0.32 mol dm^{-3}? [1 mark]

b) Hydrofluoric acid (HF) is a weaker acid than hydrochloric acid. Explain what that means in terms of hydrogen ions and pH. [1 mark]

Q2 The value of K_a for the weak acid HA, at 298 K, is 5.60×10^{-4} mol dm^{-3}.

a) Write an expression for K_a. [1 mark]

b) Calculate the pH of a 0.280 mol dm^{-3} solution of HA at 298 K. [2 marks]

Q3 The pH of a 0.150 mol dm^{-3} solution of a weak monoprotic acid, HX, is 2.65 at 298 K. Calculate the value of K_a for the acid HX at 298 K. [3 marks]

pH calculations are pH–ing great...

No, I really like them. Honestly. Although they can be a bit tricky. Just make sure you learn all the key formulae. Oh and not all calculators work the same way, so make sure you know how to work logs out on your calculator. There's loads more on pH coming up, and lots more calculations (eek), so make sure you've nailed this page before you move on.

The Ionic Product of Water

More pH calculations to come, but this time they're to do with bases. If only that meant they were basic — they're actually quite tricky. But fear not, there are loads of examples over the next two pages to guide you through K_w...

The Ionic Product of Water, K_w, Depends on the Concentration of H^+ and OH^-

Water can act as an **acid** by **donating** a proton — but it can also act as a **base** by **accepting** a proton.
So, in water there'll always be both **hydroxonium ions** and **hydroxide ions** swimming around at the **same time**.
So the following equilibrium exists in water:

$$H_2O_{(l)} + H_2O_{(l)} \rightleftharpoons H_3O^+_{(aq)} + OH^-_{(aq)}$$ or more simply: $$H_2O_{(l)} \rightleftharpoons H^+_{(aq)} + OH^-_{(aq)}$$

And, just like for any other equilibrium reaction, you can apply the equilibrium law and write an expression for the **equilibrium constant**:

$$K_c = \frac{[H^+][OH^-]}{[H_2O]}$$

Water only dissociates a **tiny amount**, so the equilibrium lies well over to the **left**. There's so much water compared to the amounts of H^+ and OH^- ions that the concentration of water is considered to have a **constant** value.

So if you multiply K_c (a constant) by $[H_2O]$ (another constant), you get a **constant**.
This new constant is called the **ionic product of water** and it is given the symbol K_w.

The units of K_w are always $mol^2\ dm^{-6}$.

$$K_w = [H^+][OH^-]$$

It doesn't matter whether water is pure or part of a solution — this equilibrium is always happening, and K_w is always the same at the same temperature.

For **pure water**, there's a **1:1** ratio of H^+ and OH^- ions due to dissociation. This means $\mathbf{[H^+] = [OH^-]}$ and $\mathbf{K_w = [H^+]^2}$.
So if you know K_w of pure water at a certain temperature, you can calculate $[H^+]$ and use this to find the pH.

The fact that K_w always has the **same value** for pure water or an aqueous solution at a **given temperature** is really useful, as you're about to discover...

At 25 °C (298 K), K_w = 1.0×10^{-14} $mol^2\ dm^{-6}$

Use K_w to Find the pH of a Strong Base

1) Sodium hydroxide (NaOH) and potassium hydroxide (KOH) are **strong bases** that **fully dissociate** in water:

$$NaOH_{(s)} \xrightarrow{H_2O} Na^+_{(aq)} + OH^-_{(aq)} \qquad KOH_{(s)} \xrightarrow{H_2O} K^+_{(aq)} + OH^-_{(aq)}$$

2) They donate **one mole of OH^- ions** per mole of base. This means that the concentration of OH^- ions is the **same** as the **concentration of the base**. So for 0.02 mol dm^{-3} sodium hydroxide solution, $[OH^-]$ is also **0.02 mol dm^{-3}**.
3) But to work out the **pH** you need to know $\mathbf{[H^+]}$ — this is linked to $\mathbf{[OH^-]}$ through the **ionic product of water, K_w**:
4) So if you know K_w and $[OH^-]$ for a **strong aqueous base** at a certain temperature, you can work out $\mathbf{[H^+]}$ (then the **pH**).

Example: Find the pH of 0.10 mol dm^{-3} NaOH at 298 K, given that K_w at 298 K is 1.0×10^{-14} $mol^2\ dm^{-6}$.

1) First put all the values you know into the expression for the ionic product of water, K_w:

$$1.0 \times 10^{-14} = [H^+][0.10]$$

2) Now rearrange the expression to find $[H^+]$:

$$[H^+] = \frac{1.0 \times 10^{-14}}{0.10} = 1.0 \times 10^{-13}\ mol\ dm^{-3}$$

3) Use your value of $[H^+]$ to find the pH of the solution:

$$pH = -\log_{10}[H^+] = -\log_{10}(1.0 \times 10^{-13}) = \mathbf{13.00}$$

The Ionic Product of Water

$pK_w = -\log_{10} K_w$ and $K_w = 10^{-pK_w}$

pK_w is calculated from K_w. And, since under standard conditions K_w is always 1.0×10^{-14}, pK_w is always:

$$pK_w = -\log_{10}K_w = -\log_{10}(1.0 \times 10^{-14}) = \mathbf{14.00}$$

The advantage of pK_w values is that they're a decent size so they're easy to work with.

$pK_a = -\log_{10} K_a$ and $K_a = 10^{-pK_a}$

Since $\boldsymbol{K_a}$ is different for different acids, pK_a is a bit trickier than pK_w.
$\boldsymbol{pK_a}$ is calculated from $\boldsymbol{K_a}$ in exactly the same way as **pH** is calculated from **$[H^+]$** — and vice versa.

Example: i) If an acid has a K_a value of 1.50×10^{-7} mol dm^3, what is its pK_a?

$$pK_a = -\log_{10}(1.50 \times 10^{-7}) = \mathbf{6.824}$$

ii) What is the K_a value of an acid if its pK_a is 4.32?

$$K_a = 10^{-4.32} = \mathbf{4.8 \times 10^{-5}\ mol\ dm^{-3}}$$

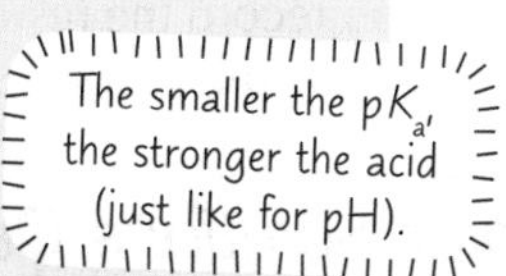

The smaller the pK_a, the stronger the acid (just like for pH).

$pK_{oink} = -\text{hog}_{10}K_{oink}$

Just to make things that bit more complicated, you might be given a **$\boldsymbol{pK_a}$** value in a question to work out concentrations or pH. If so, you just need to convert pK_a to K_a so that you can use the **$\boldsymbol{K_a}$ expression**.

Example: Calculate the pH of 0.0500 mol dm^{-3} methanoic acid (HCOOH).
Methanoic acid has a pK_a of 3.75 at this temperature.

$$K_a = 10^{-pK_a} = 10^{-3.75} = 1.77... \times 10^{-4}\ \text{mol dm}^{-3}$$

First you have to convert the pK_a to K_a.

$$K_a = \frac{[H^+]^2}{[HCOOH]} \Longrightarrow [H^+]^2 = K_a \times [HCOOH] = 1.77... \times 10^{-4} \times 0.0500 = 8.91... \times 10^{-6}$$

$$[H^+] = \sqrt{(8.91... \times 10^{-6})} = 2.98... \times 10^{-3}\ \text{mol dm}^{-3}$$

$$pH = -\log_{10}(2.98... \times 10^{-3}) = \mathbf{2.53}$$

You might also be asked to work out a pK_a value from concentrations or pH. In this case, you just work out the K_a value as usual and then convert it to pK_a.

Practice Questions

Q1 Give the equation for the ionic product of water.

Q2 What equation would you use to work out pK_w from K_w?

Exam Questions

Q1 At 298 K, a solution of sodium hydroxide contains 2.50 g dm^{-3}. K_w at 298 K is 1.0×10^{-14} mol^2 dm^{-6}.

a) What is the molar concentration of the hydroxide ions in this solution? [2 marks]

b) Calculate the pH of this solution. [2 marks]

Q2 Calculate the pH of a 0.0370 mol dm^{-3} solution of sodium hydroxide at 298 K.
K_w, the ionic product of water, is 1.0×10^{-14} mol^2 dm^{-6} at 298 K. [2 marks]

Q3 Benzoic acid is a weak acid that is used as a food preservative. It has a pK_a of 4.20 at 298 K.
Find the pH of a 1.60×10^{-4} mol dm^{-3} solution of benzoic acid at 298 K. [3 marks]

An ionic product — when your trousers have no creases in them...

You know things are getting serious when maths stuff like logs start appearing. It's fine really though, just practise a few questions and make sure you know how to use the log button on your calculator. And make sure you've learned the equations for K_w, pK_w AND pK_a. And while you're up, go and make me a nice cup of tea, lots of milk, no sugar.

Experiments Involving pH

You thought that was all there was to know about pH? Sorry to disappoint, but you're only halfway through this topic...

You Can **Measure** the pH of a Solution Using a **pH Meter**

1) A **pH meter** is an electronic gadget you can use to tell you the **pH** of a solution.
2) pH meters have a **probe** that you put into your solution and a **digital display** that shows the reading.
3) Before you use a pH meter, you need to make sure it's **calibrated correctly**. To do this...
   - Place the bulb of the pH meter into **deionised water** and allow the reading to settle. Now **adjust** the reading so that it reads **7.0**.
   - Do the same with a standard solution of pH 4 and another of pH 10. Make sure you **rinse** the probe with **deionised water** in between each reading.
4) You're now ready to take your **actual measurement**. Place the probe in the liquid you're measuring and let the reading **settle** before you record the result. After each measurement, you should **rinse** the probe in **deionised water**.

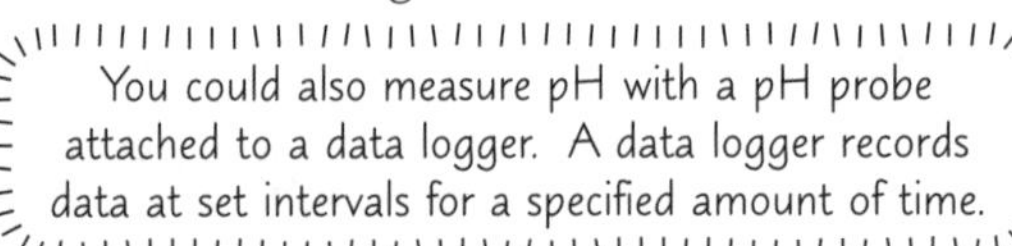

You could also measure pH with a pH probe attached to a data logger. A data logger records data at set intervals for a specified amount of time.

The **pH** of Equimolar Solutions Can Tell You About the Substances

You can learn quite a lot about the nature of a chemical just by looking at its **pH**.
By measuring the **pHs** of different equimolar solutions (solutions that contain the same number of moles), you can see whether a substance is an acid, base or a salt, and whether it is strong or weak.

Substance	pH
1 mol dm^{-3} HCl	0.00
1 mol dm^{-3} C_2H_5COOH	2.44
1 mol dm^{-3} NaCl	7.00
1 mol dm^{-3} NH_3	10.62
1 mol dm^{-3} NaOH	14.0

1 HCl has a pH of 0.00. $[H^+] = 10^{-pH} = 1$ mol dm^{-3} and the concentration of HCl is also 1 mol dm^{-3}. So HCl must be **completely dissociated** — it's a **strong acid**.

2 C_2H_5COOH has a pH of 2.44, which gives $[H^+]$ of 0.0036 mol dm^{-3}. The concentration is 1 mol dm^{-3}, so only a **small** fraction of the molecules are **dissociated**. It's a **weak acid**.

3 NaCl has a pH of 7.00 which gives $[H^+]$ of 1×10^{-7} mol dm^{-3}. Using $K_w = [H^+][OH^-] = 1.0 \times 10^{-14}$, $[OH^-]$ is also 1×10^{-7} mol dm^{-3}. $[H^+] = [OH^-]$, so the substance is **neutral**. This is true for salts of strong acids with strong bases.

4 NH_3 has $[H^+]$ of 2.4×10^{-11} which gives $[OH^-]$ of 4.2×10^{-4} mol dm^{-3} (using $K_w = [H^+][OH^-] = 1.0 \times 10^{-14}$). This shows only a **tiny fraction** of H^+ ions are accepted from the water molecules by NH_3, so it's a **weak base**.

5 NaOH has $[H^+]$ of 1.0×10^{-14} mol dm^{-3} which means $[OH^-]$ is 1 mol dm^{-3}. The concentration of NaOH is also 1 mol dm^{-3} so NaOH is **completely dissociated** — it's a **strong base**.

You Can Use **Masses** and **pH** to Work Out K_a

You can use **experimental data** to work out K_a for weak acids. The example below shows you how this works.

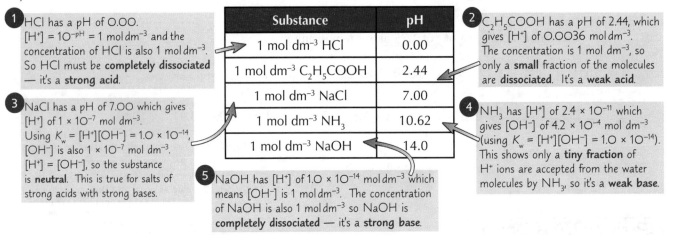

Example: 1.31 g of ethanoic acid (CH_3COOH) are dissolved in 250 cm^3 of distilled water to create a solution of ethanoic acid. The solution has a pH of 2.84. Calculate the acid dissociation constant for ethanoic acid.

1) First, you need to work out the number of moles of ethanoic acid that are in the solution.

$$\text{moles} = \text{mass} \div M \Longrightarrow \text{moles} = 1.31 \div [(2 \times 12.0) + (4 \times 1.0) + (2 \times 16.0)] = 0.02183\ldots \text{ moles}$$

2) Then, calculate the concentration of the ethanoic acid solution.

$$\text{concentration} = \frac{\text{moles} \times 1000}{\text{volume (cm}^3)} \Longrightarrow \text{concentration} = \frac{0.02183\ldots \times 1000}{250} = 0.0873\ldots \text{ mol dm}^{-3}$$

3) You can use the pH to work out $[H^+]$ at equilibrium: $[H^+] = 10^{-pH} = 10^{-2.84} = 0.00144\ldots$

4) For weak acids, $K_a = \frac{[H^+]^2}{[HA]}$, so $K_a = \frac{[0.00144\ldots]^2}{[0.0873..]} = 0.00002392\ldots = 2.4 \times 10^{-5}$

Remember, for weak acids $[HA]_{start} = [HA]_{equilibrium}$.

Experiments Involving pH

When Acids are Diluted their pH Changes

Diluting an acid reduces the **concentration of H^+** in the solution. This **increases the pH**. The table shows the pH of a strong and a weak acid at different concentrations.

Concentration of Acid ($mol\ dm^{-3}$)	HCl pH at 298 K	C_2H_5COOH pH at 298 K
1	0	2.44
0.1	1	2.94
0.01	2	3.44
0.001	3	3.94

Strong Acid — Hydrochloric Acid (HCl)

Diluting a **strong acid** by a **factor of 10** increases the pH by **1**.

It's easy to see this for yourself. Remember that for a strong acid, $[H^+] = [acid]$, so **$pH = -\log_{10}[acid]$**.

Just try sticking [acid] = 1, 0.1, 0.01, etc. into this formula.

These results may seem a bit random, but they're true. It's all in the maths...

Weak Acid — Propanoic Acid (C_2H_5COOH)

Diluting a **weak acid** by a **factor of 10** increases the pH by **0.5**.

Again, you can see this for yourself if you like by sticking numbers into the right formula, but it's a lot more fiddly this time...

Rearranging $K_a = \frac{[H^+]^2}{[Acid]}$ gives $[H^+] = \sqrt{K_a[acid]}$, and then $pH = -\log_{10}\sqrt{K_a[acid]}$

Stick [acid] = 1, 0.1, 0.01, etc. into this formula to find the pH each time. The pH will always change by 0.5, no matter what value you use for K_a.

E.g. To get the figures in the table above, K_a of propanoic acid is 1.31×10^{-5}.

So $[C_2H_5COOH] = 1\ mol\ dm^{-3}$ gives $[H^+] = 3.6 \times 10^{-3}$ which gives pH = **2.44**

$[C_2H_5COOH] = 0.1\ mol\ dm^{-3}$ gives $[H^+] = 1.14 \times 10^{-3}$ which gives pH = **2.94**

Sir John used teaH calculations to work out the optimum concentration of tea in the perfect cuppa.

Practice Questions

Q1 What pH would you expect a $1.0\ mol\ dm^{-3}$ solution of a base that completely dissociates in solution to have?

Q2 What would happen to the pH of a strong acid if you diluted it by a factor of 100?

Exam Questions

Q1 A student is measuring the pH of three $2.0\ mol\ dm^{-3}$ solutions, A, B and C, to investigate the extent of their acidity or basicity. The pHs of A, B and C, at standard temperature and pressure are 3.20, 13.80 and 6.80 respectively.

a) Suggest a piece of equipment that she could use to accurately measure the pH of the solutions. [1 mark]

b) In A, B and C, only one mole of hydrogen or hydroxide ions are released per mole of acid or base. Comment on whether A, B or C dissociates most in solution. Show your working. [4 marks]

Q2 1.22 g of benzoic acid, C_6H_5COOH, are dissolved in $100\ cm^3$ of distilled water to create a standard solution of benzoic acid. The pH of the solution is 2.60 at 298 K.

a) Calculate a value for K_a for the acid at this temperature. [5 marks]

b) Use the value of K_a that you have calculated to find the $[H^+]$ of a $0.0100\ mol\ dm^{-3}$ solution of this acid. [2 marks]

c) Calculate the pH of the $0.0100\ mol\ dm^{-3}$ solution of the acid at 298 K. [1 mark]

d) Show that the pH of a $1.00\ mol\ dm^{-3}$ solution of the acid is 2.1 at 298 K. [2 marks]

e) Without further calculations, predict the pH of a $0.001\ mol\ dm^{-3}$ solution of benzoic acid at 298 K. Explain your answer. [2 marks]

The perfect dilution — 1 part orange squash to 10 parts water...

Remember, if you dilute a weak acid by a factor of 10, you'll increase its pH by 0.5. But diluting a strong acid by a factor of 10 will increase the pH by a whole 1. Don't get them mixed up, it might cost you valuable marks...

Titration Curves and Indicators

If you add base to acid the pH changes in a squiggly sort of way.

Use Titration to Find the Concentration of an Acid or Base

You met titrations back on page 63, so here's just a quick reminder of how to do them.

1) Measure out some **base** using a pipette and put it in a flask, along with some **indicator**.
2) **Rinse** a burette with some of your **standard solution** of acid. Then **fill** it with your standard solution.
3) Do a rough titration to get an idea where the **end point** is (the point where the base is **exactly neutralised** and the indicator changes colour). To do this, take an initial reading to see how much acid is in the burette to start off with. Then, add the **acid** to the base — giving the flask a regular **swirl**. Stop when your indicator shows a permanent colour change (the end point). Record the final reading from your burette.
4) Now do an **accurate** titration. Run the acid in to within 2 cm^3 of the end point, then add the acid **dropwise** until you reach the end point.
5) **Work out** the amount of acid used to **neutralise** the base (the **titre**).
6) **Repeat** the titration a few times, making sure you get a similar answer each time — your readings should be within 0.1 cm^3 of each other. Then calculate a **mean titre** (see page 244), ignoring any anomalous results.

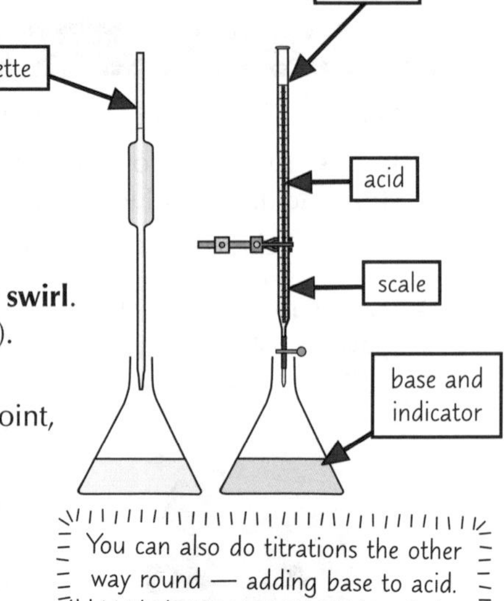

You can also do titrations the other way round — adding base to acid.

Titration Curves Plot pH Against Volume of Acid or Base Added

1) **Titrations** let you find out **exactly** how much base is needed to **neutralise** a quantity of acid.
2) All you have to do is plot the **pH** of the titration mixture against the **amount of base** added as the titration goes on. The pH of the mixture can be measured using a pH meter and the scale on the burette can be used to see how much base has been added.
3) The **shape** of your plot looks a bit different depending on the **strengths** of the acid and base that are used.
4) Here are the titration curves for the different combinations of **equimolar** strong and weak monoprotic acids and bases:

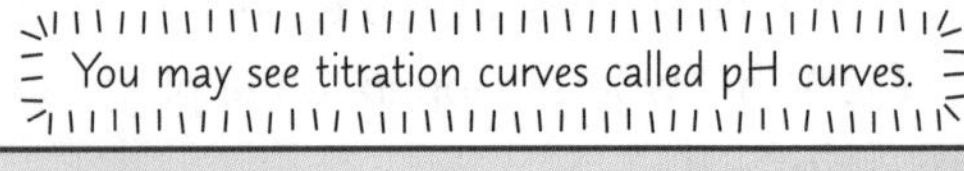

You may see titration curves called pH curves.

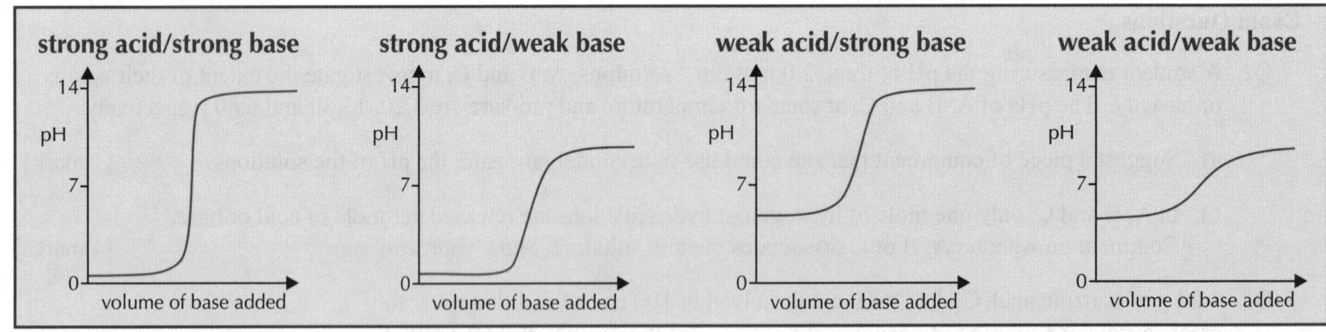

You can explain why each graph has a particular shape:

If you titrate a base with an acid instead, the shapes of the curves stay the same, but they're reversed.

- The **initial** pH depends on the **strength** of the **acid**. So a strong acid titration will start at a much **lower** pH than a weak acid.
- To start with, addition of **small** amounts of base have **little impact** on the pH of the solution.
- All the graphs (apart from the weak acid/weak base graph) have a bit that's almost vertical — this is the **equivalence line**. The point at the **centre** of the equivalence line is the **equivalence point** or **end point**. At this point $[H^+] \approx [OH^-]$ — it's here that all the acid is just **neutralised**. When this is the case, a tiny amount of base causes a sudden, big change in pH.
- The change in pH is also **less pronounced** when **strong acids** are added to **strong bases** (or vice versa), compared to when **strong acids** are added to **weak bases** (or strong bases are added to weak acids).
- The **final** pH depends on the strength of the **base** — the **stronger** the base, the **higher** the final pH.

Titration Curves and Indicators

Titration Curves Can Help you Decide which Indicator to Use

1) When carrying out a titration, you'll often need to use an **indicator** that changes **colour** to show you when your sample has been **neutralised**.
2) You need your indicator to change colour exactly at the **end point** of your titration. So you need to pick one that changes colour over a **narrow pH range** that lies entirely on the **vertical part** of the titration curve.
3) **Methyl orange** and **phenolphthalein** are **indicators** that are often used for acid-base titrations. They each change colour over a **different pH range**:

E.g. For this titration, the curve is vertical between **pH 8** and **pH 11** — so a very small amount of base will cause the pH to **change** from 8 to 11.

So you want an indicator that changes **colour** somewhere between pH 8 and pH 11.

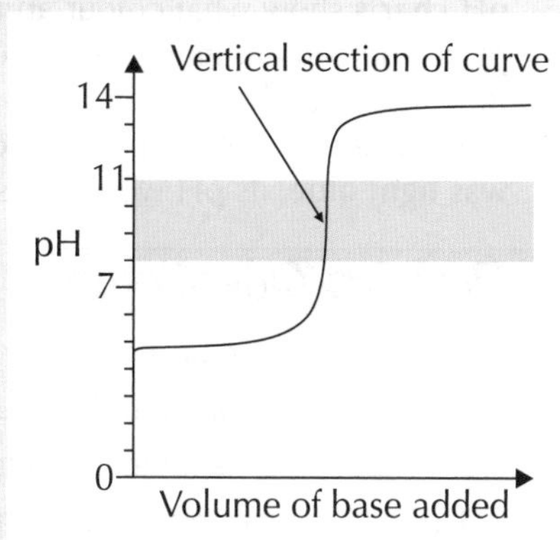

Name of indicator	Colour at low pH	Approx. pH of colour change	Colour at high pH
Methyl orange	red	3.1 – 4.4	yellow
Phenolphthalein	colourless	8.3 – 10	pink

methyl orange

- For a **strong acid/strong base** titration, you can use **either** of these indicators — there's a rapid pH change over the range for **both** indicators.
- For a **strong acid/weak base** only **methyl orange** will do. The pH changes rapidly across the range for methyl orange, but not for phenolphthalein.
- For a **weak acid/strong base**, **phenolphthalein** is the stuff to use. The pH changes rapidly over phenolphthalein's range, but not over methyl orange's.
- For **weak acid/weak base** titrations there's no sharp pH change, so **neither** of these indicators works. In fact, there aren't **any** indicators you can use in weak acid/weak base titrations, so you should just use a pH meter.

Another Great Use for Titration Curves — Finding the pK_a of a Weak Acid

1) You can work out **pK_a** of a weak acid using the titration curve for a **weak acid/strong base titration**. It involves finding the **pH** at the **half-equivalence point**.
2) **Half-equivalence** is the stage of a titration when **half** of the acid has been neutralised — it's when half of the equivalence volume of **strong base** has been added to the **weak acid**.

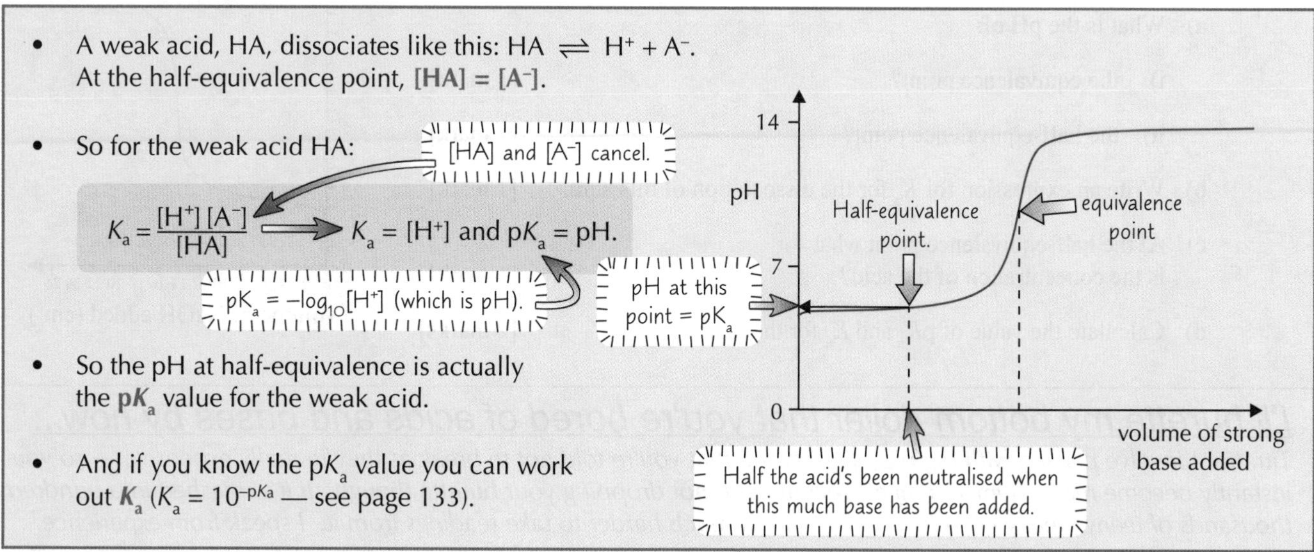

- A weak acid, HA, dissociates like this: HA $\rightleftharpoons H^+ + A^-$. At the half-equivalence point, **[HA] = [A⁻]**.
- So for the weak acid HA:

$$K_a = \frac{[H^+][A^-]}{[HA]} \Longrightarrow K_a = [H^+] \text{ and p}K_a = \text{pH}.$$

- So the pH at half-equivalence is actually the **pK_a** value for the weak acid.
- And if you know the pK_a value you can work out **K_a** ($K_a = 10^{-pKa}$ — see page 133).

Titration Curves and Indicators

You Can Follow pH Changes with a pH Chart

pH charts show what colour an **indicator** appears at different **pHs**. You can **compare** the colour of a solution containing an indicator with the indicator's pH chart to determine the **pH** of the **solution**. For example, if a solution containing **thymol blue** was **light blue**, its pH would be somewhere between **8** and **10**.

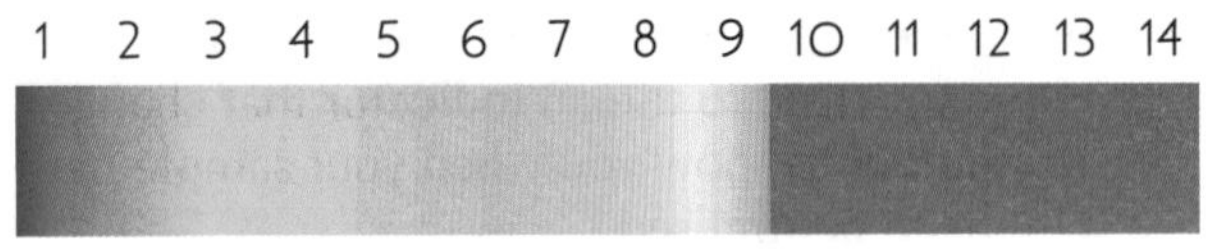

pH chart for thymol blue

Practice Questions

Q1 Sketch the titration curve for a weak acid/strong base titration.

Q2 What indicator should you use for a strong acid/weak base titration — methyl orange or phenolphthalein?

Q3 What colour is methyl orange at pH 2?

Q4 What is meant by the half-equivalence point?

Exam Questions

Q1 1.0 mol dm^{-3} NaOH (a strong base) is added separately to 25 cm^3 samples of 1.0 mol dm^{-3} nitric acid (a strong acid) and 1.0 mol dm^{-3} ethanoic acid (a weak acid). Sketch the titration curves for each of these titrations. [2 marks]

Q2 A sample of ethanoic acid (a weak acid) was titrated against potassium hydroxide (a strong base).

From the table on the right, select the best indicator for this titration, and explain your choice. [2 marks]

Name of indicator	pH range
bromophenol blue	3.0 – 4.6
methyl red	4.2 – 6.3
bromothymol blue	6.0 – 7.6
thymol blue	8.0 – 9.6

Q3 This curve shows the pH change as sodium hydroxide solution (a strong base) is added to a solution of ethanoic acid (a weak acid).

pH (0, 7, 14)
0 2 4 6 8 10 12 14 16 18 20 22 24 26
volume of NaOH added (cm^3)

a) What is the pH at the equivalence point? [1 mark]

b) What volume of base had been added at this point? [1 mark]

c) Suggest an indicator to use for the titration and explain your choice. [2 marks]

d) Sketch the curve you would get if the titration was repeated using ammonia solution (a weak base) as the base. [1 mark]

e) Why couldn't you use an indicator to identify the end point of a titration between ethanoic acid and ammonia solution? [1 mark]

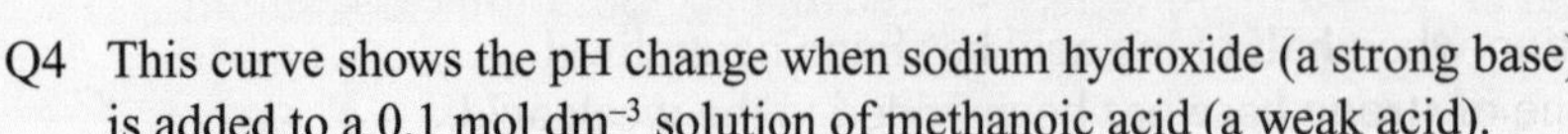

Q4 This curve shows the pH change when sodium hydroxide (a strong base) is added to a 0.1 mol dm^{-3} solution of methanoic acid (a weak acid).

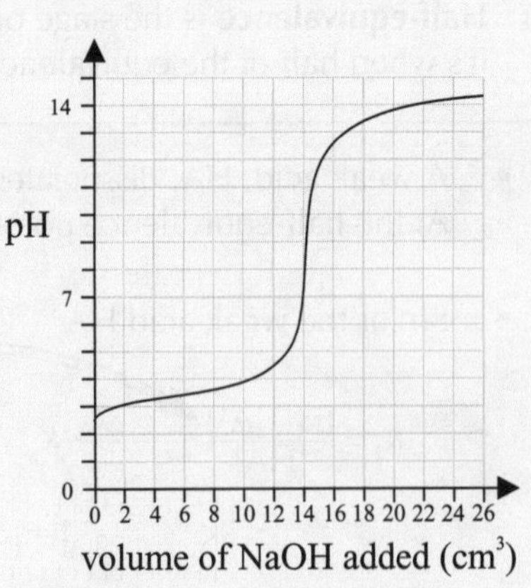

a) What is the pH of:

i) the equivalence point? [1 mark]

ii) the half-equivalence point? [1 mark]

b) Write an expression for K_a for the dissociation of this acid. [1 mark]

c) At the half-equivalence point what is the concentration of the acid? [1 mark]

d) Calculate the value of pK_a and K_a for the acid. [2 marks]

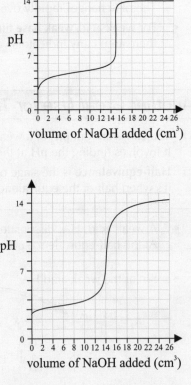

I'll burette my bottom dollar that you're bored of acids and bases by now...

Titrations involve playing with big bits of glassware that you're told not to break as they're really expensive — so you instantly become really clumsy. I highly recommend not dropping your burette though. If it's smashed into hundreds or thousands of teeny weeny tiny pieces, you'll find it much harder to take readings from it. I speak from experience...

Buffers

How can a solution resist becoming more acidic if you add acid to it? Here's where you find out...

Buffers **Resist** Changes in pH

A **buffer** is a solution that **minimises** changes in pH when **small** amounts of acid or base are added.

A buffer **doesn't** stop the pH from changing completely — it does make the changes **very slight** though. Buffers only work for small amounts of acid or base — put too much in and they won't be able to cope.

Acidic Buffers *Contain a* ***Weak Acid*** *and its* ***Conjugate Base***

Acidic buffers have a pH of less than 7 — they're made by setting up an equilibrium between a **weak acid** and its **conjugate base**. This can be done in two ways:

1) **Mix a weak acid with the salt of its conjugate base.**
   e.g. ethanoic acid and sodium ethanoate:
   - The salt **fully** dissociates into its ions when it dissolves:
     $CH_3COO^-Na^+_{(aq)} \rightarrow CH_3COO^-_{(aq)} + Na^+_{(aq)}$
   - Ethanoic acid is a **weak acid**, so only **slightly** dissociates:
     $CH_3COOH_{(aq)} \rightleftharpoons H^+_{(aq)} + CH_3COO^-_{(aq)}$

2) **Mix an excess of weak acid with a strong base.**
   e.g. ethanoic acid and sodium hydroxide:
   - **All** the base reacts with the acid:
     $CH_3COOH_{(aq)} + OH^-_{(aq)} \rightarrow CH_3COO^- + H_2O$
   - The weak acid was in **excess**, so there's still some left in solution once all the base has reacted. This acid **slightly dissociates**:
     $CH_3COOH_{(aq)} \rightleftharpoons H^+_{(aq)} + CH_3COO^-_{(aq)}$

In both cases, the following equilibrium is set up between the weak acid and its conjugate base:

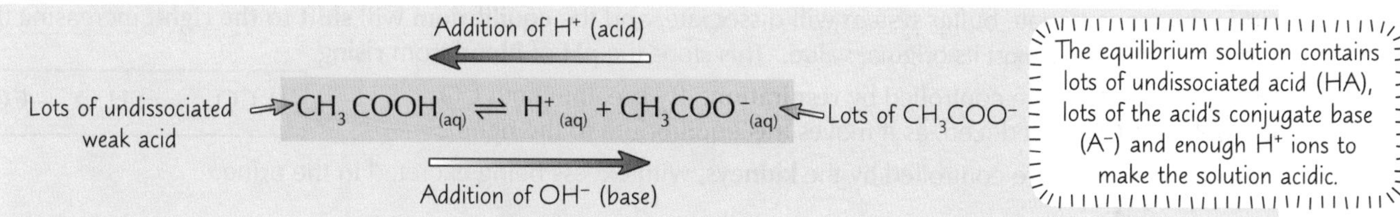

The equilibrium solution contains lots of undissociated acid (HA), lots of the acid's conjugate base (A⁻) and enough H⁺ ions to make the solution acidic.

It's the job of the conjugate pair to control the pH of a buffer solution. The **conjugate base** mops up any extra **H⁺**, while the **conjugate acid releases** H⁺ if there's too much base around.

- If you add a **small** amount of **acid** the **H⁺ concentration** increases. Most of the extra H⁺ ions combine with CH_3COO^- ions to form CH_3COOH. This shifts the equilibrium to the **left**, reducing the H⁺ concentration to close to its original value. So the **pH** doesn't change much.
- If a **small** amount of **base** (e.g. NaOH) is added, the **OH⁻ concentration** increases. Most of the extra OH⁻ ions react with H⁺ ions to form water — removing H⁺ ions from the solution. This causes more CH_3COOH to **dissociate** to form H⁺ ions — shifting the equilibrium to the **right**. The H⁺ concentration increases until it's close to its original value, so the **pH** doesn't change much.

Alkaline Buffers *are Made from a* ***Weak Base*** *and one of its* ***Salts***

A mixture of **ammonia solution** (a base) and **ammonium chloride** (a salt of ammonia) acts as an **alkaline** (or **basic**) buffer. It works in a similar way to acidic buffers:

An alkaline solution is a basic solution that's soluble in water.

1) The **salt** is fully dissociated in solution: $NH_4Cl_{(aq)} \rightarrow NH_4^+{}_{(aq)} + Cl^-_{(aq)}$.
2) An equilibrium is set up between the **ammonium ions** and **ammonia**:
   Lots of NH_4^+ — Addition of H⁺ (acid) — Lots of weak base
   $NH_4^+{}_{(aq)} \rightleftharpoons H^+_{(aq)} + NH_3{}_{(aq)}$
   Addition of OH⁻ (base)
3) If a small amount of **acid** is added, the H⁺ concentration **increases** — most of the added H⁺ reacts with NH_3 and the equilibrium shifts **left**. This reduces the H⁺ concentration to near its original value. So the pH **doesn't** change much.
4) If a small amount of **base** is added, the OH⁻ concentration **increases**. OH⁻ ions react with the H⁺ ions, removing them from the solution. There are plenty of NH_4^+ molecules around that can dissociate to generate replacement **H⁺ ions** — so the equilibrium shifts **right**, stopping the pH from changing much.

Buffers

Buffer Action can be Seen on a **Titration Curve**

1) You met **titration curves** back on pages 136 and 137. They show you how the **pH** of a solution **changes** as an **increasing volume** of **acid** or **base** is added.
2) The **titration curves** for weak acids with strong bases, and for strong acids with weak bases, have a **distinctive shape** due to the formation of **buffer solutions** as the reaction proceeds.

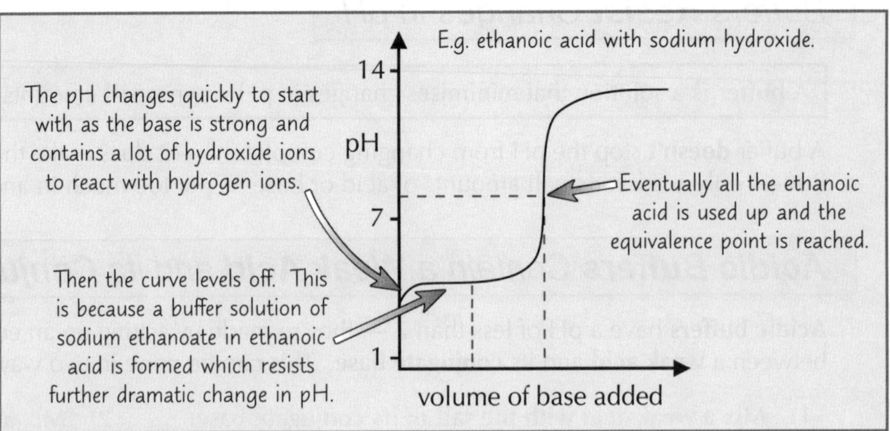

E.g. ethanoic acid with sodium hydroxide.
14
7
1
pH
volume of base added
The pH changes quickly to start with as the base is strong and contains a lot of hydroxide ions to react with hydrogen ions.
Eventually all the ethanoic acid is used up and the equivalence point is reached.
Then the curve levels off. This is because a buffer solution of sodium ethanoate in ethanoic acid is formed which resists further dramatic change in pH.

Buffer Solutions are Important in the **Blood**

1) Blood needs to be kept at around **pH 7.4**. The pH is controlled using a **carbonic acid-hydrogencarbonate buffer system**. Carbonic acid dissociates into H^+ ions and HCO_3^- ions.

$$H_2CO_{3(aq)} \rightleftharpoons H^+_{(aq)} + HCO_3^-{}_{(aq)}$$

2) If the **concentration** of **H^+ ions rises** in blood, then **HCO_3^- ions** from the carbonic acid-hydrogencarbonate buffer system will **react** with the excess H^+ ions, and the **equilibrium** will **shift to the left**, reducing the H^+ concentration to almost its original value. This stops the **pH** of **blood** from **dropping**.
3) Meanwhile, if the **concentration** of **H^+ ions falls** in blood, then more H_2CO_3 molecules from the carbonic acid-hydrogencarbonate buffer system will dissociate, and the **equilibrium** will **shift to the right**, increasing the H^+ concentration to almost its original value. This stops the **pH** of **blood** from **rising**.
4) The levels of H_2CO_3 are controlled by **respiration**. By breathing out CO_2, the level of H_2CO_3 is reduced, as it moves this equilibrium to the right.

$$H_2CO_{3(aq)} \rightleftharpoons H_2O_{(l)} + CO_{2(aq)}$$

5) The levels of HCO_3^- are controlled by the **kidneys**, with excess being excreted in the urine.

Here's How to Calculate the **pH** of a **Buffer Solution**

Calculating the **pH** of an acidic buffer isn't too tricky. You just need to know the $\boldsymbol{K_a}$ of the weak acid and the **concentrations** of the weak acid and its salt. Your calculation requires the following assumptions to be made:

- The **salt** of the **conjugate base** is **fully dissociated**, so assume that the equilibrium concentration of A^- is the **same** as the initial concentration of the salt.
- **HA** is only **slightly dissociated**, so assume that its equilibrium concentration is the **same** as its initial concentration.

The conjugate base doesn't only come from dissociation of the weak acid so $[H^+] \neq [A^-]$.

Example: At a certain temperature, a buffer solution contains 0.40 mol dm^{-3} methanoic acid, HCOOH, and 0.60 mol dm^{-3} sodium methanoate, $HCOO^-Na^+$. At this temperature, K_a for methanoic acid = 1.8×10^{-4} mol dm^{-3}. What is the pH of this buffer?

Firstly, write the expression for K_a of the weak acid:

$$HCOOH_{(aq)} \rightleftharpoons H^+_{(aq)} + HCOO^-_{(aq)} \Rightarrow K_a = \frac{[H^+][HCOO^-]}{[HCOOH]}$$

Remember — these are all equilibrium concentrations.

Then rearrange the expression and stick in the data to calculate $[H^+]$:

$$[H^+] = K_a \times \frac{[HCOOH]}{[HCOO^-]}$$

$$[H^+] = 1.8 \times 10^{-4} \times \frac{0.40}{0.60} = 1.2 \times 10^{-4} \text{ mol dm}^{-3}$$

If you wanted to find the concentration of an acid needed to make a buffer solution of a particular pH, using a salt of known concentration and the K_a of the acid, you could use this equation to find [acid]. Or you could use the Henderson-Hasselbalch equation on the next page...

Finally, convert $[H^+]$ to pH: $pH = -\log_{10}[H^+] = -\log_{10}(1.2 \times 10^{-4}) = \mathbf{3.92}$

Buffers

You Need to be Able to Calculate Concentrations

Nobody's gonna change my pH.

Acids and bases didn't mess with Jeff after he became buffer.

You may want to create a buffer with a **specific pH**.
To work out the **concentrations** of **salt** and **acid** or **base** that you'll need, you may need to use a fancy equation, known as the **Henderson-Hasselbalch** equation. Here it is:

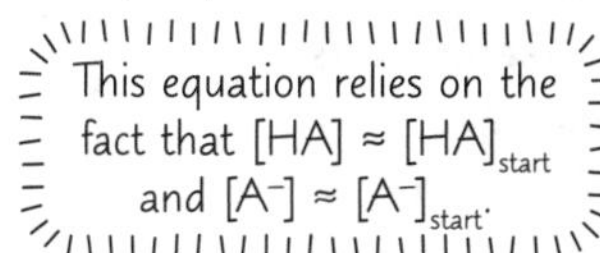

This equation relies on the fact that $[HA] \approx [HA]_{start}$ and $[A^-] \approx [A^-]_{start}$.

$$pH = pK_a + \log_{10}\left(\frac{[A^-]}{[HA]}\right)$$

Example: A buffer is made using ethanoic acid (CH_3COOH) and an ethanoic acid salt ($CH_3COO^-Na^+$). 1.20 mol dm^{-3} of the ethanoic acid salt is used. What concentration of ethanoic acid is required so that the buffer has a pH of 4.9? Under these conditions, K_a of ethanoic acid = 1.75×10^{-5}.

You know that **$pK_a = -\log K_a$**, so you can work out the pK_a of ethanoic acid: $pK_a = -\log_{10}(1.75 \times 10^{-5}) = 4.756...$

Now, substitute your value for **pK_a**, and the **desired pH** (which you were given in the question) into the Henderson-Hasselbalch equation to work out the **ratio** of **$[A^-]:[HA]$** that you need.

$$pH = pK_a + \log_{10}\left(\frac{[A^-]}{[HA]}\right)$$ ← This is the Henderson-Hasselbalch equation.

$$4.9 = 4.756... + \log_{10}\left(\frac{[CH_3COO^-]}{[CH_3COOH]}\right)$$

$$\log_{10}\left(\frac{[CH_3COO^-]}{[CH_3COOH]}\right) = 4.9 - 4.756... = 0.143...$$

$$10^{\log_{10}x} = x, \Longrightarrow \frac{[CH_3COO^-]}{[CH_3COOH]} = 10^{0.143...} = 1.39...$$

This is a log rule (from maths). You'll need to remember it to do questions like this one.

You know that the salt **fully dissociates**, so [salt] = $[A^-]$. This lets you calculate **[HA] at equilibrium**, which is equal to **[HA] at the start** of the reaction (since ethanoic acid is a **weak acid**).

$$\frac{1.20}{[CH_3COOH]} = 1.39... \Longrightarrow [CH_3COOH] = 1.20 \div 1.39...$$

$$[CH_3COOH] = \textbf{0.86 mol dm}^{-3}$$

Practice Questions

Q1 What's a buffer solution?

Q2 How can a mixture of ethanoic acid and sodium ethanoate act as a buffer?

Q3 Describe how to make an alkaline buffer.

Q4 Describe how the pH of the blood is buffered.

Exam Questions

Q1 A buffer solution contains 0.400 mol dm^{-3} benzoic acid, C_6H_5COOH, and 0.200 mol dm^{-3} sodium benzoate, $C_6H_5COO^-Na^+$. At 25 °C, K_a for benzoic acid is 6.40×10^{-5} mol dm^{-3}.

a) Calculate the pH of the buffer solution. [2 marks]

b) Explain the effect on the buffer of adding a small quantity of dilute sulfuric acid. [3 marks]

Q2 A buffer was prepared by mixing solutions of butanoic acid, $CH_3(CH_2)_2COOH$, and sodium butanoate, $CH_3(CH_2)_2COO^-Na^+$, so that they had the same concentration.

a) Write a balanced chemical equation to show butanoic acid acting as a weak acid. [1 mark]

b) Given that K_a for butanoic acid is 1.5×10^{-5} mol dm^{-3} at 298 K, calculate the pH of the buffer solution. [2 marks]

Old buffers are often resistant to change...

So that's how buffers work. There's a pleasing simplicity and neatness about it that I find rather elegant. Like watching the sun rise on a misty May morning, with only bird song for company... OK, I'll shut up now.

Lattice Energy

On these pages you can learn about lattice energy, not lettuce energy which is the energy change when 1 mole consumes salad from a veggie patch. Bu–dum cha... (that was meant to be a drum — work with me here).

Lattice Energy is a Measure of **Ionic Bond Strength**

Ionic compounds can form regular structures called **giant ionic lattices** where the positive and negative ions are held together by **electrostatic attractions**. When **gaseous ions** combine to make a solid lattice, energy is given out — this is called the **lattice energy**.

Here's the definition of **standard lattice energy** that you need to know:

> The **standard lattice energy**, $\Delta_{LE}H^\ominus$, is the energy change when **1 mole** of an **ionic solid** is formed from its **gaseous ions** under standard conditions.

Standard conditions are 298 K (25 °C) and 100 kPa.

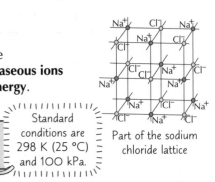

Part of the sodium chloride lattice

The standard lattice energy is a measure of **ionic bond strength**. The more **negative** the lattice energy, the **stronger** the bonding. E.g. out of NaCl and MgO, MgO has stronger bonding.

$Na^+_{(g)} + Cl^-_{(g)} \rightarrow NaCl_{(s)}$ $\Delta_{LE}H^\ominus = -787$ kJ mol^{-1}

$Mg^{2+}_{(g)} + O^{2-}_{(g)} \rightarrow MgO_{(s)}$ $\Delta_{LE}H^\ominus = -3791$ kJ mol^{-1}

Ionic Charge and **Size** Affects **Lattice Energy**

Energy changes are sometimes known as enthalpy changes — don't worry, they're the same thing.

1) The **higher the charge** on the ions, the **more energy** is released when an ionic lattice forms. This is due to the **stronger electrostatic forces** between the ions.
2) More energy released means that the lattice energy will be **more negative**. So the lattice energies for compounds with **2+** or **2– ions** (e.g. Mg^{2+} or S^{2-}) are **more exothermic** than those with **1+** or **1– ions** (e.g. Na^+ or Cl^-).

> E.g. the lattice energy of **NaCl** is only –787 kJ mol^{-1}, but the lattice energy of **$MgCl_2$** is –2526 kJ mol^{-1}. **MgS** has an even **higher** lattice energy (–3299 kJ mol^{-1}) because both Mg and S ions have **double charges**.

3) The **smaller** the **ionic radii** of the ions involved, the **more exothermic** (more negative) the **lattice energy**. Smaller ions have a higher **charge density** and their **smaller ionic radii** mean that the ions can sit **closer together** in the lattice. Both these things mean that the attractions between the ions are **stronger**.

Born-Haber Cycles can be Used to Calculate **Lattice Energies**

Hess's law says that the **total enthalpy change** of a reaction is always the **same**, no matter which route is taken — this is known as the conservation of energy.

You can't calculate a lattice energy **directly**, so you have to use a **Born-Haber cycle** to figure out what the enthalpy change would be if you took **another**, **less direct**, **route**.

Here's a Born-Haber cycle you could use to calculate the lattice energy of **NaCl**:

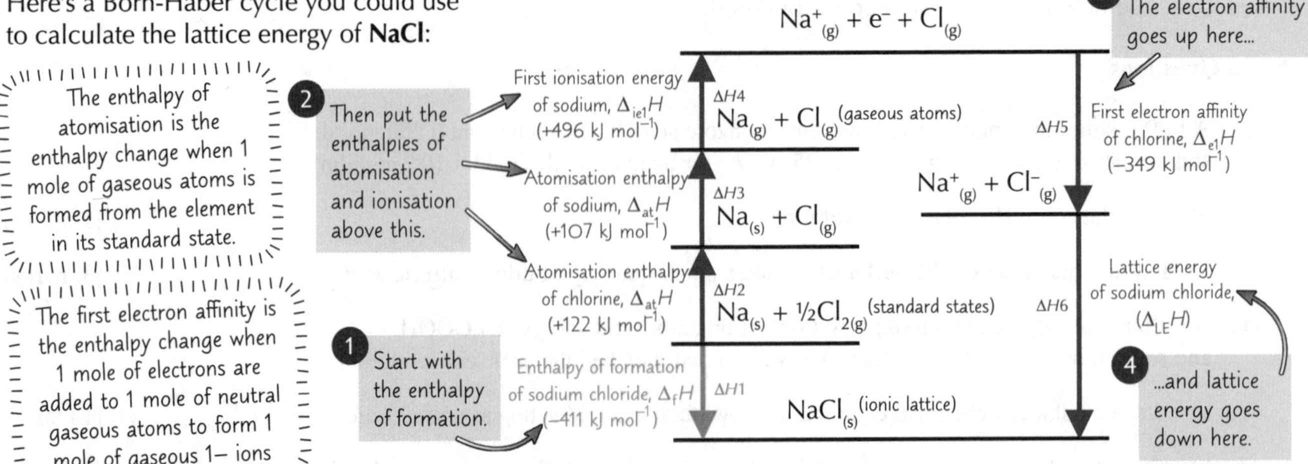

There are **two routes** you can follow to get from the elements in their **standard states** to the **ionic solid**. The green arrow shows the **direct route** and the purple arrows show the **indirect route**. The energy change for each is the **same**.

> From Hess's law: $\Delta H6 = -\Delta H5 - \Delta H4 - \Delta H3 - \Delta H2 + \Delta H1$
> $= -(-349) - (+496) - (+107) - (+122) + (-411) = \mathbf{-787}$ **kJ mol^{-1}**

You need a minus sign if you go the wrong way along an arrow.

Lattice Energy

Calculations involving Group 2 Elements are a Bit Different

Born-Haber cycles for compounds containing **Group 2 elements** have a few **changes** from the one on the previous page. Make sure you understand what's going on so you can handle whatever compound they throw at you.

Here's the Born-Haber cycle for calculating the lattice energy of **magnesium chloride** ($MgCl_2$):

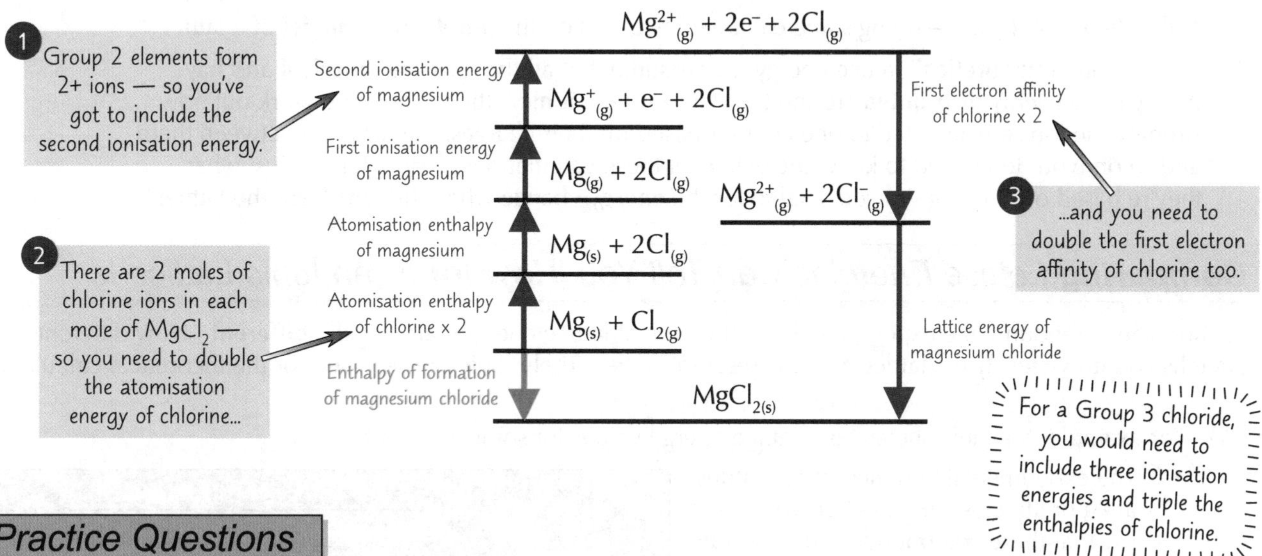

Practice Questions

Q1 What is the definition of standard lattice energy?

Q2 What does a large, negative lattice energy mean, in terms of bond strength?

Q3 Why does magnesium chloride have a more negative lattice energy than sodium chloride?

Q4 What is the definition of the enthalpy of atomisation?

Exam Questions

Q1 Using this data:

$\Delta_f H^{\ominus}$[potassium bromide] = –394 kJ mol^{-1} $\Delta_{at} H^{\ominus}$[bromine] = +112 kJ mol^{-1} $\Delta_{at} H^{\ominus}$[potassium] = +89 kJ mol^{-1}

$\Delta_{ie1} H^{\ominus}$[potassium] = +419 kJ mol^{-1} $\Delta_{e1} H^{\ominus}$[bromine] = –325 kJ mol^{-1}

a) Construct a Born-Haber cycle for potassium bromide (KBr). [3 marks]

b) Use your Born-Haber cycle to calculate the lattice energy of potassium bromide. [2 marks]

Q2 Using this data:

$\Delta_f H^{\ominus}$[aluminium chloride] = –706 kJ mol^{-1} $\Delta_{at} H^{\ominus}$[chlorine] = +122 kJ mol^{-1} $\Delta_{at} H^{\ominus}$[aluminium] = +326 kJ mol^{-1}

$\Delta_{el} H^{\ominus}$[chlorine] = –349 kJ mol^{-1} $\Delta_{iel} H^{\ominus}$[aluminium] = +578 kJ mol^{-1}

$\Delta_{ie2} H^{\ominus}$[aluminium] = +1817 kJ mol^{-1} $\Delta_{ie3} H^{\ominus}$[aluminium] = +2745 kJ mol^{-1}

a) Construct a Born-Haber cycle for aluminium chloride ($AlCl_3$). [3 marks]

b) Use your cycle to calculate the lattice energy of aluminium chloride. [2 marks]

Q3 Using this data:

$\Delta_f H^{\ominus}$[aluminium oxide] = –1676 kJ mol^{-1} $\Delta_{at} H^{\ominus}$[oxygen] = +249 kJ mol^{-1} $\Delta_{at} H^{\ominus}$[aluminium] = +326 kJ mol^{-1}

$\Delta_{iel} H^{\ominus}$[aluminium] = +578 kJ mol^{-1} $\Delta_{ie2} H^{\ominus}$[aluminium] = +1817 kJ mol^{-1} $\Delta_{ie3} H^{\ominus}$[aluminium] = +2745 kJ mol^{-1}

$\Delta_{el} H^{\ominus}$[oxygen] = –141 kJ mol^{-1} $\Delta_{e2} H^{\ominus}$[oxygen] = +844 kJ mol^{-1}

a) Construct a Born-Haber cycle for aluminium oxide (Al_2O_3). [3 marks]

b) Use your cycle to calculate the lattice energy of aluminium oxide. [2 marks]

Using Born-Haber cycles — it's just like riding a bike...

All this energy going in and out can get a bit confusing. Remember these simple rules: 1) It takes energy to break bonds, but energy is given out when bonds are made. 2) A negative ΔH means energy is given out (it's exothermic). 3) A positive ΔH means energy is taken in (it's endothermic). 4) Never return to a firework once lit.

Polarisation

And you thought you'd finished with lattice energies...

Theoretical Lattice Energies are Based on the *Ionic Model*

1) There are **two ways** to work out a lattice energy:
   - the **experimental** way — using **experimental enthalpy values** in a Born-Haber cycle (see previous page).
   - the **theoretical** way — doing some calculations based on the **purely ionic model** of a lattice.
2) To work out a '**theoretical**' lattice energy, you assume that all the ions are **spherical** and have their **charge evenly distributed** around them — a purely **ionic** lattice. Then you work out how strongly the ions are attracted to one another based on their charges, the distance between them and so on (you don't need to know the details of these calculations, fortunately — just what they're based on). That gives you a value for the **energy change** when the ions **form** the lattice.

Comparing Lattice Energies Can Tell You *'How Ionic'* an Ionic Lattice Is

For any one compound, the experimental and theoretical lattice energies are usually **different**. **How** different they are tells you **how closely** the lattice **actually** resembles the 'purely ionic' model used for the theoretical calculations.

1) For example, the table shows **both** lattice energy values for some **sodium halides**.
   - The experimental and theoretical values are a pretty close **match** — so you can say that these compounds fit the '**purely ionic**' model (spherical ions with evenly distributed charge, etc.) very **well**.
   - This indicates that the structure of the lattice for these compounds is quite close to being **purely ionic**.

	Lattice Energy (kJ mol^{-1})	
	From experimental values (in Born-Haber cycle)	From theory
Sodium chloride	−787	−756
Sodium bromide	−742	−731
Sodium iodide	−698	−686

2) Here are some more lattice energies, for **magnesium halides** this time:

	Lattice Energy (kJ mol^{-1})	
	From experimental values (in Born-Haber cycle)	From theory
Magnesium chloride	−2526	−2326
Magnesium bromide	−2440	−2097
Magnesium iodide	−2327	−1944

   - The experimental lattice energies are **more negative** than the theoretical values by a fair bit.
   - This tells you that the bonding is, in practice, **stronger** than the calculations from the ionic model predict.
   - The difference shows that the bonding in the magnesium halides **isn't** as close to 'purely ionic' as it is with sodium halides.
   - It tells you that the ionic bonds in the magnesium halides are more **polarised** — they have **some covalent character** — whereas the bonds in sodium halides have almost no polarisation and very little covalent character.

Bill was a Grizzly bear before he was polarised.

Polarisation of Ionic Bonds Leads to *Covalent Character* in Ionic Lattices

So, **magnesium** halides have more covalent character in their ionic bonds than sodium halides. Here's why...

1) In a sodium halide, e.g. NaCl, the **cation**, Na^+, has only a **small charge** (+1) so it can't really pull electrons from the anion towards itself — so the charge is distributed evenly around the ions (there's almost **no polarisation**).
2) This is pretty much what the simple **ionic model** looks like — that's why the theoretical calculations of lattice energy match the experimental ones so well for sodium halides.
3) However, the magnesium halides **don't** fit the ionic model quite so well, because charge isn't evenly distributed around the ions — the cation, Mg^{2+}, has a **bigger charge** (+2), so it can pull electrons from the anion towards itself a bit, polarising the bond.
4) In general, the greater the **charge density** of the cation (its charge compared to its volume), the poorer the match will be between experimental and theoretical values for lattice energy.

Charge Density = Charge ÷ Volume

Polarisation

Small Cations Are Very Polarising

What normally happens in ionic compounds is that the **positive charge** on the **cation** attracts electrons towards it from the **anion** — this is **polarisation**.

1) **Small** cations with a **high charge** are **very polarising** because they have a **high charge density** — the positive charge is concentrated in the ion. So the cation can pull electrons towards itself.
2) **Large anions** with a **high charge** are **polarised more easily** than smaller ones with a lower charge. This is because their electrons are **further away** from the nucleus and there is **more repulsion** between the electrons, so the electrons can be pulled away more easily towards cations.
3) If a compound contains a cation with a **high polarising ability** and an anion which is **easily polarised**, some of the anion's electron charge cloud will be dragged towards the positive cation.
4) If the compound is polarised enough, a partially **covalent bond** is formed.

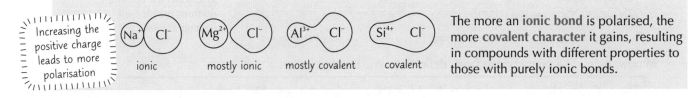

Increasing the positive charge leads to more polarisation

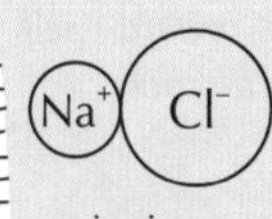

ionic

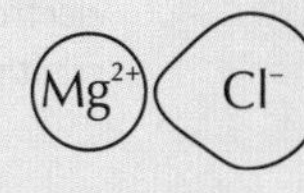

mostly ionic

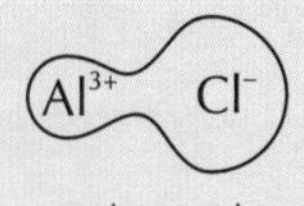

mostly covalent

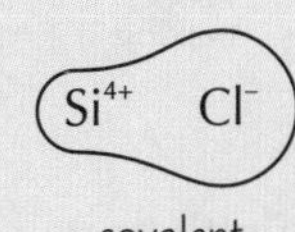

covalent

The more an **ionic bond** is polarised, the more **covalent character** it gains, resulting in compounds with different properties to those with purely ionic bonds.

Pauling Values Can Be Used to Work Out How Polar a Covalent Bond Is

1) **Electronegativity** is the ability of an atom to attract the bonding electrons in a **covalent** bond.
2) The **Pauling Scale** is usually used to measure the electronegativity of an atom.
3) The greater the **difference** in electronegativity, the greater the shift in electron density, and the **more polar** the bond.
4) Bonds are polar if the difference in Pauling electronegativity values is more than about 0.4.

Example: Predict whether a C–Cl bond will be polar, given that the Pauling electronegativity values of carbon and bromine are C = 2.5 and Cl = 3.0

The difference between the electronegativities of chlorine and carbon is: **3.0 – 2.5 = 0.5**

So the bond will be **polar**. The **chlorine atom** will have a slight **negative** charge and the **carbon atom** will have a slight **positive** charge.

5) Differences in electronegativity can also be given as **% ionic character** (see page 28).

Don't worry about remembering Pauling values — you'll be given this data in the exam. Lucky you.

Practice Questions

Q1 How can you tell, using lattice energies, whether an ionic compound is significantly polarised?

Q2 What sort of cation is highly polarising? What sort of anion is easily polarised?

Exam Questions

Q1 Metal/non-metal compounds are usually ionic, yet solid aluminium chloride exhibits many covalent characteristics. Explain why. [4 marks]

Q2 Consider the following compounds: $MgBr_2$ NaBr MgI_2

a) These compounds have differing degrees of covalent character in their bonds. Arrange the compounds in order of increasing covalent character, and explain your reasoning. [3 marks]

b) The theoretical lattice enthalpy of sodium iodide matches well with its experimental value but the theoretical lattice enthalpy of magnesium iodide does not match well with its experimental value. Explain this difference. [2 marks]

Lattice Energy — it's why rabbits have so many babies....

Is it ionic? Is it covalent? Who knows? Interpreting data is important when you're looking at the differences between theoretical and experimental values for lattice energies — you need to be able to explain what the data shows. Remember, the closer the two lattice energy values, the better the purely ionic model fits your compound.

Dissolving

Once you know what's happening when you stir sugar into your tea, your cuppa'll be twice as enjoyable.

Dissolving Involves Enthalpy Changes

When a solid **ionic lattice** dissolves in water these **two** things happen:

1) The bonds between the ions **break** — this is **endothermic**. The enthalpy change is the **opposite** of the **lattice enthalpy**.
2) Bonds between the ions and the water are **made** — this is **exothermic**. The enthalpy change here is called the **enthalpy change of hydration**.

The **enthalpy change of solution** is the overall effect of these two things.

Luckily for Geraldine, her lattice energy was greater than her enthalpy of hydration.

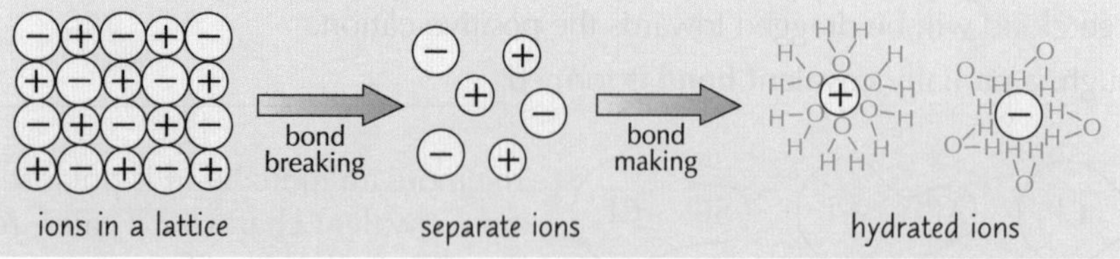

This effect happens because oxygen is more electronegative than hydrogen, so it draws the bonding electrons toward itself, creating a dipole.

$\delta-$ O, H $\delta+$, H $\delta+$

So now, here are a couple more fancy **definitions** you need to know:

> The **enthalpy change of hydration**, $\Delta_{hyd}H$, is the enthalpy change when 1 mole of gaseous ions dissolves in water.
> The **enthalpy change of solution**, $\Delta_{sol}H$, is the enthalpy change when 1 mole of solute dissolves in water.

Substances generally **only** dissolve if the energy released is roughly the same, or **greater than** the energy taken in. So soluble substances tend to have **exothermic** enthalpies of solution.

Enthalpy Change of Solution can be Calculated

You can work out the enthalpy change of solution using an energy cycle.
You just need to know the **lattice energy** of the compound and the **enthalpies of hydration** of the ions.

Here's how to draw the energy cycle for working out the **enthalpy change of solution** for **sodium chloride**:

1. Put the ionic lattice and the dissolved ions on the top — connect them by the enthalpy change of solution. This is the direct route.
2. Connect the ionic lattice to the gaseous ions by the lattice energy. The breakdown of the lattice has the opposite enthalpy change to the formation of the lattice.

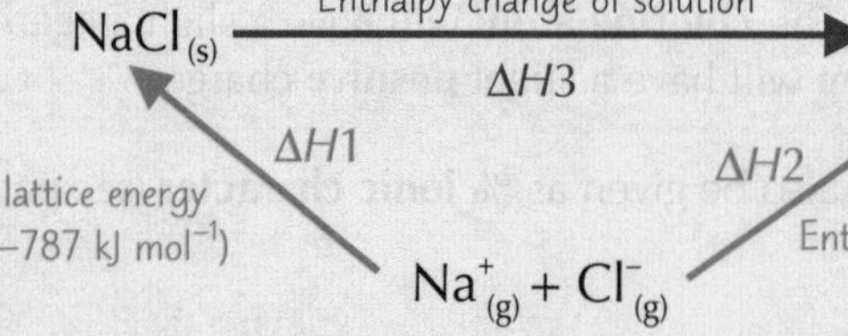

3. Connect the gaseous ions to the dissolved ions by the hydration enthalpies of **each** ion. This completes the indirect route.

From Hess's law: $\Delta H3 = -\Delta H1 + \Delta H2 = +787 + (-406 + -364) = +17$ **kJ mol^{-1}**

The enthalpy change of solution is **slightly endothermic**, but there are other factors at work that mean that sodium chloride still dissolves in water.

As long as there's only one unknown enthalpy value, you can use these cycles to work out any value on the arrows. For example, if you know the enthalpy change of solution and the enthalpy changes of hydration, you can use those values to work out the lattice energy.

You can also use energy level diagrams...

This one's for working out the **enthalpy change of solution** for **silver chloride**:

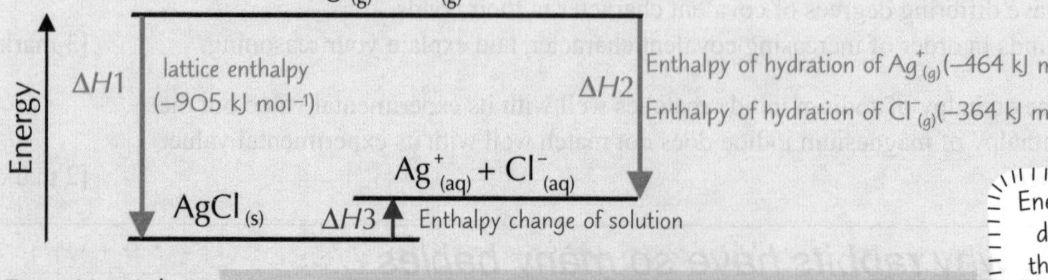

Energy level diagrams are only different to energy cycles in that substances are arranged vertically in the diagram according to their energies.

From Hess's law: $\Delta H3 = -\Delta H1 + \Delta H2 = +905 + (-464 + -364) = +77$ **kJ mol^{-1}**

This is much **more endothermic** than the enthalpy change of solution for sodium chloride. As such, silver chloride is **insoluble** in water.

Dissolving

Ionic Charge and Ionic Radius Affect the Enthalpy of Hydration

The **two** things that can affect the lattice energy (see page 142) can also affect the enthalpy of hydration. They are the **size** and the **charge** of the ions.

Ions with a greater charge have a greater enthalpy of hydration.

Ions with a **higher charge** are better at **attracting** water molecules than those with lower charges — the electrostatic attraction between the ion and the water molecules is **stronger**. This means **more energy** is released when the bonds are **made** giving them a **more exothermic** enthalpy of hydration.

Smaller ions have a greater enthalpy of hydration.

Smaller ions have a **higher** charge density than bigger ions. They **attract** the water molecules **better** and have a **more exothermic** enthalpy of hydration.

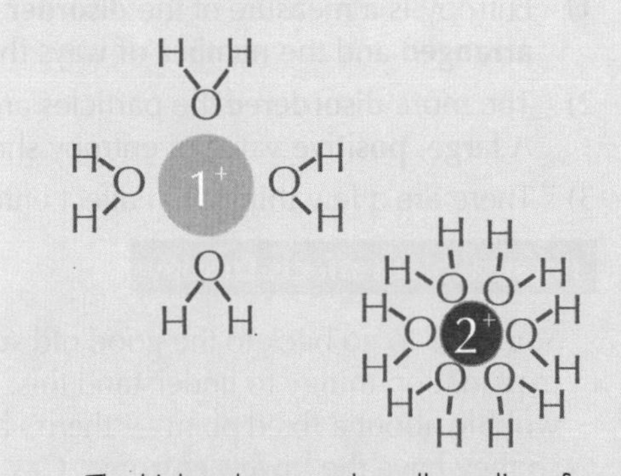

The higher charge and smaller radius of the 2+ ion create a higher charge density than the 1+ ion. This creates a stronger attraction for the water molecules and gives a more exothermic enthalpy of hydration.

E.g. a magnesium ion is smaller and more charged than a sodium ion, which gives it a much more exothermic enthalpy of hydration.

$\Delta_{hyd}H^{\ominus}[Mg^{2+}_{(g)}] = -1920$ kJ mol^{-1}
$\Delta_{hyd}H^{\ominus}[Na^{+}_{(g)}] = -406$ kJ mol^{-1}

Practice Questions

Q1 Describe the two steps that occur when an ionic lattice dissolves in water.
Q2 Define the enthalpy change of solution.
Q3 Do soluble substances have exothermic or endothermic enthalpies of solution in general?
Q4 Sketch an energy cycle that could be used to calculate the enthalpy change of solution of sodium chloride.
Q5 Name two factors that affect the enthalpy of hydration of an ion.

Exam Questions

Q1 a) Draw an energy cycle for the enthalpy change of solution of $AgF_{(s)}$. Label each enthalpy change. [2 marks]

b) Calculate the enthalpy change of solution for AgF from the following data: [2 marks]

$\Delta_{LE}H^{\ominus}[AgF_{(s)}] = -960$ kJ mol^{-1}, $\Delta_{hyd}H^{\ominus}[Ag^{+}_{(g)}] = -464$ kJ mol^{-1}, $\Delta_{hyd}H^{\ominus}[F^{-}_{(g)}] = -506$ kJ mol^{-1}.

Q2 a) Draw an energy level diagram for the dissolving of $CaCl_2$ using the data below. Label each enthalpy change. [2 marks]

$\Delta_{LE}H^{\ominus}[CaCl_{2(s)}] = -2258$ kJ mol^{-1}, $\Delta_{hyd}H^{\ominus}[Ca^{2+}_{(g)}] = -1579$ kJ mol^{-1}, $\Delta_{hyd}H^{\ominus}[Cl^{-}_{(g)}] = -364$ kJ mol^{-1}

b) Calculate the enthalpy change of solution for $CaCl_2$. [2 marks]

Q3 Show that the enthalpy of hydration of $Cl^{-}_{(g)}$ is -364 kJ mol^{-1}, given that: [3 marks]

$\Delta_{LE}H^{\ominus}[MgCl_{2(s)}] = -2526$ kJ mol^{-1}, $\Delta_{hyd}H^{\ominus}[Mg^{2+}_{(g)}] = -1920$ kJ mol^{-1}, $\Delta_{sol}H^{\ominus}[MgCl_{2(s)}] = -122$ kJ mol^{-1}.

Q4 Which of these ions will have a greater enthalpy of hydration — Ca^{2+} or K^{+}? Explain your answer. [3 marks]

Enthalpy change of solution of the Wicked Witch of the West = 939 kJ mol^{-1}...

Compared to the ones on pages 142 and 143, these energy cycles are an absolute breeze. You've got to make sure the definitions are firmly fixed in your mind though. You only need to know the lattice enthalpy and the enthalpy of hydration of your lattice ions, and you're well on your way to finding out the enthalpy change of solution.

Entropy

If you were looking for some random chemistry pages, you've just found them.

Entropy Tells you How Much Disorder There Is

1) Entropy is a measure of the **disorder** of a system — it tells you the **number of ways** that **particles** can be **arranged** and the **number of ways** that the **energy** can be shared out between the particles.
2) The more **disordered** the particles are, the higher the entropy is. A **large**, **positive** value of entropy shows a **high** level of disorder.
3) There are a few things that affect entropy:

Physical State affects Entropy

You have to go back to the good old **solid-liquid-gas** particle explanation thingy to understand this. **Solid** particles just wobble about a fixed point — there's **hardly any** randomness, so they have the **lowest entropy**. **Gas** particles whizz around wherever they like. They've got the most **random arrangements** of particles, so they have the **highest entropy**.

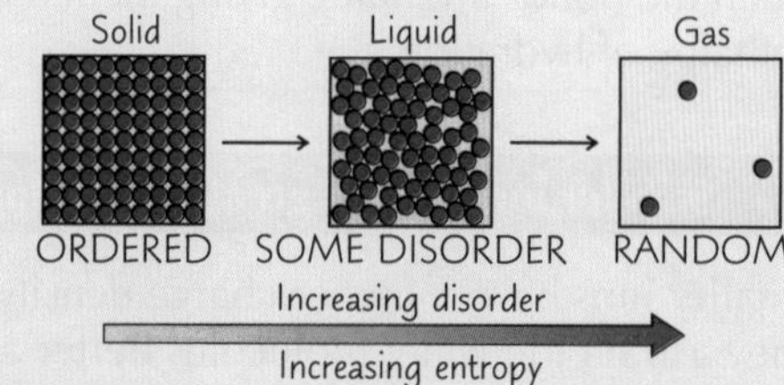

Examples:

- The **exothermic burning** of magnesium ribbon in air has a single **solid** product. One of the reactants (oxygen) is a **gas**, so in this reaction **disorder reduces** and **entropy is lowered**.

$$2Mg_{(s)} + O_{2(g)} \rightarrow 2MgO_{(s)}$$

- The reaction of **ethanoic acid** with **ammonium carbonate** produces **CO_2 gas** as a product, so in this reaction **disorder increases** and entropy is **raised**.

$$2CH_3COOH_{(aq)} + (NH_4)_2CO_{3(s)} \rightarrow 2CH_3COONH_{4(aq)} + H_2O_{(l)} + CO_{2(g)}$$

Dissolving affects Entropy

Dissolving a solid also increases its entropy — dissolved particles can **move freely** as they're no longer held in one place.

Example: Dissolving ammonium nitrate crystals in water results in an increase in entropy:

$$NH_4NO_{3(s)} \rightarrow NH_4^+{}_{(aq)} + NO_3^-{}_{(aq)}$$

A squirrel's favourite activity is to increase entropy.

More Particles means More Entropy

It makes sense — the more particles you've got, the **more ways** they and their energy can be **arranged**. So in a reaction like $N_2O_{4(g)} \rightarrow 2NO_{2(g)}$, entropy increases because the **number of moles** increases.

More Arrangements Means More Stability

1) Substances are actually more **energetically stable** when there's more disorder. So particles will move to try to **increase their entropy**.
2) This is why some reactions are **feasible** (they just happen by themselves — without the addition of energy) even when the enthalpy change is **endothermic**.

Example: The reaction of sodium hydrogencarbonate with hydrochloric acid is an **endothermic reaction** — but it is **feasible**. This is due to an **increase in entropy** as the reaction produces carbon dioxide gas and water. Liquids and gases are **more disordered** than solids and so have a **higher entropy**. This increase in entropy **overcomes** the change in enthalpy.

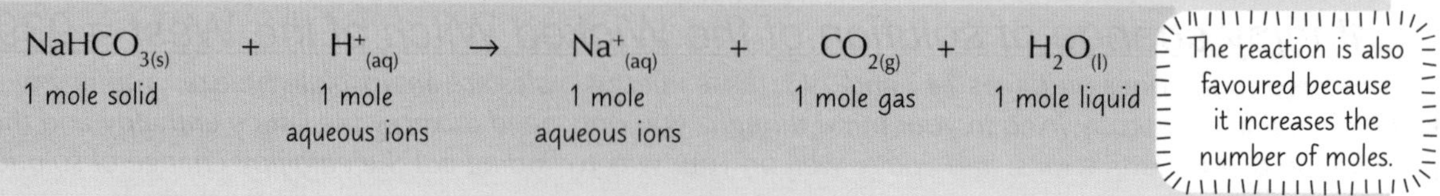

$NaHCO_{3(s)}$	+	$H^+_{(aq)}$	→	$Na^+_{(aq)}$	+	$CO_{2(g)}$	+	$H_2O_{(l)}$
1 mole solid		1 mole aqueous ions		1 mole aqueous ions		1 mole gas		1 mole liquid

The reaction is also favoured because it increases the number of moles.

Entropy

You Can Calculate the Entropy Change of a System

During a reaction there's an **entropy change** (ΔS) between the **reactants** and **products** — the entropy change of the system.

$$\Delta S_{system} = S_{products} - S_{reactants}$$

The units of entropy are $J\ K^{-1}\ mol^{-1}$.

Example: Calculate the entropy change for the reaction of ammonia and hydrogen chloride under standard conditions.

$$NH_{3(g)} + HCl_{(g)} \rightarrow NH_4Cl_{(s)}$$

$S^{\ominus}[NH_{3(g)}] = 192.3\ J\ K^{-1}\ mol^{-1}$, $S^{\ominus}[HCl_{(g)}] = 186.8\ J\ K^{-1}\ mol^{-1}$, $S^{\ominus}[NH_4Cl_{(s)}] = 94.60\ J\ K^{-1}\ mol^{-1}$

1) First find the entropy of the **products**:

$$S^{\ominus}_{products} = S^{\ominus}[NH_4Cl] = 94.60\ J\ K^{-1}\ mol^{-1}$$

2) Now find the entropy change of the **reactants**:

$$S^{\ominus}_{reactants} = S^{\ominus}[NH_3] + S^{\ominus}[HCl] = 192.3\ J\ K^{-1}\ mol^{-1} + 186.8\ J\ K^{-1}\ mol^{-1} = 379.1\ J\ K^{-1}\ mol^{-1}$$

3) Finally you can subtract the entropy of the reactants from the entropy of the products to find the **entropy change** for the system:

$$\Delta S_{system} = S^{\ominus}_{products} - S^{\ominus}_{reactants} = 94.60 - 379.1 = \mathbf{-284.5\ J\ K^{-1}\ mol^{-1}}$$

This shows a negative change in entropy. It's not surprising as 2 moles of gas have combined to form 1 mole of solid.

A positive entropy change means that a reaction is likely to be feasible, but a negative total entropy change **doesn't guarantee** the reaction **can't** happen — **enthalpy**, **temperature** and **kinetics** also play a part in whether or not a reaction occurs.

Practice Questions

Q1 What does the term 'entropy' mean?

Q2 Arrange the following compounds in order of increasing entropy values: $H_2O_{(l)}$, $MgO_{(s)}$, $CO_{2(g)}$

Q3 Write down the formula for the entropy change of a system.

Exam Questions

Q1 a) Based on just the equation below, predict whether the reaction is likely to be feasible. Give a reason for your answer.

$$Mg_{(s)} + \tfrac{1}{2}O_{2(g)} \rightarrow MgO_{(s)}$$

[2 marks]

b) Use the data on the right to calculate the entropy change for the system above. [2 marks]

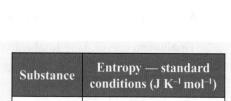

Substance	Entropy — standard conditions ($J\ K^{-1}\ mol^{-1}$)
$Mg_{(s)}$	32.7
$O_{2(g)}$	205.0
$MgO_{(s)}$	26.9

c) Does the result of the calculation indicate that the reaction will be feasible? Give a reason for your answer. [1 mark]

Q2 For the reaction $H_2O_{(l)} \rightarrow H_2O_{(s)}$:

$S^{\ominus}[H_2O_{(l)}] = 70\ J\ K^{-1}\ mol^{-1}$, $S^{\ominus}[H_2O_{(s)}] = 48\ J\ K^{-1}\ mol^{-1}$

a) Calculate the entropy change for this reaction. [1 mark]

b) Explain why this reaction might be feasible. [1 mark]

In the chemistry lab — chaos reigns...

Well, there you go. Entropy in all its glory. You haven't seen the back of it yet though, oh no. There's more where this came from. Which is why, if random disorder has left you in a spin, I'd suggest reading it again and making sure you've got your head round this lot before you turn over. You'll thank me for it... Chocolates are always welcome...

More on Entropy Change

Here we go, as promised, more entropy. Don't ever say I don't spoil you rotten...

The Total Entropy Change Includes the System and the Surroundings

1) As shown on page 149, during a reaction, there's an entropy change between the **reactants and products** — the entropy change of the **system**.
2) The entropy of the **surroundings** changes too (because **energy** is transferred to or from the system).
3) The **TOTAL entropy change** is the sum of the entropy changes of the **system** and the **surroundings**.

Remember, $\Delta S_{system} = S_{products} - S_{reactants}$

$$\Delta S_{total} = \Delta S_{system} + \Delta S_{surroundings}$$

Luckily, as well as for ΔS_{system}, there's a formula for calculating the change of entropy of the surroundings:

$$\Delta S_{surroundings} = -\frac{\Delta H}{T}$$

ΔH = enthalpy change (in J mol^{-1})
T = temperature (in K)

You can Calculate the Total Entropy Change for a Reaction

Example: Calculate the **total entropy change** for the reaction of ammonia and hydrogen chloride under standard conditions.

$$NH_{3(g)} + HCl_{(g)} \rightarrow NH_4Cl_{(s)} \qquad \Delta H = -315 \text{ kJ mol}^{-1} \text{ (at 298 K)}$$

$S^{\ominus}[NH_{3(g)}] = 192.3$ J K^{-1} mol^{-1}, $S^{\ominus}[HCl_{(g)}] = 186.8$ J K^{-1} mol^{-1}, $S^{\ominus}[NH_4Cl_{(s)}] = 94.60$ J K^{-1} mol^{-1}

First find the entropy change of the **system** — you've already done this on the previous page.

$$\Delta S_{system} = S_{products} - S_{reactants} = 94.60 - (192.3 + 186.8) = \mathbf{-284.5 \text{ J K}^{-1} \text{ mol}^{-1}}$$

Now find the entropy change of the **surroundings**:

$$\Delta H = -315 \text{ kJ mol}^{-1} = -315 \times 10^3 \text{ J mol}^{-1}$$

$$\Delta S_{surroundings} = -\frac{\Delta H}{T} = \frac{-(-315 \times 10^3)}{298} = \mathbf{+1057 \text{ J K}^{-1} \text{ mol}^{-1}}$$

The ΔH value given above is in kJ mol^{-1}, ΔH in the equation $\Delta S_{surroundings} = -\Delta H/T$ is in J mol^{-1}. You need to multiply the figure above by 1000 to convert it into J mol^{-1}.

Finally you can find the **total** entropy change:

$$\Delta S_{total} = \Delta S_{system} + \Delta S_{surroundings} = -284.5 + (+1057) = \mathbf{+772.5 \text{ J K}^{-1} \text{ mol}^{-1}}$$

Example: Calculate the **total entropy change** for ammonium nitrate crystals being dissolved in water under standard conditions.

$$NH_4NO_{3(s)} \xrightarrow{H_2O_{(l)}} NH_4^{+}{}_{(aq)} + NO_3^{-}{}_{(aq)} \qquad \Delta H = +25.70 \text{ kJ mol}^{-1} \text{ (at 298 K)}$$

$S^{\ominus}[NH_4NO_{3(s)}] = 151.1$ J K^{-1} mol^{-1}, $S^{\ominus}[NH_4^{+}{}_{(aq)}] = 113.4$ J K^{-1} mol^{-1}, $S^{\ominus}[NO_3^{-}{}_{(aq)}] = 146.4$ J K^{-1} mol^{-1}

Find the entropy change of the **system**:

$$\Delta S_{system} = S_{products} - S_{reactants} = (146.4 + 113.4) - 151.1 = \mathbf{+108.7 \text{ J K}^{-1} \text{ mol}^{-1}}$$

This makes sense if you look at the equation — you'd expect an increase in the entropy of the system because a solid is dissolving to produce freely moving ions, increasing disorder.

Now find the entropy change of the **surroundings**:

$$\Delta S_{surroundings} = -\frac{\Delta H}{T} = -\frac{(25.70 \times 10^3)}{298} = \mathbf{-86.24 \text{ J K}^{-1} \text{ mol}^{-1}}$$

So, the **total** entropy change is:

$$\Delta S_{total} = \Delta S_{system} + \Delta S_{surroundings} = 108.7 - 86.24 = \mathbf{+22.46 \text{ J K}^{-1} \text{ mol}^{-1}}$$

More on Entropy Change

You Can Relate **Reaction Results** to Changes in **Entropy** and **Enthalpy**

Example: Reaction between barium hydroxide and ammonium chloride.
First, place a flask on top of a piece of damp cardboard. Add to the flask **solid barium hydroxide crystals**, $Ba(OH)_2.8H_2O$, and **solid ammonium chloride**, then stir. Within about 30 seconds, the smell of ammonia becomes noticeable and a short time later, the bottom of the flask will be **frozen** to the cardboard. The **temperature drops** to well below 0 °C.

$$Ba(OH)_2.8H_2O_{(s)} + 2NH_4Cl_{(s)} \rightarrow BaCl_{2(s)} + 10H_2O_{(l)} + 2NH_{3(g)} \qquad \Delta H = +164.0 \text{ kJ mol}^{-1} \text{ (at 298 K)}$$

Looking at the equation, you would expect an **increase** in the entropy of the system because two solids are combining to produce a solid, a liquid and a gas — that's an **increase** in disorder.
Calculating ΔS_{system} using standard entropies confirms this:

$S^{\ominus}[Ba(OH)_2.8H_2O_{(s)}] = +427.0 \text{ J K}^{-1} \text{ mol}^{-1}$, $S^{\ominus}[NH_4Cl_{(s)}] = +94.6 \text{ J K}^{-1} \text{ mol}^{-1}$, $S^{\ominus}[BaCl_{2(s)}] = +123.7 \text{ J K}^{-1} \text{ mol}^{-1}$, $S^{\ominus}[H_2O_{(l)}] = +69.9 \text{ J K}^{-1} \text{ mol}^{-1}$, $S^{\ominus}[NH_{3(g)}] = +192.3 \text{ J K}^{-1} \text{ mol}^{-1}$

$$S_{reactants} = 427.0 + (2 \times 94.6) = +616.2 \text{ J K}^{-1} \text{ mol}^{-1}$$
$$S_{products} = 123.7 + (10 \times 69.9) + (2 \times 192.3) = +1207.3 \text{ J K}^{-1} \text{ mol}^{-1}$$

$$\Delta S_{system} = S_{products} - S_{reactants} = 1207.3 - 616.2 = +591.1 \text{ J K}^{-1} \text{ mol}^{-1}$$

The formula for barium hydroxide crystals is $Ba(OH)_2.8H_2O$. The $.8H_2O$ part of the formula tells you that there is water within the crystalline structure.

The reaction is **endothermic**, so the entropy change of the surroundings must be **negative**.

$$\Delta S_{surroundings} = -\Delta H/T = -164\,000 \div 298 = -550.3 \text{ J K}^{-1} \text{ mol}^{-1}$$

Once you know $\Delta S_{surroundings}$ and ΔS_{system} you can calculate the **total entropy change** for the reaction.

$$\Delta S_{total} = \Delta S_{system} + \Delta S_{surroundings} = 591.1 - 550.3 = \mathbf{+40.8 \text{ J K}^{-1} \text{ mol}^{-1}}$$

Practice Questions

Q1 What is the formula for calculating the total entropy change of a reaction?

Q2 What is the formula for calculating $\Delta S_{surroundings}$?

Q3 What sign will the entropy of surroundings be for an endothermic reaction?

Exam Questions

Q1 When a small amount of ammonium carbonate solid is added to 10 cm³ of 1.0 mol dm⁻³ ethanoic acid, carbon dioxide gas is evolved. This is an endothermic reaction, so the temperature of the reaction mixture drops.

$$(NH_4)_2CO_{3(s)} + 2CH_3CO_2H_{(aq)} \rightarrow 2CH_3CO_2NH_{4(aq)} + H_2O_{(l)} + CO_{2(g)} \qquad \Delta H^{\ominus} > 0$$

a) Looking at the equation, what would you expect to happen to the entropy of the system during this reaction? Explain your answer. [3 marks]

b) Explain how this reaction can be both endothermic and have a positive ΔS_{total}. [2 marks]

Q2 Thin ribbons of magnesium burn brightly in oxygen to leave a solid, white residue of magnesium oxide. The equation for this reaction is:

$$2Mg_{(s)} + O_{2(g)} \rightarrow 2MgO_{(s)} \qquad \Delta H = -1204 \text{ kJ mol}^{-1} \text{ (at 298 K)}$$

$S^{\ominus}[Mg_{(s)}] = +32.7 \text{ J K}^{-1} \text{ mol}^{-1}$, $S^{\ominus}[O_{2(g)}] = +205 \text{ J K}^{-1} \text{ mol}^{-1}$, $S^{\ominus}[MgO_{(s)}] = +26.9 \text{ J K}^{-1} \text{ mol}^{-1}$

a) Using the data given, calculate ΔS_{system} at 298 K. [3 marks]

b) Calculate ΔS_{total} for the reaction. [4 marks]

The entropy of my surrounds is always increasing, take a look at my kitchen...

Still awake? Great stuff. Let me be the first to congratulate you on making it to the end of this page — I nearly didn't. As a reward I suggest ten minutes of looking at clips of talented cats online. It'll cheer you up no end and you can think of all those lovely calculations while watching Mr Smudge walks on his hind legs. Ahh... the Internet.

Free Energy

Free energy — I could do with a bit of that. My gas bill is astronomical.

For Feasible Reactions ΔG must be **Negative** or **Zero**

1) The tendency of a process to take place is dependent on three things — the **entropy**, **ΔS**, the **enthalpy**, **ΔH**, and the **temperature**, **T**. When you put all these things **together** you get the **free energy change**, **ΔG**. ΔG tells you if a reaction is **feasible** or not — the more negative the value of ΔG, the more feasible the reaction.

Of course, there's a formula for it:

$$\Delta G = \Delta H - T\Delta S_{system}$$

ΔH = enthalpy change (in J mol^{-1})
T = temperature (in K)
ΔS_{system} = entropy change of the system (in J K^{-1} mol^{-1})

The units of ΔG are often J mol^{-1}.

Example: Calculate the free energy change for the following reaction at 298 K.

$MgCO_{3(g)} \rightarrow MgO_{(s)} + CO_{2(g)}$ $\quad \Delta H^{\circ} = +117\ 000$ J mol^{-1}, $\Delta S_{system} = +175$ J K^{-1} mol^{-1}

$\Delta G = \Delta H - T\Delta S_{system} = +117\ 000 - (298 \times (+175)) =$ **+64 900 J mol^{-1}** (3 s.f.)

ΔG is positive — so the reaction isn't feasible at this temperature.

2) When $\Delta G = 0$, the reaction is **just feasible**. So the temperature at which the reaction becomes feasible can be calculated by rearranging the equation like this:

$$\Delta H - T\Delta S_{system} = 0, \text{ so } \quad T = \frac{\Delta H}{\Delta S_{system}}$$

Example: At what temperature does the reaction $MgCO_{3(g)} \rightarrow MgO_{(s)} + CO_{2(g)}$ become feasible?

$$T = \frac{\Delta H}{\Delta S_{system}} = \frac{+117\ 000}{+175} = \mathbf{669\ K}$$

3) You can use ΔG to **predict** whether or not a reaction is **feasible**. By looking at the equation $\Delta G = \Delta H - T\Delta S$, you can see that:

Temperature is measured in Kelvin so will always have a positive value.

> When ΔH is **negative** and ΔS is **positive**, ΔG will always be **negative** and the reaction is **feasible.**
> When ΔH is **positive** and ΔS is **negative**, ΔG will always be **positive** and the reaction is **not feasible.**

In other situations, the feasibility of the reaction is dependent on the temperature.

Feasible **Reversible** Reactions have **Large Equilibrium Constants**

1) An equilibrium constant is a measure of the ratio of the concentration of products to reactants at equilibria for a reversible reaction at a specific temperature.
2) Reactions with **negative** ΔG, and so are theoretically **feasible**, have large values for their equilibrium constants — **greater** than 1.
3) Reactions with **positive** ΔG, and so **not** theoretically feasible, have small values for their equilibrium constants — **smaller** than 1.
4) This relationship is represented by the equation:

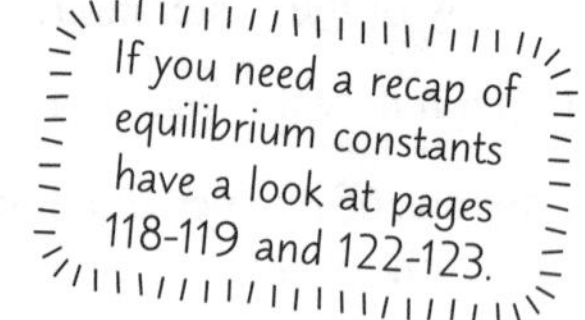
If you need a recap of
equilibrium constants
have a look at pages
118-119 and 122-123.

$$\Delta G = -RT \ln K$$

R = gas constant, 8.31 J K^{-1} mol^{-1}
T = temperature (in K)
$\ln K$ = the natural log of the equilibrium constant

Example: Ethanoic acid and ethanol were reacted together at 298 K and allowed to reach equilibrium. The equilibrium constant was calculated to be 4 at 298 K. Calculate the free energy change for the reaction.

$$CH_3COOH_{(l)} + C_2H_5OH_{(l)} \rightleftharpoons CH_3COOC_2H_{5(l)} + H_2O_{(l)}$$

The equilibrium constant is **greater than 1**, so you'd **expect** ΔG to be **negative**...

$\Delta G = -RT \ln K = -(8.31 \times 298) \times \ln(4) =$ **−3430 J mol^{-1}** (3 s.f.) ...and it **is.**

ΔG is negative — so the reaction is feasible at 298K.

Free Energy

Equilibrium Constants can be Calculated from ΔG

You may get asked to **calculate** equilibrium constants from the free energy change of a reaction.

Example: Hydrogen gas and iodine are mixed together in a sealed flask forming hydrogen iodide. Calculate the equilibrium constant at 763 K.

$$H_{2(g)} + I_{2(g)} \rightleftharpoons 2HI_{(g)} \quad \Delta G = -24287 \text{ J mol}^{-1}$$

Firstly, you need to rearrange the equation, $\Delta G = -RT \ln K$, to find $\ln K$:

$$\ln K = \frac{\Delta G}{-RT} = \frac{-24287}{-(8.31 \times 763)} = 3.8304$$

To find the value of K, you need to find the inverse of the log. To do this, use the exponential function for your value of $\ln K$:

$$\ln K = 3.8304 \text{ so } K = e^{3.8304} = 46$$

Finally, you need to calculate the units of K:

$$K = \frac{(\cancel{\text{mol dm}^{-3}})(\cancel{\text{mol dm}^{-3}})}{(\cancel{\text{mol dm}^{-3}})(\cancel{\text{mol dm}^{-3}})} = \textbf{no units}$$

So K = **46** (2 s.f.)

If you want a reminder of how to calculate the units for equilibrium constants, have a look at page 122.

Negative ΔG doesn't Guarantee a Reaction

The value of the free energy change doesn't tell you anything about the reaction's **rate**. Even if ΔG shows that a reaction is theoretically feasible, it might have a really **high activation energy** or happen so slowly that you wouldn't notice it happening at all. For example:

$H_{2(g)} + ½O_{2(g)} \rightarrow H_2O_{(g)}$ $\quad \Delta H^{\circ} = -242\,000 \text{ J mol}^{-1}$, $\Delta S^{\circ} = -44.4 \text{ J K}^{-1} \text{mol}^{-1}$

At 298 K, $\Delta G = -242\,000 - (298 \times (-44.4)) =$ **−229 000 J mol⁻¹** (3 s.f.)

But this reaction **doesn't occur** at 298 K — it needs a spark to start it off due to its **high activation energy**.

Practice Questions

Q1 What are the three things that determine the value of ΔG?

Q2 If the free energy change of a reaction is positive, what can you conclude about the reaction?

Q3 What is the relationship between the free energy change and equilibrium constants?

Q4 Why might a reaction with a negative ΔG value not always be feasible?

Exam Questions

Q1 a) Use the equation below and the table on the right to calculate the free energy change for the complete combustion of methane at 298 K. [2 marks]

$$CH_{4(g)} + 2O_{2(g)} \rightarrow CO_{2(g)} + 2H_2O_{(l)} \quad \Delta H^{\circ} = -730 \text{ kJ mol}^{-1}$$

b) Explain whether the reaction is feasible at 298 K. [1 mark]

c) What is the maximum temperature at which the reaction is feasible? [1 mark]

Substance	S° (J K⁻¹ mol⁻¹)
$CH_{4(g)}$	186
$O_{2(g)}$	205
$CO_{2(g)}$	214
$H_2O_{(l)}$	69.9
$C_3H_7OH_{(l)}$	193

Q2 At 723 K, the equilibrium constant for the exothermic reaction $H_{2(g)} + Cl_{2(g)} \rightleftharpoons 2HCl_{(g)}$ is 60. ΔS for the reaction is negative.

a) Calculate the free energy change for this reaction. [1 mark]

b) Describe the effect of increasing the temperature of the reaction on the free energy change. [2 marks]

ΔG for chemistry revision definitely has a positive value...

Okay, so ΔG won't tell you for definite whether a reaction will happen, but it will tell you if the reaction is at least theoretically feasible. Make sure you know the formulae for ΔG, how to rearrange them and how to work out the numbers to plonk in it. And don't forget to check your units, check your units, check your units.

Electrochemical Cells

On these pages there are electrons to-ing and fro-ing in redox reactions. And when electrons move, you get electricity.

If Electrons are Transferred, it's a **Redox Reaction**

Look back at your page 40 for more about redox reactions.

1) A **loss** of electrons is called **oxidation**.
   When an element is **oxidised**, its **oxidation number** will **increase**.
2) A **gain** of electrons is called **reduction**. When an element is **reduced**, its **oxidation number** will **decrease**.
3) Reduction and oxidation happen **simultaneously** — hence the term "**redox**" reaction.

- **s-block metals** tend to react by being **oxidised** — they **lose electrons** to form **positive ions** with charges the same as their group number (i.e. **Group 1** metals form **1+ ions** and **Group 2** metals form **2+ ions**).
- **p-block metals** can react by **losing electrons** (like the s-block elements), but the **non-metals** in the **p-block** react by **gaining electrons** to form **negative ions** with charges the same as their **group number minus 8**.
  p-block elements often react to form covalent species, where electrons are shared (rather than lost or gained) — see page 22.
- **d-block metals** form ions with **variable oxidation states** (see page 169) so predicting how these elements react can be tricky. But, they tend to form **positive ions** with **positive oxidation numbers**.

Electrochemical Cells Make **Electricity**

1) Electrochemical cells can be made from **two different metals** dipped in salt solutions of their **own ions** and connected by a wire (the **external circuit**). There are always **two** reactions within an electrochemical cell. One's an oxidation and one's a reduction — so it's a **redox process**.
2) Oxidation happens at the **anode** and reduction happens at the **cathode**. But unlike cells in electrolysis, in an electrochemical cell, the **anode** is the **negative** electrode and the **cathode** is the **positive** electrode.
3) **Reactive metals** form ions **more readily** than **unreactive metals**. The **more reactive metal** gives up its electrons and is **oxidised** (it becomes the **anode**, where **electrons flow** from). The **less reactive metal** becomes the **cathode**.

Here's what happens in the **zinc/copper** electrochemical cell on the right:

- Zinc **loses electrons** more easily than copper. So in the left-hand half-cell, zinc (from the zinc electrode) is **OXIDISED** to form $Zn^{2+}_{(aq)}$ ions.

  $$Zn_{(s)} \rightarrow Zn^{2+}_{(aq)} + 2e^-$$

  This releases electrons into the external circuit.
- In the other half-cell, the **same number of electrons** are taken from the external circuit, **REDUCING** the Cu^{2+} ions to copper atoms.

  $$Cu^{2+}_{(aq)} + 2e^- \rightarrow Cu_{(s)}$$

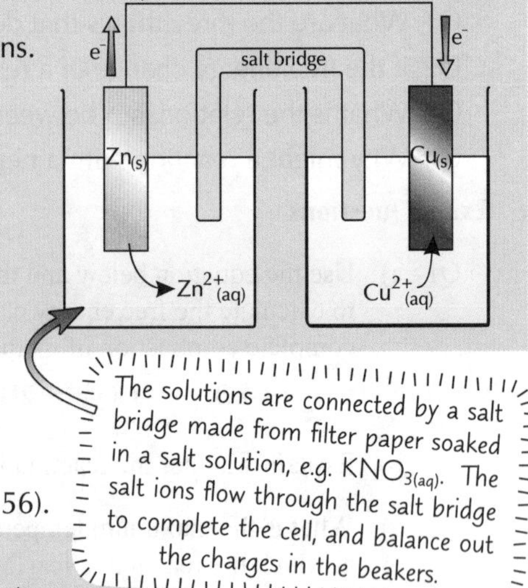

The solutions are connected by a salt bridge made from filter paper soaked in a salt solution, e.g. $KNO_{3(aq)}$. The salt ions flow through the salt bridge to complete the cell, and balance out the charges in the beakers.

4) **Electrons** flow through the wire from the most reactive metal to the least.
5) You can put a voltmeter in the external circuit to measure the **voltage** between the two half-cells. This is the **cell potential** or **EMF**, E_{cell}. Voltmeters also measure the direction of the flow of electrons (see page 156).

You can also have half-cells involving **solutions of two aqueous ions of the same element**, such as $Fe^{2+}_{(aq)}/Fe^{3+}_{(aq)}$.
The conversion from Fe^{2+} to Fe^{3+}, or vice versa, happens on the surface of the **electrode**.

$$Fe^{2+}_{(aq)} \rightarrow Fe^{3+}_{(aq)} + e^- \qquad Fe^{3+}_{(aq)} + e^- \rightarrow Fe^{2+}_{(aq)}$$

Because neither the reactants nor the products are solids, you need something else for the **electrode**.
It needs to **conduct electricity** and be very **inert**, so that it won't react with anything in the half-cell. **Platinum** is an excellent choice, but is very **expensive**, so **graphite** is often used instead.

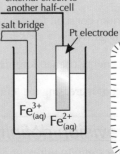

external circuit to another half-cell
salt bridge
Pt electrode
$Fe^{3+}_{(aq)}$ $Fe^{2+}_{(aq)}$

Electrochemical cells can also be made from non-metals. For systems involving a gas (e.g. chlorine), the gas can be bubbled over a platinum electrode sitting in a solution of its aqueous ions (e.g. Cl^-).

6) When drawing electrochemical cells, the half-cell where **oxidation** happens (the **anode**) should always be drawn on the **left**, and the half-cell where **reduction** happens (the **cathode**) should be drawn on the **right**.

Electrochemical Cells

The Reactions at Each Electrode are Reversible

1) The **reactions** that occur at each electrode in the **zinc/copper** cell on the last page are: ⟹ $Zn^{2+}_{(aq)} + 2e^- \rightleftharpoons Zn_{(s)}$ $Cu^{2+}_{(aq)} + 2e^- \rightleftharpoons Cu_{(s)}$
2) The **reversible arrows** show that both reactions can go in **either direction**. **Which direction** each reaction goes in depends on **how easily** each metal **loses electrons** (i.e. how easily it's **oxidised**).
3) These reactions are called **half-reactions** and, even though they're reversible, they're always written with the **reduction reaction** going in the **forward** direction, with the **electrons being added** on the **left-hand side**.

You Need to Know How to Set Up an Electrochemical Cell

You can set up an electrochemical cell and use it to take measurements of **voltage**.
Here's a method you can use to construct an **electrochemical cell** involving **two metals**.

1) Get a strip of each of the **metals** you're investigating. These are your electrodes. **Clean** the **surfaces** of the metals using a piece of **emery paper** (or **sandpaper**).
2) Clean any **grease** or **oil** from the electrodes using some **propanone**. From this point on, be careful **not to touch** the surfaces of the metals with your hands — you could transfer **grease** back onto the strips.
3) Place each electrode into a **beaker** filled with a solution containing **ions** of that metal. For example, if you had an electrode made of **zinc** metal, you could place it in a beaker of **$ZnSO_{4\,(aq)}$**. If you had an electrode made of **copper**, you could use a solution of **$CuSO_{4\,(aq)}$**. If one of the half-cells contains an oxidising agent that contains oxygen (e.g. MnO_4^-), you'll have to add acid too.
4) Create a **salt bridge** to link the two solutions together. You can do this by simply soaking a piece of filter paper in **salt solution**, e.g. $KCl_{(aq)}$ or $KNO_{3\,(aq)}$, and draping it between the two beakers. The ends of the filter paper should be **immersed** in the solutions.
5) Connect the electrodes to a **voltmeter** using **crocodile clips** and **wires**. If you've set up your circuit correctly, you'll get a **reading** on your voltmeter.

If your electrochemical cell is made up of half-cells where neither the oxidised or reduced species are solid (e.g. they're both aqueous ions), your method will be slightly different. For example, you'll need to use an inert electrode (e.g. platinum).

Practice Questions

Q1 Do s-block metals tend to react by losing or gaining electrons?

Q2 Does oxidation happen at the cathode or the anode?

Q3 How would you set up a half-cell cell between two ions of the same element in different oxidation states?

Exam Questions

Q1 A cell is made up of an iron and a zinc electrode. The half-equations for the two electrodes are:

$$Fe^{2+}_{(aq)} + 2e^- \rightleftharpoons Fe_{(s)} \qquad Zn^{2+}_{(aq)} + 2e^- \rightleftharpoons Zn_{(s)}$$

a) Describe how you would set up an electrochemical cell using an iron and a zinc half-cell. [4 marks]

b) Given that zinc is more easily oxidised than iron, draw a diagram to show this cell. Show the direction of the flow of electrons around the cell [4 marks]

Q2 A student sets up an electrochemical cell by placing strips of copper and silver metal in solutions containing copper and silver salts respectively. He connects the strips of metal to a voltmeter with wires, and connects the salt solutions together with a salt bridge.

a) What is the role of the salt bridge? [2 marks]

b) Suggest how the student could make the salt bridge. [1 mark]

c) Given that copper is a more reactive metal than silver, which metal strip will form the cathode? [1 mark]

Cells aren't just for biologists, you know...

You'll probably have to do an experiment involving electrochemical cells in your class, so make sure you read that method above really carefully so you can set up any electrochemical cell even with your eyes closed (though this is not advised...). You could be asked about this practical in your exam too, so even more reason to know it inside out...

Electrode Potentials

Time for some more electrochemical cell fun. Bet you can't wait — these pages have real potential...

Each Half-Cell has an Electrode Potential

1) Each **half-cell** in an electrochemical cell has its own **electrode potential** — this is a measure of how easily the substance in the half-cell is oxidised (i.e. loses electrons).
2) As the substances in the half-cells are oxidised or reduced, a **potential difference** builds up, due to the difference in charge between the electrode and the ions in solution. E.g., in the **zinc half-cell**, the **Zn electrode** is **negatively charged** (due to the electrons left behind when Zn^{2+} ions form) and the Zn^{2+} **ions** in solution are **positively charged.**
3) The half-reaction with the more **positive** electrode potential ($E^\ominus$) value goes **forwards**. The half-reaction with the more **negative** $E^\ominus$ value goes **backwards**.
4) The table on the right shows the electrode potentials for the copper and zinc half-cells. The **zinc half-cell** has a **more negative** electrode potential, so **zinc is oxidised** (the reaction goes **backwards**), while **copper is reduced** (the reaction goes **forwards**). The little $\ominus$ symbol next to the E shows they're **standard electrode potentials** (see below).
5) In this example, zinc is being oxidised and copper is being reduced, so **zinc** is acting as a **reducing agent** and **copper** is acting as an **oxidising agent**.

Half-cell	Electrode potential $E^\ominus$(V)
$Zn^{2+}_{(aq)} + 2e^- \rightarrow Zn_{(s)}$	−0.76
$Cu^{2+}_{(aq)} + 2e^- \rightarrow Cu_{(s)}$	+0.34

$$Cu^{2+}_{(aq)} + Zn_{(s)} \rightleftharpoons Cu_{(s)} + Zn^{2+}_{(aq)}$$

Electrode Potentials are Measured Against Standard Hydrogen Electrodes

You measure the electrode potential of a half-cell against a **standard hydrogen electrode**.

> The **standard electrode potential**, $E^\ominus$, of a half-cell is the **voltage measured** under **standard conditions** when the **half-cell** is connected to a **standard hydrogen electrode.**

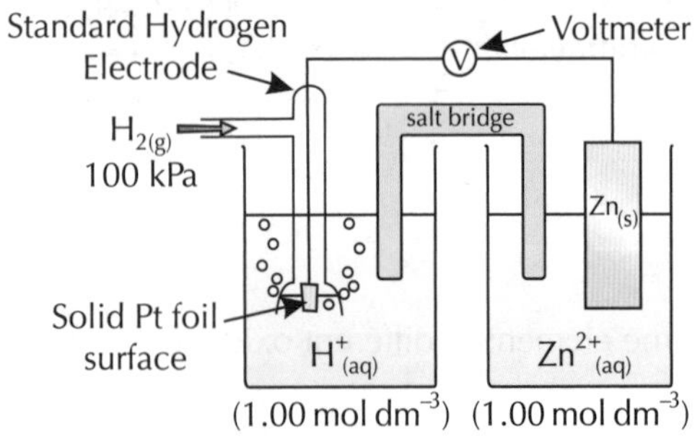

Standard conditions are:

1) The solutions of the ions you're interested in must have a concentration of **1.00 mol dm^{-3}**.
2) The temperature must be **298 K (25 °C)**.
3) The pressure must be **100 kPa**.

The equation for the reaction at the hydrogen electrode is: $2H^+_{(aq)} + 2e^- \rightleftharpoons H_{2(g)}$

The **standard hydrogen electrode** is always shown on the **left** — it doesn't matter whether or not the other half-cell is where oxidation happens.

The standard hydrogen electrode is a **reference electrode**, and allows scientists to work out and compare the electrode potentials of whatever half-cell the hydrogen electrode's connected to. The hydrogen half-cell has a value of **0.00 V**. This means the **voltage reading** will be equal to $E^\ominus$ of the other half-cell (as $E^\ominus$ for the standard hydrogen electrode is 0.00 V).

This reading could be positive or negative, depending which way the electrons flow.

Work Out E_{cell} From Standard Electrode Potentials

1) You can use standard electrode potentials to **calculate** the **cell potential,** $E^\ominus_{cell}$, of an electrochemical cell. You'll need to use this formula: $E^\ominus_{cell} = (E^\ominus_{reduction} - E^\ominus_{oxidation})$
2) The cell potential will always be a **positive voltage**, because the more negative $E^\ominus$ value is being subtracted from the more positive $E^\ominus$ value.

Example: Calculate the cell potential of a magnesium-bromine electrochemical cell: $Br_2 + Mg \rightarrow Mg^{2+} + 2Br^-$

$Mg^{2+}_{(aq)} + 2e^- \rightleftharpoons Mg_{(s)}$ $E^\ominus = -2.37$ V $\frac{1}{2}Br_{2(aq)} + e^- \rightleftharpoons Br^-_{(aq)}$ $E^\ominus = +1.09$ V

All you have to do is substitute the standard electrode potentials of Mg/Mg^{2+} and $\frac{1}{2}Br_2/Br^-$ into the equation:

$E^\ominus_{cell} = (E^\ominus_{reduction} - E^\ominus_{oxidation})$ ⟹ $E^\ominus_{cell} = +1.09 - (-2.37) = \mathbf{+3.46\ V}$

Electrode Potentials

Conditions Affect the Value of the **Electrode Potential**

Just like any other reversible reaction, the **equilibrium position** in a half-cell is affected by changes in **temperature**, **pressure** and **concentration**. Changing the equilibrium position changes the **cell potential**.
To get around this, **standard conditions** are used to measure electrode potentials — using these conditions means you always get the **same value** for the electrode potential and you can **compare values** for different cells.

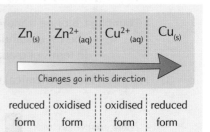

Caroline showed great potential from a young age.

There's a **Convention** for **Drawing** Electrochemical Cells

It's a bit of a faff drawing pictures of electrochemical cells.
There's a **shorthand** way of representing them though. This is known as the **conventional representation**— for example, the **Zn/Cu cell** is shown on the right.

$Zn_{(s)}$ ¦ $Zn^{2+}_{(aq)}$ ¦¦ $Cu^{2+}_{(aq)}$ ¦ $Cu_{(s)}$

Changes go in this direction

reduced form ¦ oxidised form ¦¦ oxidised form ¦ reduced form

There are a couple of important **conventions** when drawing cells:

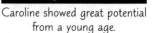

1) The **half-cell** with the **more negative** potential goes on the **left**.
2) The **oxidised forms** go in the **centre** of the cell diagram and **reduced** forms go on the **outside**.
3) **Double** vertical lines show the **salt bridge**, and **single** vertical lines separate species in **different physical states**.
4) **Commas** separate species that are in the same half-cell and in the **same physical state**.
5) In conventional representations of electrochemical cells involving the **standard hydrogen electrode**, the standard hydrogen half-cell should always go on the **left**.
6) If either of the half-cells use platinum, lead or other **inert electrodes**, show these on the outside of the diagram.

Example: Draw the conventional representation of the electrochemical cell formed between magnesium and the standard hydrogen half-cell.

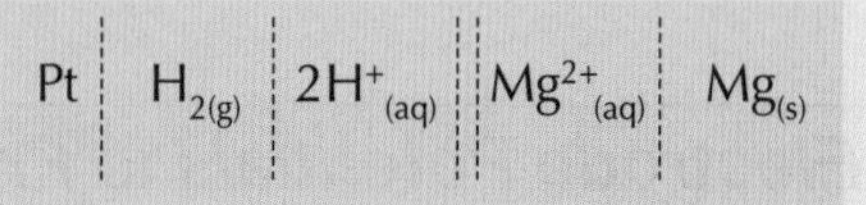

Practice Questions

Q1 What's the definition of standard electrode potential?

Q2 What is the voltage of the standard hydrogen electrode half-cell?

Q3 State the equation you could use to work out E_{cell}.

Exam Questions

Q1 A cell is made up of a lead and an iron plate, dipped in solutions of lead(II) nitrate and iron(II) nitrate respectively and connected by a salt bridge. The electrode potentials for the two electrodes are:

$Fe^{2+}_{(aq)} + 2e^- \rightleftharpoons Fe_{(s)}$ $E^\ominus = -0.44$ V $Pb^{2+}_{(aq)} + 2e^- \rightleftharpoons Pb_{(s)}$ $E^\ominus = -0.13$ V

a) Which metal becomes oxidised in the cell? Explain your answer. [2 marks]

b) Find the standard cell potential of this cell. [1 mark]

Q2 An electrochemical cell containing a zinc half-cell and a silver half-cell was set up using a potassium nitrate salt bridge. The cell potential at 25 °C was measured to be 1.40 V.

$Zn^{2+}_{(aq)} + 2e^- \rightleftharpoons Zn_{(s)}$ $E^\ominus = -0.76$ V $Ag^{+}_{(aq)} + e^- \rightleftharpoons Ag_{(s)}$ $E^\ominus = +0.80$ V

a) Use the standard electrode potentials given to calculate the standard cell potential for a zinc-silver cell. [1 mark]

b) Suggest two possible reasons why the actual cell potential was different from the value calculated in part (a). [2 marks]

This is potentially the best page I've ever read...

Standard electrode potentials are measured under standard conditions — the name kind of gives it away doesn't it? Make sure you remember what those conditions are though. Since I'm nice, I'll remind you. They're a temperature of 298 K, a pressure of 100 kPa, and all the reacting ions have to have concentrations of 1.00 mol dm^{-3}. Got it? I hope so...

The Electrochemical Series

The electrochemical series is like a pop chart of the most reactive metals — but without the pop. So it's really just a chart.

The **Electrochemical Series** Shows You What's **Reactive** and What's Not

1) The **more reactive** a **metal** is, the **more** easily it **loses electrons** to form a **positive ion**.
More reactive metals have **more negative standard electrode potentials**.

Example: Magnesium is **more reactive** than zinc — so it forms 2+ ions more easily than zinc.
The list of standard electrode potentials shows that Mg^{2+}/Mg has a **more negative** value than Zn^{2+}/Zn.
In terms of oxidation and reduction, magnesium would **reduce** Zn^{2+} (or Zn^{2+} would **oxidise** Mg).

2) The more reactive a **non-metal** is, the **more** easily it **gains electrons** to form a **negative ion**.
More reactive non-metals have **more positive standard electrode potentials**.

Example: Chlorine is **more reactive** than bromine — so it forms a negative ion more easily than bromine does.
The list of standard electrode potentials shows that $\frac{1}{2}Cl_2/Cl^-$ is **more positive** than $\frac{1}{2}Br_2/Br^-$.
In terms of oxidation and reduction, chlorine would **oxidise** Br^- (or Br^- would **reduce** Cl_2).

3) Here's an **electrochemical series** showing some standard electrode potentials:

More positive electrode potentials mean that:
1. The left-hand substances are more easily reduced.
2. The right-hand substances are more stable.

Half-reaction	$E^{\ominus}$/V
$Mg^{2+}_{(aq)} + 2e^- \rightleftharpoons Mg_{(s)}$	–2.37
$Zn^{2+}_{(aq)} + 2e^- \rightleftharpoons Zn_{(s)}$	–0.76
$H^+_{(aq)} + e^- \rightleftharpoons \frac{1}{2}H_{2(g)}$	0.00
$Cu^{2+}_{(aq)} + 2e^- \rightleftharpoons Cu_{(s)}$	+0.34
$\frac{1}{2}Br_{2(aq)} + e^- \rightleftharpoons Br^-_{(aq)}$	+1.09

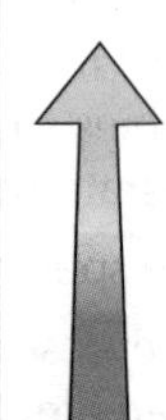

More negative electrode potentials mean that:
1. The right-hand substances are more easily oxidised.
2. The left-hand substances are more stable.

Use **Electrode Potentials** to **Predict** Whether a Reaction Will Happen

To figure out if a metal will react with the aqueous ions of another metal, you can use their $E^{\ominus}$ values. If a reaction is **thermodynamically feasible**, the overall potential will be **positive**. A reaction isn't feasible if $E^{\ominus}$ is negative.

Example: Predict whether zinc metal reacts with aqueous copper ions.

First write the two **half-equations** down as reduction reactions:

$Zn^{2+}_{(aq)} + 2e^- \rightleftharpoons Zn_{(s)}$ $E^{\ominus} = -0.76$ V $Cu^{2+}_{(aq)} + 2e^- \rightleftharpoons Cu_{(s)}$ $E^{\ominus} = +0.34$ V

Then combine them to create the reaction described in the question (in this case, you'll have to swap the direction of the zinc one, since the question is talking about the reaction of zinc metal).

The two half-equations combine to give: $Zn_{(s)} + Cu^{2+}_{(aq)} \rightarrow Zn^{2+}_{(aq)} + Cu_{(s)}$

Zinc loses electrons so is oxidised.
Copper gains electrons so is reduced.

Then, use the equation $E^{\ominus}_{cell} = (E^{\ominus}_{reduction} - E^{\ominus}_{oxidation})$
to work out the overall potential of this reaction. ⟹ $E^{\ominus}_{cell} = 0.34 - (-0.76) = \mathbf{+1.10\ V}$

The overall cell potential is **positive**, so zinc **will** react with aqueous copper ions.

Electrode Potentials can Predict Whether **Disproportionation** Reactions will Happen

During a **disproportionation** reaction, an element is simultaneously oxidised and reduced.
You can use electrode potentials to show why these sorts of reactions happen.

Example: Use the following equations to predict whether or not Ag^+ ions will disproportionate in solution.
$Ag^+_{(aq)} + e^- \rightarrow Ag_{(s)}$ $E^{\ominus} = +0.80$ V $Ag^{2+}_{(aq)} + e^- \rightarrow Ag^+_{(aq)}$ $E^{\ominus} = +2.00$ V

First combine the half-equations to create the equation for the disproportionation of Ag^+: $2Ag^+_{(aq)} \rightarrow Ag_{(s)} + Ag^{2+}_{(aq)}$

Then, use the equation $E^{\ominus}_{cell} = (E^{\ominus}_{reduction} - E^{\ominus}_{oxidation})$
to work out the overall potential of this reaction. ⟹ $E^{\ominus}_{cell} = 0.80 - (2.00) = \mathbf{-1.20\ V}$

The overall cell potential is **negative**, so silver **will not disproportionate** in solution.

The Electrochemical Series

Sometimes the Prediction is *Wrong*

A **prediction** using E° only states if a reaction is **possible** under **standard conditions**. The prediction might be **wrong if...**

...the conditions are not standard.

1) Changing the **concentration** (or temperature) of the solution can cause the electrode potential to **change**.
2) For example the zinc/copper cell has these half equations in equilibrium:

$$Zn_{(s)} \rightleftharpoons Zn^{2+}_{(aq)} + 2e^- \quad E^{\circ} = -0.76\text{ V}$$
$$Cu^{2+}_{(aq)} + 2e^- \rightleftharpoons Cu_{(s)} \quad E^{\circ} = +0.34\text{ V}$$
$$Zn_{(s)} + Cu^{2+}_{(aq)} \rightleftharpoons Zn^{2+}_{(aq)} + Cu_{(s)} \quad E_{cell} = +1.10\text{ V}$$

3) If you **increase** the concentration of Zn^{2+}, the **equilibrium** will shift to the **left**, **reducing** the ease of **electron loss** of Zn. The electrode potential of Zn/Zn^{2+} becomes **less negative** and the whole cell potential will be lower.
4) If you **increase** the concentration of Cu^{2+}, the **equilibrium** will shift to the **right**, **increasing** the ease of **electron gain** of Cu^{2+}. The electrode potential of Cu^{2+}/Cu becomes **more positive** and the whole cell potential is higher.

...the reaction kinetics are not favourable.

1) The **rate of a reaction** may be so **slow** that the reaction might **not appear** to happen.
2) If a reaction has a **high activation energy**, this may stop it happening.

Cell Potential is Related to *Entropy* and the *Equilibrium Constant*

The bigger the **cell potential**, the bigger the **total entropy change** taking place during the reaction in the cell. This gives the following equations:

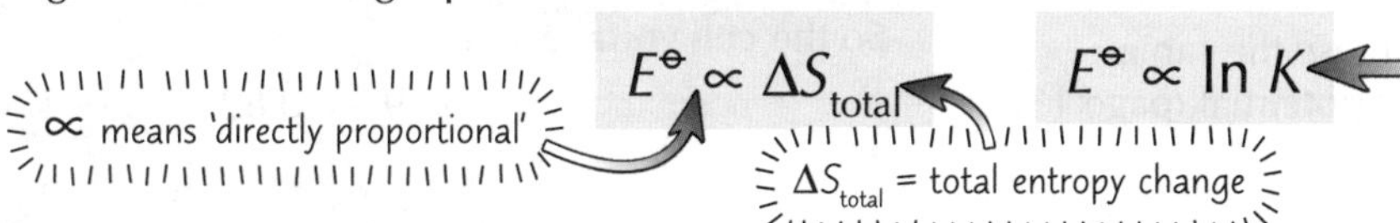

$E^{\circ} \propto \Delta S_{total}$
$E^{\circ} \propto \ln K$
∝ means 'directly proportional'
ΔS_{total} = total entropy change
This one comes from the fact that entropy and the equilibrium constant, K, are linked — see page 152.

Practice Questions

Q1 Use electrode potentials to show that zinc metal will react with Cu^{2+} ions.

Q2 How are cell potential and the total entropy change during a reaction related?

Exam Questions

Q1 Use the E° values in the table on the right and on the previous page to determine the outcome of mixing the following solutions. If there is a reaction, determine the E° value and write the equation. If there isn't a reaction, state this and explain why.

a) Zinc metal and Ni^{2+} ions. [2 marks]

b) Acidified MnO_4^- ions and Sn^{2+} ions. [2 marks]

c) $Br_{2(aq)}$ and acidified $Cr_2O_7^{2-}$ ions. [2 marks]

Half-reaction	E°/V
$MnO_4^-{}_{(aq)} + 8H^+_{(aq)} + 5e^- \rightleftharpoons Mn^{2+}_{(aq)} + 4H_2O_{(l)}$	+1.51
$Cr_2O_7^{2-}{}_{(aq)} + 14H^+_{(aq)} + 6e^- \rightleftharpoons 2Cr^{3+}_{(aq)} + 7H_2O_{(l)}$	+1.33
$Sn^{4+}_{(aq)} + 2e^- \rightleftharpoons Sn^{2+}_{(aq)}$	+0.14
$Ni^{2+}_{(aq)} + 2e^- \rightleftharpoons Ni_{(s)}$	–0.25

Q2 Potassium manganate(VII), $KMnO_4$, and potassium dichromate, $K_2Cr_2O_7$, are both used as oxidising agents. From their electrode potentials (given in the table above), which would you predict is the stronger oxidising agent? Explain why. [2 marks]

Q3 A cell is set up with copper and nickel electrodes in 1 mol dm^{-3} solutions of their ions, Cu^{2+} and Ni^{2+}, connected by a salt bridge.

a) What is the overall equation for this reaction? [1 mark]

b) How would the voltage of the cell change if a more dilute copper solution was used? [1 mark]

My Gran's in a rock band — they call themselves the electrochemical dearies...

All these positive and negative electrode potentials get me in a spin. Fortunately, you'll be given all the electrode potential data you need in the data booklet in your exam, so you don't need to memorise it — you just need to know how to use it.

Storage and Fuel Cells

More electrochemical reactions on these pages. It's like Christmas come early (if electrochemistry is your sort of thing)...

Energy Storage Cells are Like **Electrochemical Cells**

Energy storage cells (fancy name for a battery) have been around for ages and modern ones **work** just like an **electrochemical cell**. For example the nickel-iron cell was developed way back at the start of the 1900s and is often used as a back-up power supply because it can be repeatedly charged and is very robust. You can work out the **voltage** produced by these **cells** by using the **electrode potentials** of the substances used in the cell.

There are **lots** of different cells and you **won't** be asked to remember the E° for the reactions, but you might be **asked** to work out the **cell potential** or **cell voltage** for a given cell... so here's an example I prepared earlier.

Example: The nickel-iron cell has a nickel oxide hydroxide (NiO(OH)) cathode and an iron (Fe) anode with potassium hydroxide as the electrolyte. Using the half equations given:

a) write out the full equation for the reaction.

b) calculate the cell voltage produced by the nickel-iron cell.

$Fe(OH)_2 + 2e^- \rightleftharpoons Fe + 2OH^-$ $\quad E^{\circ} = -0.89$ V

$NiO(OH) + H_2O + e^- \rightleftharpoons Ni(OH)_2 + OH^-$ $\quad E^{\circ} = +0.49$ V

You have to double everything in the second equation so that the electrons balance those in the first equation.

For the first part you have to **combine** the two half-equations together in the feasible direction (when E° is positive). This involves switching the reaction with the less positive electode potential around. The e^- and the OH^- are not shown because they get cancelled out.

The **overall** reaction is...

$2NiO(OH) + 2H_2O + Fe \rightarrow 2Ni(OH)_2 + Fe(OH)_2$

To calculate the **cell voltage** you use the **same formula** for working out the **cell potential** (page 156).

So the **cell voltage** = $E^{\circ}_{reduction} - E^{\circ}_{oxidation}$

$= +0.49 - (-0.89) = \mathbf{1.38\ V}$

Fuel Cells can **Generate Electricity** From **Hydrogen** and **Oxygen**

In most cells the **chemicals** that generate the electricity are contained in the **electrodes** and the **electrolyte** that form the cell. In a **fuel cell** the chemicals are **stored separately** outside the cell and fed in when electricity is required. One example of this is the **alkaline hydrogen-oxygen fuel cell**, which can be used to **power electric vehicles**. **Hydrogen** and **oxygen gases** are fed into two separate platinum-containing electrodes. The electrodes are separated by an **anion-exchange membrane** that **allows anions** (OH^-) and water to pass through it, but **not hydrogen and oxygen gas**. The **electrolyte** is an aqueous alkaline (KOH) solution.

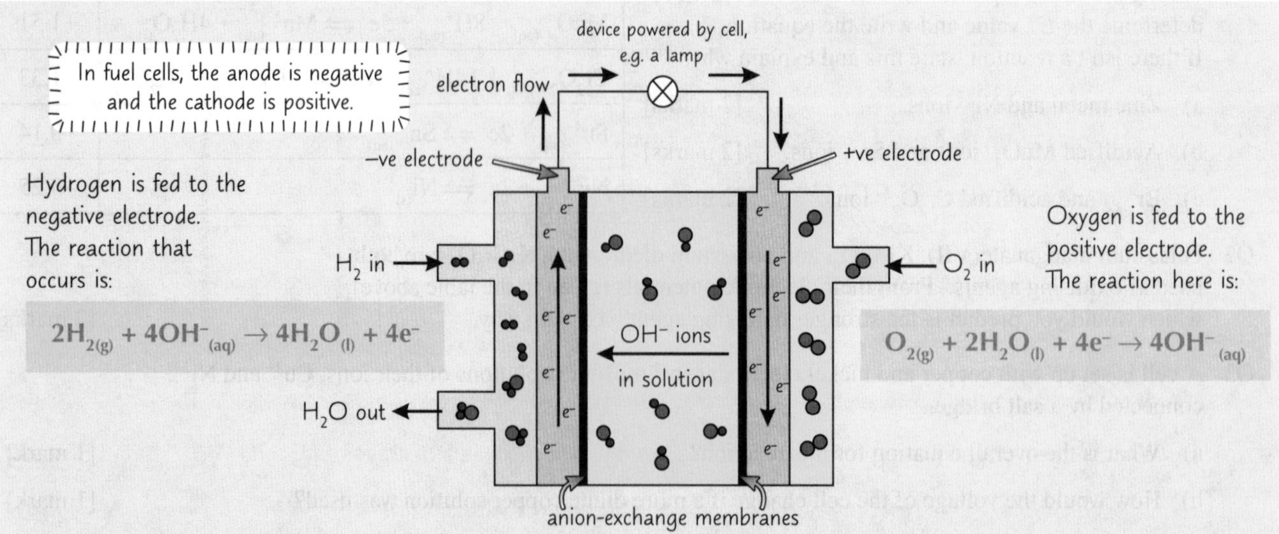
In fuel cells, the anode is negative and the cathode is positive.
device powered by cell, e.g. a lamp
electron flow
–ve electrode
+ve electrode
Hydrogen is fed to the negative electrode. The reaction that occurs is:
$2H_{2(g)} + 4OH^-_{(aq)} \rightarrow 4H_2O_{(l)} + 4e^-$
H₂ in
H₂O out
OH⁻ ions
in solution
O₂ in
Oxygen is fed to the positive electrode. The reaction here is:
$O_{2(g)} + 2H_2O_{(l)} + 4e^- \rightarrow 4OH^-_{(aq)}$
anion-exchange membranes

The **electrons** flow from the **negative electrode** through an **external circuit** to the **positive electrode**.
The **OH^- ions** pass through the **anion-exchange membrane** towards the negative electrode.

The **overall effect** is that H_2 and O_2 react to make **water**: $2H_{2(g)} + O_{2(g)} \rightarrow 2H_2O_{(l)}$

Storage and Fuel Cells

Hydrogen-Oxygen Fuel Cells Work in Acidic Conditions Too

1) At the **anode** the platinum catalyst **splits** the H_2 into protons and electrons.
2) The **polymer electrolyte membrane** (PEM) **only** allows the H^+ across and this **forces** the e^- to travel **around** the circuit to get to the cathode.
3) An **electric current** is created in the circuit, which is used to **power** something like a car or a bike or a dancing Santa.
4) At the **cathode**, O_2 **combines** with the H^+ from the anode and the e^- from the circuit to make H_2O. This is the only waste product.

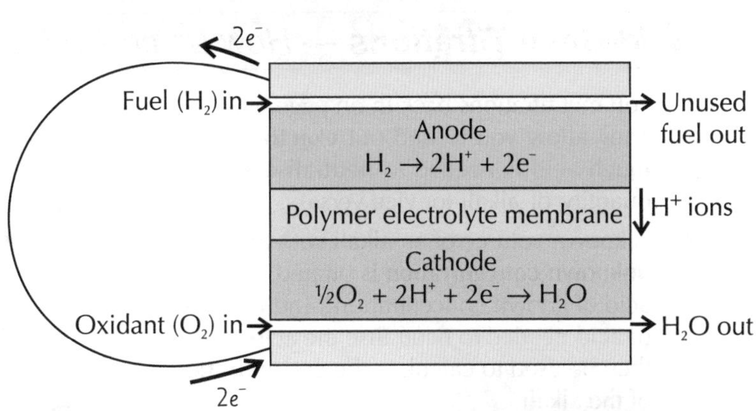

Fuel Cells Don't Just Use Hydrogen

Scientists in the car industry are developing fuel cells that use **hydrogen-rich fuels** — these have a high percentage of hydrogen in their molecules and can be converted into H_2 in the car by a **reformer**. Such fuels include the two simplest alcohols, **methanol** and **ethanol**. There is also a **new generation** of fuel cells that can use alcohols **directly** without having to reform them to produce hydrogen.

A rowdy, ethanol-fuelled brawl had broken out in Hastings.

In these new fuel cells, the alcohol is **oxidised** at the **anode** in the presence of **water**. → E.g. $CH_3OH + H_2O \rightarrow CO_2 + 6e^- + 6H^+$

The **H^+ ions** pass through the electrolyte and are **oxidised** themselves to water. → $6H^+ + 6e^- + \frac{3}{2}O_2 \rightarrow 3H_2O$

Practice Questions

Q1 Name a metal that is used in the electrodes of an alkaline hydrogen-oxygen fuel cell.

Q2 What electrolyte is used in an alkaline hydrogen-oxygen fuel cell?

Exam Questions

Q1 The diagram on the right shows the structure of an alkaline hydrogen-oxygen fuel cell.

a) i) Label the site of oxidation and the site of reduction on the diagram. [1 mark]

ii) Draw an arrow to show the direction of the flow of electrons. [1 mark]

b) Write a half-equation for the reaction at each electrode. [2 marks]

c) Explain the purpose of the anion-exchange membrane in the fuel cell. [1 mark]

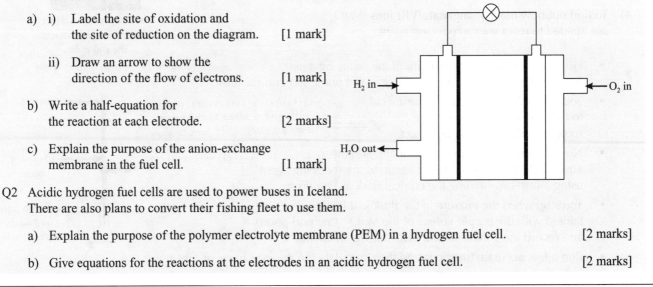

H_2 in → ← O_2 in

H_2O out ←

Q2 Acidic hydrogen fuel cells are used to power buses in Iceland. There are also plans to convert their fishing fleet to use them.

a) Explain the purpose of the polymer electrolyte membrane (PEM) in a hydrogen fuel cell. [2 marks]

b) Give equations for the reactions at the electrodes in an acidic hydrogen fuel cell. [2 marks]

Fuel sells — £1.15 per litre of petrol, £1.20 per litre of diesel...

These fuel cells are pretty nifty aren't they? Make sure you can draw the hydrogen-oxygen fuel cells in both acidic and alkaline conditions. Make sure you know the equations happening at the anode and cathode in each one too.

Redox Titrations

Better check your Year 1 notes and brush up on acid-base titrations. Redox titrations work like acid-base titrations but they're used to find out how much oxidising agent is needed to exactly react with a quantity of reducing agent (or vice versa).

Acid-Base Titrations — How Much Acid is Needed to Neutralise a Base

1) You met titrations back in on page 63. They allow you to find out **exactly** how much acid is needed to **neutralise** a quantity of alkali (or vice versa).
2) A known volume of an alkali with an **unknown concentration** is titrated with an acid of known concentration. The **volume** of acid needed to neutralise the acid can then be used to calculate the **concentration** of the alkali.
3) To carry out a titration, you'll need to apparatus a bit like this:

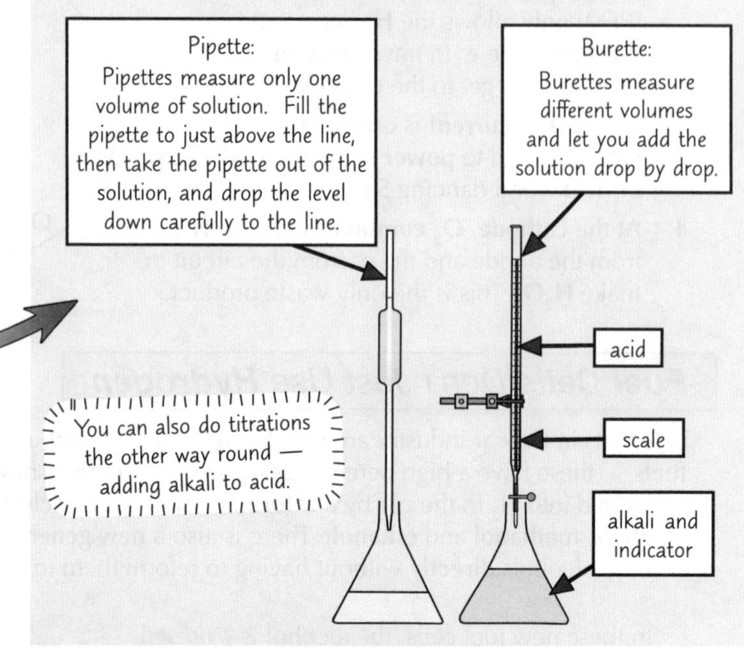
Pipette:
Pipettes measure only one volume of solution. Fill the pipette to just above the line, then take the pipette out of the solution, and drop the level down carefully to the line.
Burette:
Burettes measure different volumes and let you add the solution drop by drop.
acid
scale
alkali and indicator
You can also do titrations the other way round — adding alkali to acid.

Titrations Using Transition Element Ions are Redox Titrations

1) An **oxidising agent** accepts electrons and gets reduced. A **reducing agent** donates electrons and gets oxidised.
2) Transition (d-block) elements are good at changing **oxidation number** (see page 169). This makes them useful as oxidising and reducing agents as they'll readily **give out** or **receive** electrons.
3) To work out the **concentration** of a reducing agent, you just need to titrate a **known volume** of it against an oxidising agent of **known concentration**. This allows you to work out how much oxidising agent is needed to **exactly react** with your sample of reducing agent.
4) To find out how many **manganate(VII) ions** (MnO_4^-) are needed to react with a reducing agent:

Fred's celebration dance was a good indicator of the end point.

- First you measure out a quantity of the **reducing agent**, e.g. aqueous Fe^{2+} ions, using a pipette, and put it in a conical flask.
- You then add some **dilute sulfuric acid** to the flask — this is an excess, so you don't have to be too exact.
- Now do a rough titration — gradually add the aqueous MnO_4^- (the **oxidising agent**) to the reducing agent using a **burette**, **swirling** the conical flask as you do so.
- You stop when the mixture in the flask **just** becomes tainted with the **purple colour** of the MnO_4^- (the **end point**) and record the volume of the oxidising agent added.
- Run a few accurate **titrations** and then calculate the **mean volume** of MnO_4^-.

The acid is added to make sure there are plenty of H^+ ions to allow the oxidising agent to be reduced.

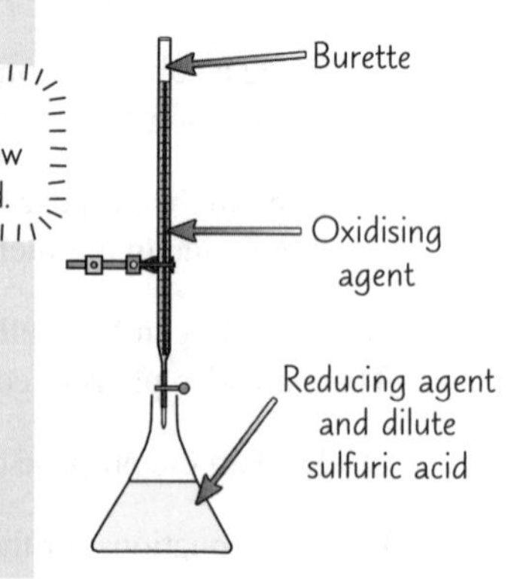
Burette
Oxidising agent
Reducing agent and dilute sulfuric acid

5) You can also do titrations the **other way round** — adding the reducing agent to the oxidising agent. The rule tends to be that you add the substance of **known** concentration to the substance of **unknown** concentration.

You can also work out the concentration of an oxidising agent by titrating it with a reducing agent of known concentration.

Redox Titrations

You Don't Always Need an *Indicator* During *Redox Titrations*

1) As transition metals change oxidation state they often also change **colour**, so it's easy to spot when the reaction is finished. Here are a couple of examples:

Acidified **potassium manganate(VII)** solution, $KMnO_{4\,(aq)}$, is used as an **oxidising agent**. It contains **manganate(VII) ions** (MnO_4^-), in which manganese has an oxidation number of **+7**. They can be reduced to Mn^{2+} ions during a **redox reaction**.

Example: The oxidation of Fe^{2+} to Fe^{3+} by manganate(VII) ions in solution.

Half-equations:

$MnO_4^- + 8H^+ + 5e^- \rightarrow Mn^{2+} + 4H_2O$ Manganese is reduced

$5Fe^{2+} \rightarrow 5Fe^{3+} + 5e^-$ Iron is oxidised

$MnO_4^- + 8H^+ + 5Fe^{2+} \rightarrow Mn^{2+} + 4H_2O + 5Fe^{3+}$

$MnO_{4\,(aq)}^-$ is purple. $Mn^{2+}_{(aq)}$ is colourless. During this reaction, you'll see a colour change from purple to colourless.

Acidified **potassium dichromate** solution, $K_2Cr_2O_{7\,(aq)}$, is another **oxidising agent**. It contains **dichromate(VI) ions** ($Cr_2O_7^{2-}$) in which chromium has an oxidation number of **+6**. They can be reduced to Cr^{3+} ions during a **redox reaction**.

Example: The oxidation of Zn to Zn^{2+} by dichromate(VI) ions in solution.

Half-equations:

$Cr_2O_7^{2-} + 14H^+ + 6e^- \rightarrow 2Cr^{3+} + 7H_2O$ Chromium is reduced

$3Zn \rightarrow 3Zn^{2+} + 6e^-$ Zinc is oxidised

$Cr_2O_7^{2-} + 14H^+ + 3Zn \rightarrow 2Cr^{3+} + 7H_2O + 3Zn^{2+}$

$Cr_2O_{7\,(aq)}^{2-}$ is orange. $Cr^{3+}_{(aq)}$ is violet, but usually looks green. During this reaction, you'll see a colour change from orange to green.

2) So, when you're carrying out redox titrations, you need to watch out for a **sharp colour change**.
3) When you're adding an oxidising agent to a reducing agent, they start reacting. This reaction will continue until **all** of the reducing agent is used up. The **very next drop** into the flask will give the mixture the **colour of the oxidising agent**. The trick is to spot **exactly** when this happens. (You could use a coloured reducing agent and a colourless oxidising agent instead — then you'd be watching for the moment that the colour in the flask disappears.)
4) Doing the reaction in front of a **white surface** can make colour changes easier to spot.

You Can *Calculate* the *Concentration* of a Reagent from the *Titration Results*

It wouldn't be a titration without some horrid calculations...

Example: 27.5 cm³ of 0.0200 mol dm⁻³ aqueous potassium manganate(VII) reacted with 25.0 cm³ of acidified iron(II) sulfate solution. Calculate the concentration of Fe^{2+} ions in the solution.

$$MnO^-_{4\,(aq)} + 8H^+_{(aq)} + 5Fe^{2+}_{(aq)} \rightarrow Mn^{2+}_{(aq)} + 4H_2O_{(l)} + 5Fe^{3+}_{(aq)}$$

1) Work out the number of **moles of MnO_4^- ions** added to the flask.

$$\text{Number of moles } MnO_4^- \text{ added} = \frac{\text{concentration} \times \text{volume}}{1000} = \frac{0.0200 \times 27.5}{1000} = 5.50 \times 10^{-4} \text{ moles}$$

2) Look at the balanced equation to find how many moles of Fe^{2+} react with **one mole** of MnO_4^-. Then you can work out the **number of moles of Fe^{2+}** in the flask.

5 moles of Fe^{2+} react with 1 mole of MnO_4^-. So moles of $Fe^{2+} = 5.50 \times 10^{-4} \times 5 = 2.75 \times 10^{-3}$ moles.

3) Work out the **number of moles of Fe^{2+}** that would be in 1000 cm³ (1 dm³) of solution — this is the **concentration.**

25.0 cm³ of solution contained 2.75×10^{-3} moles of Fe^{2+}.

1000 cm³ of solution would contain $\frac{(2.75 \times 10^{-3}) \times 1000}{25.0} = 0.110$ moles of Fe^{2+}.

So the concentration of Fe^{2+} is **0.110 mol dm⁻³**.

Redox Titrations

You Can Also Estimate the **Percentage of Iron** in **Iron Tablets**

This titration can be used to find out the percentage of iron in the iron tablets that are used to treat people with the blood disorder anaemia. The iron is usually in the form of iron(II) sulfate.

Example: A 2.56 g iron tablet was dissolved in dilute sulfuric acid to give 250 cm³ of solution. 25.0 cm³ of this solution was found to react with 12.5 cm³ of 0.0250 mol dm⁻³ potassium manganate(VII) solution. Calculate the percentage of iron in the tablet.

$$MnO_4^-{}_{(aq)} + 8H^+{}_{(aq)} + 5Fe^{2+}{}_{(aq)} \rightarrow Mn^{2+}{}_{(aq)} + 4H_2O_{(l)} + 5Fe^{3+}{}_{(aq)}$$

The first two steps are the same as the example on the previous page.

1) Work out the number of moles of **manganate(VII) ions** which took part in the reaction:

   Number of moles of MnO_4^- = $\frac{\text{concentration} \times \text{volume}}{1000} = \frac{0.0250 \times 12.5}{1000}$ = **3.125 × 10⁻⁴ moles**

2) From the equation, you can see that **5 moles** of iron(II) ions react with **1 mole** of manganate(VII) ions.

   So in 25.0 cm³ of the iron solution there must be: 5 × 3.125 × 10⁻⁴ = **1.5625 × 10⁻³ moles of iron(II) ions.**

3) Now you can work out the number of moles of iron in **250 cm³** of the solution — this will be the number of moles of iron in the **whole tablet**:

   Number of moles of Fe^{2+} = 1.5625 × 10⁻³ × 10 = **1.5625 × 10⁻² moles**

4) From this, you can work out the **mass** of iron in the tablet:

   1 mole of iron weighs **55.8 g**, so 1 tablet contains: 1.5625 × 10⁻² × 55.8 = 0.871... g of iron

5) Finally, you can calculate the percentage of iron in the tablet. The total weight of the tablet is **2.56 g**.

   So, the percentage of iron = (0.871... ÷ 2.56) × 100 = **34.1%**

Practice Questions

Q1 Write a half equation to show manganate(VII) ions acting as an oxidising agent.

Q2 Why is dilute acid added to the reaction mixture in redox titrations involving MnO_4^- ions?

Exam Questions

Q1 A 3.20 g iron tablet was dissolved in dilute sulfuric acid and made up to 250 cm³ with deionised water. 25.0 cm³ of this solution was found to react with 15.0 cm³ of 0.00900 mol dm⁻³ potassium manganate(VII) solution.

a) Calculate the number of moles of iron in 25.0 cm³ of the solution. [2 marks]

b) Calculate the number of moles of iron in the tablet. [1 mark]

c) What percentage, by mass, of the tablet is iron? [2 marks]

Q2 A 10.0 cm³ sample of 0.500 mol dm⁻³ $SnCl_2$ solution was titrated with acidified potassium manganate(VII) solution. Exactly 20.0 cm³ of 0.100 mol dm⁻³ potassium manganate(VII) solution was needed to fully oxidise the tin(II) chloride.

a) What type of reaction is this? [1 mark]

b) How many moles of tin(II) chloride were present in the 10.0 cm³ sample? [2 marks]

c) How many moles of potassium manganate(VII) were needed to fully oxidise the tin(II) chloride? [2 marks]

The half-equation for acidified MnO_4^- acting as an oxidising agent is: $MnO_4^- + 8H^+ + 5e^- \rightarrow Mn^{2+} + 4H_2O$

d) Find the oxidation number of the oxidised tin ions present in the solution at the end of the titration. [4 marks]

And how many moles does it take to change a light bulb...

...two, one to change the bulb, and another to ask "Why do we need light bulbs? We're moles — most of the time that we're underground, we keep our eyes shut. And the electricity costs a packet. We haven't thought this through..."

More on Redox Titrations

This is another example of a redox titration — it's a nifty little reaction that you can use to find the concentration of an oxidising agent. And since it's a titration, that also means a few more calculations to get to grips with...

Iodine-Sodium Thiosulfate Titrations are Dead Handy

Iodine-sodium thiosulfate titrations are a way of finding the concentration of an **oxidising agent**.

The **more concentrated** an oxidising agent is, the **more ions will be oxidised** by a certain volume of it.
So here's how you can find out the concentration of a solution of the oxidising agent **potassium iodate(V)**:

STAGE 1: Use a sample of oxidising agent to oxidise as much iodide as possible.

1) Measure out a certain volume of **potassium iodate(V)** solution (**KIO_3**) (the oxidising agent) — say **25.0 cm³**.
2) Add this to an excess of acidified **potassium iodide** solution (**KI**).
   The iodate(V) ions in the potassium iodate(V) solution **oxidise** some of the **iodide ions** to **iodine**. ⟹ $IO_{3\,(aq)}^- + 5I^-_{(aq)} + 6H^+_{(aq)} \rightarrow 3I_{2(aq)} + 3H_2O_{(l)}$

STAGE 2: Find out how many moles of iodine have been produced.

You do this by **titrating** the resulting solution with **sodium thiosulfate** (**$Na_2S_2O_3$**).
(You need to know the concentration of the sodium thiosulfate solution.)

The iodine in the solution reacts with **thiosulfate ions** like this: ⟹ $I_{2\,(aq)} + 2S_2O_3{}^{2-}{}_{(aq)} \rightarrow 2I^-_{(aq)} + S_4O_6{}^{2-}{}_{(aq)}$

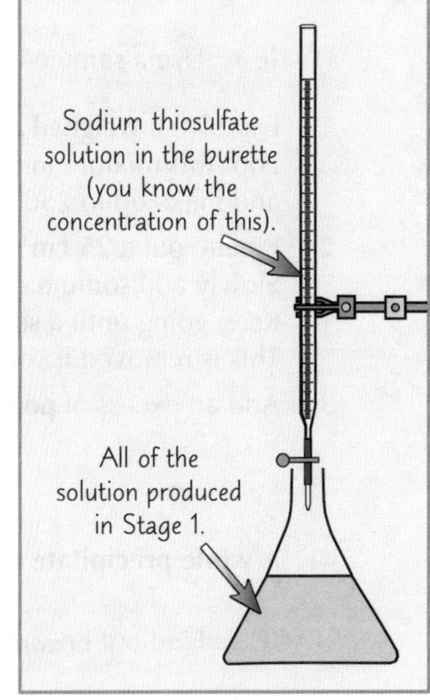

Sodium thiosulfate solution in the burette (you know the concentration of this).
All of the solution produced in Stage 1.

Titration of Iodine with Sodium Thiosulfate

1) Take the flask containing the solution that was produced in Stage 1.
2) From a burette, add sodium thiosulfate solution to the flask **drop by drop**.
3) It's hard to see the end point, so when the iodine colour fades to a **pale yellow** (this is close to the end point), add 2 cm³ of **starch solution** (to detect the presence of iodine). The solution in the conical flask will go **dark blue**, showing there's still some iodine there.
4) Add sodium thiosulfate **one drop at a time** until the blue colour disappears.
5) When this happens, it means all the iodine has **just** been reacted.
6) Now you can **calculate** the number of moles of iodine in the solution.

Here's how you'd do the titration calculation to find the **number of moles of iodine** produced in Stage 1.

Example: The iodine in the solution produced in Stage 1 reacted fully with 11.0 cm³ of 0.120 mol dm⁻³ thiosulfate solution. Work out the number of moles of iodine present in the starting solution.

$$I_2 + 2S_2O_3{}^{2-} \rightarrow 2I^- + S_4O_6{}^{2-}$$

11.0 cm³ (under $2S_2O_3{}^{2-}$)
0.120 mol dm⁻³

Number of moles of thiosulfate $= \frac{\text{concentration} \times \text{volume}(\text{cm}^3)}{1000} = \frac{0.120 \times 11.0}{1000} = \mathbf{1.32 \times 10^{-3}}$ **moles**

1 mole of iodine reacts with **2 moles** of thiosulfate.

So number of **moles of iodine** in the solution = $1.32 \times 10^{-3} \div 2 = \mathbf{6.60 \times 10^{-4}}$ **moles**

More on Redox Titrations

STAGE 3: Calculate the concentration of the oxidising agent.

1) Now look back at your original equation: $IO_3^-{}_{(aq)} + 5I^-_{(aq)} + 6H^+_{(aq)} \rightarrow 3I_{2(aq)} + 3H_2O_{(l)}$
2) 25.0 cm³ of potassium iodate(V) solution produced **6.60×10^{-4} moles of iodine**.
   The equation shows that **one mole** of iodate(V) ions will produce **three moles** of iodine.
3) That means there must have been **$6.60 \times 10^{-4} \div 3 = 2.20 \times 10^{-4}$ moles of iodate(V) ions** in the original solution. So now it's straightforward to find the **concentration** of the potassium iodate(V) solution, which is what you're after:

$$\text{number of moles} = \frac{\text{concentration} \times \text{volume}(\text{cm}^3)}{1000} \qquad 2.20 \times 10^{-4} = \frac{\text{concentration} \times 25.0}{1000}$$

$$\Rightarrow \text{concentration of potassium iodate(V) solution} = \mathbf{0.00880\ mol\ dm^{-3}}$$

You Can Use the **Titration** to Find the **Percentage of Copper** in an **Alloy**

Copper(II) ions will **oxidise** iodide ions to **iodine**.
This can be used to find the percentage of copper in an alloy, e.g. brass...

STAGE 1: Use a sample of oxidising agent to oxidise as much iodide as possible.

1) Dissolve a **weighed amount** of the alloy in some **concentrated nitric acid**.
   Pour this mixture into a **250 cm³** volumetric flask and make up to 250 cm³ with **deionised water**.
2) Pipette out a **25 cm³** portion of the diluted solution and transfer to a flask.
   Slowly add **sodium carbonate solution** to neutralise any remaining nitric acid.
   Keep going until a slight precipitate forms.
   This is removed if you add a few drops of **ethanoic acid**.
3) Add an excess of **potassium iodide solution** which reacts with the copper ions:

$$2Cu^{2+}_{(aq)} + 4I^-_{(aq)} \rightarrow 2CuI_{(s)} + I_{2(aq)}$$

4) A **white precipitate** of **copper(I) iodide** forms. The copper(II) ions have been reduced to copper(I).

King Henry was 30% steel, 20% velvet and 50% bravery.

STAGE 2: Find out how many moles of iodine have been produced.

Titrate the **product mixture** against **sodium thiosulfate solution** to find the number of moles of **iodine** present.

STAGE 3: Calculate the concentration of the oxidising agent.

1) Now you can work out the **number of moles of copper** present in both the 25 cm³ and 250 cm³ solutions (from the equation above, you can see that **2 moles** of copper ions produce **1 mole** of iodine).
2) From this you can calculate the **mass of copper** in the whole piece of brass.
3) Finally, you can work out the **percentage** of copper in the alloy.

There are a Few **Sources of Error** in These Titrations...

1) The **starch indicator** for the sodium thiosulfate titration needs to be added at the right point, when most of the iodine has **reacted**, or else the blue colour will be very **slow to disappear**.
2) The starch solution needs to be **freshly made** or else it won't behave as expected.
3) The **precipitate of copper(I) iodide** makes seeing the **colour of the solution** quite hard.
4) The **iodine** produced in the reaction can **evaporate** from the solution, giving a **false titration reading**.
   The final figure for the percentage of copper would be **too low** as a result. It helps if the solution is kept **cool**.

More on Redox Titrations

Practice Questions

Q1 How can an iodine-sodium thiosulfate titration help you to work out the concentration of an oxidising agent?

Q2 How many moles of thiosulfate ions react with one mole of iodine molecules?

Q3 What is added during an iodine-sodium thiosulfate titration to make the end point easier to see?

Q4 Describe the colour change at the end point of the iodine-sodium thiosulfate titration.

Exam Questions

Q1 10.0 cm^3 of potassium iodate(V) solution was reacted with excess acidified potassium iodide solution. All of the resulting solution was titrated with 0.150 mol dm^{-3} sodium thiosulfate solution. It fully reacted with 24.0 cm^3 of the sodium thiosulfate solution.

a) Write an equation showing how iodine is formed in the reaction between iodate(V) ions and iodide ions in acidic solution. [1 mark]

b) How many moles of thiosulfate ions were there in 24.0 cm^3 of the sodium thiosulfate solution? [1 mark]

c) In the titration, iodine reacted with sodium thiosulfate according to this equation:

$$I_{2(aq)} + 2Na_2S_2O_{3(aq)} \rightarrow 2NaI_{(aq)} + Na_2S_4O_{6(aq)}$$

Calculate the number of moles of iodine that reacted with the sodium thiosulfate solution. [1 mark]

d) How many moles of iodate(V) ions produce 1 mole of iodine from potassium iodide? [1 mark]

e) What was the concentration of the potassium iodate(V) solution? [2 marks]

Q2 An 18.0 cm^3 sample of potassium manganate(VII) solution was reacted with an excess of acidified potassium iodide solution. The resulting solution was titrated with 0.300 mol dm^{-3} sodium thiosulfate solution. 12.5 cm^3 of sodium thiosulfate solution were needed to fully react with the iodine.

When they were mixed, the manganate(VII) ions reacted with the iodide ions according to this equation:

$$2MnO_4^-{}_{(aq)} + 10I^-{}_{(aq)} + 16H^+ \rightarrow 5I_{2(aq)} + 8H_2O_{(aq)} + 2Mn^{2+}{}_{(aq)}$$

During the titration, the iodine reacted with sodium thiosulfate according to this equation:

$$I_{2(aq)} + 2Na_2S_2O_{3(aq)} \rightarrow 2NaI_{(aq)} + Na_2S_4O_{6(aq)}$$

Calculate the concentration of the potassium manganate(VII) solution. [4 marks]

Q3 A 4.20 g coin, made of a copper alloy, was dissolved in acid and the solution made up to 250 cm^3 with distilled water. 25.0 cm^3 of this solution was added to excess potassium iodide solution. The following reaction occurred:

$$2Cu^{2+}{}_{(aq)} + 4I^-{}_{(aq)} \rightarrow 2CuI_{(s)} + I_{2(aq)}$$

The resulting solution was neutralised and then titrated with 0.150 mol dm^{-3} sodium thiosulfate. The iodine and thiosulfate reacted according to this equation:

$$I_{2(aq)} + 2S_2O_3^{2-}{}_{(aq)} \rightarrow 2I^-{}_{(aq)} + S_4O_6^{2-}{}_{(aq)}$$

The average titration result was 19.3 cm^3.

a) How many moles of iodine were present in the solution used in the titration? [2 marks]

b) How many moles of copper ions must have been in the 25.0 cm^3 of solution used for the titration? [2 marks]

c) What percentage of the coin, by mass, was copper? [3 marks]

Two vowels went out for dinner — they had an iodate...

This might seem like quite a faff — you do a redox reaction to release iodine, titrate the iodine solution, do a sum to find the iodine concentration, write an equation, then do another sum to work out the concentration of something else. The thing is, it does work, and you do have to know how. If you're rusty on the calculations, look back at pages 165-166.

Transition Metals

The d-block can be found slap bang in the middle of the periodic table. It's here you'll find the transition metals. You'll also find the most precious metals in the world here. That's got to make it worth a look...

Transition Metals are Found in the *d-Block*

The **d-block** is the block of elements in the middle of the periodic table. Most of the elements in the d-block are **transition metals** (or transition elements).

You mainly need to know about the ones in the first row of the d-block. These are the elements from **titanium** to **copper**.

s-block d-block p-block

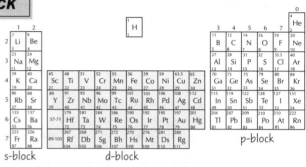

You Need to Know the *Electronic Configurations* of the *Transition Metals*

Transition metals are d-block elements that can form **one** or **more stable ions** with **incompletely filled d-orbitals.**

A d subshell has **5 orbitals** so can hold **10** electrons. So transition metals can form **at least one ion** that has **between 1 and 9 electrons** in its d-orbitals. All the period 4 d-block elements are transition metals apart from **scandium** and **zinc** (see below). The diagram below shows the 3d and 4s subshells of the period 4 transition metals:

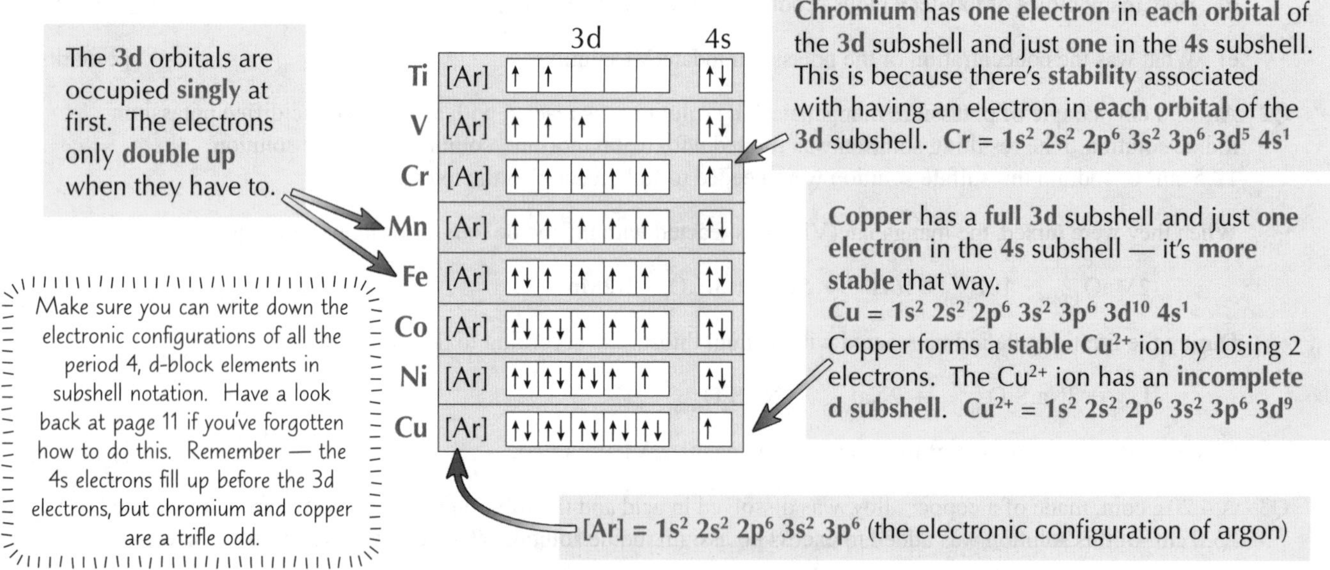

The 3d orbitals are occupied singly at first. The electrons only double up when they have to.
Make sure you can write down the electronic configurations of all the period 4, d-block elements in subshell notation. Have a look back at page 11 if you've forgotten how to do this. Remember — the 4s electrons fill up before the 3d electrons, but chromium and copper are a trifle odd.
3d
4s
Ti [Ar]
V [Ar]
Cr [Ar]
Mn [Ar]
Fe [Ar]
Co [Ar]
Ni [Ar]
Cu [Ar]
Chromium has one electron in each orbital of the 3d subshell and just one in the 4s subshell. This is because there's stability associated with having an electron in each orbital of the 3d subshell. Cr = 1s² 2s² 2p⁶ 3s² 3p⁶ 3d⁵ 4s¹
Copper has a full 3d subshell and just one electron in the 4s subshell — it's more stable that way.
Cu = 1s² 2s² 2p⁶ 3s² 3p⁶ 3d¹⁰ 4s¹
Copper forms a stable Cu²⁺ ion by losing 2 electrons. The Cu²⁺ ion has an incomplete d subshell. Cu²⁺ = 1s² 2s² 2p⁶ 3s² 3p⁶ 3d⁹
[Ar] = 1s² 2s² 2p⁶ 3s² 3p⁶ (the electronic configuration of argon)

When *Ions* are Formed, the *s Electrons* are *Removed First*

When transition metals form **positive** ions, outer **s electrons** are removed **first**, then the d electrons.

Example: Titanium can form Ti^{2+} ions and Ti^{3+} ions. Give the electronic configurations for these two ions.

When titanium forms 2+ ions, it loses **both its 4s electrons.**
$Ti = 1s^2\ 2s^2\ 2p^6\ 3s^2\ 3p^6\ 3d^2\ 4s^2 \rightarrow Ti^{2+} = 1s^2\ 2s^2\ 2p^6\ 3s^2\ 3p^6\ 3d^2$

To form 3+ ions, it loses both its 4s electrons, and then a **3d electron** as well.
$Ti^{2+} = 1s^2\ 2s^2\ 2p^6\ 3s^2\ 3p^6\ 3d^2 \rightarrow Ti^{3+} = 1s^2\ 2s^2\ 2p^6\ 3s^2\ 3p^6\ 3d^1$

Titanium can also form 4+ ions, with the electronic configuration [Ar].

Sc and Zn *Aren't* Transition Metals

1) **Scandium** only forms one ion, Sc^{3+}, which has an **empty d subshell**. Scandium has the electronic configuration **[Ar]$3d^1\ 4s^2$**, so when it loses three electrons to form Sc^{3+}, it ends up with the electronic configuration **[Ar]**.
2) **Zinc** only forms one ion, Zn^{2+}, which has a **full d subshell**. Zinc has the electronic configuration **[Ar]$3d^{10}\ 4s^2$**. When it forms Zn^{2+} it loses 2 electrons, both from the 4s subshell. This means it keeps its full 3d subshell.

Transition Metals

Transition Metals have Variable Oxidation Numbers

1) Most transition metals can form multiple **stable ions**.
In each ion, the transition metal is present with a different oxidation number.
For example, **vanadium** has **four** stable oxidation numbers:
vanadium(II) V^{2+}, vanadium(III) V^{3+}, vanadyl(IV) VO^{2+} and vanadate(V) VO_2^+.

Oxidation numbers tell you how many electrons an atom has gained or lost in an ion or a compound.

2) To form a **compound** or a **complex** (see page 170) containing an ion with a certain oxidation number, the energy given out when the ion forms a compound or a complex needs to be greater than the energy taken to remove the outer electrons and form the ion (the **ionisation energy**).

Other terms, such as entropy, play a part too, but they're less important.

3) **Transition metals** form ions by losing electrons from both their **4s** and **3d subshells**. The **4s** and **3d** subshells are at **similar energy levels**, so it takes a similar amount of energy to remove an electron from the 4s subshell as it does to remove an electron from the 3d subshell. There is not a large increase between the ionisation energies of removing successive electrons either, so multiple electrons can be removed from these subshells, to form ions with different oxidation numbers.

4) The energy released when ions form a complex or compound increases with the **ionic charge** (see page 142). Therefore, the increase in the energy required to remove outer electrons to form transition metal ions with higher oxidation numbers is usually **counteracted** by the increase in the energy released.

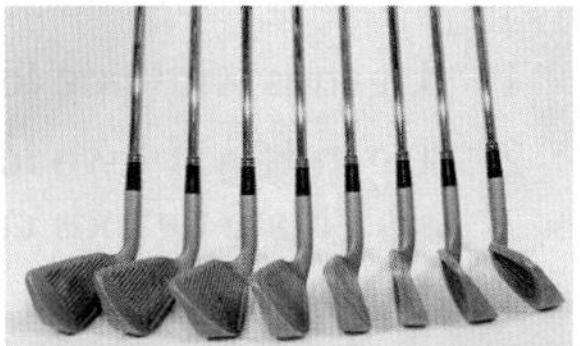
Priesh had many stable irons.

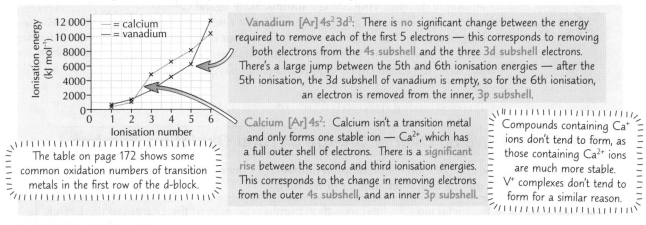

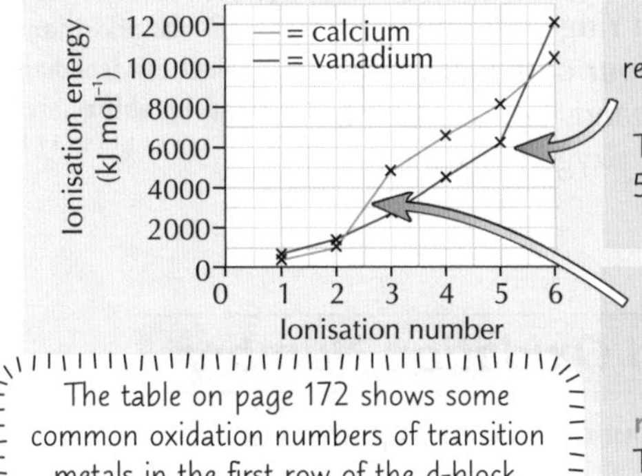

Vanadium [Ar] $4s^2 3d^3$: There is no significant change between the energy required to remove each of the first 5 electrons — this corresponds to removing both electrons from the 4s subshell and the three 3d subshell electrons. There's a large jump between the 5th and 6th ionisation energies — after the 5th ionisation, the 3d subshell of vanadium is empty, so for the 6th ionisation, an electron is removed from the inner, 3p subshell.

Calcium [Ar] $4s^2$: Calcium isn't a transition metal and only forms one stable ion — Ca^{2+}, which has a full outer shell of electrons. There is a significant rise between the second and third ionisation energies. This corresponds to the change in removing electrons from the outer 4s subshell, and an inner 3p subshell.

The table on page 172 shows some common oxidation numbers of transition metals in the first row of the d-block.

Compounds containing Ca^+ ions don't tend to form, as those containing Ca^{2+} ions are much more stable. V^+ complexes don't tend to form for a similar reason.

Practice Questions

Q1 What is the definition of a transition metal?

Q2 Why doesn't chromium have 2 electrons in its 4s subshell?

Q3 When vanadium forms an ion, which subshell does it lose its electrons from first?

Q4 Why is zinc not counted as a transition metal?

Exam Questions

Q1 Manganese is a transition metal. It forms stable manganese(II) ions, Mn^{2+}, and stable permanganate(VII) ions, MnO_4^-. With reference to the electronic configurations of these ions, explain why manganese shows variable oxidation numbers. [3 marks]

Q2 Iron and copper are two common transition metals.

a) Write the electronic configuration of an iron atom and a copper atom. [2 marks]

b) Explain what is unusual about the electronic configuration of copper among transition metals, and explain why this feature occurs. [2 marks]

c) Explain, in terms of iron's orbital and electronic configuration, what happens when Fe^{2+} and Fe^{3+} ions are formed. [2 marks]

Scram Sc and Zn — we don't take kindly to your types round these parts...

As long as you're up to speed with your electronic configuration rules, these pages are a bit of a breeze. Chromium and copper do throw a couple of spanners in the works (those banterous scamps), so make sure you don't get complacent.

Complex Ions

Transition metals are always forming complex ions. These aren't as complicated as they sound, though. Honest.

Complex Ions are Metal Ions Surrounded by Ligands

Transition metals can form **complex ions**. E.g. iron forms a **complex ion with water** — $[Fe(H_2O)_6]^{2+}$.

A **complex ion** is a **metal ion** surrounded by **dative covalently (coordinately) bonded ligands.**

A dative covalent bond is a covalent bond in which both electrons in the shared pair come from the same atom.

Ligands Form Bonds Using Lone Pairs of Electrons

A **ligand** is an atom, ion or molecule that **donates a pair of electrons** to a central metal atom or ion. A ligand must have **at least one lone pair of electrons**, otherwise it won't have anything to form a **dative covalent bond** with.

1) Ligands with **one lone pair** are called **monodentate** — e.g. $H_2O:$, $:NH_3$, $:Cl^-$, $:OH^-$.
2) Ligands with **two lone pairs** are called **bidentate** — e.g. 1,2-diaminoethane. Bidentate ligands can each form **two dative covalent bonds** with a metal ion.
3) Ligands with **more than two lone pairs** are called **multidentate** — e.g. **EDTA⁴⁻** has six lone pairs (so it's **hexadentate**). It can form **six dative bonds** with a metal ion.

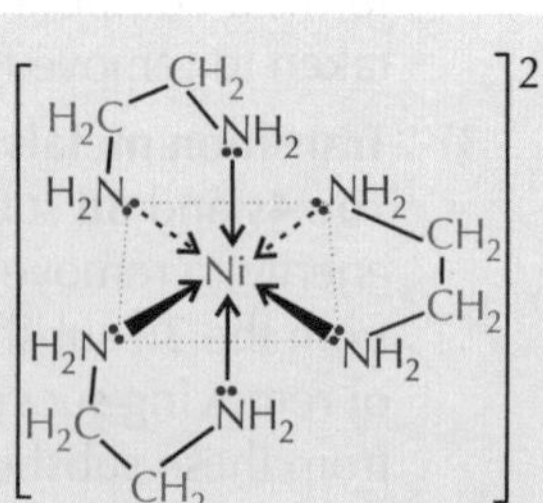

In this complex, the nickel ion is bonded to three bidentate 1,2-diaminoethane $(NH_2CH_2CH_2NH_2)$ ligands.

1,2-diaminoethane is also called ethylenediamine and can be abbreviated to 'en'.

4) **Haemoglobin** is used to transport **oxygen** around the body. It's an iron(II) complex containing a **multidentate ligand** called a **haem** group. The haem group is made up of a **ring** containing **4 nitrogen atoms**. This means it's able to form **four dative covalent bonds** to the iron(II) ion. There are two other ligands bonded to the iron(II) ion — a protein called globin and either oxygen or water.

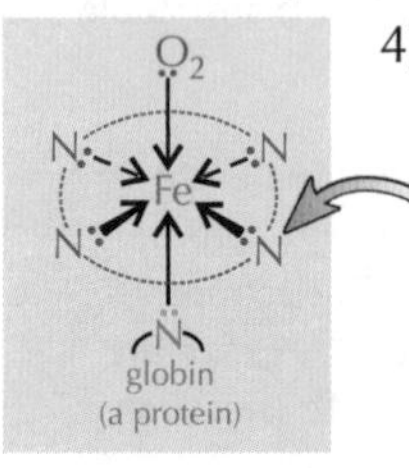

There's more on haemoglobin on page 176.

Complex Ions Have an Overall Charge or Total Oxidation Number

The **overall charge** on the complex ion is its **oxidation number**. It's put **outside** the **square** brackets. You can use this to work out the **oxidation number of the metal**:

oxidation number of the metal ion = total oxidation number – sum of the charges of the ligands

E.g. $[Fe(CN)_6]^{4-}_{(aq)}$: The total oxidation number is **–4** and each CN^- ligand has a charge of **–1**. So in this complex, iron's oxidation number = –4 – (6 × –1) = **+2**.

Complex Ions Can Have Different Numbers of Ligands

1) The **coordination number** is the **number** of **dative covalent** (**coordinate**) **bonds** formed with the central metal ion.
2) The usual coordination numbers are **6** and **4**. If the ligands are **small**, like H_2O or NH_3, **6** can fit around the central metal ion. But if the ligands are **larger**, like Cl^-, **only 4** can fit around the central metal ion.
3) The bonding electrons in the dative covalent bonds of a complex **repel** each other. This means that, in general, the ligands are positioned **as far away** from each other as possible. This causes complexes with different **coordination numbers** to have **distinctive shapes**.

There's more about the shapes of molecules on pages 24 and 25.

Complexes with Six-Fold Coordination

Six-fold coordination means an **octahedral shape.** In octahedral complexes, the **bond angles** are all **90°**.

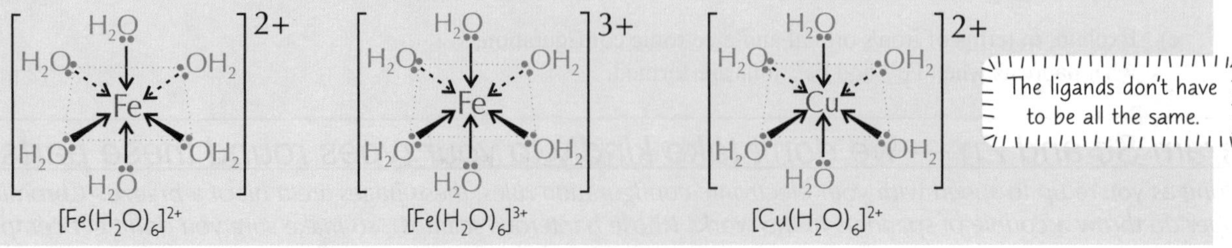

The ligands don't have to be all the same.

Complex Ions

Complexes With **Four-Fold Coordination**

Four-fold coordination usually means a **tetrahedral shape**.
E.g. the $[CuCl_4]^{2-}$ complex, which is yellow, and the $[Co(Cl)_4]^{2-}$ complex ion, which is deep blue.

The **bond angles** are **109.5°**.

Make sure you learn the shapes of these complexes. The d subshells mean you can't always use electron pair repulsion theory (see pages 24-25) to predict the shapes.

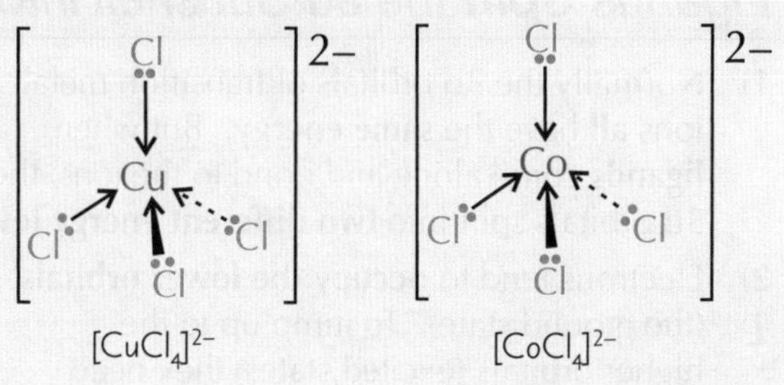

Occasionally, **four-fold coordination** results in a **square planar shape**. E.g. **cis-platin** (shown on the right).
The **bond angles** are **90°**.

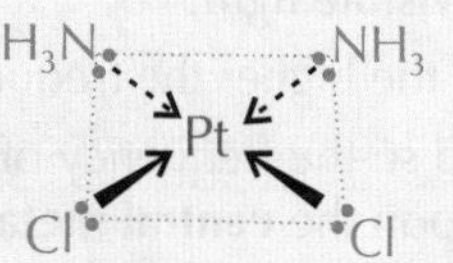

The Leow family were proud of their colour coordination.

Complex Ions Can Show **Cis/Trans Isomerism**

Cis/trans isomerism is a special case of **E/Z isomerism** (see page 85).
Square planar and **octahedral** complex ions that have at least **two pairs** of identical ligands show **cis/trans isomerism**. **Cis** isomers have the **same groups** on the **same side**, **trans** have the **same groups opposite** each other. For example:

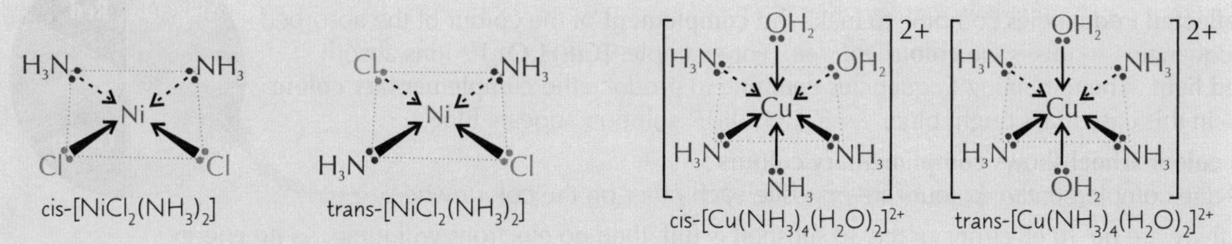

Cis-platin is a complex of platinum(II) with two chloride ions and two ammonia molecules in a square planar shape. It is used as an **anti-cancer** drug.
The two chloride ions are **next to each other**, so this complex is **cis-platin**. If they were **opposite** each other you would have **trans-platin**, which is toxic. It's therefore important that only the **cis** form of the complex is given to patients being treated for cancer.

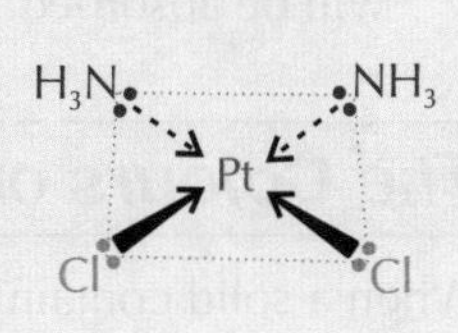

Practice Questions

Q1 What is meant by the term 'complex ion'?

Q2 Describe how a ligand, such as ammonia, bonds to a central metal ion.

Q3 Draw the shape of the complex ion $[Cu(H_2O)_6]^{2+}$. Name the shape and state the size(s) of the bond angles.

Exam Question

Q1 When concentrated hydrochloric acid is added to an aqueous solution of $Cu^{2+}_{(aq)}$ a yellow solution is formed.

a) State the coordination number and shape of the $Cu^{2+}_{(aq)}$ complex ion in the initial solution. [2 marks]

b) State the coordination number, shape, bond angles and formula of the complex ion responsible for the yellow solution. [4 marks]

c) Explain why the coordination number is different in the yellow solution than in the starting aqueous copper solution. [2 marks]

Put your hands up — we've got you surrounded...

You'll never get transition element ions floating around by themselves in a solution — they'll always be surrounded by other molecules. It's kind of like what'd happen if you put a dish of sweets in a room of eight (or eighteen) year-olds.

Complex Ions and Colour

One property of transition metals is that they form coloured complexes. You're about to find out why...

Ligands **Split** the 3d Subshell into **Two Energy Levels**

1) Normally the 3d orbitals of transition metal ions **all** have the **same energy**. But when **ligands** come along and bond to the ions, the 3d orbitals split into **two different energy levels**.
2) Electrons tend to **occupy the lower orbitals** (the ground state). To jump up to the higher orbitals (excited states) they need **energy** equal to the energy gap, ΔE. They get this energy from **visible light**.

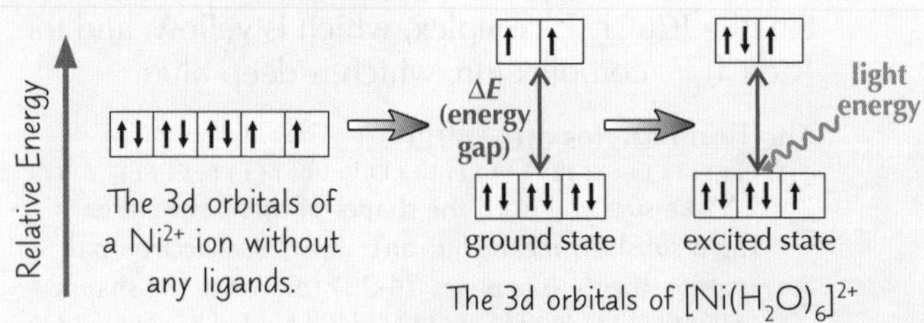

3) The larger the energy gap, the higher the frequency of light that is absorbed.
4) The amount of energy (and so the frequency of the light) needed to make electrons jump depends upon the **central metal ion**, its **oxidation number**, the **ligands** and the **coordination number** — these affect the **size of the energy gap** (ΔE).

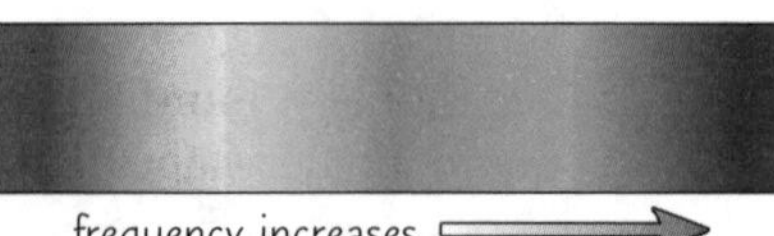

The **Colours** of Compounds are the **Complement** of Those That are **Absorbed**

1) As you saw above, the splitting of the d-orbitals in transition metals by ligands causes some frequencies of light to be absorbed by the complexes.
2) The rest of the frequencies of light are **transmitted** (or **reflected**). These **transmitted** or **reflected** frequencies combine to make the **complement** of the colour of the absorbed frequencies — this is the **colour** you see. For example, $[Cu(H_2O)_6]^{2+}$ ions absorb **red light**. The remaining frequencies **combine** to produce the **complementary colour** — in this case that's bright blue. So $[Cu(H_2O)_6]^{2+}$ solution appears **blue**.
3) A **colour wheel** shows **complimentary colours** — the complementary colours are opposite each other on the colour wheel.

Magenta, Red, Yellow, Green, Cyan, Blue

4) If there are **no** 3d electrons or the 3d subshell is **full**, then no electrons will jump, so **no energy** will be absorbed. If there's no energy absorbed, the compound will look **white** or **colourless**.

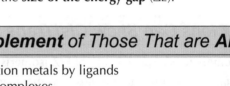

The **Colours** of **Aqueous Complexes** Can Help to **Identify** Transition Metal Ions

When a solid containing a **transition metal ion** is dissolved in **water**, the transition metal ion will form an **aqueous complex** in solution (the metal ion will be surrounded by water ligands). The **colour** of this aqueous solution can help to identify the transition metal ion that is present.

Oxidation No.	+7	+6	+5	+4	+3	+2
Titanium					**Ti^{3+} (purple)**	Ti^{2+} (violet)
Vanadium			VO_2^+ (yellow)	**VO^{2+} (blue)**	V^{3+} (green)	V^{2+} (violet)
Chromium		$Cr_2O_7^{2-}$ (orange)			Cr^{3+} (green)	
Manganese	**MnO_4^- (purple)**	MnO_4^{2-} (green)				Mn^{2+} (pale pink)
Iron					Fe^{3+} (yellow)	Fe^{2+} (pale green)
Cobalt						Co^{2+} (pink)
Nickel						**Ni^{2+} (green)**
Copper						Cu^{2+} (pale blue)

You don't need to learn the colours of aqueous titanium, manganese or nickel complexes.

Complex Ions and Colour

Vanadium Forms **Stable Ions** with Different **Oxidation Numbers**

1) You learnt on page 169 that one of the properties of transition metals is that they can exist in variable oxidation numbers. For example, vanadium can exist in **four oxidation numbers** in solution — +2, +3, +4 and +5. You can tell them apart by their colours, which are shown on the previous page.
2) When you switch between oxidation numbers, it's a **redox reaction** — ions are either oxidised (they lose electrons and their oxidation number increases) or reduced (they gain electrons and their oxidation number decreases).
3) You can write ionic half-equations to show the reduction of ions or atoms. Each reaction also has its own **reduction potential**. Here are the ionic half-equations for the reduction reactions of the different vanadium ions:

Oxidation Number of Vanadium	Reduction Half-Equation	Reduction Potential ($E^\ominus$)
+5	$VO_2^{+}{}_{(aq)} + 2H^+_{(aq)} + e^- \rightleftharpoons VO^{2+}_{(aq)} + H_2O_{(l)}$	+1.00 V
+4	$VO^{2+}_{(aq)} + 2H^+_{(aq)} + e^- \rightleftharpoons V^{3+}_{(aq)} + H_2O_{(l)}$	+0.34 V
+3	$V^{3+}_{(aq)} + e^- \rightleftharpoons V^{2+}_{(aq)}$	–0.26 V
+2	$V^{2+}_{(aq)} + 2e^- \rightleftharpoons V_{(s)}$	–1.18 V

4) You can use the **reduction potentials** to work out whether redox reactions involving transition metals are likely to happen. The method for this is the same as the one on page 158.

Reduction potentials is just another name for electrode potentials.

Example: Use the table above to determine the colour change(s) observed when zinc metal is added to an acidified solution containing $VO^{2+}_{(aq)}$ ions. $Zn^{2+}_{(aq)} + 2e^- \rightleftharpoons Zn_{(s)}$ $E^\ominus = -0.76$ V

First work out the **cell potential** for each of the reduction reactions of the vanadium ions by zinc:

$2VO_2^{+}{}_{(aq)} + 4H^+_{(aq)} + Zn_{(s)} \rightleftharpoons 2VO^{2+}_{(aq)} + 2H_2O_{(l)} + Zn^{2+}_{(aq)}$ $E^\ominus = +1.76$ V

$2VO^{2+}_{(aq)} + 4H^+_{(aq)} + Zn_{(s)} \rightleftharpoons 2V^{3+}_{(aq)} + 2H_2O_{(l)} + Zn^{2+}_{(aq)}$ $E^\ominus = +1.10$ V

$2V^{3+}_{(aq)} + Zn_{(s)} \rightleftharpoons 2V^{2+}_{(aq)} + Zn^{2+}_{(aq)}$ $E^\ominus = +0.50$ V

$V^{2+}_{(aq)} + Zn_{(s)} \rightleftharpoons V_{(s)} + Zn^{2+}_{(aq)}$ $E^\ominus = -0.42$ V

Redox reactions are only feasible if $E^\ominus$ is positive.

$E^\ominus$ for the first three reactions is **positive**, so zinc metal is able to reduce **vanadium(V)** to **vanadium(IV)**, which will then be reduced to **vanadium(III)**, which in turn will be reduced to **vanadium(II)**.
The reduction potential for the reaction of vanadium(II) with zinc is **negative**.
So under standard conditions, vanadium(II) **won't** be reduced by zinc to vanadium metal.
So the solution will change from **yellow** to **blue** to **green** to **violet**.

The mixture of yellow $VO_2^{+}{}_{(aq)}$ ions and blue $VO^{2+}_{(aq)}$ ions might make the solution look green.

Practice Questions

Q1 Which subshell is split by the presence of ligands?

Q2 State three factors that can affect the frequency of light absorbed by a transition metal complex.

Q3 What colour are VO^{2+} ions in solution?

Exam Questions

Q1 a) Using a noble gas core, [Ar], complete the electron arrangements for the following ions:

i) Cu^+ ii) Cu^{2+} [2 marks]

b) Which one of the above ions has coloured compounds? Explain your answer. [1 mark]

Q2* Transition metal ions form a wide range of different colours when bonded to ligands.
Using your knowledge of 3d orbitals, explain how ligands cause transition metals to be coloured. [6 marks]

Blue's not my complementary colour — it clashes with my hair...

Finally, some real Chemistry, with pretty colours and everything. It only took you 173 pages to get there. Make sure you understand how the colours are made — there have to be electrons in the d-orbitals that are able to jump up from the lower energy d-orbitals to the higher energy d-orbitals. Otherwise you'll just have a colourless solution. Yawn.

* The quality of your extended response will be assessed for this question.

Chromium

Can't get enough of transition metals? Well, you're in luck, because it's time for the chemistry of chromium...

Chromium Ions Usually Exist in the +2, +3 or +6 Oxidation Numbers

1) Chromium exists in compounds in many oxidation numbers. The +3 state is the most stable, followed by the +6 and then +2.
2) Chromium forms **two ions** with oxygen in the +6 oxidation number — **chromate(VI) ions**, CrO_4^{2-}, and **dichromate(VI) ions**, $Cr_2O_7^{2-}$. These ions are **good oxidising agents** because they are easily reduced to Cr^{3+}.
3) When **Cr^{3+} ions** are surrounded by 6 water ligands they're **violet**. But the water ligands are usually **substituted** with impurities in the water, e.g. Cl^-. This makes the solution look green.

Oxidation number	Formula of ion	Colour of ion in water
+6	$Cr_2O_7^{2-}{}_{(aq)}$	Orange
+6	$CrO_4^{2-}{}_{(aq)}$	Yellow
+3	$Cr^{3+}{}_{(aq)}$	Green (Violet)
+2	$Cr^{2+}{}_{(aq)}$	Blue

Chromium Ions can be Oxidised and Reduced

Chromium has lots of different oxidation numbers and can take part in lots of redox reactions.

1) Dichromate(VI) ions can be **reduced** using a reducing agent such as **zinc** and **dilute acid**.

Oxidation no: +6 (Cr), 0 (Zn), +2 (Zn), +3 (Cr)

$$Cr_2O_7^{2-}{}_{(aq)} + 14H^+{}_{(aq)} + 3Zn_{(s)} \rightarrow 3Zn^{2+}{}_{(aq)} + 2Cr^{3+}{}_{(aq)} + 7H_2O_{(l)} \quad E^\ominus = +2.09\text{ V}$$

2) Zinc will **reduce** Cr^{3+} further to Cr^{2+}. You'll need to use an inert atmosphere — Cr^{2+} is so **unstable** that it oxidises straight back to Cr^{3+} in air.

Oxidation no: +3 (Cr), 0 (Zn), +2 (Zn), +2 (Cr)

$$2Cr^{3+}{}_{(aq)} + Zn_{(s)} \rightarrow Zn^{2+}{}_{(aq)} + 2Cr^{2+}{}_{(aq)} \quad E^\ominus = +0.35\text{ V}$$

3) You can oxidise Cr^{3+} to chromate(VI) ions with **hydrogen peroxide** in an **alkaline** solution.

Oxidation no: +3 (Cr), +6 (Cr)

$$2Cr^{3+}{}_{(aq)} + 10OH^-{}_{(aq)} + 3H_2O_{2(aq)} \rightarrow 2CrO_4^{2-}{}_{(aq)} + 8H_2O_{(l)} \quad E^\ominus = +1.08\text{ V}$$

4) If you add some **acid** to this yellow solution, you form an **orange solution** that contains **dichromate(VI) ions**. This is a reversible reaction, so an equilibrium exists between **chromate(VI)** and **dichromate(VI) ions**.

Adding acid shifts the equilibrium to the right. Adding alkali shifts it to the left.

Oxidation no: +6, +6

$$2CrO_4^{2-}{}_{(aq)} + 2H^+{}_{(aq)} \rightleftharpoons Cr_2O_7^{2-}{}_{(aq)} + H_2O_{(l)}$$

Chromium Hydroxide is Amphoteric

1) When you mix an aqueous solution of **chromium(III) ions** with aqueous **sodium hydroxide** (NaOH) or aqueous **ammonia** (NH_3) you get a **chromium hydroxide precipitate** — $Cr(OH)_3(H_2O)_{3(s)}$.

$$[Cr(H_2O)_6]^{3+}{}_{(aq)} + 3OH^-{}_{(aq)} \rightarrow [Cr(OH)_3(H_2O)_3]_{(s)} + 3H_2O_{(l)}$$
green solution → grey-green precipitate

$$[Cr(H_2O)_6]^{3+}{}_{(aq)} + 3NH_{3(aq)} \rightarrow [Cr(OH)_3(H_2O)_3]_{(s)} + 3NH_4^+{}_{(aq)}$$
green solution → grey-green precipitate

2) Chromium hydroxide $[Cr(H_2O)_3(OH)_3]$ is **amphoteric**. This means it can react with **both** acids and bases.

$$[Cr(H_2O)_6]^{3+}{}_{(aq)} \xleftarrow[\text{With acid}]{+3H^+{}_{(aq)}} [Cr(OH)_3(H_2O)_3]_{(s)} \xrightarrow[\text{With base}]{+3OH^-{}_{(aq)}} [Cr(OH)_6]^{3-}{}_{(aq)} + 3H_2O_{(l)}$$

3) So if you add **excess sodium hydroxide** to a chromium hydroxide precipitate, the H_2O ligands **deprotonate**, and a solution containing $[Cr(OH)_6]^{3-}{}_{(aq)}$ forms.

$$[Cr(OH)_3(H_2O)_3]_{(s)} + 3OH^-{}_{(aq)} \rightarrow [Cr(OH)_6]^{3-}{}_{(aq)} + 3H_2O_{(l)}$$
grey-green precipitate → dark green solution

4) If you add **acid** to the chromium hydroxide precipitate, the OH^- ligands **protonate** and a solution containing $[Cr(H_2O)_6]^{3+}{}_{(aq)}$ forms.

$$[Cr(OH)_3(H_2O)_3]_{(s)} + 3H^+{}_{(aq)} \rightarrow [Cr(H_2O)_6]^{3+}{}_{(aq)}$$
grey-green precipitate → green solution

5) The **reactions** above are **NOT** ligand exchanges (see page 176). Instead, they're acid-base reactions — the ligands are **chemically modified** by the acid or the alkali (by the addition or removal of an H^+ ion).
6) But, if you add **excess ammonia** to the chromium hydroxide precipitate, a **ligand exchange reaction** occurs.

$$[Cr(OH)_3(H_2O)_3]_{(s)} + 6NH_{3(aq)} \rightarrow [Cr(NH_3)_6]^{3+}{}_{(aq)} + 3OH^-{}_{(aq)} + 3H_2O_{(l)}$$
grey-green precipitate → purple solution

Chromium

You Can Prepare Transition Metal Complexes

Making transition metal complexes can be as simple as adding a solution or solid containing your **transition metal ion** to a solution containing your **ligand** and giving it a mix. This is how you would prepare the complexes on page 177.

It's not always that easy, however. Take the **chromium** complex **chromium(II) ethanoate**, $Cr_2(CH_3COO)_4(H_2O)_2$, for instance. To make it, you start off with sodium dichromate(VI) solution. The reaction happens in **two parts**.

1) **Orange** sodium dichromate(VI) is **reduced** with zinc in acid solution to first form a **green** solution containing Cr^{3+} ions, and then to give a **blue** solution of Cr^{2+} ions (like you saw on the previous page).

$$Cr_2O_7^{2-}{}_{(aq)} + 14H^+{}_{(aq)} + 3Zn_{(s)} \rightarrow 3Zn^{2+}{}_{(aq)} + 2Cr^{3+}{}_{(aq)} + 7H_2O_{(l)}$$

$$2Cr^{3+}{}_{(aq)} + Zn_{(s)} \rightarrow 2Cr^{2+}{}_{(aq)} + Zn^{2+}{}_{(aq)}$$

2) **Sodium ethanoate** is mixed with this solution and a **red precipitate** of **chromium(II) ethanoate** forms.

$$2Cr^{2+}{}_{(aq)} + 4CH_3COO^-{}_{(aq)} + 2H_2O_{(l)} \rightarrow [Cr_2(CH_3COO)_4(H_2O)_2]_{(s)}$$

3) Unfortunately it's not that simple as Cr^{2+} ions are **very easily oxidised.** You have to do the whole experiment in an **inert atmosphere** (such as nitrogen) to keep the air out and remove the oxygen from all the liquids in your experiment before using them (e.g. by bubbling nitrogen though them).

Though you could be tested on the preparation of a complex in the exam, it won't necessarily be this one. Any specific details that you need will be given to you.

- Slowly add **hydrochloric acid** to a flask containing sodium dichromate(VI) solution and zinc mesh. As well as reducing the dichromate(VI) ions, some of the zinc metal will react with the acid to produce **hydrogen gas**, which can escape through a rubber tube into a beaker of water.
- As soon as you see the solution turn a **clear blue** colour, **pinch the rubber tube shut** so hydrogen can **no longer escape** from the flask.
- The build up of **pressure** in the flask will force the Cr^{2+} solution through the open glass tube and into a flask of **sodium ethanoate.**
- As soon as the blue solution reacts with the sodium ethanoate, a **red precipitate** forms. Ta-da, you've made **chromium(II) ethanoate.**
- **Filter** off the precipitate and **wash** it using **water**, then **ethanol**, then **ether** (while still keeping the chromium(II) ethanoate in an inert atmosphere to stop it getting oxidised).

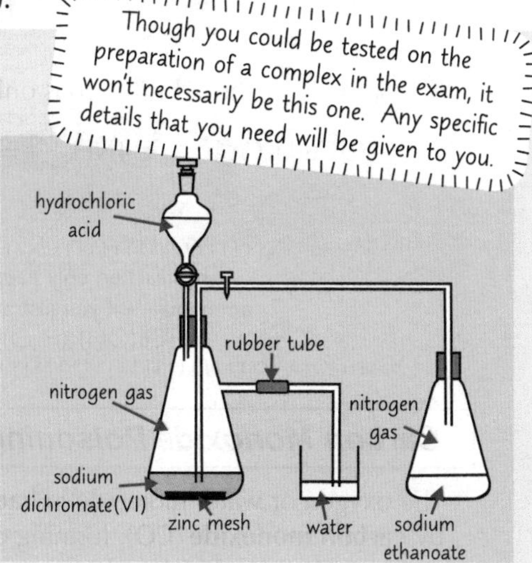

Practice Questions

Q1 What colours are the +3 and +2 chromium aqua-ions?

Q2 Write an equation for the reaction between chromium(III) ions and hydrogen peroxide in an alkaline solution.

Exam Questions

Q1 Potassium dichromate(VI) ($K_2Cr_2O_7$) is a powerful oxidising agent in acidic solution. When potassium dichromate(VI) is acidified and mixed with zinc powder in air, a colour change is seen.

a) Describe the colour change seen in the solution. [1 mark]

b) Give the changes in oxidation number for Cr and Zn and write an ionic equation for the reaction. [3 marks]

c) If the reaction is carried out in an inert atmosphere, a different result will occur. State how the result will differ and explain why. [3 marks]

Q2 Chromium hydroxide, $Cr(OH)_3(H_2O)_3$, is an amphoteric complex.

a) Explain what is meant by the term 'amphoteric', and give equations that demonstrate the amphoteric behaviour of the chromium hydroxide complex. [3 marks]

b) Write an equation for the reaction between chromium hydroxide and excess ammonia. Include any observations you would expect to see. [2 marks]

What do you call a bird's mother? Crow-mum...

Sorry, all these equations seem to be getting to my head a bit. Time for an emergency biscuit. First, have another look at the reactions of chromium hydroxide and make sure you know whether the ligands are being exchanged or modified.

Reactions of Ligands

There are more substitutions on this page than the number of elephants you can fit in a mini.

Ligands can *Exchange* Places with One Another

One ligand can be **swapped** for another ligand — this is **ligand exchange**. It usually causes a **colour change**.

1) If the ligands are of **similar size**, e.g. H_2O, NH_3, CN^- or OH^-, then the **coordination number** of the complex ion **doesn't change**, and neither does the **shape**.

$$[Cr(H_2O)_6]^{3+}_{(aq)} + 6NH_{3(aq)} \rightleftharpoons [Cr(NH_3)_6]^{3+}_{(aq)} + 6H_2O_{(l)}$$

octahedral, green → octahedral, purple

Like ligands, a large, charged rugby player can also lead to a change in coordination.

2) If a **small, uncharged** ligand (e.g. H_2O) is substituted for a **large, charged** ligand (e.g. Cl^-), or vice versa, there's a **change of coordination number** and a **change of shape**.

$$[Cu(H_2O)_6]^{2+}_{(aq)} + 4Cl^-_{(aq)} \rightleftharpoons [CuCl_4]^{2-}_{(aq)} + 6H_2O_{(l)}$$

octahedral, pale blue → tetrahedral, yellow

$$[Co(H_2O)_6]^{2+}_{(aq)} + 4Cl^-_{(aq)} \rightleftharpoons [CoCl_4]^{2-}_{(aq)} + 6H_2O_{(l)}$$

octahedral, pale pink → tetrahedral, blue

3) Sometimes the substitution is only **partial**.

$$[Cu(H_2O)_6]^{2+}_{(aq)} + 4NH_{3(aq)} \rightleftharpoons [Cu(NH_3)_4(H_2O)_2]^{2+}_{(aq)} + 4H_2O_{(l)}$$

octahedral, pale blue → octahedral, deep blue

This reaction only happens when you add an excess of ammonia — if you just add a bit, you get a blue precipitate of $[Cu(OH)_2(H_2O)_4]$ instead (see the next page).

As it's in solution and contains ligands that aren't water, you need to include all the water ligands when writing the formula of a complex like $[Cu(NH_3)_4(H_2O)_2]^{2+}$. But if you're writing out the formula of a precipitate, such as $[Cu(H_2O)_4(OH)_2]$, you can leave out the water ligands and just write $Cu(OH)_2$.

Carbon Monoxide Poisoning Happens Because of *Ligand Exchange*

The oxygen or water molecule in **haemoglobin** (see page 170) can be replaced in a ligand exchange reaction by **carbon monoxide** (**CO**), forming **carboxyhaemoglobin**. This is bad news because carbon monoxide forms **strong** dative covalent bonds (see page 23) with the **iron** ion and **doesn't** readily exchange with oxygen or water ligands, meaning the haemoglobin **can't transport oxygen** any more. This leads to **carbon monoxide poisoning**.

A *Positive Entropy Change* Makes a *More Stable* Complex

1) When a **ligand exchange reaction** occurs, dative bonds are **broken** and **formed**. The **strength** of the bonds being broken is often very **similar** to the strength of the new bonds being made. So the **enthalpy change** for a ligand exchange reaction is usually very **small**. For example, the reaction substituting ammonia with ethane-1,2-diamine in a nickel complex has a very **small** enthalpy change of reaction:

$$[Ni(NH_3)_6]^{2+} + 3NH_2CH_2CH_2NH_2 \rightarrow [Ni(NH_2CH_2CH_2NH_2)_3]^{2+} + 6NH_3 \quad \Delta H = -13 \text{ kJ mol}^{-1}$$

Break 6 coordinate bonds between Ni and N. — Form 6 coordinate bonds between Ni and N.

2) This is actually a **reversible** reaction, but the equilibrium lies so **far to the right** that it is thought of as being irreversible — $[Ni(NH_2CH_2CH_2NH_2)_3]^{2+}$ is **much more stable** than $[Ni(NH_3)_6]^{2+}$. This isn't accounted for by an enthalpy change. Instead, it's to do with the **entropy change** of the reaction:

> When monodentate ligands are substituted with bidentate or multidentate ligands, the number of particles in solution increases — the **more particles**, the **greater the entropy**. Reactions that result in an increase in entropy are **more likely** to occur.

3) When the **hexadentate ligand EDTA^{4-}** replaces monodentate or bidentate ligands, the complex formed is **a lot more stable**.

$$[Cr(NH_3)_6]^{3+} + EDTA^{4-} \rightarrow [Cr(EDTA)]^- + 6NH_3 \quad \textbf{2 particles} \rightarrow \textbf{7 particles}$$

The enthalpy change for this reaction is almost zero and the entropy change is big and positive. This makes the free energy change ($\Delta G = \Delta H - T\Delta S$) negative, so the reaction is feasible (see page 152).

Reactions of Ligands

Transition Element Hydroxides are Brightly Coloured Precipitates

1) When you mix an aqueous solution of **transition element ions** with aqueous **sodium hydroxide** (NaOH) or aqueous **ammonia** (NH_3), the water ligands are **deprotonated** in an acid-base reaction and you get a **coloured hydroxide precipitate**.
2) You can reverse these reactions by adding an **acid** to the **hydroxide precipitate** — the hydroxide ligands will **protonate** and the precipitate will dissolve as the soluble **metal-aqua ions** are reformed.
3) In **aqueous solutions**, transition elements take the form $[M(H_2O)_6]^{n+}$. They can also be written as $M^{n+}_{(aq)}$, as long as the metal ion is **only** bonded to **water**. If it's bonded to anything else you need to write out the whole formula.
4) You need to know the **equations** for the following reactions, and the **colours** of the hydroxide precipitates:

A metal-aqua ion is a metal ion complex that only contains water ligands.

copper(II): $[Cu(H_2O)_6]^{2+}_{(aq)} + 2OH^-_{(aq)} \rightarrow [Cu(OH)_2(H_2O)_4]_{(s)} + 2H_2O_{(l)}$

this can also be written as: $Cu^{2+}_{(aq)} + 2OH^-_{(aq)} \rightarrow Cu(OH)_{2(s)}$

$[Cu(H_2O)_6]^{2+}_{(aq)} + 2NH_{3(aq)} \rightarrow [Cu(OH)_2(H_2O)_4]_{(s)} + 2NH_4{}^+_{(aq)}$

This goes from a pale blue solution to a blue precipitate.

In excess ammonia, copper(II) hydroxide undergoes a **ligand exchange reaction**:

$[Cu(OH)_2(H_2O)_4]_{(s)} + 4NH_{3(aq)} \rightarrow [Cu(NH_3)_4(H_2O)_2]^{2+}_{(aq)} + 2OH^-_{(aq)} + 2H_2O_{(l)}$

This goes from a blue precipitate to a deep blue solution.

iron(II): $[Fe(H_2O)_6]^{2+}_{(aq)} + 2OH^-_{(aq)} \rightarrow [Fe(OH)_2(H_2O)_4]_{(s)} + 2H_2O_{(l)}$

$[Fe(H_2O)_6]^{2+}_{(aq)} + 2NH_{3(aq)} \rightarrow [Fe(OH)_2(H_2O)_4]_{(s)} + 2NH_4{}^+_{(aq)}$

This goes from a pale green solution to a green precipitate, which darkens on standing (as the precipitate is oxidised by water and oxygen in the air to form **iron(III) hydroxide**).

iron(III): $[Fe(H_2O)_6]^{3+}_{(aq)} + 3OH^-_{(aq)} \rightarrow [Fe(OH)_3(H_2O)_3]_{(s)} + 3H_2O_{(l)}$

$[Fe(H_2O)_6]^{3+}_{(aq)} + 3NH_{3(aq)} \rightarrow [Fe(OH)_3(H_2O)_3]_{(s)} + 3NH_4{}^+_{(aq)}$

This goes from a yellow solution to an orange precipitate, which darkens on standing.

cobalt(II): $[Co(H_2O)_6]^{2+}_{(aq)} + 2OH^-_{(aq)} \rightarrow [Co(OH)_2(H_2O)_4]_{(s)} + 2H_2O_{(l)}$

$[Co(H_2O)_6]^{2+}_{(aq)} + 2NH_{3(aq)} \rightarrow [Co(OH)_2(H_2O)_4]_{(s)} + 2NH_4{}^+_{(aq)}$

This goes from a pale pink solution to a blue precipitate, which turns brown on standing.

In excess ammonia, cobalt(II) hydroxide undergoes a **ligand exchange reaction**:

$[Co(OH)_2(H_2O)_4]_{(s)} + 6NH_{3(aq)} \rightarrow [Co(NH_3)_6]^{2+}_{(aq)} + 2OH^-_{(aq)}\ 4H_2O_{(l)}$

The blue (or pink) precipitate dissolves to form a yellow-brown solution.

On standing, this is oxidised to form a brown solution containing $[Co(NH_3)_6]^{3+}_{(aq)}$ ions.

Have a look at page 174 to see how chromium(II) reacts with sodium hydroxide and ammonia.

Practice Questions

Q1 Give an example of a ligand substitution reaction that involves a change of coordination number.

Q2 What do you see when ammonia solution is slowly added to a copper(II) sulfate solution until it's in excess?

Q3 Why does adding excess NH_3 give different results from adding excess NaOH to copper(II) sulfate solution?

Exam Questions

Q1 When a solution of $EDTA^{4-}$ ions is added to an aqueous solution of $[Fe(H_2O)_6]^{3+}$ ions, a ligand substitution reaction occurs.

a) Write an equation for the reaction that takes place. [1 mark]

b) The new complex that is formed is more stable than $[Fe(H_2O)_6]^{3+}$. Explain why. [1 mark]

Q2 Ammonia solution is added to a pale pink solution containing a hydrated transition metal complex. Initially, a blue precipitate is formed. When an excess of ammonia is added, the precipitate dissolves to form a yellow-brown solution.

a) Identify the transition metal complex present in the initial pale pink solution. [1 mark]

b) Write equations for both reactions, and state the type of reaction taking place each time. [4 marks]

Where do transition metals sell their shares? On the ligand exchange...

Ligands generally don't mind swapping with other ligands, so long as they're not too tightly attached to the central metal ion. They also won't fancy changing if it means forming fewer molecules and having less entropy. Fussy things...

Transition Metals and Catalysis

As if you haven't seen enough evidence for the greatness of transition metals, here's more. They're darn good catalysts...

Transition Metals and their Compounds make **Good Catalysts**

Transition metals and their compounds make **good catalysts** because they can **change oxidation number** by gaining or losing electrons within their **d-orbitals**. This means they can **transfer electrons** to **speed up** reactions.

Example: In the Contact Process, SO_2 is oxidised to SO_3: $SO_2 + ½O_2 \rightarrow SO_3$.
Vanadium(V) oxide is used as a catalyst as it can be reduced to vanadium(IV) oxide and oxidise SO_2.
It's then oxidised back to vanadium(V) oxide by oxygen ready to start all over again.

This example uses a heterogeneous catalyst (see the next page), but the principle also applies to homogeneous catalysts.

Vanadium oxidises SO_2 to SO_3 and is reduced itself.

$$V_2O_5 + SO_2 \rightarrow V_2O_4 + SO_3$$

vanadium(V) → vanadium(IV)

The reduced catalyst is then oxidised by oxygen gas back to its original state.

$$V_2O_4 + {}^1/_2O_2 \rightarrow V_2O_5$$

vanadium(IV) → vanadium(V)

Transition Metal Compounds are Good **Homogeneous Catalysts**

1) **Homogeneous catalysts** are in the **same physical state** as the reactants.
   Usually a **homogeneous** catalyst is an **aqueous catalyst** for a reaction between two **aqueous solutions**.
2) Homogeneous catalysts work by combining with the reactants to form an **intermediate species** which then reacts to form the **products** and **reform the catalyst**.
3) The activation energy needed to form the **intermediates** (and to form the products from the intermediates) is **lower** than that needed to make the products directly from the reactants.
4) The catalyst is always **reformed** so it can carry on catalysing the reaction.

Example: Peroxodisulfate ions oxidising iodide ions.

The **redox** reaction between iodide ions and peroxodisulfate ($S_2O_8^{2-}$) ions takes place **annoyingly slowly** because both ions are **negatively charged**. The ions **repel** each other, so it's unlikely they'll **collide** and **react**.

$$S_2O_8^{2-}{}_{(aq)} + 2I^-{}_{(aq)} \rightarrow I_{2(aq)} + 2SO_4^{2-}{}_{(aq)}$$

But if **Fe^{2+} ions** are added, things really **speed up** because each stage of the reaction involves a **positive and a negative ion**, so there's **no repulsion**.

1) First, the Fe^{2+} ions are **oxidised** to Fe^{3+} ions by the $S_2O_8^{2-}$ ions. $S_2O_8^{2-}{}_{(aq)} + 2Fe^{2+}{}_{(aq)} \rightarrow 2Fe^{3+}{}_{(aq)} + 2SO_4^{2-}{}_{(aq)}$
2) The newly formed intermediate Fe^{3+} ions now **easily oxidise** the I^- ions to iodine, and the **catalyst is regenerated**. $2Fe^{3+}{}_{(aq)} + 2I^-{}_{(aq)} \rightarrow I_{2(aq)} + 2Fe^{2+}{}_{(aq)}$

The Fe^{2+} is a homogeneous catalyst — it's in the same phase as the reactants.

Autocatalysis is when a **Product** Catalyses the Reaction

Another example of a **homogeneous catalyst** is Mn^{2+} in the reaction between $C_2O_4^{2-}$ and MnO_4^-.
It's an **autocatalysis reaction** because Mn^{2+} is a **product** of the reaction and **acts as a catalyst** for the reaction.
This means that as the reaction progresses and the **amount** of the **product increases**, the reaction **speeds up**.

The reactant ions are both negatively charged so repel each other and cause the rate of the uncatalysed reaction to be very slow.

$$2MnO_4^-{}_{(aq)} + 16H^+{}_{(aq)} + 5C_2O_4^{2-}{}_{(aq)} \rightarrow 2Mn^{2+}{}_{(aq)} + 8H_2O_{(l)} + 10CO_{2(g)}$$

1) Mn^{2+} catalyses the reaction by first reacting with MnO_4^- to form **Mn^{3+}** ions: $MnO_4^-{}_{(aq)} + 4Mn^{2+}{}_{(aq)} + 8H^+{}_{(aq)} \rightarrow 5Mn^{3+}{}_{(aq)} + 4H_2O_{(l)}$
2) The newly formed **Mn^{3+}** ions then react with $C_2O_4^{2-}$ ions to form carbon dioxide and **re-form** the Mn^{2+} catalyst ions: $2Mn^{3+}{}_{(aq)} + C_2O_4^{2-}{}_{(aq)} \rightarrow 2Mn^{2+}{}_{(aq)} + 2CO_{2(g)}$

Transition Metals and Catalysis

Transition Metals and Their Compounds can be **Heterogeneous Catalysts**

A **heterogeneous catalyst** is in a **different phase** from the reactants. Usually the reactants are gases or in solution and the catalyst is a solid — the reaction occurs on the surface of the catalyst. Transition metals make good heterogeneous catalysts because they can use their partially filled **d-orbitals** to make weak **bonds** with the reactant molecules.

Catalytic converters are used in cars to reduce emissions of **nitrogen monoxide** and **carbon monoxide** produced by internal combustion engines. They use a **platinum** or **rhodium** catalyst to convert these gases into nitrogen and carbon dioxide.

$$2NO_{(g)} + 2CO_{(g)} \rightarrow N_{2(g)} + 2CO_{2(g)}$$

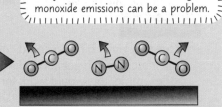

Have a look at page 80 to see why carbon monoxide and nitrogen monoxide emissions can be a problem.

Here's how it works —

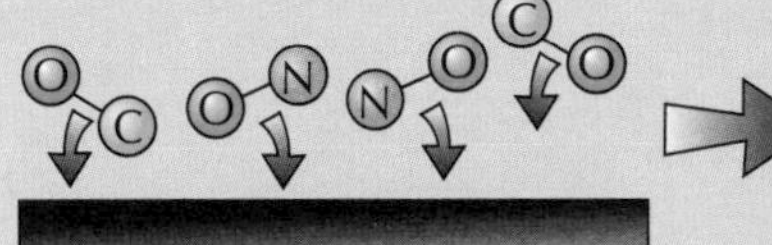

1) The **reactant** molecules are **attracted** to the surface of the solid catalyst and stick to it — this is called **adsorption**.

2) The surface of the catalyst **activates** the molecules so they react more easily. In the reaction between nitrogen monoxide and carbon dioxide, the bonds between the **reactants'** atoms are **weakened** making them **easier** to **break** and reform as the products.

3) The **product** molecules **leave** the surface of the catalyst making way for fresh reactants to take their place. This is called **desorption**.

Practice Questions

Q1 What property of transition metals makes them good catalysts?

Q2 Why is the rate of the uncatalysed reaction between iodide and peroxodisulfate ions so slow?

Q3 What term describes the process when a product catalyses a reaction?

Q4 Which two transition metals are used in catalytic converters?

Exam Questions

Q1 Transition metal compounds are used as both heterogeneous and homogeneous catalysts.

a) Explain the meaning of the terms 'heterogeneous' and 'homogeneous'. [1 mark]

b) How does the fact that a transition metal has partially filled d-orbitals help it act as a heterogeneous catalyst? [1 mark]

c) How does the fact that transition metals have variable oxidation numbers allow them to act as homogeneous catalysts? [2 marks]

Q2 A student is measuring the rate of the reaction between MnO_4^- ions and $C_2O_4^{2-}$ over time. She predicts that the rate will decrease with time, but discovers instead that the rate of reaction over the first five minutes increases. Explain the student's results with use of appropriate equations. [5 marks]

Q3 Catalytic converters use a platinum or rhodium catalyst to reduce emissions of carbon monoxide and nitrogen monoxide from internal combustion engines.

a) The first step in the catalysis reaction is the adsorption of nitrogen monoxide and carbon monoxide onto the surface of the catalyst. What is meant by the term 'adsorption'? [1 mark]

b) Explain how adsorption helps to catalyse the reaction. [2 marks]

Burmese cats are top of my cat list...

Transition metals are able to do so many different things. And it's all down to those d-orbital electron thingies. Unfortunately that means there's a lot for you to remember. It's not even as if there's only one sort of catalyst to remember. There are two — homogeneous catalysts and heterogeneous catalysts... And you need to know both.

Reaction Rates

Welcome, one and all to Kinetics. Your emergency exits are located here, here and here. Thank you.

The Reaction Rate Tells You How Fast Reactants are Converted to Products

The **reaction rate** is the **change in the amount** of reactants or products **per unit time** (normally per second).

There are Loads of Ways to Follow the Rate of a Reaction

Although there are a lot of ways to follow reactions, not every method works for every reaction. You've got to pick a property that changes as the reaction goes on. The following methods are all **continuous monitoring** methods of following the rate of reaction — continuous monitoring means measurements are taken over the duration of the reaction.

Gas volume

If a gas is given off, you could collect it in a gas syringe and record how much you've got at regular time intervals (e.g. every 15 seconds). For example, this would work for the reaction between an acid and a carbonate in which carbon dioxide gas is given off.

To find the concentration of a reactant at each time point, use the ideal gas equation (page 61) to work out how many moles of gas you've got, then use the molar ratio to work out the concentration of the reactant.

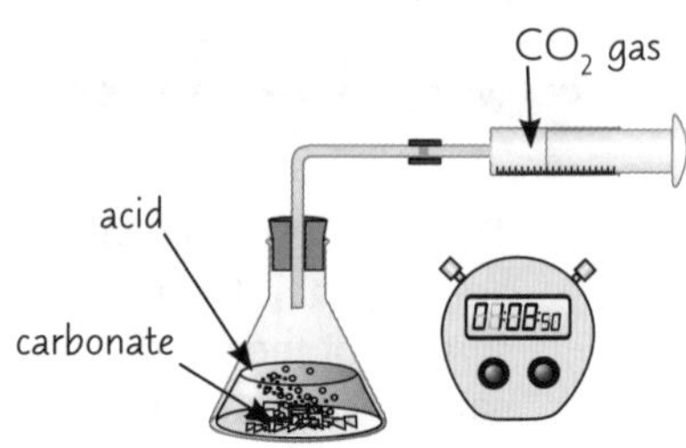

Loss of mass

If a gas is given off, the system will lose mass. You can measure this at regular intervals with a balance.

Use mole calculations to work out how much gas you've lost, and therefore how many moles of reactants are left.

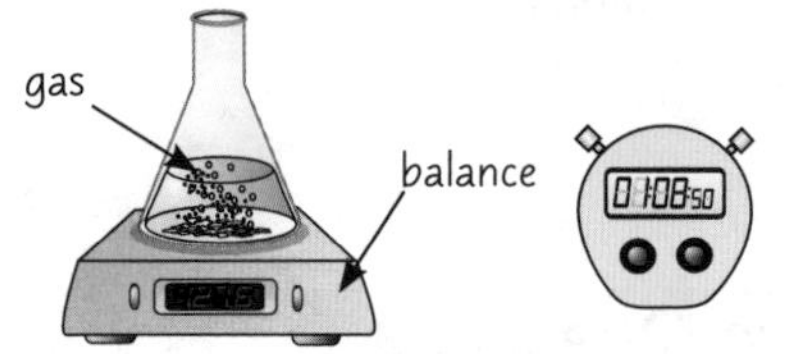

Colour change

You can sometimes track the colour change of a reaction using a gadget called a colorimeter. A colorimeter measures absorbance (the amount of light absorbed by the solution). The more concentrated the colour of the solution, the higher the absorbance is.

For example, in the reaction between propanone and iodine, the brown colour fades. So the absorbance of the solution will decrease.

$$CH_3COCH_{3(aq)} + I_{2(aq)} \rightarrow CH_3COCH_2I_{(aq)} + H^+_{(aq)} + I^-_{(aq)}$$

colourless (propanone), brown (iodine), colourless (products)

You measure the change in absorbance like this:

1) Plot a calibration curve — a graph of known concentrations of the coloured solution (in this case I_2) plotted against absorbance.
2) During the experiment, take a small sample from your reaction solution at regular intervals and read the absorbance.
3) Use your calibration curve to convert the absorbance at each time point into a concentration.

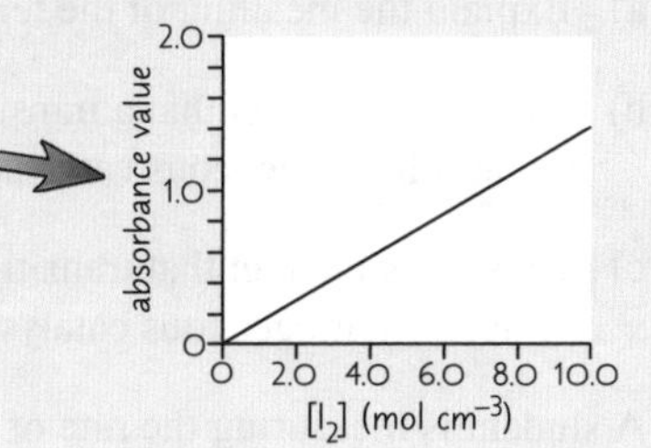

Change in pH

If the reaction produces or uses up H^+ ions, the pH of the solution will change. So you could measure the pH of the solution at regular intervals and calculate the concentration of H^+.

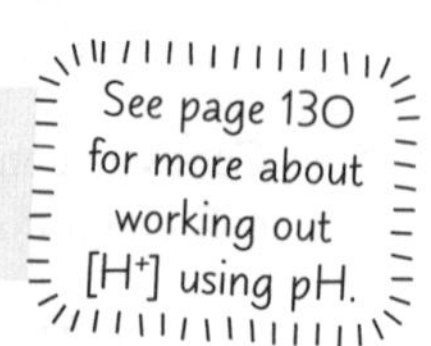

Titration

You can take small samples of a reaction at regular time intervals and titrate them using a standard solution. The rate can be found from measuring the change in concentration of the products or reactant over time.

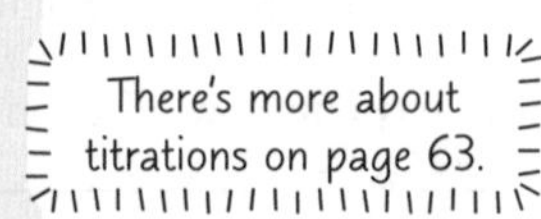

Electrical conductivity

If the number of ions changes, so will the electrical conductivity.

Reaction Rates

Work Out **Reaction Rate** from a **Concentration-Time Graph**

1) By repeatedly taking **measurements** during a reaction (continuous monitoring) you can draw a graph of the **amount of reactant** or **product** (on the *y*-axis) against **time** (on the *x*-axis).
2) The rate at any point in the reaction is given by the **gradient** (slope) at that point on the graph.
3) If the graph is a curve, you'll have to draw a **tangent** to the curve and find the gradient of that.

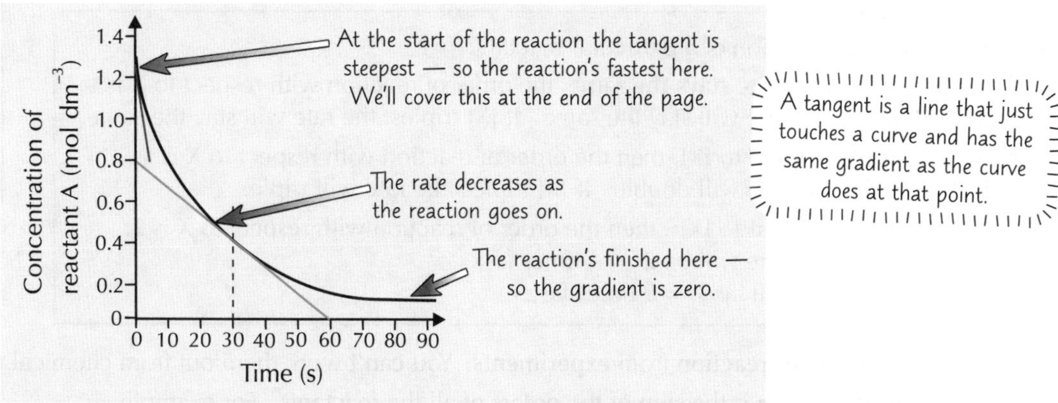

Concentration of reactant A (mol dm⁻³)
1.4
1.2
1.0
0.8
0.6
0.4
0.2
0
0 10 20 30 40 50 60 70 80 90
Time (s)
At the start of the reaction the tangent is steepest — so the reaction's fastest here. We'll cover this at the end of the page.
The rate decreases as the reaction goes on.
The reaction's finished here — so the gradient is zero.

A tangent is a line that just touches a curve and has the same gradient as the curve does at that point.

Example: Use the graph above to find the rate of reaction after 30 seconds.

$$\text{Gradient} = \frac{\text{change in } y}{\text{change in } x} = \frac{-0.8}{60} = \mathbf{-0.013}$$

So, the rate after 30 seconds is **0.013 mol dm^{-3} s^{-1}**.

Don't forget the units — you've divided mol dm^{-3} by s, so it's mol dm^{-3} s^{-1}.

4) The **sign** of the gradient doesn't really matter — it's a **negative** gradient when you're measuring **reactant concentration** because the reactant decreases. If you measured the **product concentration**, it'd be a **positive** gradient.

Practice Questions

Q1 What is the definition of reaction rate?

Q2 Give an example of a reaction where gas volume can be measured to follow reaction rate.

Q3 For a straight line graph of concentration of reactants against time, how do you work out reaction rate?

Exam Question

Q1 The reaction between iodine and propanone in acidic conditions was investigated.

$$I_{2(aq)} + CH_3COCH_{3(aq)} \xrightarrow{H^+_{(aq)}} CH_3COCH_2I_{(aq)} + H^+_{(aq)} + I^-_{(aq)}$$

a) Apart from colorimetry, suggest, with a reason, one method that could be used to follow the reaction rate. [1 mark]

b) Outline how the rate of reaction with respect to propanone, at any particular time, could be determined. [2 marks]

The following data was collected at 25 °C.

Time (s)	0	10	20	30	40
Concentration of CH_3COCH_3 (mol dm^{-3})	0.2	0.07	0.025	0.0098	0.0031

c) Plot a graph, using the data provided. From the graph, determine the rate of reaction at 25 °C after 15 seconds. [3 marks]

My concentration-time graph for chemistry revision has a negative gradient...

This kinetics topic really comes at you at a fast rate... I can't promise the jokes are going to get a whole lot better throughout the topic but I can promise it's gonna cover a lot of different stuff to do with reaction rates. So it's worth making sure you understand the gradient = rate thing now, as well as how to find the gradient of different graphs.

Orders of Reactions

You might think the rate of a reaction will change if you change the concentration of the reactants. But this isn't always the case... Read on for some juicy information about the orders of reactions. Speaking of orders... can I order a pizza?

Orders Tell You How a Reactant's Concentration Affects the Rate

1) The **order of reaction** with respect to a particular reactant tells you how the **reactant's concentration** affects the **rate**.

Where [X] is the concentration of a particular reactant:
- If [X] changes and the rate **stays the same**, the order of reaction with respect to X is **0**. So if [X] doubles, the rate will stay the same. If [X] triples, the rate will stay the same.
- If the rate is **proportional to [X]**, then the order of reaction with respect to X is **1**. So if [X] doubles, the rate will double. If [X] triples, the rate will triple.
- If the rate is **proportional to $[X]^2$**, then the order of reaction with respect to X is **2**. So if [X] doubles, the rate will be $2^2 = 4$ times faster. If [X] triples, the rate will be $3^2 = 9$ times faster.

No matter how hard Jane concentrated, she couldn't increase the rate of the meeting.

2) You can only find **orders of reaction** from **experiments**. You **can't** work them out from chemical equations.
3) The **overall order of reaction** is the **sum** of the orders of all the reactants. For example, if the reaction, $A + B + C \rightarrow D$ is **first order** with respect to A and B and **zero order** with respect to C, then the **overall order** of reaction is **2**.

The Shape of a Rate-Concentration Graph Tells You the Order

You can use data from a **concentration-time graph** to construct a **rate-concentration graph**, which can tell you the **reaction order**. Here's how...

1) Find the **gradient** at various points on the graph. This will give you the **rate** at that particular **concentration**. With a **straight-line graph**, this is easy, but if it's a **curve**, you need to draw **tangents** and find their gradients.
2) Now plot each point on a new graph with the axes **rate** and **concentration**. Then draw a smooth line or curve through the points. The shape of the line will tell you the order of the reaction with respect to that reactant.

The notation [X] means the concentration of reactant X.

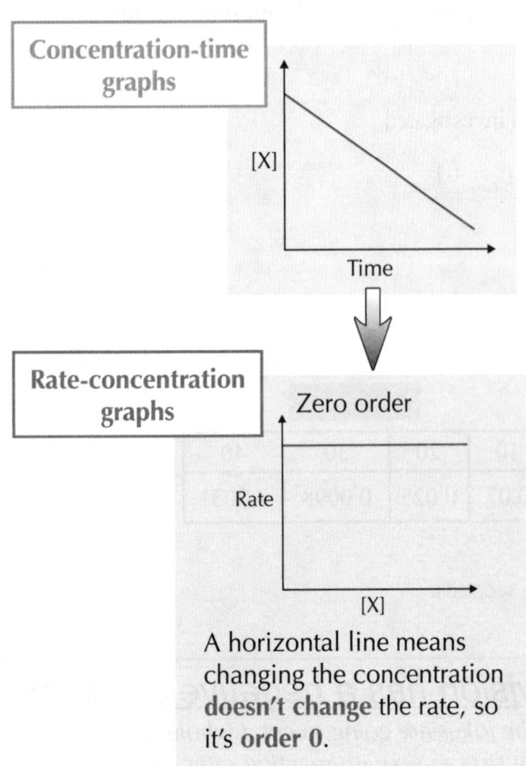

A horizontal line means changing the concentration **doesn't change** the rate, so it's **order 0**.

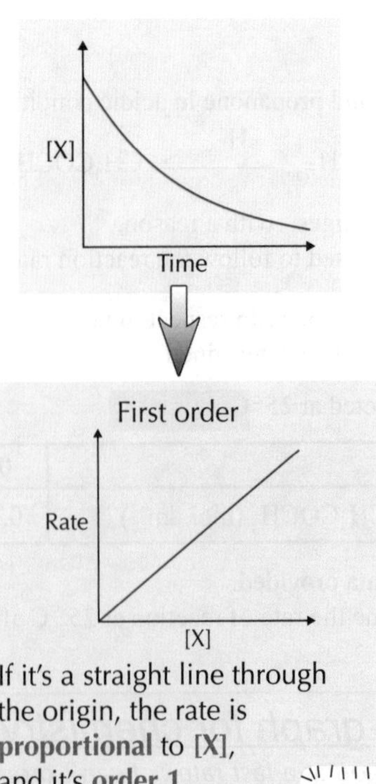

If it's a straight line through the origin, the rate is **proportional** to **[X]**, and it's **order 1**.

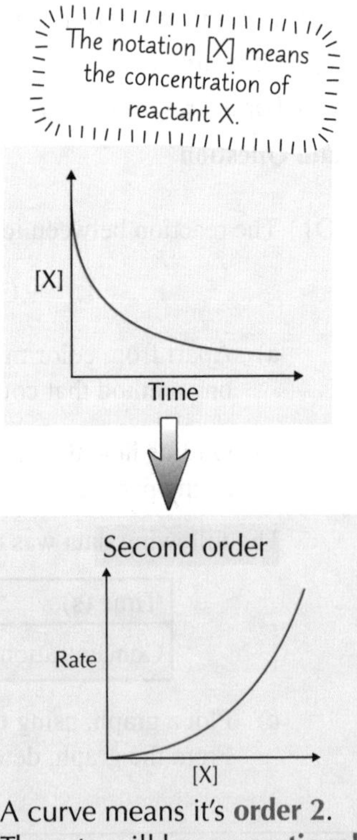

A curve means it's **order 2**. The rate will be **proportional** to **$[X]^2$**.

In theory, a curve could mean a higher order than 2, but you won't be asked about them.

Orders of Reactions

The ***Half-Life*** *is the* ***Time*** *it takes for* ***Half*** *of the* ***Reactant*** *to be* ***Used Up***

To work out the **half-life** ($t_{½}$) of a reaction, plot a **concentration–time graph**. Then **draw lines** across from the *y*-axis at points where the concentration has **halved** and read off the time taken.

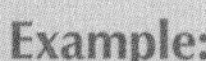

Example:

The graph shows the decomposition of hydrogen peroxide:

$$2H_2O_{2(aq)} \rightarrow O_{2(g)} + 2H_2O_{(l)}$$

$[H_2O_2]$ from 4 to 2 mol dm^{-3} = 200 sec,
$[H_2O_2]$ from 2 to 1 mol dm^{-3} = 200 sec,
$[H_2O_2]$ from 1 to 0.5 mol dm^{-3} = 200 sec.

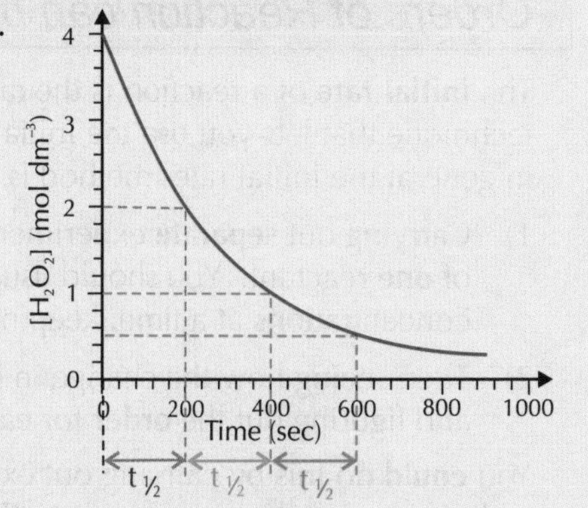

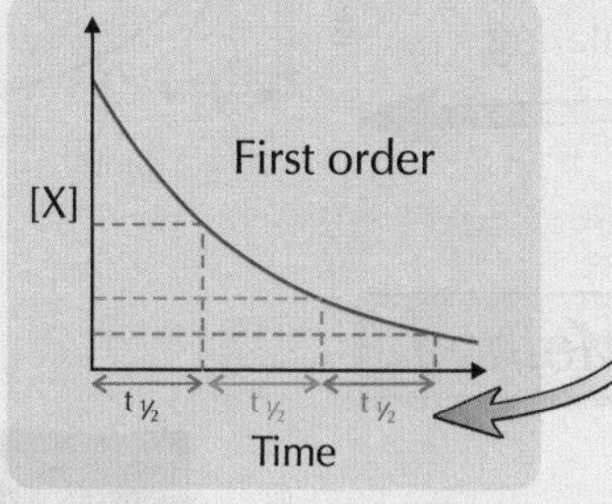

Half-lives are useful for identifying a first order reaction **without** having to draw a rate-concentration graph. This is because the half-life is always constant for a first order reaction.

For example, for this reaction, $t_{½}$ is **constant** — it always takes the **same** amount of **time** for the concentration to halve. The half-life is independent of the concentration and so the reaction must be first order.

Volume-time graphs can also be used in exactly the same way, e.g. the half-life is the time it takes the volume of reactant to half.

Practice Questions

Q1 Sketch rate-concentration graphs for zero, first and second order reactions.

Q2 How does the half-life change with time in a first order reaction?

Exam Questions

Q1 The table shows the results of an experiment on the decomposition of nitrogen(V) oxide at constant temperature.

$$2N_2O_5 \rightarrow 4NO_2 + O_2$$

Time (s)	0	50	100	150	200	250	300
$[N_2O_5]$ (mol dm^{-3})	2.5	1.66	1.14	0.76	0.5	0.33	0.22

a) Plot a graph of these results. [2 marks]

b) From the graph, find the times for the concentration of N_2O_5 to decrease:

i) to half its original concentration, [1 mark]

ii) from 2.0 mol dm^{-3} to 1.0 mol dm^{-3}. [1 mark]

c) Giving a reason, deduce the order of this reaction. [1 mark]

Q2 A student measures the rate for the following reaction.

$$A + B \rightarrow C$$

The rate of reaction is found to be first order with respect to A and second order with respect to B.

a) What would be the change in the rate if the concentration of B was doubled and the concentration of A was halved? [1 mark]

b) What is the overall order for the reaction? [1 mark]

Describe the link between concentration and rate, soldier — that's an order...

There's quite a lot on this page, graphically speaking. And graphs are always great, easy marks. Just remember — labelled axes, accurately plotted points and a smoooooth curve or a smoooooth line of best fit. If you do these things then all the other calculations will become a lot easier. And remember smoooooth — like a freshly licked lollipop.

The Initial Rates Method

The initial rate is just what it sounds like — the rate of reaction right at the start of the reaction. They're not very imaginative these chemists, but they do love using experiments to calculate the orders of reactions, as you'll soon see...

Orders of Reaction can be Worked Out by the ***Initial Rates Method***

The **initial rate** of a reaction is the rate right at the **start** of the reaction. The **initial rates method** is a technique that lets you use the initial rate of an experiment to work out the orders of reaction.
In general the initial rates method is done by:

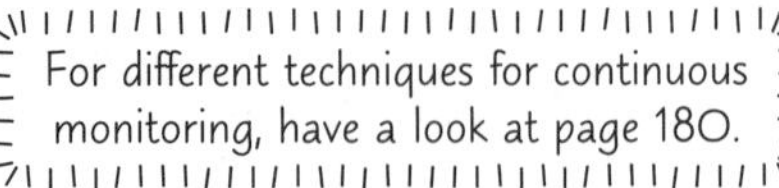

For different techniques for continuous monitoring, have a look at page 180.

1) Carrying out **separate** experiments using **different initial concentrations** of **one** reactant. You should usually only change **one** of the concentrations at a time, keeping the rest constant.
2) Then seeing how the change in **initial concentrations** affects the **initial rates** and figuring out the **order** for each reactant. (See page 186 for how to do this.)

You **could** do this by carrying out experiments using **continuous monitoring** techniques and drawing **concentration-time** or **volume-time graphs**. By calculating the **gradient** of the tangent at time = 0, you can find the initial rate.

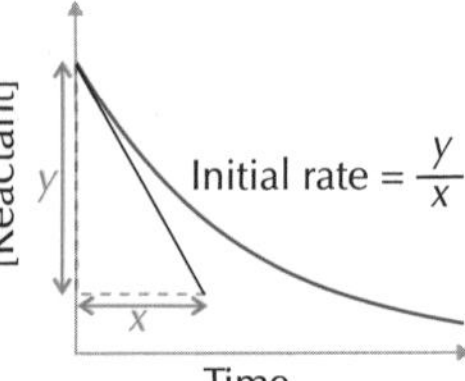

Or, you could carry out a **clock reaction**...

A ***Clock Reaction*** is an ***Example*** of the Initial Rates Method

The method above involves lots of graph drawing and calculations.
Another, simpler, example of an initial rates method is a **clock reaction**.

1) In a clock reaction, you measure how the **time taken** for a set amount of product to form **changes** as you **vary the concentration** of one of the reactants.
2) As part of a clock reaction, there will be a **sudden increase** in the concentration of a certain product as a **limiting reactant** is used up.
3) There's usually an **easily observable end point**, such as a colour change, to tell you when the desired amount of product has formed.
4) The **quicker** the clock reaction finishes, the **faster** the initial rate of the reaction.
5) When carrying out a clock reaction you need to make the following assumptions:
    - The **concentration** of each reactant **doesn't change** significantly over the time period of your clock reaction.
    - The **temperature** stays **constant**.
    - When the end point is seen, the reaction has not proceeded **too far**.

A tanned gent.

The ***Iodine Clock Reaction*** is a Well-Known ***Clock Reaction***

In an iodine clock reaction, the reaction you're monitoring is:

$$H_2O_{2(aq)} + 2I^-_{(aq)} + 2H^+_{(aq)} \rightarrow 2H_2O_{(l)} + I_{2(aq)}$$

The iodine clock is also known as the Harcourt-Esson Reaction.

1) A **small amount of sodium thiosulfate** solution and starch are added to an **excess of hydrogen peroxide** and iodide ions in acid solution. (Starch is used as an indicator — it turns blue-black in the presence of iodine.)
2) The sodium thiosulfate that is added to the reaction mixture reacts **instantaneously** with any iodine that forms:

$$2S_2O_3^{2-}{}_{(aq)} + I_{2(aq)} \rightarrow 2I^-_{(aq)} + S_4O_6^{2-}{}_{(aq)}$$

3) To begin with, all the iodine that forms in the first reaction is **used up straight away** in the **second reaction**. But once all the sodium thiosulfate is **used up**, any more iodine that forms will **stay in solution**, so the starch indicator will suddenly turn the solution **blue-black**. This is the end of the clock reaction.
4) Varying the iodide or hydrogen peroxide concentration, while keeping the others constant, will give **different times** for the colour change.
5) The **time it takes** for the reaction to occur along with the **concentration** of reactants allows you to calculate the **initial rate** with respect to iodide or hydrogen peroxide.

The Initial Rates Method

Here's How to Carry Out the **Iodine Clock Reaction** in the **Lab**...

To find the order with respect to **potassium iodide**:

1) Rinse a **clean** pipette with **sulfuric acid**. Then, use this pipette to transfer a small amount of sulfuric acid, of **known concentration** (e.g. 0.25 mol dm^{-3}), to a clean beaker. This beaker is your reaction vessel.
2) Using a clean pipette or measuring cylinder, add **distilled water** to the beaker containing the sulfuric acid.
3) Using a dropping pipette, add a few drops of **starch solution** to the same beaker.
4) Measure a known amount of **potassium iodide solution** of a known concentration, using either a pipette or a burette, rinsed with potassium iodide solution. Transfer this volume to the reaction vessel.
5) Next, using a pipette rinsed with **sodium thiosulfate solution**, or a clean measuring cylinder, add sodium thiosulfate to the reaction vessel. Swirl the contents of the beaker so all the solutions are evenly mixed.
6) Finally, rinse a pipette with **hydrogen peroxide solution**. Then, use the pipette to transfer hydrogen peroxide solution to the reaction vessel while stirring the contents and simultaneously **start a stop watch**.
7) Continue to stir, and stop the stop watch when the contents of the beaker turn from **colourless to blue-black**, this marks the **end point**. Record this time in a results table, along with the quantities of sulfuric acid, water, potassium iodide and sodium thiosulfate solutions you used in that experiment.
8) **Repeat** the experiment varying the volume of potassium iodide solution. Keep the volume of sulfuric acid, sodium thiosulfate and hydrogen peroxide **constant** and use **varying** amounts of **distilled water** in each experiment so the **overall volume** of the reaction mixture remains **constant**.

An example of how to work out orders of reaction from initial rates data is on page 186.

An **approximation** of the initial rate at each concentration can be found from the **time** it took to reach the end point. By **comparing** these initial rates you can find the reaction order with **respect to** potassium iodide.

The **Initial Rate** of the **Iodination** of **Propanone** can be Found by Titrating

The rate of reaction for the iodine-propanone reaction can be followed by a **continuous monitoring** titrimetric method.

$$CH_3COCH_{3(aq)} + I_{2(aq)} \xrightarrow{H^+_{(aq)}} CH_3COCH_2I_{(aq)} + H^+_{(aq)} + I^-_{(aq)}$$

A titrimetric method uses titrations to find out information about a reaction.

You can monitor the reaction by **taking samples** at regular intervals. You first need to **stop** the reaction in each sample by adding **sodium hydrogencarbonate** to neutralise the acid. Then **titrate** each sample against sodium thiosulfate and starch to work out the **concentration** of the **iodine**. You'll need to carry out the experiment several times and in each experiment change the concentration of just **one reactant**.

Practice Questions

Q1 How do you find the initial rate of reaction from a concentration-time graph?

Q2 Why is sodium hydrogen carbonate added to samples from the reaction between propanone and iodine?

Exam Questions

Q1 A student carried out an iodine clock reaction:

$$H_2O_{2(aq)} + 2I^-_{(aq)} + 2H^+_{(aq)} \rightarrow 2H_2O_{(l)} + I_{2(aq)}$$

$$2S_2O_3^{2-}{}_{(aq)} + I_{2(aq)} \rightarrow 2I^-_{(aq)} + S_4O_6^{2-}{}_{(aq)}$$

a) After some time, the starch indicator in solution turns blue-black. State why this change occurs. [1 mark]

b) The amount of sodium thiosulfate added to the reaction mixture was increased. Explain what change this would have on the time it takes for the colour change to occur. [1 mark]

Q2 Propanone can be reacted with iodine to form iodopropanone via an acid-catalysed reaction. Describe how you could use titration to investigate how the rate of reaction changes as the concentration of iodine varies. [3 marks]

The alarm clock reaction — the end point is a broken bedside table...

I know experiments like these might not seem the most exciting in the world. But you've got to learn them. Besides, once upon a time they were thrilling. People would go crazy for a chemical colour change. Honest...

Rate Equations

This is when it all gets a bit mathsy. You've just got to take a deep breath and dive in...

*The **Rate Equation** links **Reaction Rate** to **Reactant Concentrations***

Rate equations look ghastly, but all they really do is tell you how the **rate** is affected by the **concentrations of reactants**. For a general reaction: **A + B → C + D**, the **rate equation** is:

$$\text{Rate} = k[A]^m[B]^n$$

The units of rate are normally mol dm^{-3} s^{-1}.

1) k is the **rate constant** — the **bigger** it is, the **faster** the reaction.
2) **m** and **n** are the **orders of the reaction** with respect to reactant A and reactant B.
   m tells you how the **concentration of reactant A** affects the **rate** and **n** tells you the same for **reactant B**.
3) The overall order of the reaction is **m + n**.

Example: The chemical equation below shows the acid-catalysed reaction between propanone and iodine.

$$CH_3COCH_{3(aq)} + I_{2(aq)} \xrightarrow{H^+_{(aq)}} CH_3COCH_2I_{(aq)} + H^+_{(aq)} + I^-_{(aq)}$$

This reaction is first order with respect to propanone and $H^+_{(aq)}$ and zero order with respect to iodine. Write down the rate equation.

Even though $H^+_{(aq)}$ is a catalyst, rather than a reactant, it can still appear in the rate equation.

The rate equation is: rate = $k[CH_3COCH_{3(aq)}]^1[H^+_{(aq)}]^1[I_{2(aq)}]^0$

But $[X]^1$ is usually written as $[X]$, and $[X]^0$ equals 1 so is usually left out of the rate equation.

So you can simplify the rate equation to: rate = $k[CH_3COCH_{3(aq)}][H^+_{(aq)}]$

Think about the powers laws from maths.

Spectator ions (ions that don't take part in the chemical reaction) are normally not included in rate equations.

*You can use the **Initial Rates Method** to Work Out **Orders of Reaction***

1) By using the **initial rates method** (see pages 184-185) to collect data about the initial rate of a reaction.
2) By comparing the initial rate of a reaction with varying concentrations of reactants, you can find the **orders of reaction** for reactants in a reaction.
3) Once you know the chemical **equation** for a reaction, along with the orders of reaction, you can **write the rate equation**.

Example:
The table on the right shows the results of a series of initial rate experiments for the reaction:

$$NO_{(g)} + CO_{(g)} + O_{2(g)} \rightarrow NO_{2(g)} + CO_{2(g)}$$

The experiments were carried out at a constant temperature.
Write down the rate equation for the reaction.

Experiment number	[NO] (mol dm^{-3})	[CO] (mol dm^{-3})	[O_2] (mol dm^{-3})	Initial rate (mol dm^{-3} s^{-1})
1	2.0×10^{-2}	1.0×10^{-2}	1.0×10^{-2}	0.17
2	6.0×10^{-2}	1.0×10^{-2}	1.0×10^{-2}	1.53
3	2.0×10^{-2}	2.0×10^{-2}	1.0×10^{-2}	0.17
4	4.0×10^{-2}	1.0×10^{-2}	2.0×10^{-2}	0.68

1) Look at experiments 1 and 2 — when [NO] triples (and all the other concentrations stay constant) the rate is nine times faster, and $9 = 3^2$. So the reaction is second order with respect to NO.
2) Look at experiments 1 and 3 — when [CO] doubles (but all the other concentrations stay constant), the rate stays the same. So the reaction is zero order with respect to CO.
3) Look at experiments 1 and 4 — the rate of experiment 4 is four times faster than experiment 1. The reaction is second order with respect to [NO], so the rate will quadruple when you double [NO]. But in experiment 4, [O_2] has also been doubled. As doubling [O_2] hasn't had any additional effect on the rate, the reaction must be zero order with respect to O_2.
4) Now that you know the order with respect to each reactant you can write the rate equation: rate = $k[NO]^2$.

Rate Equations

You can Calculate the Rate Constant from the Orders and Rate of Reaction

Once the rate and the orders of the reaction have been found by experiment, you can work out the **rate constant**, ***k***. The rate constant is always the **same** for a certain reaction at a **particular temperature** — but if you **increase** the temperature, the rate constant's going to **rise** too. The units **vary**, so you have to work them out. The example below shows you how.

Example: The reaction below was found to be second order with respect to NO and zero order with respect to CO and O_2. The rate is 1.76×10^{-3} mol dm^{-3} s^{-1} when $[NO_{(g)}] = [CO_{(g)}] = [O_{2(g)}] = 2.00 \times 10^{-3}$ mol dm^{-3}.

$$NO_{(g)} + CO_{(g)} + O_{2(g)} \rightarrow NO_{2(g)} + CO_{2(g)}$$

Find the value of the rate constant.

First write out the **rate equation**: Rate $= k[NO_{(g)}]^2[CO_{(g)}]^0[O_{2(g)}]^0 = k[NO_{(g)}]^2$

Next insert the **concentration** and the **rate**. **Rearrange** the equation and calculate the value of k:

Rate $= k[NO_{(g)}]^2$, so $1.76 \times 10^{-3} = k \times (2.00 \times 10^{-3})^2 \Longrightarrow k = \frac{1.76 \times 10^{-3}}{(2.00 \times 10^{-3})^2} = 440$

Find the **units for k** by putting the other units in the rate equation:

Rate $= k[NO_{(g)}]^2$, so mol dm^{-3} s^{-1} $= k \times$ (mol dm^{-3})^2 $\Longrightarrow k = \frac{\text{mol dm}^{-3}\text{ s}^{-1}}{(\text{mol dm}^{-3})^2} = \frac{\text{s}^{-1}}{\text{mol dm}^{-3}} = \text{dm}^3\text{ mol}^{-1}\text{ s}^{-1}$

So the answer is: **$k = 440$ dm^3 mol^{-1} s^{-1}**

Practice Questions

Q1 What does the size of the rate constant tell you about the reaction rate?

Q2 How do you find the overall order for a reaction?

Q3 How does the rate constant change with an increase in temperature?

Exam Questions

Q1 The following reaction is second order with respect to NO and first order with respect to H_2.

$$2NO_{(g)} + 2H_{2(g)} \rightarrow 2H_2O_{(g)} + N_{2(g)}$$

a) Write a rate equation for the reaction and state the overall order of the reaction. [2 marks]

b) The rate of the reaction at 800 °C was determined to be 0.0027 mol dm^{-3} s^{-1} when $[H_2] = 0.0020$ mol dm^{-3} and $[NO] = 0.0040$ mol dm^{-3}.

i) Calculate a value for the rate constant at 800 °C, including units. [2 marks]

ii) Predict the effect on the rate constant of decreasing the temperature of the reaction to 600 °C. [1 mark]

Q2 An experiment is carried out with reactants X, Y, Z. The initial rates method is used to find the orders of reaction with respect to each reactant. The table to the right shows the results obtained.

a) Give the order with respect to X, Y and Z. Explain your reasoning [3 marks]

b) Give the initial rate if Experiment 2 was repeated, but the concentration of Z was tripled. [1 mark]

Experiment	[X]	[Y]	[Z]	Initial rate (mol dm^{-3} s^{-1})
1	0.25	0.1	0.4	1.30×10^{-3}
2	0.5	0.1	0.4	1.30×10^{-3}
3	0.25	0.2	0.4	5.20×10^{-3}
4	0.25	0.2	0.8	0.0104

c) Write the rate equation for the reaction investigated. [1 mark]

This kinetics joke is so good — it's a gag of the first order...

Working with rate equations is actually pretty fun when you get the hang of it. No, really. And speaking of things that are fun can I recommend to you flying kites, peeling bananas, making models of your friends out of apples, the literary works of Jan Pieńkowski, counting spots on the carpet, the 1980s, goats, eating all the pies, darts... All fantastic fun.

The Rate-Determining Step

You know when you're trying to get out of a room to go to lunch, but it takes ages because not everyone can get through the door at the same time? Well getting through that door is the rate determining step. Talking about lunch...

The **Rate-Determining Step** is the **Slowest Step** in a Multi-Step Reaction

Reaction mechanisms can have **one step** or a **series of steps**.
In a series of steps, each step can have a **different rate**.
The **overall rate** is decided by the step with the **slowest** rate — the **rate-determining step**.

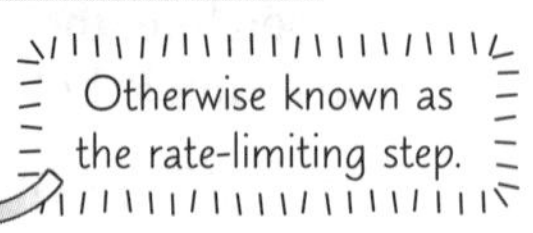
Otherwise known as the rate-limiting step.

Reactants in the **Rate Equation** Affect the **Rate**

The rate equation is handy for helping you work out the **mechanism** of a chemical reaction.
You need to be able to pick out which reactants from the chemical equation are involved in the **rate-determining step**.
Here are the **rules** for doing this:

- If a reactant appears in the **rate equation**, it must affect the **rate**. So this reactant, or something derived from it, must be in the **rate-determining step**.
- If a reactant **doesn't** appear in the **rate equation**, then it **isn't** involved in the **rate-determining step** (and neither is anything derived from it).

Catalysts can appear in rate equations, so they can be in rate-determining steps too.

Some **important points** to remember about rate-determining steps and mechanisms are:

1) The rate-determining step **doesn't** have to be the first step in a mechanism.
2) The reaction mechanism **can't** usually be predicted from **just** the chemical equation.

You Can Predict the **Rate Equation** from the **Rate-Determining Step**...

The **order of a reaction** with respect to a reactant shows the **number of molecules** of that reactant which are involved **in** or **before** the **rate-determining step**.

So, if a reaction's second order with respect to X, there'll be two molecules of X in the rate-determining step.

Example: The mechanism for the reaction between **chlorine free radicals** and **ozone**, O_3, consists of **two steps**:

$$Cl\bullet_{(g)} + O_{3(g)} \rightarrow ClO\bullet_{(g)} + O_{2(g)} \text{ — slow (rate-determining step)}$$

$$ClO\bullet_{(g)} + O_{(g)} \rightarrow Cl\bullet_{(g)} + O_{2(g)} \text{ — fast}$$

Predict the rate equation for this reaction.

$Cl\bullet$ and O_3 must both be in the rate equation, so the rate equation is of the form: **rate = $k[Cl\bullet]^m[O_3]^n$**.
There's only **one** $Cl\bullet$ radical and **one** O_3 molecule in the rate-determining step, so the **orders**, m and n, are both **1**. So the rate equation is **rate = $k[Cl\bullet][O_3]$**.

...And You Can Predict the **Mechanism** from the **Rate Equation**

Knowing exactly which reactants are in the **rate-determining step** gives you an idea of the reaction **mechanism**.

For example, here are two possible mechanisms for the reaction: $(CH_3)_3CBr + OH^- \rightarrow (CH_3)_3COH + Br^-$.

① $$(CH_3)_3C\text{—}Br + OH^- \rightarrow (CH_3)_3C\text{—}OH + Br^-$$

② $$(CH_3)_3C\text{—}Br \rightarrow (CH_3)_3C^+ + Br^- \text{ — slow (rate-determining step)}$$

$$(CH_3)_3C^+ + OH^- \rightarrow (CH_3)_3C\text{—}OH \text{ — fast}$$

The actual **rate equation** was worked out by rate experiments:

rate = $k[(CH_3)_3CBr]$

OH^- isn't in the **rate equation**, so it **can't** be involved in the reaction until **after** the rate-determining step. So, **mechanism 2** is most likely to be correct — there is **1 molecule** of **$(CH_3)_3CBr$** (and **no molecules of OH^-**) in the **rate determining step**. This agrees with the **rate equation**.

The Rate-Determining Step

Example — Propanone and Iodine... again

You've seen it before and it's back again. The reaction between **propanone** and **iodine**, catalysed by hydrogen ions. The full equation for this reaction is...

$$CH_3COCH_{3(aq)} + I_{2(aq)} \xrightarrow{H^+_{(aq)}} CH_3COCH_2I_{(aq)} + H^+_{(aq)} + I^-_{(aq)}$$

And the rate equation for the reaction is...

$$\text{Rate} = k[CH_3COCH_3][H^+]$$

So, using the rules from the previous page, here's what you can say about the reaction —

1) Propanone and H^+ are **in** the **rate equation** — so they, or something **derived** from them, must be **in the rate-determining step**.
2) Iodine is **not in the rate equation** so it's **not** involved until **after** the **rate determining step.**
3) The **order** of reaction for both propanone and H^+ is **1** — so the rate-determining step must use **1 molecule** of each.
4) H^+ is a **catalyst** — so it must be **regenerated** in another step.

And when you put all that together you could come up with a reaction mechanism like this...

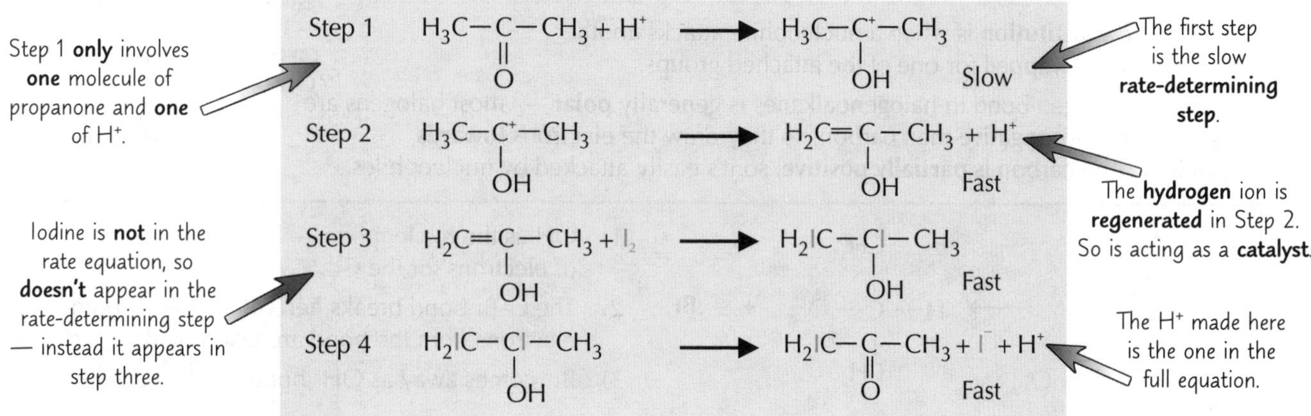
Step 1 only involves one molecule of propanone and one of H⁺.
Iodine is not in the rate equation, so doesn't appear in the rate-determining step — instead it appears in step three.
Step 1
Step 2
Step 3
Step 4
Slow
Fast
Fast
Fast
The first step is the slow rate-determining step.
The hydrogen ion is regenerated in Step 2. So is acting as a catalyst.
The H⁺ made here is the one in the full equation.

Practice Questions

Q1 Can catalysts appear in rate equations?

Q2 Knowing the order of reaction is important for suggesting a rate-determining step. Why?

Q3 In the reaction of iodine with propanone, why doesn't iodine appear in the rate equation?

Exam Questions

Q1 For the reaction; $CH_3COOH_{(aq)} + C_2H_5OH_{(aq)} \rightarrow CH_3COOC_2H_{5(aq)} + H_2O_{(l)}$, the rate equation is:

$$\text{rate} = k[CH_3COOH][H^+]$$

What can you deduce about the role that H^+ plays in the reaction? Explain your answer. [2 marks]

Q2 Hydrogen reacts with iodine monochloride as in the equation; $H_{2(g)} + 2ICl_{(g)} \rightarrow I_{2(g)} + 2HCl_{(g)}$.
The rate equation for this reaction is: rate = $k[H_2][ICl]$.

a) The mechanism for the reaction consists of two steps.
Identify the molecules that affect the rate-determining step. Justify your answer. [2 marks]

b) A chemist suggested the following mechanism for the reaction:

$2ICl_{(g)} \rightarrow I_{2(g)} + Cl_{2(g)}$ slow

$H_{2(g)} + Cl_{2(g)} \rightarrow 2HCl_{(g)}$ fast

Suggest, with reasons, whether this mechanism is likely to be correct. [2 marks]

I found rate-determining step aerobics a bit on the slow side...

These pages show you how rate equations, orders of reaction, and reaction mechanisms all tie together and how each actually means something in the grand scheme of A-Level Chemistry. It's all very profound. So get it all learnt, answer the questions and then you'll have plenty of time to practise the cha-cha-cha for your Strictly Come Dancing routine.

Halogenoalkanes and Reaction Mechanisms

'Lean hog on a lake' is an anagram of halogenoalkane. A good thing to know...

Halogenoalkanes can be Hydrolysed by Hydroxide Ions

There are three different types of halogenoalkane. They can all be hydrolysed (split) by heating them with sodium hydroxide — but they react using different mechanisms.

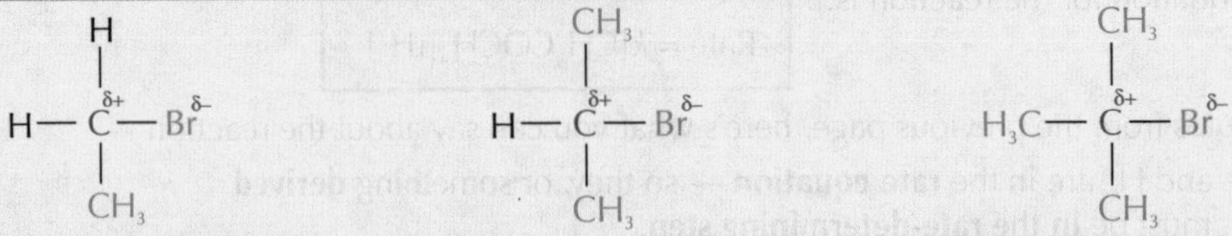

In primary halogenoalkanes, the halogen is joined to a carbon with just one alkyl group attached.

In secondary halogenoalkanes the halogen is joined to a carbon with two alkyl groups attached.

In tertiary halogenoalkanes, the halogen is attached to a carbon with three alkyl groups attached.

Halogenoalkanes Undergo Nucleophilic Substitution

Nucleophiles are electron pair donors — they're attracted to positive charge. OH^- and CN^- are both nucleophiles.

Nucleophilic substitution is when a nucleophile attacks another molecule and is **swapped** for one of the attached groups.

The carbon–halogen bond in halogenoalkanes is generally **polar** — most halogens are much more **electronegative** than carbon, so they draw the electrons **towards** themselves. The carbon is **partially positive**, so it's easily attacked by nucleophiles.

$C^{\delta+}–Br^{\delta-}$

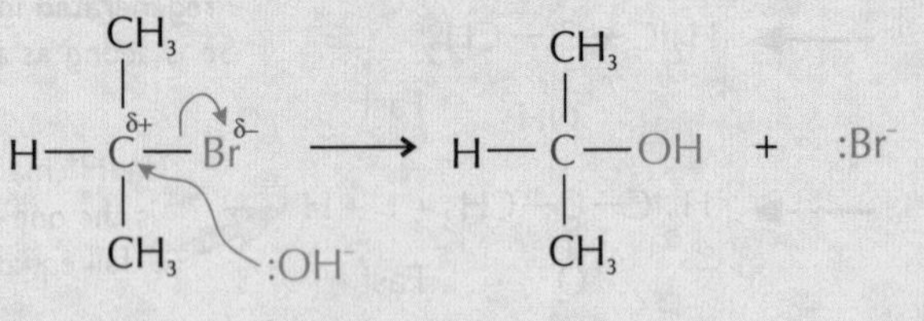

1) OH^- is the **nucleophile** — it provides a pair of electrons for the $C^{\delta+}$.
2) The C–Br bond breaks **heterolytically** — both electrons from the bond are taken by Br^-.
3) Br^- comes away as OH^- bonds to the carbon.

There are two different types of mechanism for nucleophilic substitution — $\mathbf{S_N1}$ and $\mathbf{S_N2}$.

S_N1 reactions only involve **1** molecule or ion in the **rate-determining step.**
S_N2 reactions involve **2** molecules, 1 molecule and 1 ion, or 2 ions in the **rate-determining step.**

Primary halogenoalkanes only react by the $\mathbf{S_N2}$ mechanism.
Secondary halogenoalkanes can react by **both** the S_N1 and S_N2 mechanisms.
Tertiary halogenoalkanes only react by the $\mathbf{S_N1}$ mechanism.

The Rate Equation for an S_N2 Reaction Will Include Both Reactants

The equation for the reaction of the primary halogenoalkane **bromoethane** with **hydroxide ions** is:

$$CH_3CH_2Br + OH^- \rightarrow CH_3CH_2OH + Br^-$$

As there is a single step, a transition state is formed.

This occurs via an S_N2 reaction with a **single**, rate-determining **step**.

The rate equation for the reaction is:

$$\text{rate} = k[CH_3CH_2Br][OH^-]$$

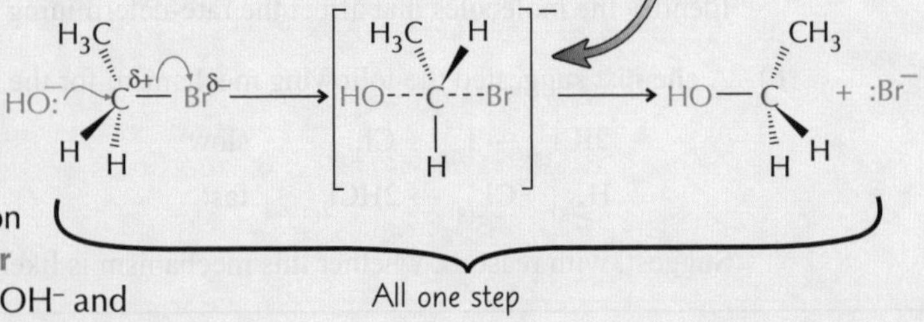

All one step

The rate equation shows that the **rate is dependent** on the concentration of **both** the reactants and the **order** with respect to **each** is **1**. So, one molecule of **both** OH^- and CH_3CH_2Br must be involved in the reaction **in** (or **before**) the rate-determining step, which fits with an $\mathbf{S_N2}$ **mechanism.**

Primary halogenoalkanes have lots of space around the carbon, which is surrounded mostly by H groups. This means there is space for the hydroxide ion to attack.

Halogenoalkanes and Reaction Mechanisms

The **Rate Equation** shows **Tertiary** Halogenoalkanes Use S_N1

The equation for the reaction of the tertiary halogenoalkane **2-bromo-2-methylpropane** with **hydroxide ions** looks similar to the reaction with bromoethane on the previous page:

$$(CH_3)_3CBr + OH^- \rightarrow (CH_3)_3COH + Br$$

But the rate equation for this reaction is different: rate = $k[(CH_3)_3CBr]$

The **rate is only dependent** on the concentration of the **halogenoalkane.** So the hydroxide ion is only involved in the reaction **after** the **rate-determining** step.

The reaction happens in two steps. In the first step, the halogen leaves the halogenoalkane. The nucleophile is then able to attack in the second step.

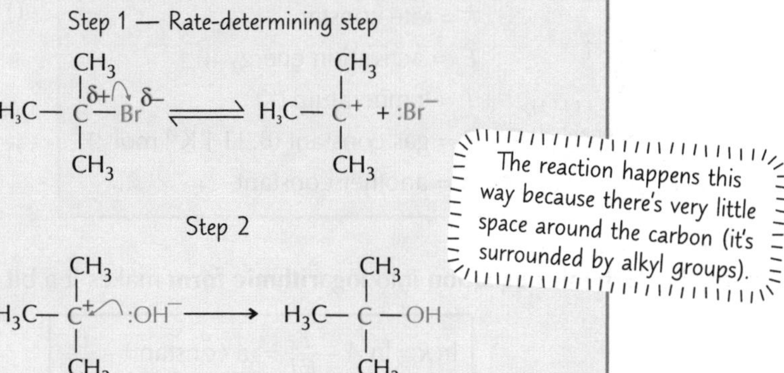

Step 1 — Rate-determining step
Step 2
The reaction happens this way because there's very little space around the carbon (it's surrounded by alkyl groups).

Practice Questions

Q1 How many alkyl groups are attached to a tertiary halogenoalkane?

Q2 What is the role of the hydroxide ion in the hydrolysis of a halogenoalkane?

Q3 How many molecules/ions are involved in the rate determining step of an S_N2 reaction?

Q4 In which step does the nucleophile attack in an S_N2 reaction?

Exam Questions

Q1 For the reaction between sodium hydroxide and 1-chloropropane:

$$CH_3CH_2CH_2Cl + NaOH \rightarrow CH_3CH_2CH_2OH + NaCl$$

Predict which one of the following is the correct rate equation.

A Rate = $k[OH^-]$ **B** Rate = $k[CH_3CH_2CH_2Cl]$

C Rate = $k[CH_3CH_2CH_2Cl]_2$ **D** Rate = $k[CH_3CH_2CH_2Cl][OH^-]$ [1 mark]

Q2 The following equation shows the hydrolysis of 1-iodobutane by hydroxide ions:

$$CH_3CH_2CH_2CH_2I + OH^- \rightarrow CH_3CH_2CH_2CH_2OH + I^-$$

a) Is 1-iodobutane a primary, secondary or tertiary iodoalkane? [1 mark]

b) Write the rate equation for this reaction. [1 mark]

c) What type of mechanism is involved in this reaction? [1 mark]

d) Draw the mechanism of this reaction. [3 marks]

Q3 2-bromo-2-methylpentane is hydrolysed via a reaction with hydroxide ions.

a) Suggest a likely rate equation for the reaction. [1 mark]

b) Draw the mechanism of this reaction and label the rate determining step. [3 marks]

Way-hay!!! — It's the curly arrows...

Whenever I talk to someone who's studied chemistry the one thing they've remembered is curly arrows. They have no idea how they work. But they know they exist. The thing is, they don't have an exam, but you do — so make sure you understand where the arrows are coming from and going to. Check back to your Year 1 stuff if you're unsure.

Activation Energy

It's more maths on this page. But keep going, the end is in sight — even though it's over the page.

Use the Arrhenius Equation to Calculate the Activation Energy

The **Arrhenius equation** (nasty-looking thing in the blue box) links the **rate constant** (k) with **activation energy** (E_a, the minimum amount of kinetic energy particles need to react) and **temperature** (T). This is probably the **worst** equation there is in A-Level Chemistry. But the good news is, you **don't** have to learn it — you'll be given it in the exam if you need it — so you just have to understand what it's showing you. Here it is:

$$k = A e^{\frac{-E_a}{RT}}$$

It's an exponential relationship. This 'e' is the e^x button on your calculator.

k = rate constant
E_a = activation energy (J)
T = temperature (K)
R = gas constant (8.31 J K^{-1} mol^{-1})
A = another constant

1) As the activation energy, E_a, gets **bigger**, k gets **smaller**. So, a **large E_a** will mean a **slow rate**. You can **test** this out by trying **different numbers** for E_a in the equation... ahh go on, be a devil.
2) The equation also shows that as the temperature **rises**, k **increases**. Try this one out too.

Putting the **Arrhenius equation** into **logarithmic form** makes it a bit easier to use.

$$\ln k = \ln A - \frac{E_a}{RT} = \text{(a constant)} - \frac{E_a}{RT}$$

There's a handy 'ln' button on your calculator for this.

You can use this equation to create an **Arrhenius plot** by plotting **ln *k*** against $\frac{1}{T}$.
This will produce a graph with a gradient of $\frac{-E_a}{R}$. And once you know the gradient, you can find **activation energy**.

Example: The graph on the right shows an Arrhenius plot for the decomposition of hydrogen iodide. Calculate the activation energy for this reaction. R = 8.31 J K^{-1} mol^{-1}.

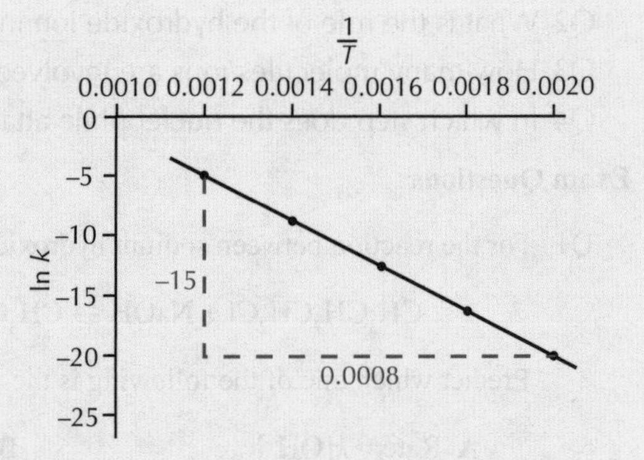

The gradient, $\frac{-E_a}{R} = \frac{-15}{0.0008} = -18\,750$

So, $E_a = -(-18\,750 \times 8.31) = 155\,812.5$ J mol^{-1} ≈ **156 kJ mol^{-1}**

To Calculate the Activation Energy, First Collect and Process the Data...

Here's another example of how to work out the activation energy.

$$S_2O_8{}^{2-}{}_{(aq)} + 2I^-{}_{(aq)} \rightarrow 2SO_4{}^{2-}{}_{(aq)} + I_{2(aq)}$$

You can only do this kind of mathematical trickery if all the concentrations are kept the same.

You can use the **iodine-clock reaction** to monitor when a fixed amount of I_2 has been made. The **rate of the reaction** is **inversely proportional** to the **time taken** (**t**) for the solution to change colour — a faster rate means a shorter time taken.
So, mathematically speaking, the rate is **proportional** to **1/time**. This means that 1/t can be used instead of k in the Arrhenius equation, which means you can calculate the activation energy. Hurrah!!

Time, t (s)	Temp, *T* (K)	1/t (s^{-1})	ln 1/t	1/*T* (K^{-1})
204	303	0.0049	-5.32	0.0033
138	308	0.0072	-4.93	0.00325
115	312	0.0087	-4.74	0.00321
75	318	0.0133	-4.32	0.00314
55	323	0.0182	-4.01	0.0031

Here's some collected data for this reaction at different temperatures. The first two columns show the raw data and the other columns show the data that's needed to draw a graph of **ln (1/t)** against **1/*T*** (see the next page).

Activation Energy

...Then Draw an **Arrhenius Plot** to Find E_a

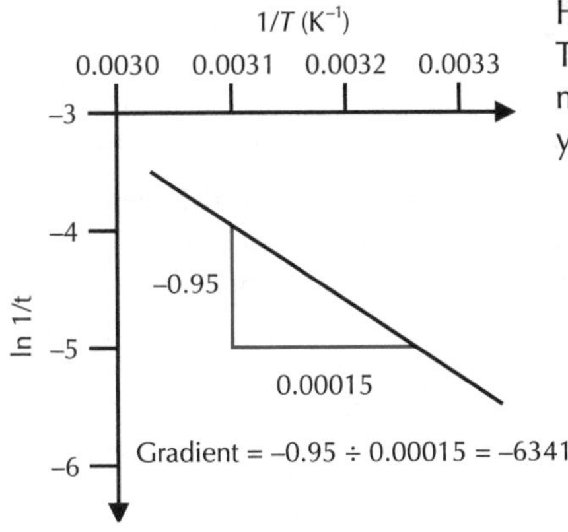

Here's an **Arrhenius plot** of the data at the bottom of the last page. The graph will **always** show a **straight line**, which makes it easy to work out the gradient — and once you know the gradient, you can find E_a.

> The gradient of the line = −6341 = $\frac{-E_a}{R}$
> R = 8.31 J K⁻¹ mol⁻¹ so...
> $E_a = -(-6341 \times 8.31)$ = **52700 J mol⁻¹ = 52.7 kJ mol⁻¹**

To convert from J mol⁻¹ to kJ mol⁻¹ you need to divide your answer by 1000.

Looking at the gradient, Amara decided the activation energy needed to walk up the mountain was too high.

Catalysts Lower the **Activation Energy** of a **Reaction**

You can use **catalysts** to make chemical reactions happen **faster**. A **catalyst** increases the **rate** of a reaction by providing an **alternative reaction pathway** with a **lower activation energy**. The catalyst is **chemically unchanged** at the end of the reaction — they don't get used up. Catalysts can be classified into two different types:

1. **Homogeneous catalysts** are in the **same state** as the reactant. So for example, if the reactants are **gases**, the catalyst must be a **gas** too. An example of **homogeneous catalysis** would be the $H^+_{(aq)}$ catalysis of the iodination of propanone — all reactants are aqueous (dissolved in water).

Physical state and phase mean the same thing.

2. **Heterogeneous catalysts** are in a **different physical state** from the reactants:
   - **Solid** heterogeneous catalysts provide a **surface** for the reaction to take place on. The catalyst is usually a **mesh** or a **fine powder** to increase the **surface area**. Alternatively it might be spread over an **inert support**.
   - Heterogeneous catalysts can be easily **separated** from the products and leftover reactants.
   - **Heterogeneous catalysts** can be poisoned though. A **poison** is a substance that clings to the catalyst's surface **more strongly** than the reactant does, **preventing** the catalyst from getting involved in the reaction it's meant to be **speeding up**. For instance, **sulfur** can poison the **iron catalyst** used in the **Haber process**.

Practice Questions

Q1 The Arrhenius equation can be written as ln k = a constant $-E_a/RT$. What do the terms k, T and R represent?

Q2 In an Arrhenius plot, where $1/T$ on the x-axis is plotted against ln k on the y-axis, what will the gradient show?

Exam Questions

Q1 The table gives values for the rate constant of the reaction between hydroxide ions and bromoethane at different temperatures

a) Complete the table and then plot a graph of ln k (y-axis) against $1/T$ (x-axis). [4 marks]

b) Calculate the gradient of the straight line produced. [1 mark]

c) Using the Arrhenius equation, ln k = a constant $-E_a/RT$, calculate the activation energy of the reaction. (R = 8.31 J K⁻¹ mol⁻¹) [2 marks]

T (K)	k	$1/T$ (K⁻¹)	ln k
305	0.181	0.00328	−1.709
313	0.468		
323	1.34		
333	3.29	0.00300	1.191
344	10.1		
353	22.7	0.00283	3.127

Q2 State the major difference between homogeneous and heterogeneous catalysts. [1 mark]

Aaaaaaaaggggggggggghhhhhhhhhh...

The thing to remember here is you'll be given the Arrhenius equation in the exam if you need it. So concentrate on learning how to use it — which bits to put on an Arrhenius plot and what things to calculate to work out the E_a.

Optical Isomerism

You know you were crying out for some organic chemistry? Well here you go... This time we're looking at what the spatial arrangement of atoms can tell us about the molecule. Can you think of anything more exciting? Thought not...

***Optical Isomers** are **Mirror Images** of Each Other*

Sometimes molecules can have more than one chiral centre.

1) **Optical isomerism** is a type of stereoisomerism. Stereoisomers have the **same structural formula**, but have their atoms arranged differently in **space**.
2) A **chiral** (or **asymmetric**) carbon atom (known as a **chiral centre**) is a carbon atom that has **four different groups** attached to it. It's possible to arrange the groups in two different ways around the carbon atom so that two different molecules are made — these molecules are called **enantiomers** or **optical isomers**.
3) The enantiomers are **mirror images** and no matter which way you turn them, they can't be **superimposed**.
4) You have to be able to **draw** optical isomers. But first you have to identify the chiral centre...

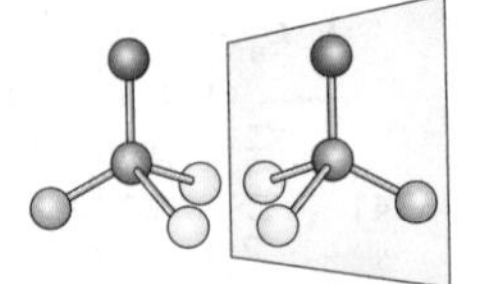

If molecules can be superimposed, they're achiral — and there's no optical isomerism.

1) **Locating any chiral centres:** Look for any carbon atoms with **four different groups** attached. Here it's the carbon with the four groups H, OH, COOH and CH_3 attached.

chiral centre

2-hydroxypropanoic acid

A solid wedge shows a bond coming out of the page towards you. A dotted line shows a bond going into the page away from you.

2) **Drawing isomers:** Once you know the **chiral centre**, draw one enantiomer in a **tetrahedral shape**. Don't try to draw the full structure of each group — it gets confusing. Then draw a **mirror image** beside it. If there's more than one chiral centre, mirror each chiral centre one by one to get all the possible isomers.

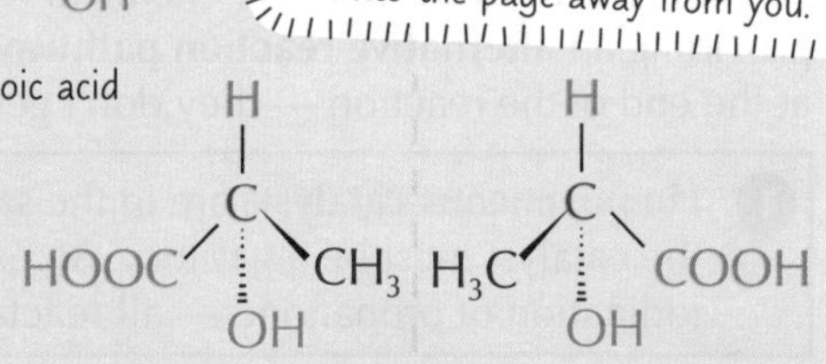

enantiomers of 2-hydroxypropanoic acid

*Optical Isomers **Rotate Plane-Polarised Light***

1) Normal light is made up of a range of different wavelengths and vibrates in all directions. **Monochromatic, plane-polarised light** has a single wavelength and only vibrates in one direction.
2) Optical isomers are **optically active** — they **rotate** the plane of polarisation of plane-polarised monochromatic light.
3) One enantiomer rotates it in a **clockwise** direction, and the other rotates it in an **anticlockwise** direction.

Christmas is a time to embrace your choral centre.

*A **Racemic Mixture** is a **Mixture** of Both **Optical Isomers***

A **racemic mixture** (or **racemate**) contains **equal quantities** of each enantiomer of a chiral compound.

Racemic mixtures **don't** rotate plane polarised light — the two enantiomers **cancel** each other's light-rotating effect.
Chemists often react two **achiral** things together and get a **racemic** mixture of a **chiral** product.
This is because when two molecules react there's often an **equal chance** of forming each of the enantiomers.
Look at the reaction between butane and chlorine:

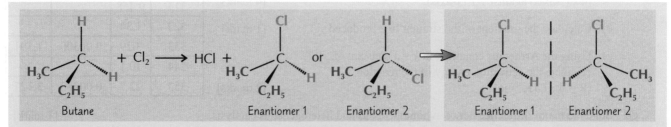

Butane + Cl_2 ⟶ HCl + Enantiomer 1 or Enantiomer 2 ⟹ Enantiomer 1 | Enantiomer 2

A **chlorine** atom replaces one of the **H atoms**, to give **2-chlorobutane**.
Either of the H atoms can be replaced, so the reaction produces a **mixture** of the two possible **enantiomers**.
Each hydrogen has an **equal chance** of being replaced, so the two optical isomers are formed in **equal amounts**.

Optical Isomerism

You Can Use **Optical Activity** to **Work Out** a Reaction **Mechanism**

Optical activity can give you some insight into how the **mechanism** of a reaction works.
For example, **nucleophilic substitution reactions** (see page 92) can take place by one of two mechanisms.

S_N1 mechanism

Have a look at pages 190-191 for a reminder on this.

If it's an S_N1 mechanism and you start with a **single enantiomer** reactant, the product will be a **racemic mixture** of **two optical isomers** of each other, so won't rotate plane-polarised light.

Step 1: $H_3C-C(H)(C_2H_5)-X$ ($\delta+$ C, $\delta-$ X) ⇌ H_3C, H, C^+, C_2H_5 + $:X^-$

Step 2: C^+ :Y^- Or Y^-: C^+ → C_2H_5, H_3C, C, Y, H | C_2H_5, Y, C, CH_3, H

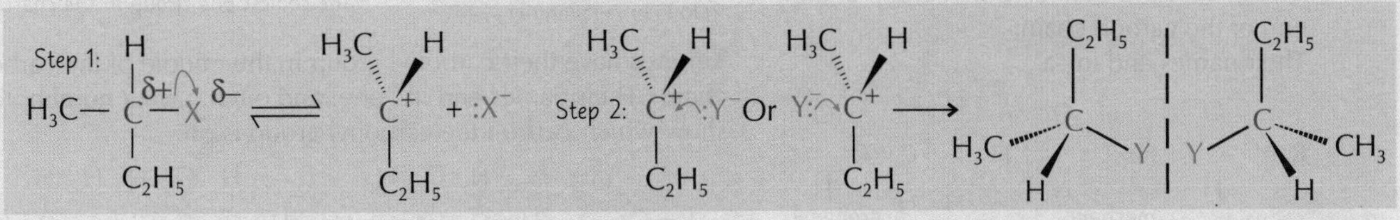

In **step 1**, a group breaks off, leaving a **planar** (flat) ion.
In **step 2**, the planar ion can be **attacked** by a nucleophile from **either side** — this results in two optical isomers.

S_N2 mechanism

In an S_N2 mechanism, a **single enantiomer** reactant produces a **single enantiomer** product.

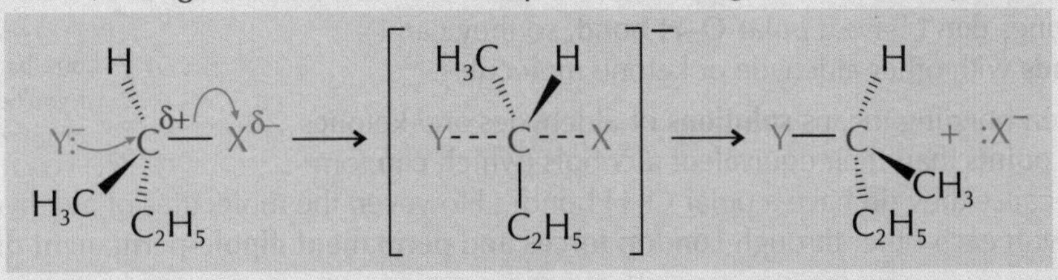

$Y:^-$ → $C(H)(H_3C)(C_2H_5)$ ($\delta+$) — X ($\delta-$) → $[Y\text{---}C(H_3C)(H)(C_2H_5)\text{---}X]^-$ → $Y-C(H)(CH_3)(C_2H_5)$ + $:X^-$

There's only one step in this mechanism — the **nucleophile** always attacks the **opposite side** to the leaving group, so only one product is produced. The product will rotate plane-polarised light **differently** to the reactant, the extent and direction of rotation occurs can be measured experimentally.

So if you know the **optical activity** of the **reactant** and **products**, you can sometimes work out the reaction **mechanism**.

Practice Questions

Q1 What is meant by a chiral carbon atom?

Q2 What is a racemic mixture?

Q3 Which nucleophilic substitution reaction mechanism produces a racemic mixture?

Q4 Which nucleophilic substitution reaction mechanism has a single enantiomer as a product?

Exam Question

Q1 The molecule 2-bromobutane displays optical isomerism.

a) Draw the structure of 2-bromobutane, and mark the chiral centre of the molecule on the diagram. [1 mark]

A sample of a single, pure optical isomer of 2-bromobutane is dissolved in an ethanol and water solvent and mixed with dilute sodium hydroxide solution. This mixture is gently heated under reflux and a substitution reaction occurs. The product of the reaction is a racemic mixture of butan-2-ol.

b) Explain why the butan-2-ol solution produced will not rotate plane-polarised light. [1 mark]

c) Has the substitution reaction proceeded via an S_N1 mechanism or an S_N2 mechanism? Explain your answer. [2 marks]

Time for some quiet reflection...

This optical isomer stuff's not all bad — you get to draw pretty little pictures of molecules. If you're having difficulty picturing them as 3D shapes, you could always make some models with matchsticks and some balls of coloured clay.

Aldehydes and Ketones

The sun is shining outside, the birds are singing, flowers are in bloom. Alas, you have to stay in and learn about the properties and reactions of organic compounds... It's tough, but that's the life you've chosen, my friend.

Aldehydes and *Ketones* Contain a *Carbonyl Group*

Aldehydes and ketones are **carbonyl compounds** — they contain the **carbonyl** functional group, **C=O**.

Introducing the carbonyl group — the coolest pop group in the charts.

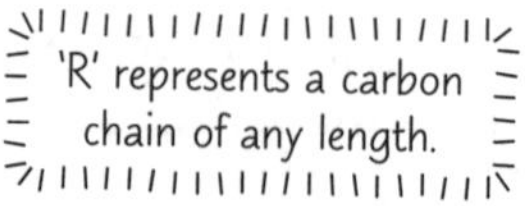
'R' represents a carbon chain of any length.

Aldehydes have their carbonyl group at the **end** of the carbon chain. Their names end in **–al**.

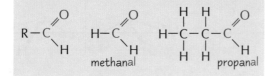

methanal   propanal

Ketones have their carbonyl group in the middle of the carbon chain. Their names end in **–one**, and often have a number to show which **carbon** the carbonyl group is on.

propanone   pentan-2-one

Aldehydes and Ketones *Don't Hydrogen Bond* with *Themselves...*

Look back at pages 28-33 if you're rusty on polarity or intermolecular forces.

Aldehydes and ketones **don't** have a **polar O–H bond**, so they can't form **hydrogen bonds** with other aldehyde or ketone molecules.

This lack of hydrogen bonding means **solutions** of aldehydes and ketones have **lower boiling points** than their equivalent alcohols (which **can** form hydrogen bonds because they **do** have a polar O–H bond). However, the molecules of aldehydes and ketones still bond with each other through **London forces** and **permanent dipole-permanent dipole bonds**.

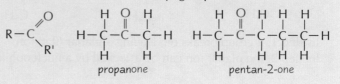

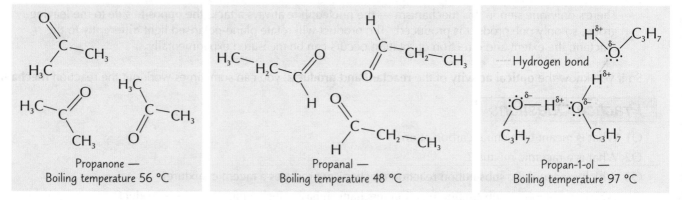

Propanone — Boiling temperature 56 °C

Propanal — Boiling temperature 48 °C

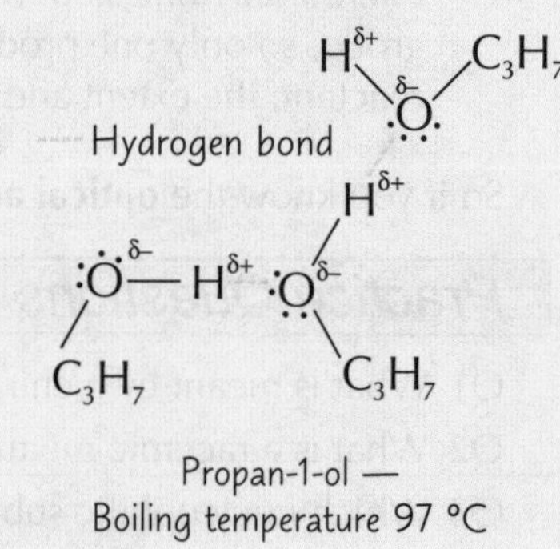
Hydrogen bond

Propan-1-ol — Boiling temperature 97 °C

...But Aldehydes and Ketones can Hydrogen Bond *with* Water

1) Although aldehydes and ketones don't have polar -OH groups, they do have a **lone pair of electrons** on the **O atom** of the C=O group.
2) The oxygen can use its lone pairs to form **hydrogen bonds** with hydrogen atoms on **water** molecules. So **small** aldehydes and ketones will **dissolve** in water.
3) Large aldehydes and ketones have **longer** carbon chains which aren't able to form hydrogen bonds with water. When larger aldehydes or ketones are mixed with water, these hydrocarbon chains **disrupt** the hydrogen bonding between the water molecules, but **aren't able** to form hydrogen bonds themselves.
4) So if an aldehyde or ketone is **large enough**, the intermolecular forces (in this case **London forces**) between the **aldehyde** or **ketone** molecules, and the hydrogen bonding between water molecules will be stronger than the hydrogen bonds that could form between the aldehyde/ketone and water. So the compound **won't dissolve**.

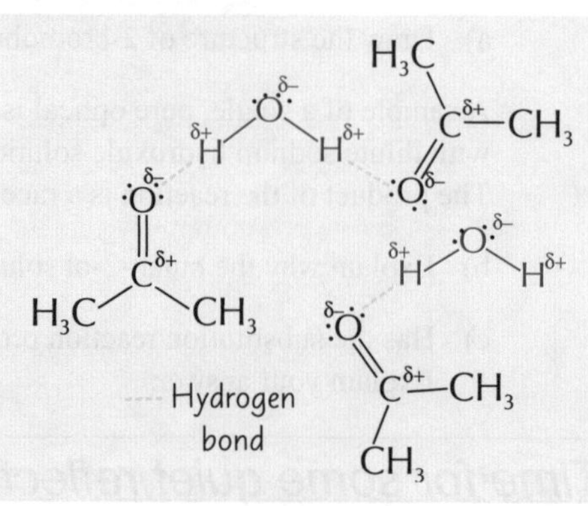
Hydrogen bond

Aldehydes and Ketones

There are a Few Ways of Testing for **Aldehydes**

Although aldehydes and ketones have similar physical properties, there are tests that let you distinguish between them.
They all work on the idea that an **aldehyde** can be **easily oxidised** to a carboxylic acid, but a ketone can't.
As an aldehyde is oxidised, another compound is **reduced** — so a reagent is used that **changes colour** as it's reduced.

aldehyde $R{-}CHO \xrightarrow{+[O]} R{-}COOH$ carboxylic acid

Tollens' Reagent

Tollens' reagent is a **colourless** solution of **silver nitrate** dissolved in **aqueous ammonia**.
If it's heated in a test tube with an aldehyde, a **silver mirror** forms after a few minutes.

$$Ag(NH_3)_2{}^+{}_{(aq)} + e^- \rightarrow Ag_{(s)} + 2NH_{3(aq)}$$
colourless → silver

You shouldn't heat the test tube directly over a flame — most organic compounds are flammable. Use a water bath or heating mantle instead.

$$2Ag(NH_3)_2{}^+{}_{(aq)} + RCHO_{(aq)} + 3OH^-{}_{(aq)} \rightarrow 2Ag_{(s)} + RCOO^-{}_{(aq)} + 4NH_{3(aq)} + 2H_2O$$

Fehling's solution or Benedict's solution

Fehling's solution is a **blue** solution of complexed **copper(II) ions** dissolved in **sodium hydroxide**.
If it's heated with an aldehyde, the copper(II) ions are reduced to a **brick-red precipitate** of **copper(I) oxide**.

$$Cu^{2+}{}_{(aq)} + e^- \rightarrow Cu^+{}_{(s)}$$
blue → brick-red

$$RCHO_{(aq)} + 2Cu^{2+} + 5OH^- \rightarrow RCOO^-{}_{(aq)} + Cu_2O_{(s)} + 3H_2O_{(l)}$$

Benedict's solution is exactly the same as Fehling's solution except the copper(II) ions are dissolved in **sodium carbonate** instead. You still get a **brick-red precipitate** of copper(I) oxide though.

Acidified dichromate(VI) ions

If you **heat** an **aldehyde** with **acidified dichromate(VI) ions,** you get a carboxylic acid.
The **dichromate(VI) ions** are the oxidising agent, [O].
Potassium dichromate(VI) with dilute sulfuric acid is often used. The solution turns orange to green as the dichromate(VI) ions are reduced.

$$Cr_2O_7{}^{2-} + 14H^+ + 6e^- \rightarrow 2Cr^{3+} + 7H_2O$$
Orange → Green

Ketones won't oxidise with acidified **dichromate(VI) ions.**

Practice Questions

Q1 Why do short chain aldehydes and ketones readily dissolve in water?

Q2 Describe how you'd use Tollens' reagent to test for the presence of aldehydes.

Q3 What would you see if you heated Fehling's solution with an aldehyde?

Q4 Describe the colour change seen when an aldehyde is heated with acidified dichromate(VI) ions.

Exam Question

Q1 The skeletal formulae of three compounds are shown on the right.

A (aldehyde, O) B (ketone, O) C (OH)

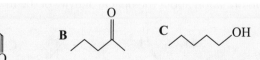

a) Predict which compound has the highest boiling point. [1 mark]

b) Which compound(s) do not form silver precipitates when reacted with Tollens' reagent? [1 mark]

c) Compound B is heated with potassium dichromate(VI) and dilute sulfuric acid. No colour changes occur. Explain why. [1 mark]

Silver mirror on the wall, who's the most 'aldehydey' of them all...

Benedict Cumberbatch. What a guy. Unfortunately he's not the Benedict who the solution is named after. Better luck next time Cumberbatch... You don't have to be Sherlock Holmes to know you have to learn the tests for an aldehyde.

Reactions of Aldehydes and Ketones

So I bet you were wondering 'I know how to distinguish between aldehydes and ketones and have learnt about their properties but what more reactions can they do?' Well, wonder no more my brave chemistry friend.

*You can **Reduce** Aldehydes and Ketones Back to **Alcohols***

Using a **reducing agent** [H] you can:

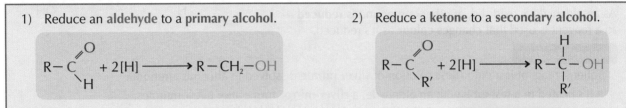

1) Reduce an **aldehyde** to a **primary alcohol**.

$$RCHO + 2[H] \longrightarrow R{-}CH_2{-}OH$$

2) Reduce a **ketone** to a **secondary alcohol**.

$$RCOR' + 2[H] \longrightarrow R{-}CH(OH){-}R'$$

For the **reducing agent,** you could use **$LiAlH_4$** (lithium tetrahydridoaluminate(III) or lithium aluminium hydride) in **dry ether** — it's a very powerful reducing agent, which reacts violently with water, bursting into flames. Eeek.

These are nucleophilic addition reactions (see below) — the reducing agent supplies an H^- that acts as a nucleophile and attacks the δ+ carbon.

Mrs Desai went OTT with the $LiAlH_4$ again...

Hydrogen Cyanide** will React with Carbonyls by **Nucleophilic Addition

Hydrogen cyanide reacts with carbonyl compounds to produce **hydroxynitriles** (molecules with a CN and an OH group). It's a **nucleophilic addition reaction** — a **nucleophile** attacks the molecule, and adds itself.

You can also use acidified potassium cyanide (which dissociates in water to form K^+ ions and CN^- ions). It needs to be acidified so there's a source of H^+ for this step.

Hydrogen cyanide is a **weak acid** — it partially dissociates in water to form H^+ and CN^- ions.

$$HCN \rightleftharpoons H^+ + CN^-$$

1) The CN^- ion **attacks** the slightly positive carbon atom and **donates** a pair of electrons to it. Both electrons from the double bond transfer to the oxygen.
2) H^+ (from either hydrogen cyanide or water) bonds to the oxygen to form the **hydroxyl group** (OH).

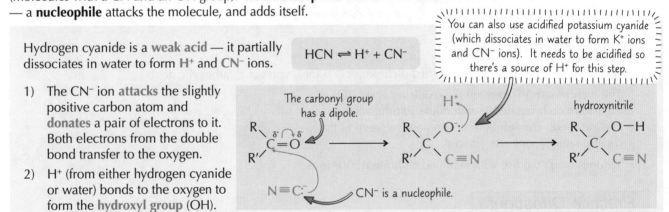

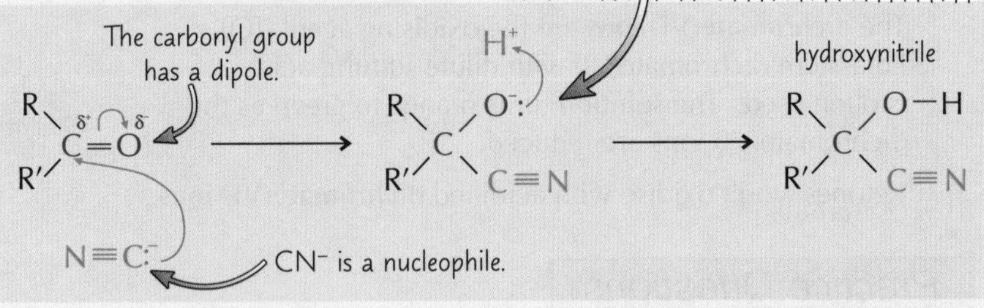

The carbonyl group has a dipole.
hydroxynitrile
CN⁻ is a nucleophile.

Hydrogen cyanide is a **highly toxic** gas. When this reaction is done in the laboratory, a solution of **acidified potassium cyanide** is used instead, to reduce the risk. Even so, the reaction should be done in a **fume cupboard** while wearing a **lab coat, gloves** and **safety glasses.**

Information about the optical activity of the **hydroxynitrile** can provide **evidence** for the reaction mechanism.

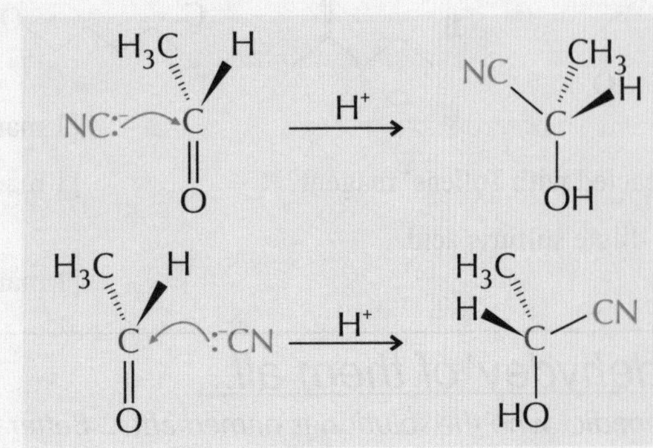

- The groups surrounding the carbonyl carbon in a ketone or aldehyde are **planar**. The nucleophile (CN^- ion) can attack it from **either side**.
- When you react an aldehyde or asymmetric ketone with CN^-, you get a **racemic mixture** of **two optical isomers**. This is exactly what you'd expect from the mechanism — the carbonyl group gets attacked equally from **each side**, producing **equal amounts** of the two products, which are optical isomers.
- Because the product is present in a racemic mixture, you would expect the product to be **optically inactive**.

Reactions of Aldehydes and Ketones

2,4-dinitrophenylhydrazine Tests for a *Carbonyl Group*

2,4-dinitrophenylhydrazine (2,4-DNPH) is dissolved in methanol and concentrated sulfuric acid.

The **2,4-dinitrophenylhydrazine** reacts to form a **bright orange precipitate** if a carbonyl group is present.

This only happens with **C=O groups**, not with more complicated ones like -COOH, so it only tests for **aldehydes** and **ketones**.

You have to be careful when handling 2,4-DNPH — it's harmful, flammable and can be explosive when dry.

The Melting Point of the Precipitate Identifies the Carbonyl Compound

The orange precipitate is a **derivative** of the carbonyl compound which can be purified by **recrystallisation**. Each different carbonyl compound gives a crystalline derivative with a **different melting point**.

For details of how to do a recrystallisation, have a look at page 226.

If you measure the melting point of the crystals and compare it to a table of **known** melting points of the possible derivatives, you can **identify** the carbonyl compound.

Some Carbonyls will React with Iodine

Carbonyls that contain a **methyl carbonyl** group react when heated with **iodine** in the presence of an alkali. If there's a methyl carbonyl group you'll get a **yellow precipitate** of triiodomethane (CHI_3) and an antiseptic smell.

This is a methyl carbonyl group: $\Rightarrow$ $-C(=O)-CH_3$

$$RCOCH_3 + 3I_2 + 4OH^- \rightarrow RCOO^- + CHI_3 + 3I^- + 3H_2O$$

If something contains a **methyl carbonyl** group, it must be:

Ethanal. $H-C(=O)-CH_3$ or A **ketone** with **at least one** methyl group. $R-C(=O)-CH_3$

Practice Questions

Q1 What are the reagents and conditions necessary to convert an aldehyde into an alcohol?

Q2 What are the reagents and conditions necessary to convert a carbonyl into a hydroxynitrile?

Q3 Which aldehyde will react with iodine in the presence of an alkali?

Exam Questions

Q1 Substance Q reacts to give an orange precipitate with 2,4-dinitrophenylhydrazine. It produces a secondary alcohol when reduced. It reacts with iodine to give a yellow precipitate. The molecular formula of Q is $C_7H_{14}O$.

a) Use the information to draw a possible structure for Q. Explain how each piece of information is useful. [4 marks]

b) Suggest and explain how the precipitate formed when Q reacts with 2,4-DNPH reagent could be used to confirm your suggested structure. [2 marks]

c) Draw the structure of the substance produced when Q reacts with $LiAlH_4$ in dry ether. [1 mark]

Q2 Propanone and propanal are isomers with the molecular formula C_3H_6O.

a) Name the type of reaction that occurs when hydrogen cyanide reacts with carbonyl compounds. [1 mark]

b) Draw: i) the product obtained when hydrogen cyanide reacts with propanone. [1 mark]

ii) the mechanism of the reaction between HCN and propanone. [4 marks]

c) When propanal reacts with HCN the resulting product forms a racemic mixture. Give reasons why. [3 marks]

Spot the difference...

If you can't remember which is aldehyde and which is ketone, this might help — 'a' comes at one end of the alphabet, so CO is at the end of the molecule, 'k' is in the middle of the alphabet, so the CO is in the middle. Just an idea.

Carboxylic Acids

Carboxylic acids are more interesting than cardboard boxes — as you're about to discover...

Carboxylic Acids Contain –COOH

A carboxyl group contains a carbonyl group and a hydroxyl group.

1) **Carboxylic acids** contain the **carboxyl** functional group **–COOH**.
2) To name a carboxylic acid, you find and name the longest alkane chain containing the –COOH group, take off the 'e' and add **'–oic acid'**.

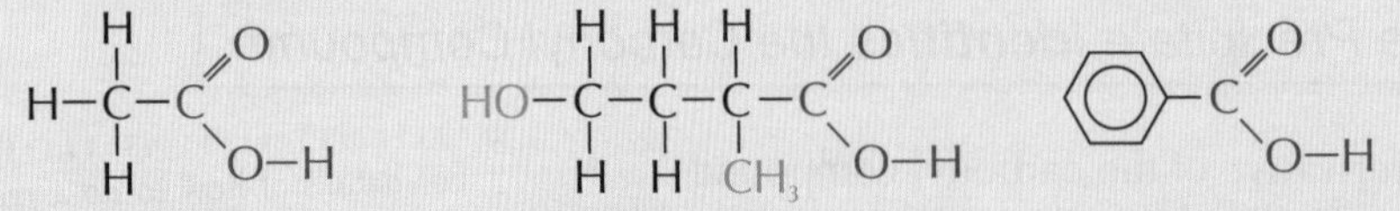

ethanoic acid — 4-hydroxy-2-methylbutanoic acid — benzoic acid

The branches and other groups of carboxylic acids are named using the IUPAC rules. If you're unsure have a look back at page 70.

3) The carboxyl group is always at the **end** of the molecule and when naming it's more important than any other functional groups — so all the other functional groups in the molecule are numbered starting from this carbon.
4) Carboxylic acids are **weak acids** — in water they partially dissociate into **carboxylate ions** and **H^+ ions**.

This equilibrium lies to the left because most of the molecules don't dissociate.

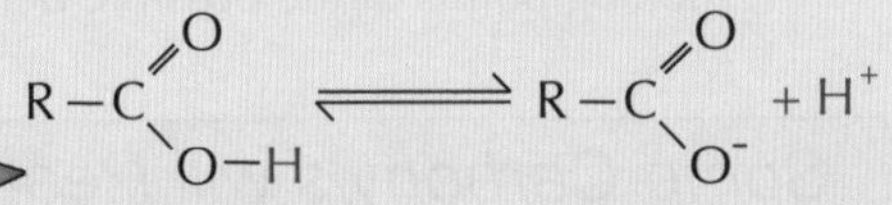

$$R{-}COOH \rightleftharpoons R{-}COO^- + H^+$$

carboxylic acid — carboxylate ion

Carboxylic Acids are Very Soluble

1) Carboxylic acids molecules can form **hydrogen bonds** with each other. Because of this, carboxylic acids have relatively **high boiling points**.
2) The ability to form hydrogen bonds make small carboxylic acids **very soluble** in water, as they can form H bonds with the water molecules.
3) As with aldehydes and ketones (see page 196), the solubility of carboxylic acids **decreases** as the length of the carbon chain **increases**. The hydrocarbon chains can't form hydrogen bonds with water but, when mixed with water, disrupt the hydrogen bonds present between the water molecules. So, large carboxylic acids **don't dissolve** in water.

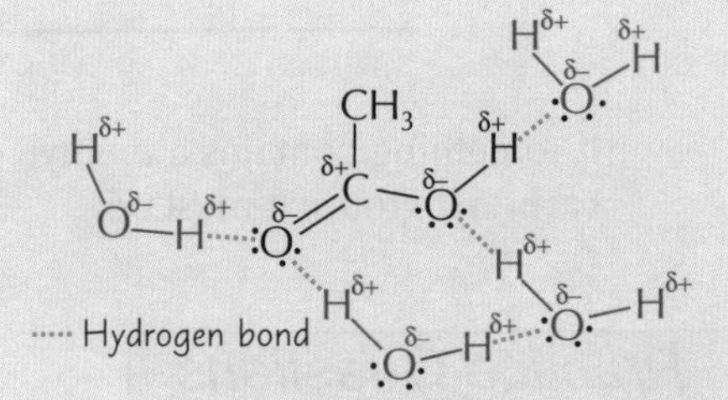

····· Hydrogen bond

In pure, liquid carboxylic acids, **dimers** can also form. This is when a molecule hydrogen bonds with just **one** other molecule. This effectively **increases** the **size** of the molecule, **increasing** the intermolecular forces, and so the boiling point.

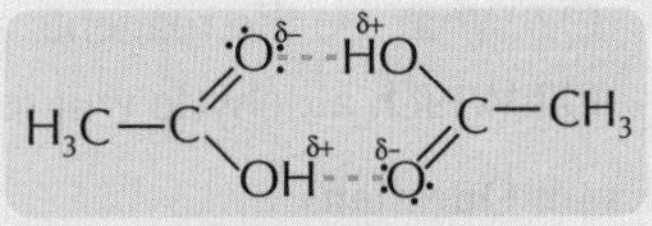

Carboxylic Acids Can Be Formed from Alcohols, Aldehydes and Nitriles

Oxidation of Primary Alcohols and Aldehydes

[O] represents an oxidising agent, for example, acidified dichromate(VI) ions, $Cr_2O_7^{2-}$.

You can make a carboxylic acid by **oxidising** a **primary alcohol** to an **aldehyde**, and then to a carboxylic acid. Often, acidified potassium dichromate is used ($K_2Cr_2O_7/H_2SO_4$).

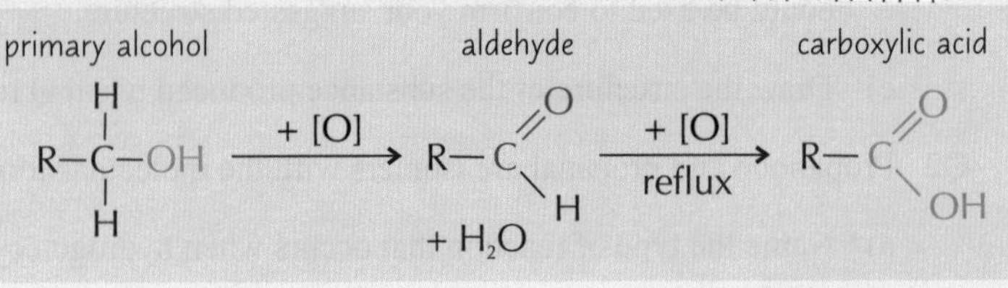

primary alcohol $\xrightarrow{+[O]}$ aldehyde $+ H_2O$ $\xrightarrow[\text{reflux}]{+[O]}$ carboxylic acid

$$R{-}CH_2{-}OH \xrightarrow{+[O]} R{-}CHO + H_2O \xrightarrow[\text{reflux}]{+[O]} R{-}COOH$$

Hydrolysis of Nitriles

Carboxylic acids can also be made by **hydrolysing** a **nitrile**. You reflux the nitrile with dilute hydrochloric acid, and then distil off the carboxylic acid.

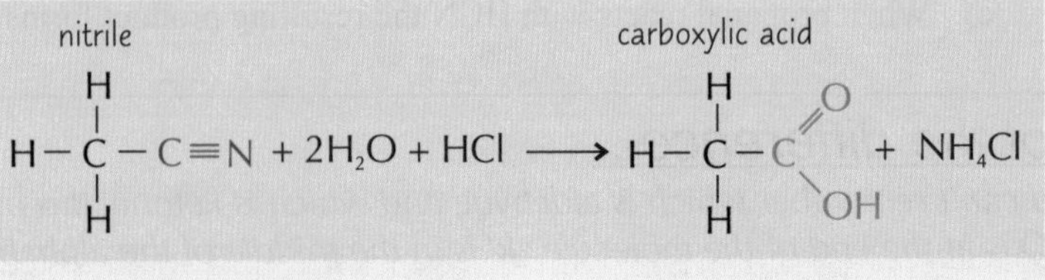

$$\underset{\text{nitrile}}{H{-}CH_2{-}C{\equiv}N} + 2H_2O + HCl \longrightarrow \underset{\text{carboxylic acid}}{H{-}CH_2{-}COOH} + NH_4Cl$$

Look back at page 98 for more on distillation.

Carboxylic Acids

Carboxylic Acids React with **Bases** to Form **Salts**

1) Carboxylic acids are **neutralised** by **aqueous bases (alkalis)** to form **salts** and **water**.

$CH_3COOH + NaOH \rightarrow CH_3COONa + H_2O$
ethanoic acid — sodium ethanoate

Salts of carboxylic acids are called carboxylates and their names end with –oate.

2) Carboxylic acids react with **carbonates (CO_3^{2-})** or **hydrogencarbonates (HCO_3^-)** to form a **salt, carbon dioxide** and **water**.

$2CH_3COOH_{(aq)} + Na_2CO_{3(s)} \rightarrow 2CH_3COONa_{(aq)} + H_2O_{(l)} + CO_{2(g)}$

$CH_3COOH_{(aq)} + NaHCO_{3(s)} \rightarrow CH_3COONa_{(aq)} + H_2O_{(l)} + CO_{2(g)}$
ethanoic acid — sodium ethanoate

In these reactions, carbon dioxide fizzes out of the solution. This can be used as a test for carboxylic acids.

Other Reactions You'll Need to Know

It's quite **hard** to reduce a carboxylic acid, so you have to use a **powerful reducing agent** like **$LiAlH_4$** in **dry ether**. It reduces the carboxylic acid right down to an **alcohol** in one go — you can't get the reduction to stop at the aldehyde.

carboxylic acid $R{-}C({=}O){-}OH \xrightarrow[2.\ H_2O]{1.\ 4[H]} R{-}CH_2{-}OH$ primary alcohol

carboxylic acid $R{-}C({=}O){-}OH + PCl_5 \longrightarrow R{-}C({=}O){-}Cl + POCl_3 + HCl$ acyl chloride

Mix a carboxylic acid with **phosphorus(V) chloride** (Phosphorous pentachloride) and you'll get an **acyl chloride**.

Acyl chlorides are covered on page 204.

Practice Questions

Q1 Draw the structure of ethanoic acid.

Q2 Explain the relatively high boiling points of carboxylic acids.

Q3 Describe two ways of preparing carboxylic acids.

Q4 How can you make an acyl chloride from a carboxylic acid?

Exam Questions

Q1 A student is carrying out an experiment to synthesise propanoic acid from propan-1-ol.

a) Describe how the student could make propanoic acid from propan-1-ol. [2 marks]

b) The student wants to know whether the synthesis has been successful. Describe a simple test tube reaction to distinguish between propan-1-ol and propanoic acid. Give the reagent(s) and state the observations expected. [2 marks]

Q2 Methanoic acid, H_2COOH, and pentanoic acid, $CH_3(CH_2)_3COOH$, are carboxylic acids.

a) Draw the structures of both compounds. [2 marks]

b) Explain why methanoic acid is more soluble in water than pentanoic acid. [2 marks]

c) Write a balanced equation for the reaction of 2-ethylpentanoic acid with phosphorous(V) chloride. [1 mark]

Alright, so maybe cardboard boxes do have the edge after all...

So a few new reactions for you to get your head around here. When you think about it though, the reactions with bases and carbonates are just the same as they would be for any old acid. Also, learning the last section on forming acyl chlorides will be really useful for when we get on to their reactions later on. You'll have to wait for that treat though.

Esters

Time to embrace another functional group. You'll like this one, some of the compounds smell of fruit.

Esters have the Functional Group –COO–

The **name** of an **ester** is made up of **two parts** — the **first** bit comes from the **alcohol**, and the **second** bit from the **carboxylic acid**.

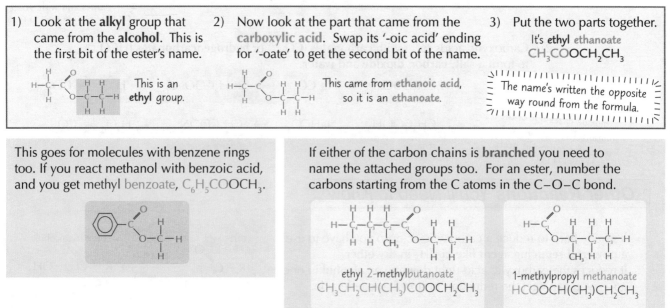

1) Look at the **alkyl** group that came from the **alcohol**. This is the first bit of the ester's name.

   This is an **ethyl** group.

2) Now look at the part that came from the **carboxylic acid**. Swap its '-oic acid' ending for '-oate' to get the second bit of the name.

   This came from **ethanoic acid**, so it is an **ethanoate**.

3) Put the two parts together.

   It's **ethyl ethanoate**

   $CH_3COOCH_2CH_3$

   The name's written the opposite way round from the formula.

This goes for molecules with benzene rings too. If you react methanol with benzoic acid, and you get methyl benzoate, $C_6H_5COOCH_3$.

If either of the carbon chains is **branched** you need to name the attached groups too. For an ester, number the carbons starting from the C atoms in the C–O–C bond.

ethyl 2-**methyl**butanoate
$CH_3CH_2CH(CH_3)COOCH_2CH_3$

1-**methyl**propyl methanoate
$HCOOCH(CH_3)CH_2CH_3$

Esters can be Made From Alcohols and Carboxylic Acids

1) If you heat a **carboxylic acid** with an **alcohol** in the presence of an **acid catalyst**, such as concentrated H_2SO_4 or HCl, you get an ester. The reaction is called **esterification**.
2) For example, to make **ethyl ethanoate** you reflux ethanoic acid with ethanol and concentrated sulfuric acid as the catalyst:

This oxygen comes from the alcohol.

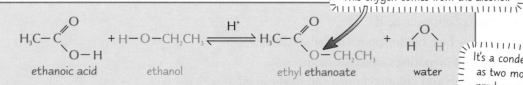

$$\underset{\text{ethanoic acid}}{CH_3COOH} + \underset{\text{ethanol}}{H{-}O{-}CH_2CH_3} \overset{H^+}{\rightleftharpoons} \underset{\text{ethyl ethanoate}}{CH_3COOCH_2CH_3} + \underset{\text{water}}{H_2O}$$

It's a condensation reaction as two molecules react to produce a large molecule, and a small molecule (in this case water) is released.

3) The reaction is **reversible**, so you need to separate out the product **as it's formed**. You do this by **distillation**, collecting the liquid that comes off just **below** 80 °C.
4) The product is then mixed with **sodium carbonate** solution to react with any **carboxylic acid** that might have snuck in. The **ethyl ethanoate** forms a layer on the **top** of the aqueous layer and can be easily separated using a separating funnel.
5) Ethyl ethanoate is often used as a **solvent** in chromatography and as a **pineapple flavouring**.

Esters can be Broken Up in Hydrolysis Reactions

Acid Hydrolysis

As it's a reversible reaction, you need to use lots of water to push the equilibrium over to the right.

Acid hydrolysis splits the ester into an **acid** and an **alcohol** — it's just the **reverse** of the condensation reaction above. You have to **reflux** the ester with a **dilute acid**, such as hydrochloric or sulfuric. For example:

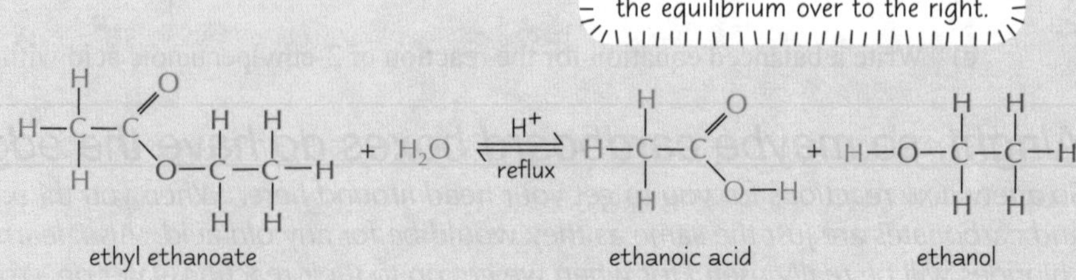

Esters

Base Hydrolysis

This time you have to **reflux** the ester with a **dilute alkali**, such as sodium hydroxide. You get a **carboxylate ion** and an **alcohol**. This reaction is **irreversible**. For example:

$$CH_3COOCH_2CH_3 + OH^- \xrightarrow{\text{reflux}} CH_3COO^- + HOCH_2CH_3$$

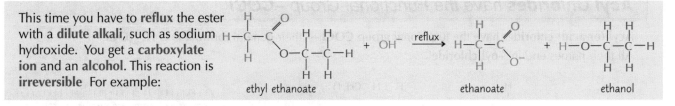

ethyl ethanoate → ethanoate + ethanol

Polyesters Contain lots of Ester Links

1) **Diols** contain **two** –OH functional groups and **dicarboxylic** acids contain **2** –COOH functional groups.
2) Dicarboxylic acids and diols can **react together** to form long **ester chains**, called **polyesters**. This reaction is known as a **condensation polymerisation** reaction.

$$HO-C(=O)-R-C(=O)-OH + H-O-R'-O-H \rightarrow HO-C(=O)-R-C(=O)-O-R'-O-H + H_2O$$

dicarboxylic acid, diol, ester link — a water molecule is eliminated

For more on condensation polymers, have a look at pages 216-217.

Example: Terylene™ (PET) — formed from **benzene-1,4-dicarboxylic acid** and **ethane-1,2-diol**.

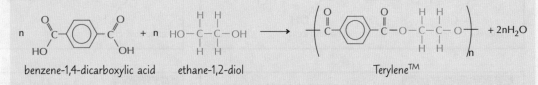

$$n\ HOOC-C_6H_4-COOH + n\ HO-CH_2-CH_2-OH \rightarrow -[-CO-C_6H_4-CO-O-CH_2-CH_2-O-]_n- + 2nH_2O$$

benzene-1,4-dicarboxylic acid, ethane-1,2-diol, Terylene™

Jeremy didn't know the chemistry behind his outfit — he just knew he looked good.

Polyester fibres are **strong**, **flexible** and **abrasion-resistant**. Terylene™ is used in **clothes** to keep them crease-free and make them last longer. Polyesters are also used in **carpets**.

You can treat polyesters (by stretching and heat-treating them) to make them stronger. Treated Terylene™ is used to make fizzy drink bottles and food containers.

Practice Questions

Q1 Draw the structure of ethyl ethanoate.

Q2 Suggest the reactants necessary to form ethyl ethanoate via an esterification reaction.

Q3 Name the products formed when ethyl ethanoate undergoes acid hydrolysis.

Exam Questions

Q1 Compound C, shown on the right, is found in raspberries.

$$HCOO-CH_2-CH(CH_3)-CH_3$$

a) Name compound C. [1 mark]

b) Draw and name the structures of the products formed when compound C is refluxed with dilute sulfuric acid. What kind of reaction is this? [5 marks]

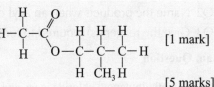

Q2 1-methylethyl methanoate is an ester.

a) Draw the structure of this ester. [1 mark]

b) Write an equation to show the formation of this ester from a suitable acid and an alcohol. [3 marks]

c) Name the type of reaction that is taking place to form this ester. [1 mark]

Carboxylic acid + alcohol produces ester — well, that's life...

Those two ways of hydrolysing esters are just similar enough that it's easy to get in a muddle. Remember — hydrolysis in acidic conditions is reversible, and you get a carboxylic acid as well as an alcohol. Hydrolysis with a base is a one way reaction that gives you an alcohol and a carboxylate ion. Now we've got that sorted, I think it's time for a cuppa.

Acyl Chlorides

Told you we'd get on to acyl chlorides later. Can you imagine a better way to end the topic? OK, maybe ice cream...

Acyl Chlorides have the Functional Group –COCl

Acyl (or acid) chlorides have the functional group **COCl** — their general formula is $\mathbf{C_nH_{2n-1}OCl}$.
All their names end in '**–oyl chloride**'.

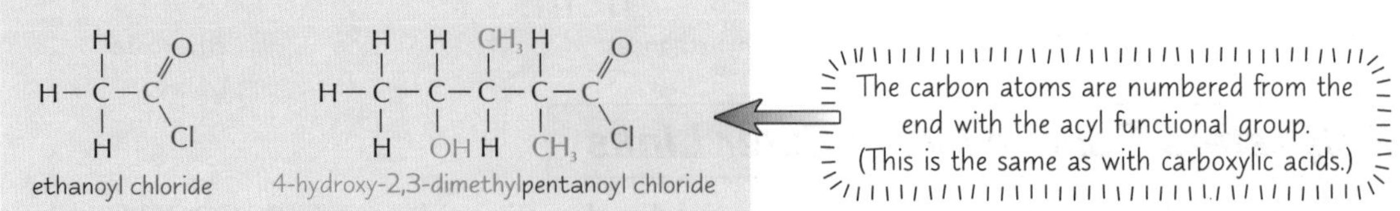

*Acyl Chlorides Easily **Lose** Their **Chlorine***

This irreversible reaction is a much easier, faster way to produce an ester than esterification.

Acyl chlorides react with...

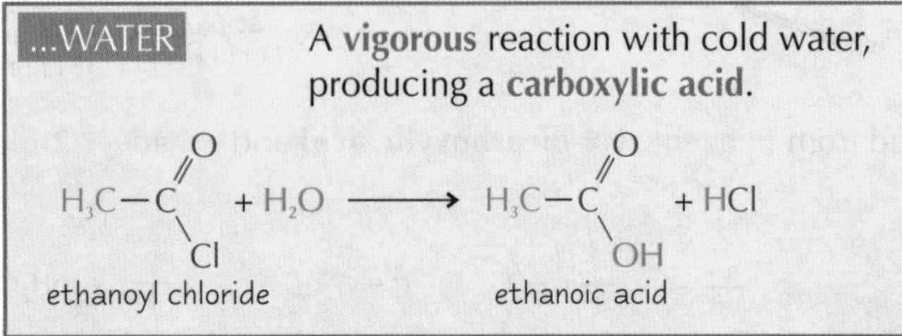

...WATER
A vigorous reaction with cold water, producing a carboxylic acid.
H₃C–C(=O)Cl + H₂O ⟶ H₃C–C(=O)OH + HCl
ethanoyl chloride
ethanoic acid

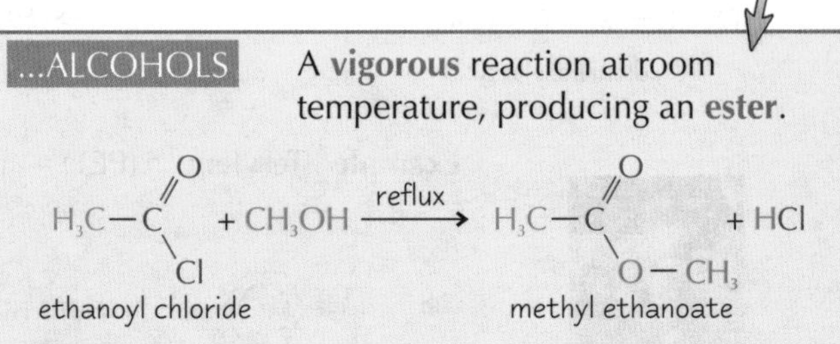

...ALCOHOLS
A vigorous reaction at room temperature, producing an ester.
H₃C–C(=O)Cl + CH₃OH ⟶(reflux) H₃C–C(=O)O–CH₃ + HCl
ethanoyl chloride
methyl ethanoate

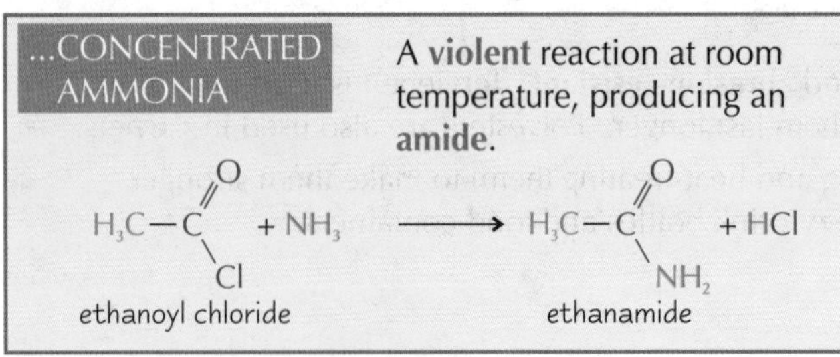

...CONCENTRATED AMMONIA
A violent reaction at room temperature, producing an amide.
H₃C–C(=O)Cl + NH₃ ⟶ H₃C–C(=O)NH₂ + HCl
ethanoyl chloride
ethanamide

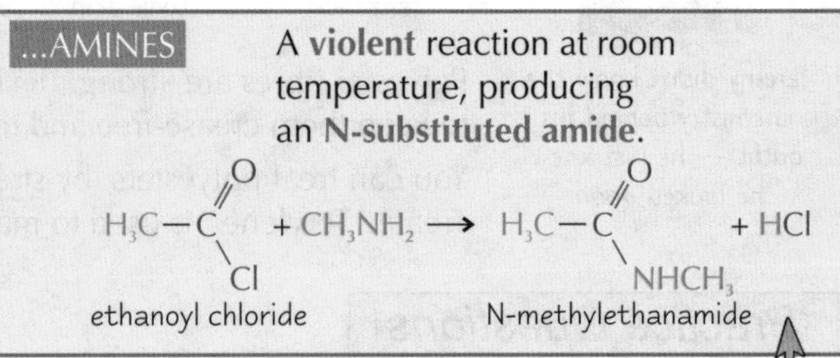

...AMINES
A violent reaction at room temperature, producing an N-substituted amide.
H₃C–C(=O)Cl + CH₃NH₂ ⟶ H₃C–C(=O)NHCH₃ + HCl
ethanoyl chloride
N-methylethanamide

Each time, **Cl** is **substituted** by an oxygen or nitrogen group and **hydrogen chloride** fumes are given off.

See page 212-215 for amines and amides.

Practice Questions

Q1 What is the organic product produced when cold water and an acyl chloride react together?

Q2 Name the products when an acyl chloride and an alcohol react.

Q3 Give the reagent(s) required to form an amide from an acyl chloride.

Exam Question

Q1 2-methylbutanoyl chloride is an acyl chloride.

a) Draw the structure of 2-methylbutanoyl chloride. [1 mark]

b) 2-methylbutanoyl chloride is reacted with compound X to give N-propyl 2-methylbutanamide.

i) Give the structure of compound X. [1 mark]

ii) Write a balance equation for the reaction. [1 mark]

Learn this page and you can become a real ace at acyl chloride reactions...

Acyl chlorides love to react. I just stared at one once, and it lost it's chlorine right there and then... You might find it useful to learn the structure of the functional group and get to grips with their various reactions. And when I say useful, I mean really very important. Better get to it. Once you're done, congratulate yourself on finishing the topic unscathed.

Aromatic Compounds

We begin this topic with a fantastical tale about the discovery of the magical rings of Benzene. Our story opens in a shire where four hobbits are getting up to mischief... Actually no, that's something else...

Benzene has a **Ring Of Carbon Atoms**

Benzene has the formula C_6H_6. It has a cyclic structure, with its six carbon atoms joined together in a ring. There are two ways of representing it — the **Kekulé model** and the **delocalised model**.

The **Kekulé Model** Came First

1) In 1865, the German chemist Friedrich August Kekulé proposed that **benzene** was made up of a **planar** (flat) **ring** of **carbon** atoms with **alternating single** and **double** bonds between them.
2) In Kekulé's model, each carbon atom is also bonded to **one hydrogen** atom.
3) He later adapted the model to say that the benzene molecule was constantly **flipping** between two forms (**isomers**) by switching over the double and single bonds:

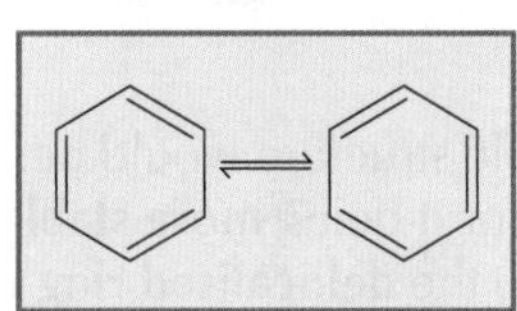

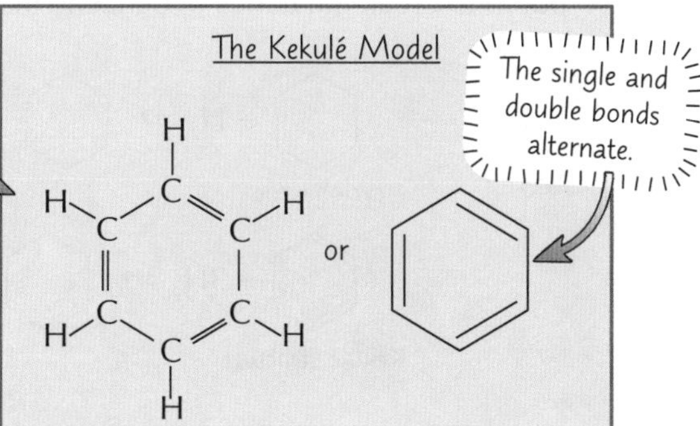

4) If the Kekulé model was correct, you'd expect benzene to have three bonds with the length of a **C–C bond** (154 pm) and three bonds with the length of a **C=C bond** (134 pm).
5) However **X-ray diffraction studies** have shown that all the carbon-carbon bonds in benzene have the **same length** of 140 pm — i.e. they're **between** the length of a single bond and a double bond. So the Kekulé structure **can't** be completely right...

Even though it's not completely right, chemists still draw the Kekulé structure of benzene as it's useful when drawing reaction mechanisms.

The **Delocalised Model** Replaced Kekulé's Model

The bond-length observations are explained by a different model — the **delocalised** model.

1) In the delocalised model, each carbon atom forms three σ-bonds — one to a hydrogen atom, and one to each of its neighbouring carbon atoms. These bonds form due to **head-on** overlap of their atomic orbitals.
2) Each carbon atom then has **one remaining** p-orbital, containing one electron, which sticks out **above** and **below** the plane of the ring. These p-orbitals on each of the carbon atoms overlap **sideways** to form a **ring** of π-bonds that are **delocalised** around the carbon ring.
3) The delocalised π-bonds are made up of two **ring-shaped** clouds of electrons — one above and one below the plane of the six carbon atoms.
4) All the bonds in the ring are the same — so, they're all the **same length**.
5) The electrons in the rings are said to be **delocalised** because they don't belong to a **specific** carbon atom. They are represented as a **circle** inside the ring of carbons rather than as double or single bonds.

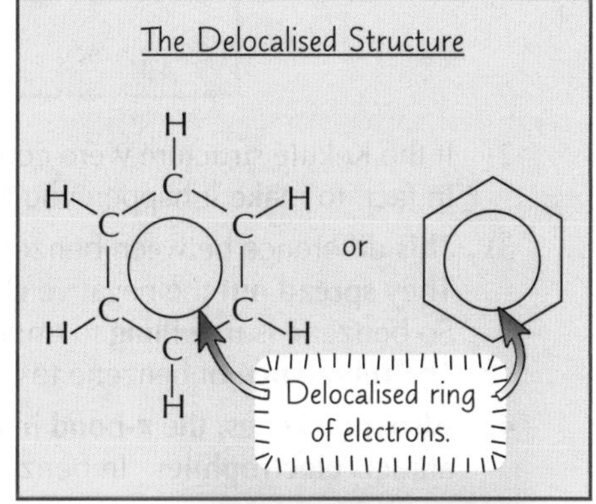

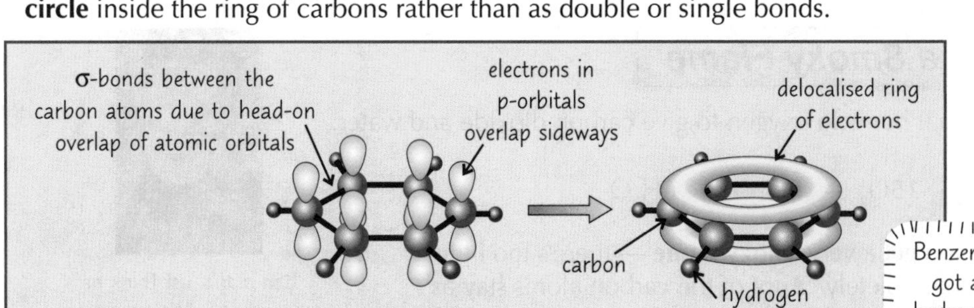

Gary woke up after the stag party to find himself in a delocalised orbit.

Benzene is a planar (flat) molecule — it's got a ring of carbon atoms with their hydrogens sticking out all on a flat plane.

Aromatic Compounds

Enthalpy Changes of Hydrogenation Give More Evidence for Delocalisation

1) If you react an **alkene** with **hydrogen gas**, two atoms of hydrogen add across the **double bond**. This is called **hydrogenation**, and the enthalpy change of the reaction is the **enthalpy change of hydrogenation**.
2) Cyclohexene has **one** double bond. When it's hydrogenated, the enthalpy change is **-120 kJ mol^{-1}**. If benzene had three double bonds (as in the Kekulé structure), you'd expect the enthalpy of hydrogenation to be ($3 \times 120 =$) **-360 kJ mol^{-1}**.
3) But the **experimental** enthalpy of hydrogenation of benzene is **-208 kJ mol^{-1}** — far **less exothermic** than expected.
4) Energy is put in to break bonds and released when bonds are made. So **more energy** must have been put in to break the bonds in benzene than would be needed to break the bonds in the Kekulé structure.

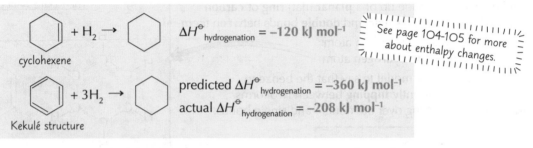

cyclohexene $+ H_2 \rightarrow$ cyclohexane $\quad \Delta H^{\ominus}_{hydrogenation} = -120$ kJ mol^{-1}

Kekulé structure $+ 3H_2 \rightarrow$ cyclohexane

predicted $\Delta H^{\ominus}_{hydrogenation} = -360$ kJ mol^{-1}

actual $\Delta H^{\ominus}_{hydrogenation} = -208$ kJ mol^{-1}

See page 104-105 for more about enthalpy changes.

5) This difference indicates that benzene is **more stable** than the Kekulé structure would be. Benzene's **resistance to reaction** (see below) gives more evidence for it being **more stable** than the Kekulé structure suggests. The extra stability is thought to be due to the **delocalised ring of electrons**.

Alkenes usually like Addition Reactions, but Not Benzene

1) **Alkenes** react easily with **bromine** water at room temperature. This **decolourises** the brown bromine water. It's an **electrophilic addition reaction** — the bromine atoms are added across the double bond of the alkene (see page 86). For example:

$$H_2C{=}CH_2 + Br{-}Br \longrightarrow H{-}CHBr{-}CHBr{-}H$$

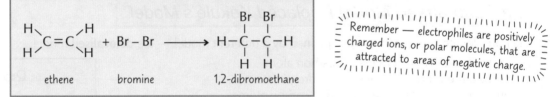

ethene + bromine → 1,2-dibromoethane

Remember — electrophiles are positively charged ions, or polar molecules, that are attracted to areas of negative charge.

2) If the Kekulé structure were correct, you'd expect a **similar reaction** between benzene and bromine. In fact, to make it happen you need **hot benzene** and **ultraviolet light** — and it's still a real **struggle**.
3) This difference between benzene and other alkenes is explained by the **delocalised π-bonds** in benzene. They **spread out** the negative charge and make the benzene ring very **stable**. So benzene is **unwilling** to undergo **addition reactions** which would destroy the stable ring. The **reluctance** of benzene to undergo addition reactions is **more evidence** supporting the **delocalised model**.
4) Also, in alkenes, the **π-bond** in the C=C double bond is an area of localised **high electron density** which strongly attracts **electrophiles**. In benzene, this attraction is reduced due to the negative charge being spread out.
5) So benzene prefers to react by **electrophilic substitution** (see pages 208-210).

Benzene Burns with a Smoky Flame

Benzene is a **hydrocarbon**, so it burns in oxygen to give carbon dioxide and water:

$$2C_6H_6 + 15O_2 \rightarrow 12CO_2 + 6H_2O$$

If you burn benzene in **air**, you get a very **smoky flame** — there's too little oxygen to burn the benzene completely. A lot of the carbon atoms stay as carbon and form particles of **soot** in the hot gas — making the flame **smoke**.

Ben didn't just think he was hot... He thought he was smoking hot.

Aromatic Compounds

Aromatic Compounds are Derived from Benzene

1) Compounds containing a **benzene ring** are called **arenes** or **'aromatic compounds'**. There are **two** ways of **naming** arenes, but there's no easy rule to know which name to give them. Here are some examples:

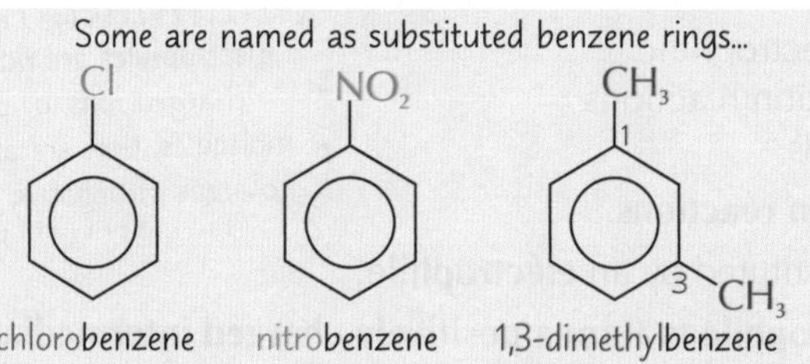

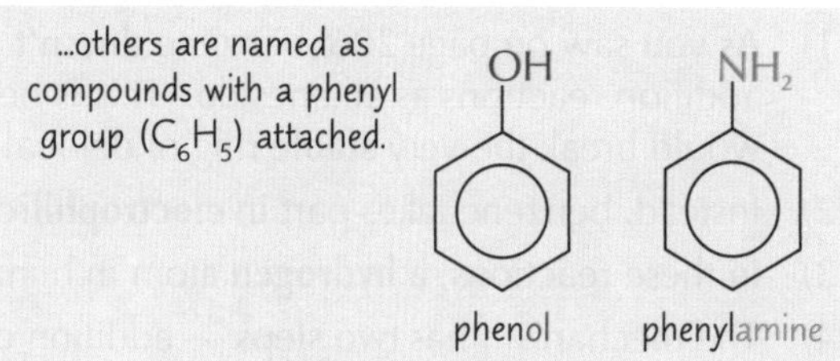

2) If there's **more than one** functional group attached to the benzene ring you have to **number** the **carbons** to show where the groups are.
   - If all the functional groups are the **same**, pick the group to start from that gives the **smallest** numbers when you count round.
   - If the functional groups are **different**, start from whichever functional group gives the molecule its **suffix** (e.g. the -OH group for a phenol) and continue counting round the way that gives the **smallest** numbers.

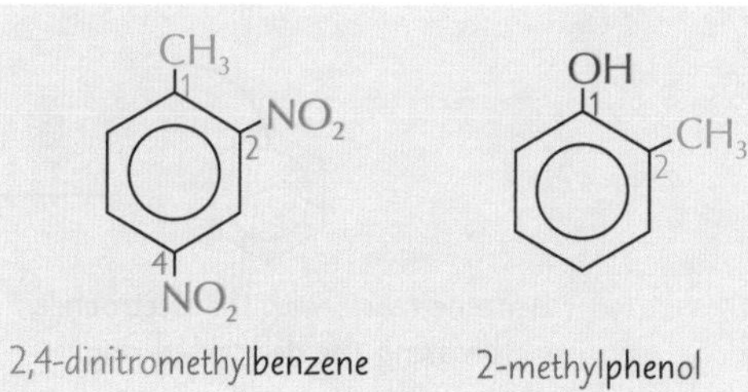

Practice Questions

Q1 Draw the Kekulé and delocalised models of benzene.

Q2 Write an equation for the combustion of benzene in excess oxygen.

Exam Questions

Q1 When cyclohexene reacts with hydrogen, one mole of H_2 adds across the double bond in one mole of cyclohexene. 120 kJ of energy is released.

$$\text{cyclohexene} + H_2 \rightarrow \text{cyclohexane} \qquad \Delta H = -120 \text{ kJ mol}^{-1}$$

Use the structures of the following molecules, along with the information above, to answer the following questions:

Cyclohexa-1,3-diene   Benzene (Kekulé structure)

a) i) Predict the number of moles of H_2 that one mole of cyclohexa-1,3-diene will react with. [1 mark]

ii) Predict how much energy will be released during this reaction. [1 mark]

b) Look at the Kekulé structure for benzene. Explain why this model would lead to the prediction that 360 kJ of energy would be released during the reaction between benzene and H_2. [1 mark]

c) One mole of benzene actually releases 208 kJ of energy when it reacts with hydrogen. Suggest how the delocalised model of benzene explains the difference between this number and the prediction of 360 kJ based on the Kekulé structure. [2 marks]

d) By referring to the structure and reactivity of benzene, outline two further pieces of evidence which support the delocalised structure as a better representation of benzene than the Kekulé structure. [4 marks]

Q2 A student takes two test tubes, each containing bromine water. He adds cyclohexene to one of the test tubes and benzene to the other. Describe and explain what the student will see. [3 marks]

Everyone needs a bit of stability in their life...

The structure of benzene is bizarre — even top scientists struggled to find out what its molecular structure looked like. Make sure you can draw all the different representations of benzene given on these pages, including the ones showing the Cs and Hs. Yes, and don't forget there's a hydrogen at every point on the ring — it's easy to forget they're there.

Electrophilic Substitution Reactions

Benzene is an alkene but it often doesn't behave like one — whenever this is the case, you can pretty much guarantee that our kooky friend Mr Delocalised Electron Ring is up to his old tricks again...

Arenes Undergo **Electrophilic Substitution** Reactions

1) As you saw on page 206, benzene **doesn't** undergo electrophilic addition reactions as alkenes do. This is because addition reactions would break the very **stable** ring of delocalised π-bonds.
2) Instead, benzene takes part in **electrophilic substitution reactions**.
3) In these reactions, a **hydrogen** atom in benzene is substituted by an **electrophile**.
4) The mechanism has two steps — addition of the **electrophile** to form a **positively charged intermediate**, followed by loss of **H⁺** from the carbon atom attached to the electrophile. This **reforms** the delocalised ring.

Electrophiles are positively charged ions, or polar molecules, that are attracted to areas of negative charge.

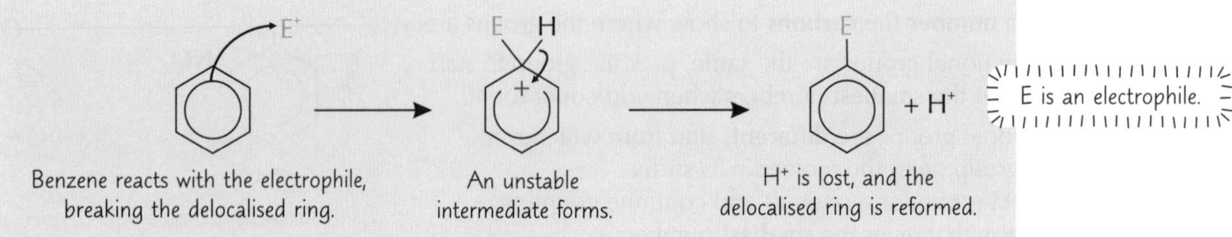

E⁺
E H
E
+ H⁺
Benzene reacts with the electrophile, breaking the delocalised ring.
An unstable intermediate forms.
H⁺ is lost, and the delocalised ring is reformed.

E is an electrophile.

Halogen Carriers Help to Make **Good Electrophiles**

1) The **delocalised** π-bonds in benzene means that the charge density is **spread out** across the ring. This means that an electrophile has to have a pretty strong **positive charge** to be able to attack the benzene ring. Most compounds just **aren't polarised enough** — but some can be made into **stronger electrophiles** using a catalyst called a **halogen carrier**.
2) A halogen carrier accepts a **lone pair of electrons** from a **halogen** atom on an **electrophile**. As the lone pair of electrons is pulled away, the **polarisation** in the molecule **increases** and sometimes a **carbocation** forms. This makes the electrophile **stronger**.

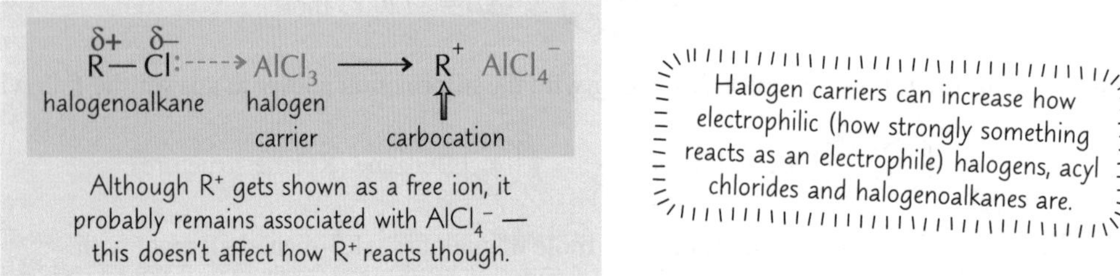

δ+ δ–
R—Cl: ----> AlCl₃ ⟶ R⁺ AlCl₄⁻
halogenoalkane
halogen carrier
carbocation
Although R⁺ gets shown as a free ion, it probably remains associated with AlCl₄⁻ — this doesn't affect how R⁺ reacts though.

Halogen carriers can increase how electrophilic (how strongly something reacts as an electrophile) halogens, acyl chlorides and halogenoalkanes are.

3) Halogen carriers include **aluminium halides**, **iron halides** and **iron**.

Halogen Carriers Help **Halogens Substitute** into the Benzene Ring

1) Benzene will react with **halogens** (e.g. Br_2) at room temperature in the presence of a halogen carrier catalyst, e.g **iron(III) bromide**, $FeBr_3$.
2) The catalyst **polarises** the halogen, allowing one of the halogen atoms to act as an **electrophile**.
3) During the reaction, a halogen atom is **substituted** in place of a H atom — this is called **halogenation**.

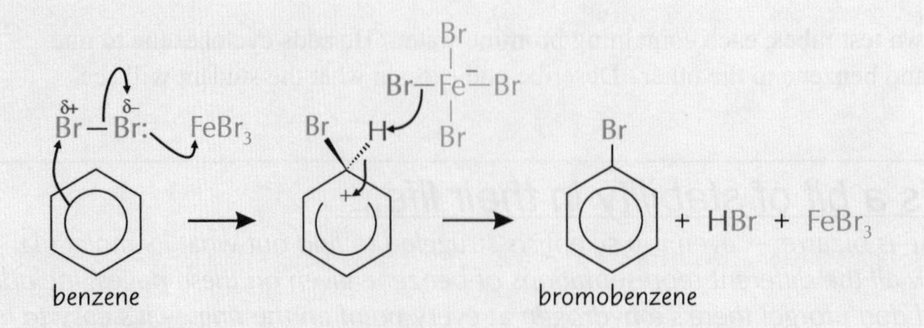

Electrophilic Substitution Reactions

Friedel-Crafts *Reactions Form* ***C–C*** *Bonds*

Friedel-Crafts reactions are really useful for forming C–C bonds in organic synthesis. They are carried out by refluxing benzene with a halogen carrier and either a **halogenoalkane** or an **acyl chloride**. There are two types:

Friedel-Crafts Alkylation *Puts an* ***Alkyl Group*** *on Benzene*

Friedel-Crafts alkylation puts **any alkyl group** onto a benzene ring using a **halogenoalkane** and a halogen carrier. The general reaction is:

$$C_6H_6 + R\text{–}X \xrightarrow[\text{Reflux}]{AlCl_3} C_6H_5R + HX$$

Here's how the **mechanism** for the reaction works, using a chloroalkane and $AlCl_3$ as an example:

A carbocation is formed from the chloroalkane and $AlCl_3$.

$$R\text{–}Cl + AlCl_3 \rightarrow R^+ + AlCl_4^-$$

The carbocation then reacts with benzene via electrophilic substitution:

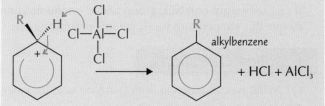

1) The carbocation is the electrophile. It attracts the electrons in the delocalised ring to form a new C–C bond. The delocalised ring of electrons is broken and an unstable intermediate forms.

2) $AlCl_4^-$ reacts with the unstable intermediate to remove a hydrogen ion and the delocalised ring is reformed. An alkylbenzene and hydrogen chloride are made and the $AlCl_3$ catalyst is regenerated.

Friedel-Crafts alkylation can also occur with other **electrophiles**.

Electrophiles that are made up of alkyl chains containing $OAlCl_3^-$ groups can be added to benzene rings to create **alcohols**.

Because the oxygen in the alkyl chain has a **lone pair** of electrons, it can act as a nucleophile.

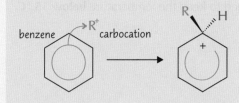

Friedel-Crafts Acylation *Produces* ***Phenylketones***

Friedel-Crafts acylation substitutes an **acyl group** for an H atom on benzene. You have to reflux benzene with an **acyl chloride** instead of a halogenoalkane. This produces **phenylketones** (unless R = H, in which case an aldehyde called benzenecarbaldehyde, or benzaldehyde, is formed). The reactants need to be **heated under reflux** in a **non-aqueous solvent** (like dry ether) for the reaction to occur.

The general reaction is:

$$C_6H_6 + RCOCl \xrightarrow[\text{Reflux}]{AlCl_3} C_6H_5COR + HCl$$

The mechanism for this is the same as for the formation of a carbocation in Friedel-Crafts alkylation, except with an acyl chloride instead of a halogenoalkane.

Again, the **carbocation** is formed from the acyl chloride and $AlCl_3$: $CH_3COCl + AlCl_3 \rightarrow CH_3CO^+ + AlCl_4^-$

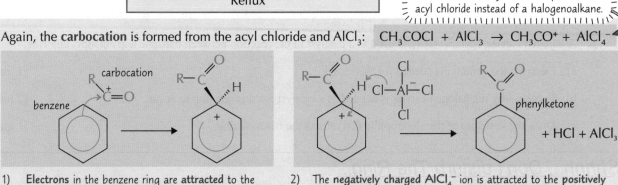

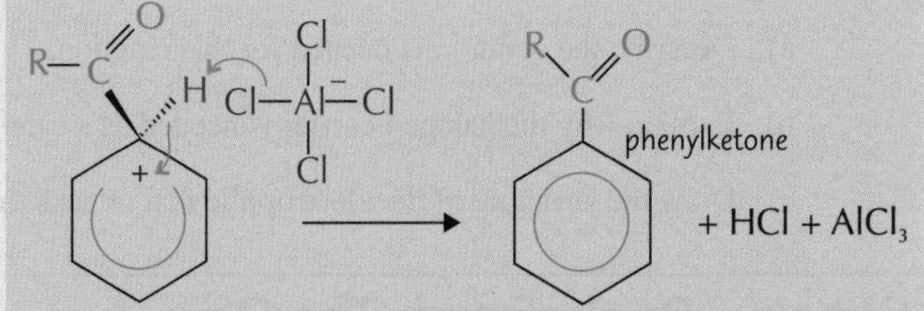

1) **Electrons** in the benzene ring are **attracted** to the positively charged **carbocation**. Two electrons from the benzene **bond** with the carbocation. This **partially breaks** the **delocalised ring** and gives it a **positive charge**.

2) The **negatively charged** $AlCl_4^-$ ion is attracted to the **positively charged ring**. One **chloride ion** breaks away from the aluminium chloride ion and **bonds** with the **hydrogen** ion. This **removes the hydrogen** from the ring forming HCl. It also reforms the catalyst.

Electrophilic Substitution Reactions

Nitric Acid Acts as an Electrophile with a Sulfuric Acid Catalyst

When you warm **benzene** with **concentrated nitric acid** and **concentrated sulfuric acid**, you get a **nitration reaction** and **nitrobenzene** is formed.
Sulfuric acid is a **catalyst** — it helps make the nitronium ion, $\mathbf{NO_2^+}$, which is the **electrophile**:

$$HNO_3 + H_2SO_4 \rightarrow H_2NO_3^+ + HSO_4^-$$
$$H_2NO_3^+ \rightarrow NO_2^+ + H_2O$$

The NO_2^+ electrophile then reacts with the benzene ring to form nitrobenzene:

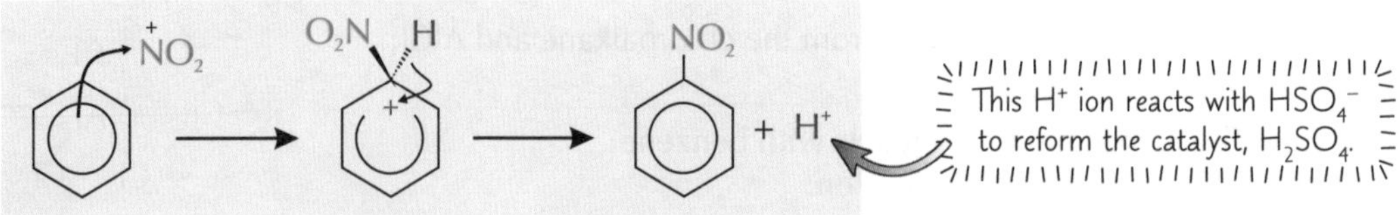

If you only want one NO_2 group added (**mononitration**), you need to keep the temperature **below 55 °C**. Above this temperature you'll get lots of substitutions.

Practice Questions

Q1 What type of reaction does benzene tend to undergo?

Q2 Describe the role of a halogen carrier in electrophilic substitution reactions.

Q3 Name two substances that are used as halogen carriers in substitution reactions of benzene.

Q4 Describe two ways of making C–C bonds with benzene.

Q5 What type of compounds are normally formed in Friedel-Crafts acylation reactions?

Q6 Which two acids are used in the production of nitrobenzene?

Exam Questions

Q1 Two electrophilic substitution reactions of benzene are summarised in the diagram below:

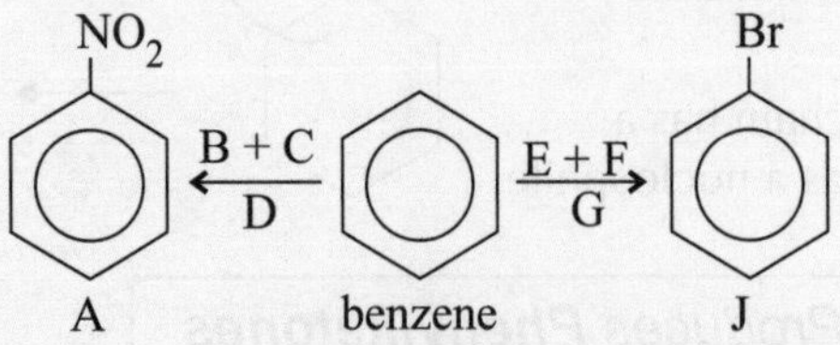

a) i) Name product A, the reagents B and C, and give the conditions, D. [4 marks]

ii) Write equations to show the formation of the electrophile in this reaction. [2 marks]

iii) Outline a mechanism for the reaction of benzene with the electrophile formed in ii). [2 marks]

b) i) Name product J. [1 mark]

ii) Name reagents E and F, and give the conditions, G, needed in the reaction to make J. [3 marks]

Q2 A halogen carrier, such as $AlCl_3$, is used as a catalyst in the reaction between benzene and ethanoyl chloride.

a) Describe the conditions needed for this reaction. [1 mark]

b) Explain why the halogen carrier is needed as a catalyst for this reaction to occur. [2 marks]

c) Draw the structure of the electrophile that attacks the benzene ring. [1 mark]

Shhhh... Don't disturb The Ring...

Benzene really likes Mr Delocalised Electron Ring and it won't give him up for nobody, at least not without one heck of a fight. It'd much rather get tangled up in an electrophilic substitution reaction. I mean, those hydrogen atoms weren't good for much anyway, so it's not as if anyone's going to miss them. Anything not to bother The Ring.

Phenols

Phenols are like benzene, but they have a hydroxyl group on the benzene ring. This changes their reactivity.

Phenols Have Benzene Rings with -OH Groups Attached

Phenol has the formula C_6H_5OH.
Other phenol derivatives have various groups attached to the benzene ring:

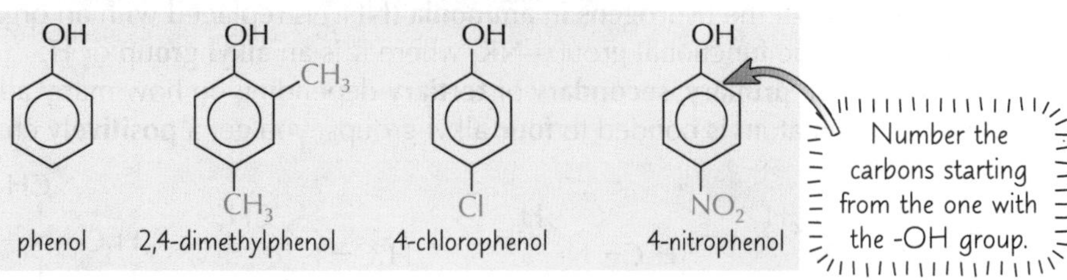

phenol 2,4-dimethylphenol 4-chlorophenol 4-nitrophenol

Number the carbons starting from the one with the -OH group.

Phenol is More Reactive than Benzene

delocalised ring of electrons
electrons in p-orbitals
oxygen
carbon
hydrogen

1) The -OH group means that phenol is more likely to undergo **electrophilic substitution** than benzene.
2) One of the lone pairs of electrons in a **p-orbital** of the oxygen atom **overlaps** with the delocalised π-bonds in the benzene ring.
3) So the lone pair of electrons from the oxygen atom is **partially delocalised** into the π-system.
4) This increases the **electron density** of the ring, making it more likely to be attacked by electrophiles.

Phenol is **more reactive** than **benzene**, so if you shake phenol with orange bromine water, it will **react, decolourising** it.
The -OH group makes the ring very attractive to electrophiles, so substitution happens **more than once**. The product is called **2,4,6-tribromophenol** — it's insoluble in water and **precipitates** out of the mixture. It smells of antiseptic.

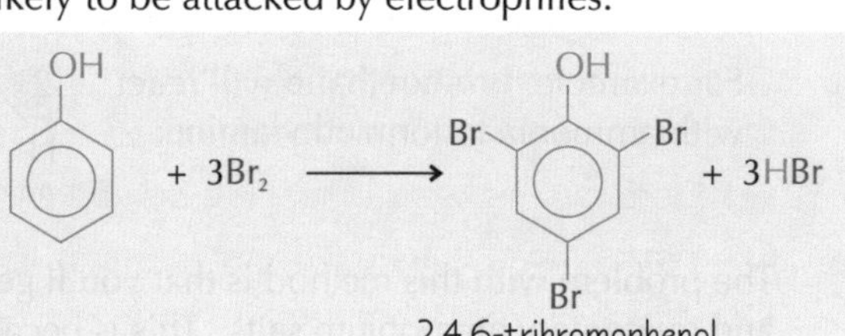

2,4,6-tribromophenol

You Can Synthesise Aspirin From Salicylic Acid

The -OH group in phenol can take part in esterification reactions, like an alcohol. For example, aspirin can be synthesised by an **esterification** reaction of salicylic acid (a phenol derivative).

Ethanoic anhydride reacts a bit like an acyl chloride, but it's cheaper and safer.

1) Add some ethanoic anhydride and a few drops of phosphoric acid to salicylic acid in a test tube. Warm the reaction mixture to 50 °C and leave for about 15 minutes.
2) Add some cold water to the reaction mixture, and then cool on ice. Aspirin crystals should form.
3) Filter the crystals under reduced pressure.
4) Recrystallise the aspirin in a mixture of water and ethanol.

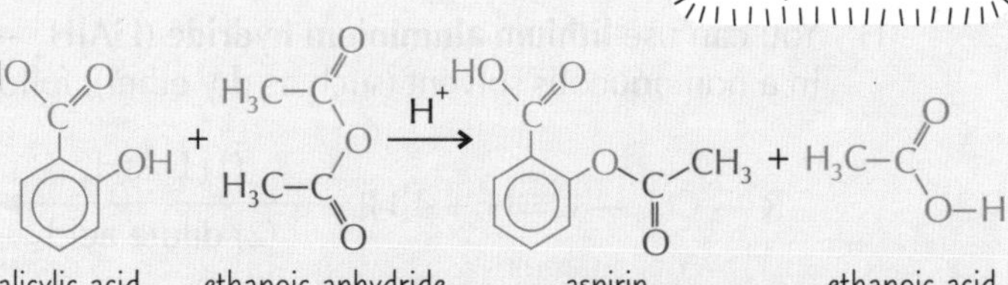

salicylic acid ethanoic anhydride aspirin ethanoic acid

See page 202 for more on esterification.

Practice Questions

Q1 What is the formula and structure of phenol?

Q2 Write a balanced equation for the reaction between phenol and bromine (Br_2).

Exam Question

Q1 a) Bromine water can be used to distinguish between benzene and phenol.
Describe what you would observe in each case and name any products formed. [2 marks]

b) Explain why phenol reacts differently from benzene. [2 marks]

c) Name the type of reaction that occurs between phenol and bromine. [1 mark]

Phenol Destination 4 — more compounds, more equations, more horror...

The electrophilic substitution reactions of phenol are all pretty similar to benzene — phenol's just more reactive so the reaction conditions can be a bit milder. Make sure you can explain why phenol is more reactive than benzene.

Amines

Another type of organic compound coming up. Amines all contain nitrogen. Luckily, they're not as mean as they sound.

Amines are Organic Derivatives of Ammonia

If one or more of the **hydrogens** in **ammonia** (NH_3) is replaced with an organic group, you get an **amine**.
Amines have the functional group **$-NR_2$** where R is an **alkyl group** or **H**.
Amines can be **primary**, **secondary** or **tertiary** depending on how many **alkyl** groups the nitrogen atom is bonded to.
If the nitrogen atom is bonded to **four** alkyl groups, you get a **positively** charged **quaternary ammonium** ion.

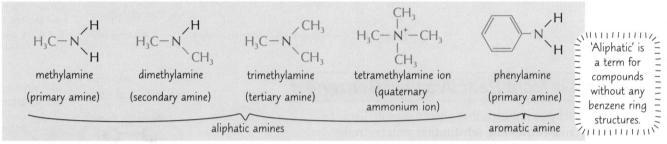

H_3C-NH_2	$H_3C-NH(CH_3)$	$H_3C-N(CH_3)_2$	$H_3C-N^+(CH_3)_3$	$C_6H_5-NH_2$
methylamine (primary amine)	dimethylamine (secondary amine)	trimethylamine (tertiary amine)	tetramethylamine ion (quaternary ammonium ion)	phenylamine (primary amine)
aliphatic amines				aromatic amine

'Aliphatic' is a term for compounds without any benzene ring structures.

Aliphatic Amines Can Be Made From Halogenoalkanes...

Amines can be made by heating a **halogenoalkane** with an excess of **ethanolic ammonia**.

For example, **bromoethane** will react with ammonia to form **ethylamine**:

$$2NH_3 + CH_3CH_2Br \longrightarrow CH_3CH_2NH_2 + NH_4Br$$

(ammonia → ethylamine)

This is a nucleophilic substitution reaction.

The problem with this method is that you'll get a **mixture** of primary, secondary and tertiary amines, and quaternary ammonium salts. This is because the nitrogen atom in primary, secondary and tertiary amines has a **lone pair** of electrons, meaning it can act as a **nucleophile**. It can therefore take part in **nucleophilic substitution reactions** with any halogenoalkane in the reaction mixture (see page 214), which causes more substituted amines to be produced, where more than one hydrogen is replaced.

...Or By Reducing a Nitrile

You can **reduce** a nitrile to a **primary amine** by a number of different methods:

1) You can use **lithium aluminium hydride** (**$LiAlH_4$** — a strong reducing agent) in a non-aqueous solvent (such as dry ether), followed by some **dilute acid**.

$$\underset{\text{nitrile}}{R-CH_2-C\equiv N} + 4[H] \xrightarrow[\text{(2) dilute acid}]{\text{(1) } LiAlH_4} \underset{\text{primary amine}}{R-CH_2-CH_2NH_2}$$

[H] is just the reducing agent (here it's $LiAlH_4$).

2) This method is fine in the lab, but $LiAlH_4$ is too **expensive** for industrial use.
In industry, nitriles are reduced using **hydrogen gas** with a **metal catalyst**, such as platinum or nickel, at high temperature and pressure. This is called **catalytic hydrogenation**.

$$\underset{\text{nitrile}}{R-CH_2-C\equiv N} + 2H_2 \xrightarrow[\text{high temperature and pressure}]{\text{nickel catalyst}} \underset{\text{primary amine}}{R-CH_2-CH_2NH_2}$$

Becky was reduced to tears by lithium aluminium hydride.

Aromatic Amines are Made by Reducing a Nitro Compound

Aromatic nitro compounds, e.g. **nitrobenzene**, are reduced in two steps:

1) Heat a mixture of a **nitro compound**, **tin metal** and **concentrated hydrochloric acid** under **reflux** — this makes a **salt**.
2) To get the **aromatic amine**, add **sodium hydroxide**.

$$\underset{\text{nitrobenzene}}{C_6H_5NO_2} + 6[H] \xrightarrow[\text{(2) NaOH}]{\text{(1) tin, conc. HCl reflux}} \underset{\text{phenylamine}}{C_6H_5NH_2} + 2H_2O$$

Amines

Amines Are Bases

1) Amines act as **weak bases** because they **accept protons**. There's a **lone pair of electrons** on the **nitrogen** atom that can form a **dative covalent (coordinate) bond** with an H^+ ion.

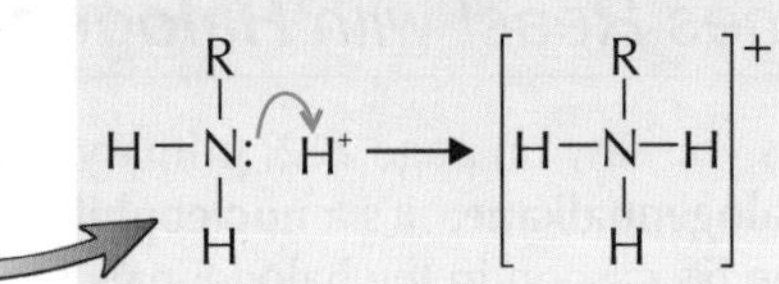

2) The **strength** of the **base** depends on how **available** the nitrogen's lone pair of electrons is. The more **available** the **lone pair** is, the more likely the amine is to **accept a proton**, and the **stronger** a base it will be. A **lone pair** of electrons will be **more available** if its **electron density** is **higher**.

Primary aliphatic amines are **stronger** bases than **ammonia**, which is a **stronger** base than **aromatic amines.**

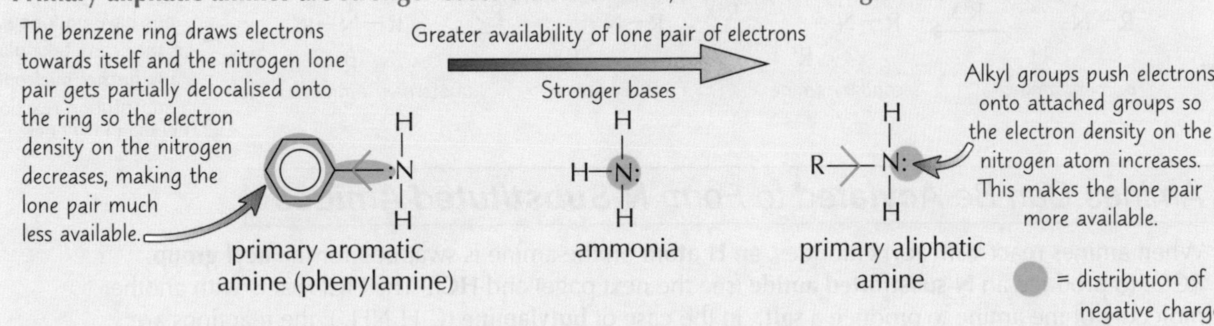

The benzene ring draws electrons towards itself and the nitrogen lone pair gets partially delocalised onto the ring so the electron density on the nitrogen decreases, making the lone pair much less available.
Greater availability of lone pair of electrons
Stronger bases
Alkyl groups push electrons onto attached groups so the electron density on the nitrogen atom increases. This makes the lone pair more available.
primary aromatic amine (phenylamine)
ammonia
primary aliphatic amine
= distribution of negative charge

3) The lone pair of electrons also means that amines are **nucleophiles**. They react with **halogenoalkanes** in a **nucleophilic substitution reaction** (see next page), or with **acyl chlorides** to form **N-substituted amides** (p.215).

4) Amines are **neutralised** by **acids** to make **ammonium salts**. E.g. **butylamine** reacts with **hydrochloric acid** to form butylammonium chloride:

$$CH_3CH_2CH_2CH_2NH_2 + HCl \rightarrow CH_3CH_2CH_2CH_2NH_3^+Cl^-$$

Small Amines Dissolve in Water to Form an Alkaline Solution

1) **Small amines** are **soluble in water** as the amine group can form **hydrogen bonds** with the water molecules.

2) The **bigger** the amine, the **greater** the **London forces** (see pages 30-31) between the amine molecules and the more energy it takes to overcome the London forces. The larger carbon chains in larger amines also disrupt the hydrogen bonding in water, but can't form hydrogen bonds with water themselves. So **large amines** are **less soluble** in water than small ones.

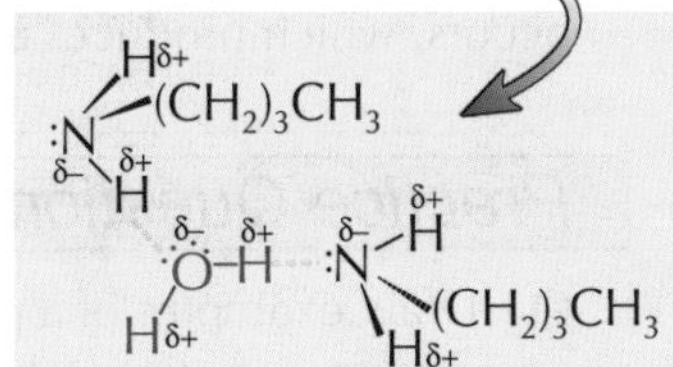

3) When they dissolve, amines form **alkaline** solutions. Some of the amine molecules in the solution take a hydrogen ion from water, forming **alkyl ammonium ions** and **hydroxide ions**.

$$CH_3CH_2CH_2CH_2NH_{2(aq)} + H_2O_{(l)} \rightleftharpoons CH_3CH_2CH_2CH_2NH_3^+{}_{(aq)} + OH^-_{(aq)}$$

Amines will Form a Complex Ion With Copper(II) Ions

1) In **copper(II) sulfate** solution, the Cu^{2+} ions form $\mathbf{[Cu(H_2O)_6]^{2+}}$ complexes with water. This solution's **blue**.

2) If you add a **small** amount of **butylamine solution** to copper(II) sulfate solution you get a **pale blue precipitate** — the amine acts as a **base** (proton acceptor) and takes two H^+ ions from the complex. This leaves a pale blue precipitate of copper hydroxide, $\mathbf{[Cu(OH)_2(H_2O)_4]}$, which is insoluble.

3) Add more butylamine solution, and the **precipitate dissolves** to form a beautiful **deep blue solution**. Some of the ligands are replaced by butylamine molecules, which donate their lone pairs to form dative covalent bonds with the Cu^{2+} ion. This forms soluble $\mathbf{[Cu(CH_3(CH_2)_3NH_2)_4(H_2O)_2]^{2+}}$ complex ions.

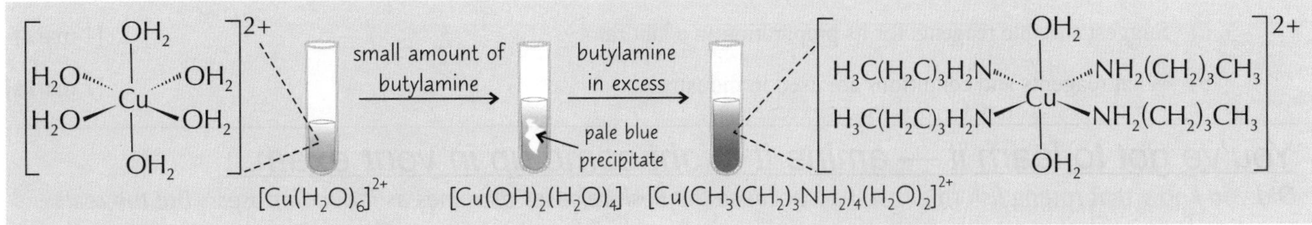

4) The **same** set of reactions will happen with **other** amine molecules. For **larger** amines, the final product may **change** because the amine molecules just **can't fit** around the copper ion.

Amines

Amines React with Halogenoalkanes in Nucleophilic Substitution Reactions

1) As you saw on page 212, primary amines can be made from the reaction between **ammonia** and a **halogenoalkane**. It's a **nucleophilic substitution reaction** — the **lone pair** on the ammonia molecule is attracted to the δ+ carbon in the halogenoalkane and reacts with it to remove the halogen and form a primary amine.
2) The nitrogen atom in the primary amine that is formed has a lone pair of electrons, so it is **also** a **nucleophile**. In fact, **primary**, **secondary** and **tertiary** amines all have a lone pair of electrons on their nitrogen atom, so are able to react with halogenoalkanes in nucleophilic substitution reactions to form more substituted amines:

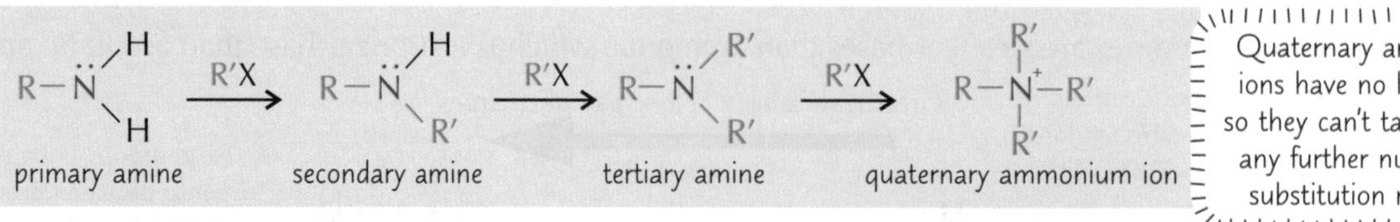

Quaternary ammonium ions have no lone pairs, so they can't take place in any further nucleophilic substitution reactions.

Amines Can Be Acylated to Form N-Substituted Amides

When amines react with acyl chlorides, an **H atom** on the amine is swapped for the **acyl group**, RCO, to produce an **N-substituted amide** (see the next page) and **HCl**. The HCl reacts with another molecule of the amine to produce a **salt**. In the case of **butylamine** ($C_4H_9NH_2$), the reactions are:

Stage 1: $CH_3COCl + CH_3(CH_2)_3NH_2 \rightarrow HCl + CH_3CONH(CH_2)_3CH_3$

ethanoyl chloride + butylamine → N-butyl ethanamide

Stage 2: $CH_3(CH_2)_3NH_2 + HCl \rightarrow CH_3(CH_2)_3NH_3^+\ Cl^-$

butylamine → butylammonium chloride

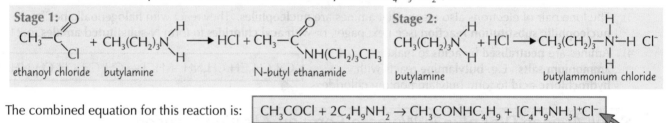

The combined equation for this reaction is: $CH_3COCl + 2C_4H_9NH_2 \rightarrow CH_3CONHC_4H_9 + [C_4H_9NH_3]^+Cl^-$

This is the 'halogenoalkane + ammonia' reaction you met on page 93.

To carry out this reaction, ethanoyl chloride is added to a **concentrated aqueous solution** of the amine. A violent reaction occurs, which produces a **solid, white mixture** of the products.

Practice Questions

Q1 Draw examples of a primary, secondary and tertiary amine, and a quaternary ammonium ion.

Q2 What conditions are needed to reduce nitrobenzene to phenylamine?

Q3 Explain why small amines dissolve in water but large ones don't.

Exam Questions

Q1 Butylamine solution will react with ethanoyl chloride, CH_3COCl, to form N-butylethanamide, $CH_3CONH(C_4H_9)$.

a) Butylamine solution is alkaline. Explain why this is. [2 marks]

b) Write balanced equations for the two stages of the reaction between butylamine and ethanoyl chloride. [2 marks]

Q2 a) Explain how methylamine, CH_3NH_2, can act as a base. [1 mark]

b) Methylamine is a stronger base than ammonia, NH_3. However, phenylamine, $C_6H_5NH_2$, is a weaker base than ammonia. Explain these differences in base strength. [2 marks]

Q3 Propylamine can be synthesised from propanenitrile, CH_3CH_2CN.

a) Suggest suitable reagents for its preparation in a laboratory. [1 mark]

b) What reagents and conditions are used in industry? [2 marks]

You've got to learn it — amine it might come up in your exam...

Did you know that rotting fish smells so bad because the flesh releases diamines as it decomposes? But the real question is: is it fish that smells of amines or amines that smell of fish — it's one of those chicken or egg things that no one can answer. Well, enough philosophical pondering — we all know the answer to the meaning of life. It's 42.

Amides

Some more nitrogen-containing organic compounds to keep you entertained. Amides look like carboxylic acids, but the -OH group is replaced by $-NH_2$ or -NHR. You need to be able to recognise them and know how they're made.

Amides are Carboxylic Acid Derivatives

Amides contain the functional group **$-CONH_2$**.

The **carbonyl group** pulls electrons away from the rest of the $-CONH_2$ group, so amides behave differently from amines.

You get **primary amides** and **N-substituted amides** depending on how many **carbon atoms** the nitrogen is bonded to.

R–C(=O)–N(–H)–H — primary amide

R–C(=O)–N(–H)–R′ — N-substituted amide

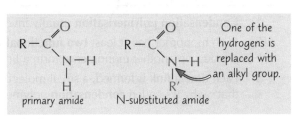

One of the hydrogens is replaced with an alkyl group.

You Name Amides Using the Suffix '-amide'

1) Amides all have the suffix **-amide**. If the molecule is a **primary amide**, then the name is simply the stem of the carbon chain, followed by -amide.
2) **N-substituted amides** also have a prefix to describe the alkyl chain that is attached directly to the nitrogen atom. The prefix has the general form **N-alkyl-**.

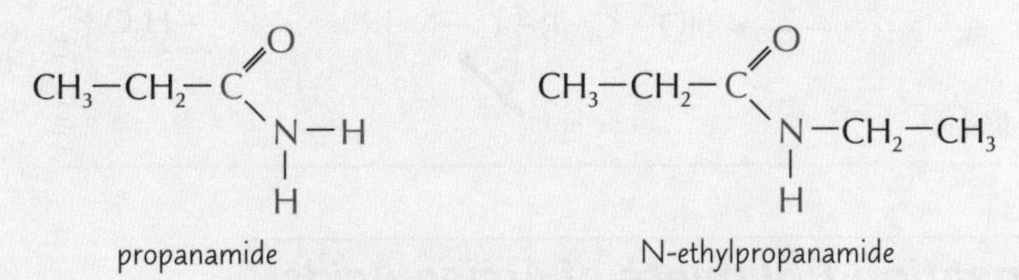

Jayda was trying the new, protein-heavy hen-substituted diet.

Amides Can Be Made From Acyl Chlorides

If you can react an acyl chloride with **ammonia** or a **primary amine**, you'll form an **amide**.

1) The reaction with concentrated **ammonia** at **room temperature** forms a **primary amide**:

$$H_3C-C(=O)Cl + NH_3 \longrightarrow H_3C-C(=O)NH_2 + HCl$$

ethanoyl chloride → ethanamide

2) The reaction with a **primary amine** at **room temperature** forms an **N-substituted amide**:

$$H_3C-C(=O)Cl + CH_3NH_2 \longrightarrow H_3C-C(=O)NHCH_3 + HCl$$

ethanoyl chloride → N-methylethanamide

Practice Questions

Q1 Draw the general structures of a primary amide and an N-substituted amide, using R and R′ to represent any alkyl groups.

Q2 Give the reagents and conditions you could use to make a primary amide from an acyl chloride.

Exam Question

Q1 An N-substituted amide is shown on the right.

$CH_3CH_2CH_2-C(=O)NHCH_2CH_2CH_3$

a) Name the amide. [1 mark]

b) The amide can be made through the reaction of an acyl chloride. Name the acyl chloride, and give any other reagents and conditions needed for this reaction. [3 marks]

I think, therefore I amide...

'Amine' and 'amide' might sound pretty similar, but that C=O group makes a world of difference. Check that you can tell the difference between them, and make sure you know how to make both primary and N-substituted amides.

Condensation Polymers

You met addition polymerisation back on page 88. Now it's time for a second type — condensation polymerisation.

Condensation Polymers Include **Polyesters, Polyamides** and **Polypeptides**

1) **Condensation polymerisation** usually involves two different types of monomers.
2) Each monomer has at least **two functional groups**. Each functional group reacts with a group on another monomer to form a link, creating polymer chains.
3) Each time a link is formed, a small molecule (often water) is lost — that's why it's called **condensation** polymerisation.

Reactions Between **Dicarboxylic Acids** and **Diamines** Make **Polyamides**

1) **Carboxyl** (–COOH) groups react with **amino** ($-NH_2$) groups to form **amide** (–CONH–) links.
2) A water molecule is lost each time an amide link is formed — it's a **condensation** reaction.
3) The condensation polymer formed is a **polyamide**.

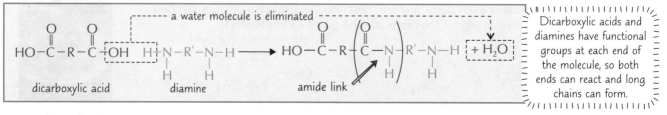

a water molecule is eliminated

$$\text{HO-C(=O)-R-C(=O)-OH} + \text{H-N(H)-R'-N(H)-H} \longrightarrow \text{HO-C(=O)-R-C(=O)-N(H)-R'-N(H)-H} + H_2O$$

dicarboxylic acid — diamine — amide link

Dicarboxylic acids and diamines have functional groups at each end of the molecule, so both ends can react and long chains can form.

Proteins are **Condensation Polymers** of Amino Acids

1) Amino acids are molecules that contain **both** an **amine** and a **carboxylic acid** group (see page 218).
2) Amino acid monomers can react together in condensation polymerisation reactions to form **proteins**. The **amino acid monomers** are connected by amide links — in proteins these are called **peptide links**.
3) The **amine group** of one amino acid can react with the **carboxylic acid group** of another in a **condensation** reaction.

Proteins are really polyamides.

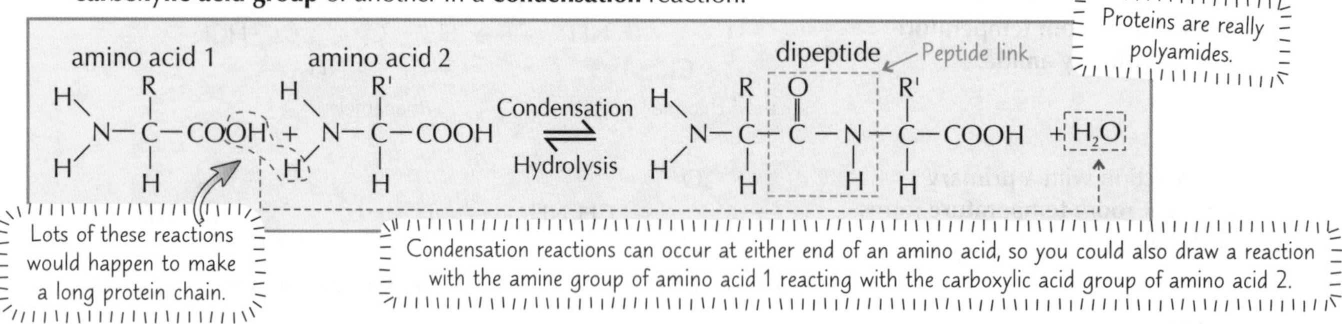
amino acid 1
amino acid 2
Condensation
Hydrolysis
dipeptide
Peptide link
$+H_2O$
Lots of these reactions would happen to make a long protein chain.
Condensation reactions can occur at either end of an amino acid, so you could also draw a reaction with the amine group of amino acid 1 reacting with the carboxylic acid group of amino acid 2.

4) You can break down (**hydrolyse**) a protein into its individual amino acids, but you need pretty harsh conditions. **Hot aqueous 6 mol dm^{-3} hydrochloric acid** is added, and the mixture is heated under reflux for 24 hours. This produces the **ammonium salts** of the amino acids. The final mixture is then neutralised using a base.
5) Once you've hydrolysed a protein, you can use **chromatography** (see page 219) to identify the amino acid monomers that it was made from.

Reactions Between **Dicarboxylic Acids** and **Diols** Make **Polyesters**

Carboxyl groups (–COOH) react with **hydroxyl** (–OH) groups to form **ester links** (–COO–). It's another **condensation** reaction, and the polymer formed is a **polyester**

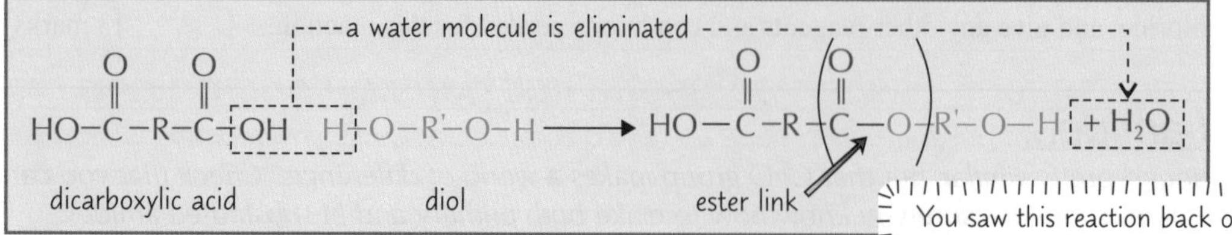
a water molecule is eliminated
dicarboxylic acid
diol
ester link
$+H_2O$

You saw this reaction back on page 203.

Pretty Polymer.

Condensation Polymers

Break the **Amide** or **Ester** Link to Find the **Monomers** of a **Condensation** Polymer

You can find the formulae of the **monomers** used to make a condensation polymer by looking at its repeat unit.

1) First find the amide **(HN–CO)** or ester **(CO–O)** link. Break it down the middle.

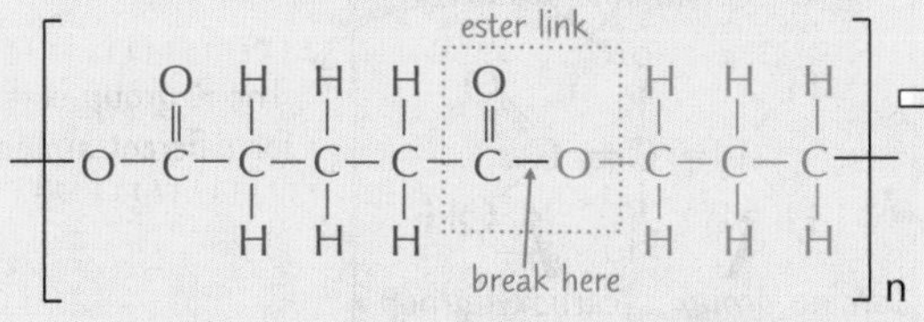

ester link

break here

2) Then add an **H** or an **OH** to **both ends** of **both molecules** to find the monomers.
(Always add Hs to O or N atoms, and OH groups to C atoms.)

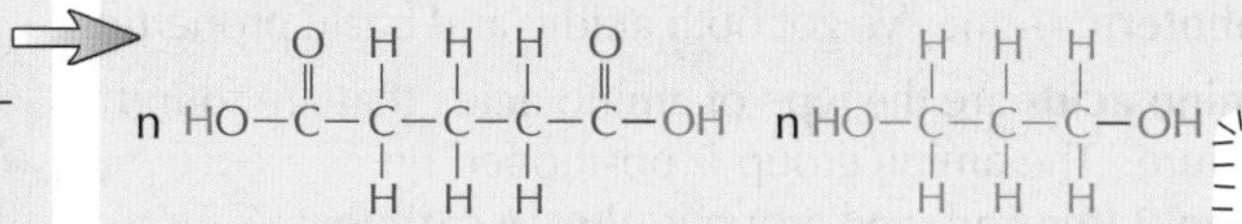

n = a large number of.

Join the **Monomer Functional Groups** to Find a **Condensation Polymer**

If you know the **formulae** of a pair of **monomers** that react together in a **condensation polymerisation** reaction, you can work out the **repeat unit** of the condensation polymer that they would form.

Example: A condensation polymer is made from 1,4-diaminobutane, $H_2N(CH_2)_4NH_2$, and decanedioic acid, $HOOC(CH_2)_8COOH$. Draw the repeat unit of the polymer that is formed.

1) Draw out the two **monomer** molecules next to each other.
2) Remove an **OH** from the **dicarboxylic acid**, and an **H** from the **diamine** — that gives you a water molecule.
3) Join the C and the N together to make an **amide link**.
4) Take another **H** and **OH** off the ends of your molecule, and there's your **repeat unit**.

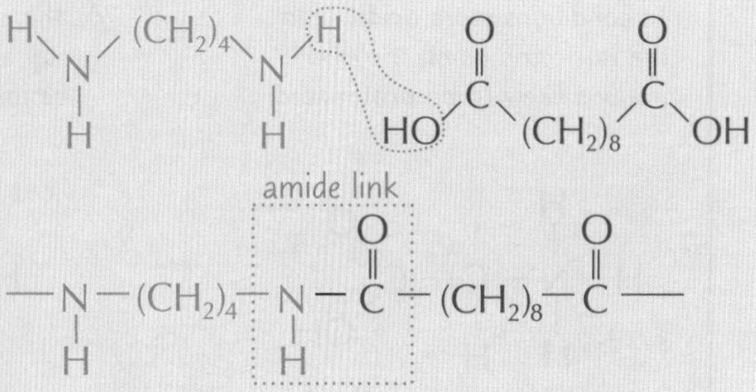

amide link

If the monomer molecules are a **dicarboxylic acid** and a **diol**, then you take an **H** atom from the **diol** and an **-OH** group from the **dicarboxylic acid**, and form an **ester** link instead.

Practice Questions

Q1 Why are polyamides and polyesters called 'condensation polymers'?

Q2 Which two types of molecules react together to make a polyamide?

Q3 What type of molecules react together to form a polypeptide?

Exam Questions

Q1 The monomers shown on the right are used to make a polymer called poly(butylene succinate), or PBS.

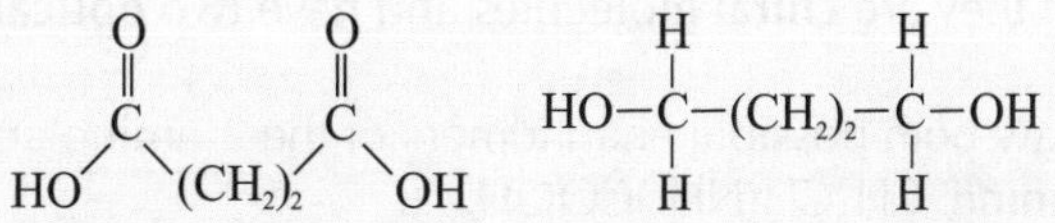

butanedioic acid   butane-1,4-diol

a) Draw the repeat unit of the polymer made from these two monomers.
(It is not necessary to draw the carbon chains out in full.) [2 marks]

b) Give a name for the type of link formed between the monomers. [1 mark]

Q2 The polyamide nylon (6,6) is formed by the reaction between the monomers hexanedioic acid and 1,6-hexanediamine.

a) Draw the repeat unit for nylon (6,6). [2 marks]

b) Explain why this is an example of condensation polymerisation. [1 mark]

Conversation polymerisation — when someone just goes on and on and on...

If you need to work out a repeat unit for a polymer that's made up of two complicated looking monomers, don't worry. All that matters is finding the carboxylic acid group and the amine or alcohol group and linking them up. Then write down everything that comes in between just as it's been given to you, take off an -H and an -OH, and there you go.

Amino Acids

Amino acids are often called the building blocks of life. They're like little plastic building bricks, but hurt less if you tread on one. Instead of putting them together to make houses and rockets, they're used to make all the proteins in your body.

Amino Acids have an **Amino Group** and a **Carboxyl Group**

1) An amino acid has a **basic amino group** (NH_2) and an **acidic carboxyl group** (COOH). This makes them **amphoteric** — they've got both acidic and basic properties.
2) **2-amino acids** are the type of amino acids that are found in nature. The **amino** group is positioned on **carbon-2** (the carboxyl group is always carbon-1).

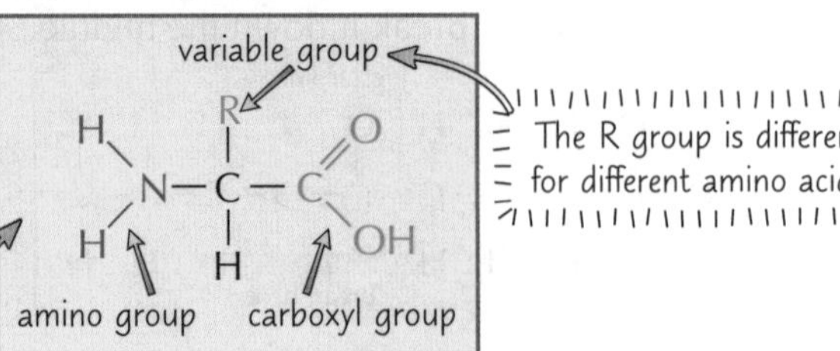

The R group is different for different amino acids.

Amino Acids Can Exist As **Zwitterions**

A **zwitterion** is an **overall neutral** molecule that has both a **positive** and a **negative charge** in different parts of the molecule. An amino acid can only exist as a zwitterion near its **isoelectric point** — this is the **pH** where the **overall charge** on the amino acid is zero. It's different for different amino acids — it depends on their R group.

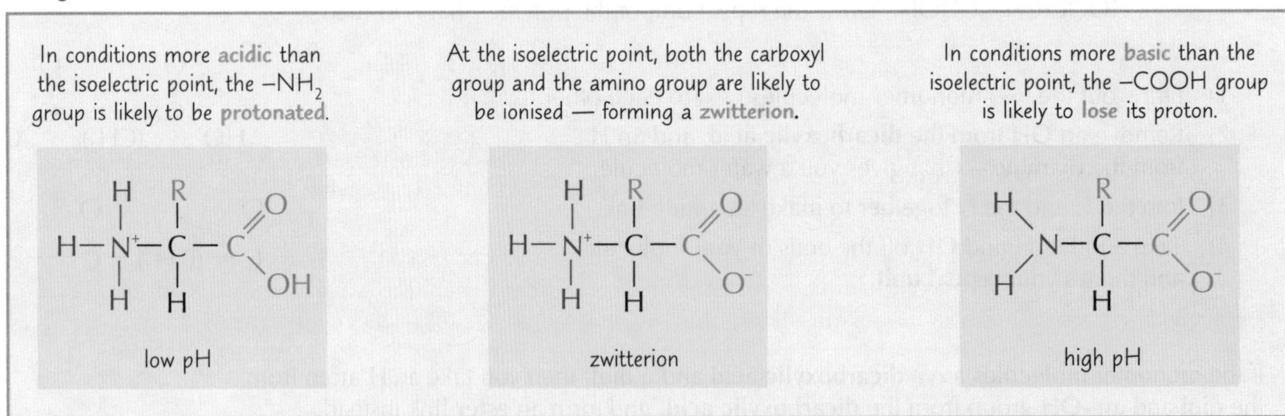

In conditions more acidic than the isoelectric point, the –NH_2 group is likely to be protonated.
At the isoelectric point, both the carboxyl group and the amino group are likely to be ionised — forming a zwitterion.
In conditions more basic than the isoelectric point, the –COOH group is likely to lose its proton.
low pH
zwitterion
high pH

In general, if the amino acid contains **the same number** of carboxyl groups as amino groups, it will exist as a zwitterion when it is dissolved in solution, and will have a pH of about 7 (it will be roughly **neutral**).

Most **2-Amino Acids** Are **Chiral**

1) There are usually **four** different groups attached to carbon-2 of a 2-amino acid — the carboxyl group, the amino group, a hydrogen atom and the R group. This means that they are **chiral** molecules and have two **optical isomers** (see page 194).

Example: Draw both possible enantiomers of the 2-amino acid alanine, $CH_3CH(NH_2)COOH$.

1) First draw one isomer with the groups arranged in a **tetrahedral shape** around the **chiral carbon**.
2) Draw a **mirror line** next to the isomer.
3) Draw its **mirror image** next to it.

COOH, H_2N, C, H, H_3C | HOOC, C, H, NH_2, CH_3

mirror line

See page 194 for more on drawing optical isomers.

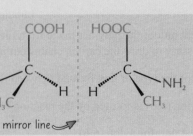

Sweet dreams are made of cheese..

A choral protein.

2) If **plane-polarised, monochromatic light** is shone through an aqueous solution that contains just **one** of the enantiomers of a 2–amino acid, the plane of the light gets **rotated** because of the **chiral carbon**.
3) The exception to this is **glycine** where the **R group** is a hydrogen atom. It has two H atoms attached to the central carbon, so it **isn't chiral** (it's **achiral**), and it won't rotate the plane of plane-polarised light.

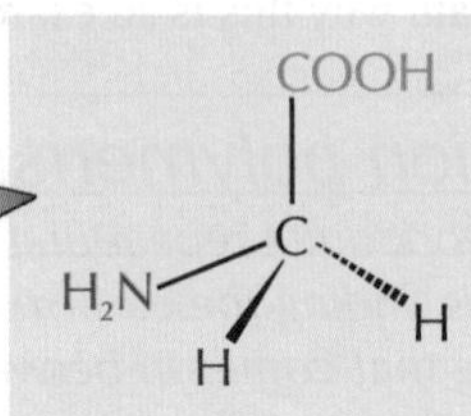

Amino Acids

Paper Chromatography can be used to *Identify Unknown* Amino Acids

You can easily identify amino acids in a mixture using a simple **paper** (one-way) **chromatography experiment**.

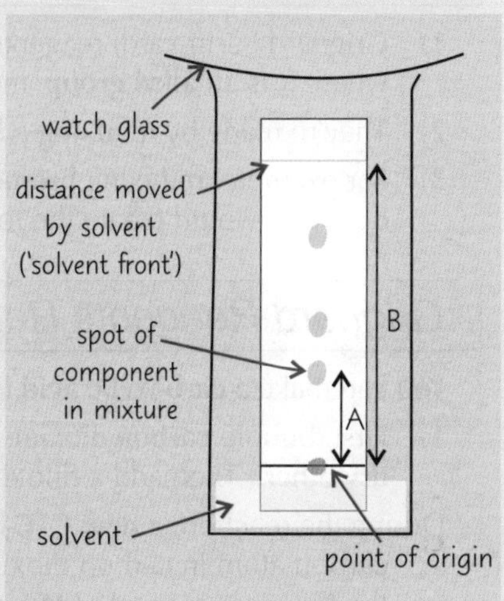

1) Draw a **pencil line** near the bottom of a piece of chromatography paper and put a **concentrated spot** of the mixture you want to investigate on it.
2) Place the paper into a **beaker** containing a small amount of **solvent**, so that the solvent level is **below** the spot of mixture. Place a **watch glass** on top of the beaker to stop any solvent **evaporating** out.
3) Different substances have **different solubilities** in the solvent. As the solvent spreads up the paper, the different chemicals in the mixture move with it, but at **different rates**, so they separate out.
4) When the solvent's **nearly** reached the top, take the paper out and **mark** where the solvent has reached with a pencil. This is the **solvent front**.
5) Identify the positions of the spots of different chemicals on the paper. Some chemicals, such as amino acids, aren't coloured so you first have to make them **visible**. You can do this by spraying **ninhydrin solution** (a developing agent) on the paper to turn them purple. You can also dip the paper into a jar containing a few crystals of **iodine**. Iodine **sublimes** from a solid straight to a gas, and the iodine gas causes the spots to turn **brown**. However you visualise your spots, you should **circle** their positions with a pencil.
6) You can work out the **R_f values** of the substances using this formula: $R_f \text{ value} = \frac{A}{B} = \frac{\text{distance travelled by spot}}{\text{distance travelled by solvent}}$

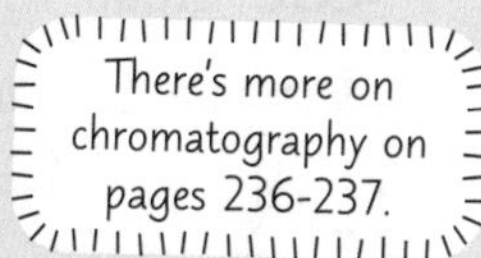
There's more on chromatography on pages 236-237.

7) If you've done your experiment under **standard conditions**, you can use a **table of known R_f values** to identify the components of the mixture. Otherwise, you should **repeat** the experiment with a spot of a substance you think is in the mixture, alongside the mixture, to see if they have the same R_f value.

Thin-layer chromatography can also be used to separate and identify amino acids. The method is the same as for paper chromatography, but instead of chromatography paper, you use a plate covered in a **thin layer** of **silica** (SiO_2) or **alumina** (Al_2O_3) as the **stationary phase**.

Practice Questions

Q1 Draw the general structure of a 2-amino acid.

Q2 What is a zwitterion?

Exam Questions

Q1 Glycine and cysteine, shown on the right, are two naturally occurring 2-amino acids.

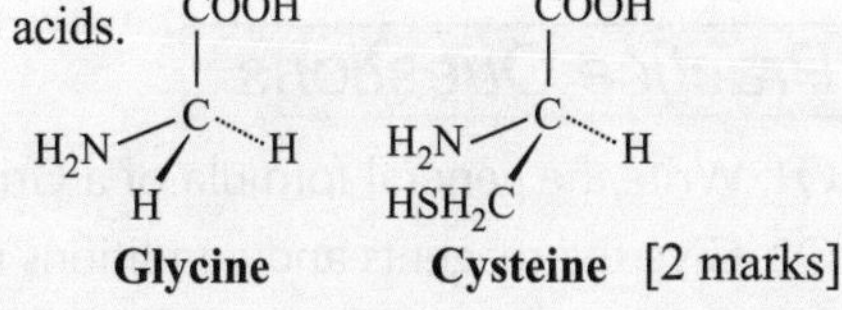

a) One way of distinguishing between glycine and cysteine is to observe their effect on plane-polarised monochromatic light. Explain why this method works. [2 marks]

b)* Explain how paper chromatography could be used to separate and identify a mixture of amino acids. [6 marks]

Q2 Amino acids are organic molecules that contain both a carboxyl group and an amino group.

a) Explain what is meant by the 'isoelectric point' of an amino acid. [1 mark]

b) The 2-amino acid serine has the formula $HOOCCH(NH_2)CH_2OH$.

i) Draw the displayed formula of serine. [1 mark]

ii) Draw the structure that serine will take in a solution with a high pH. [1 mark]

Twitterions — when amino acids get let loose on social media...

Well, these pages aren't too bad. Another organic structure, a bit of drawing chiral molecules, and a nice experimental technique. Make sure you know how chromatography is used to separate and identify amino acids and you're away.

* The quality of your extended response will be assessed for this question.

Grignard Reagents

The whole of Organic Chemistry revolves around carbon compounds and how they react, but getting one carbon to react with another and form a new carbon-carbon bond is surprisingly hard. Fortunately, Grignard reagents let you do it.

Grignard Reagents Are **Made** by Reacting **Halogenoalkanes** With **Magnesium**

1) Grignard (Grin-yard) reagents have the general formula **RMgX**, where R is an **alkyl group** and X is a **halogen**.
2) They're made by refluxing a halogenoalkane with magnesium in **dry ether**.

3) For example, refluxing **bromoethane** with magnesium in dry ether would create the following Grignard reagent:

$$CH_3CH_2Br + Mg \xrightarrow{\text{dry ether}} CH_3CH_2MgBr$$

Grignard Reagents React With **Carbon Dioxide...**

You can make a **carboxylic acid** from a Grignard reagent in **two steps**.

1) First, bubble **carbon dioxide gas** through a Grignard reagent in **dry ether**. Then add a dilute acid, such as hydrochloric acid.

$$\underset{\text{Grignard reagent}}{R{-}MgBr} + O{=}C{=}O \xrightarrow[\text{(2) dilute HCl}]{\text{(1) dry ether}} \underset{\text{carboxylic acid}}{RCOOH} + MgBrCl$$

During the reaction, **a new C–C bond** forms between the carbon atom in carbon dioxide and the C–Mg carbon from the Grignard reagent. One of the C=O bonds in carbon dioxide is broken to form a **-COO⁻ group**, which is **protonated** when the dilute acid is added to form -COOH.

Example: Butanoic acid can be synthesised from bromopropane in three steps. Give the reagents and conditions needed for each step, and the product formed at each stage of the synthesis.

$$CH_3CH_2CH_2Br \xrightarrow[\text{dry ether}]{\text{Mg}} CH_3CH_2CH_2MgBr \xrightarrow[\text{(2) dilute HCl}]{\text{(1) } CO_2\text{, dry ether}} CH_3CH_2CH_2COOH + MgBrCl$$

...And With **Carbonyl Compounds**

1) Grignard reagents react with aldehydes and ketones to make **alcohols**. A **new C–C bond** forms between the C–Mg carbon atom from the Grignard reagent and the C=O carbon of the carbonyl. This causes the C=O bond to break and, when acid is added, an **-OH group** is formed.
2) Again, there are **two steps** to the reaction. First the carbonyl compound is added to the **Grignard reagent** in **dry ether**, and then **dilute acid** is added to the reaction mixture.

$$\underset{\text{Grignard reagent}}{R{-}MgBr} + R'C(=O)R' \xrightarrow[\text{(2) dilute HCl}]{\text{(1) dry ether}} \underset{\text{alcohol}}{R'{-}C(OH)(R){-}R'} + MgBrCl$$

Reacting a Grignard reagent with an aldehyde will make a secondary alcohol (unless it's methanal which makes a primary alcohol). Reacting a Grignard reagent with a ketone will make a tertiary alcohol.

Practice Questions

Q1 Write the general formula of a Grignard reagent.

Q2 Give the reagents and conditions needed to make a Grignard reagent from a bromoalkane.

Q3 What type of organic product is formed when a Grignard reagent is reacted with carbon dioxide and then hydrolysed with dilute acid?

Exam Question

Q1 a) Give the reagents and conditions needed to make the Grignard reagent, **X**. (skeletal structure of butyl–MgBr, **X**) [1 mark]

b) Give the reagent and conditions needed to make the following compounds using Grignard reagent **X**:

i) Hexan-2-ol [1 mark]

ii) Pentanoic acid [1 mark]

You may not like Organic Chemistry, but you'll have to Grignard bear it...

Grignard reagents are quite unstable, so you can't just get them out of a bottle. Instead, you need to know how they're made. Don't forget that the reactions are in dry ether except in the last step — otherwise the reaction won't work.

Organic Synthesis

There are lots of organic compounds and reactions coming up. Don't panic. It's a summary of things you've met before.

***Functional Groups** are the **Most Important Parts** of a Molecule*

Functional groups are the parts of a molecule that are responsible for the way the molecule reacts.
Substances are grouped into families called **homologous series** based on what functional groups they contain.
Here's a round-up of all the ones you've studied:

Homologous series	Functional group	Properties	Typical reactions
Alkane	C–C	Non-polar, unreactive.	Radical substitution
Alkene	C=C	Non-polar, electron-rich double bond.	Electrophilic addition
Aromatic compounds	C_6H_5-	Stable delocalised ring of electrons.	Electrophilic substitution
Alcohol	C-OH	Polar C-OH bond.	Nucleophilic substitution Dehydration/elimination
		Lone pair on oxygen can act as a nucleophile.	Esterification Nucleophilic substitution
Halogenoalkane	C–X	Polar C–X bond.	Nucleophilic substitution Elimination
Amine	$C–NH_2$ / $C–NR_2$	Lone pair on nitrogen is basic and can act as a nucleophile.	Neutralisation Nucleophilic substitution
Amide	$-CONH_2$ / -CONHR	–	–
Nitrile	C−C≡N	Electron deficient carbon centre.	Reduction Hydrolysis
Aldehyde/Ketone	C=O	Polar C=O bond.	Nucleophilic addition Reduction Aldehydes will oxidise.
Carboxylic acid	-COOH	Electron deficient carbon centre.	Neutralisation Esterification Reduction
Ester	RCOOR′	Electron deficient carbon centre.	Hydrolysis
Acyl chloride	-COCl	Electron deficient carbon centre.	Nucleophilic addition-elimination Condensation (lose HCl) Friedel-Crafts acylation

The functional groups in a molecule give you clues about its **properties** and **reactions**.
For example, a **–COOH group** will (usually) make the molecule **acidic** and mean it will **form esters** with alcohols.

*Chemists Use **Synthetic Routes** to Get from One Compound to Another*

1) Chemists need to be able to make one compound from another. It's vital for things such as **designing medicines**.
2) It's not always possible to synthesise a desired product from a starting material in **just one** reaction.
3) A **synthetic route** shows how you get from one compound to another. It shows all the **reactions** with the **intermediate products**, and the **reagents** needed for each reaction.

Example: Starting with ethene, you can synthesise ethanamide in four steps. The synthetic route is:

$$H_2C{=}CH_2 \xrightarrow[\text{high temperature and pressure}]{\text{steam, } H_3PO_4 \text{ (cat.)}} CH_3CH_2OH \xrightarrow[\text{reflux}]{K_2Cr_2O_7/\,H_2SO_4} CH_3COOH \xrightarrow{PCl_5,\ 20\ °C} CH_3COCl \xrightarrow[20\ °C]{\text{conc. } NH_3} CH_3CONH_2$$

If you're asked how to make one compound from another in the exam, make sure you include:

1) Any **special procedures**, such as refluxing.
2) The **conditions** needed, e.g. high temperature or pressure, or the presence of a catalyst.
3) Any **safety** precautions, e.g. do it in a fume cupboard.

Jon and Patricia loved their new synthetic roots.

Organic Synthesis

Chemists Have to Carefully **Plan** a **Synthetic Route**

When chemists plan the synthesis of a molecule there are some things they need to keep in mind:

1) **Stereoisomers**: Making the correct stereoisomer is important in the pharmaceutical industry because different **stereoisomers** might have **different properties**. Understanding the **mechanism** of a reaction lets chemists plan which stereoisomer will be produced (for example, see page 195). E.g. **S_N2 nucleophilic substitution** can produce a **single isomer** product if a single isomer is used as the starting molecule.
2) **Safety**: To reduce the risks posed by any of the organic chemicals or reagents used in an organic synthesis method, **safety measures** must be considered. For example, reactions can be performed in **fume hoods** to remove toxic gases and **electric mantles**, **water baths** or **sand baths** can be used to heat solutions so there are no naked flames near flammable reagents.

Synthesis Routes for Making **Aliphatic Compounds**

Here's a round-up of the reactions to convert between functional groups that you've covered in the A-Level course:

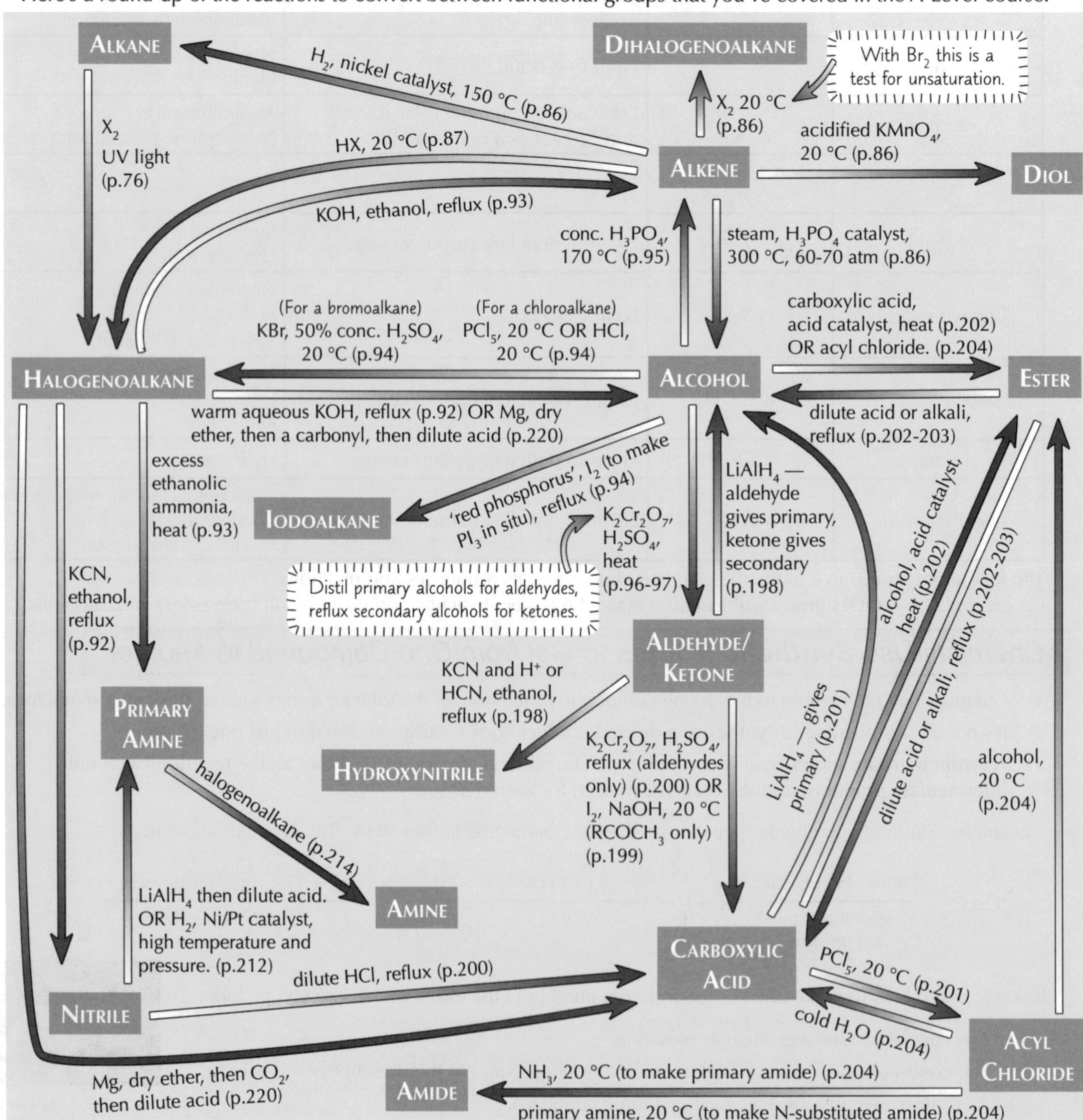

Organic Synthesis

Synthesis Routes for Making **Aromatic Compounds**

There aren't so many of these reactions to learn — so make sure you know all the itty-bitty details.
If you can't remember any of the reactions, look back to the relevant pages and take a quick peek over them.

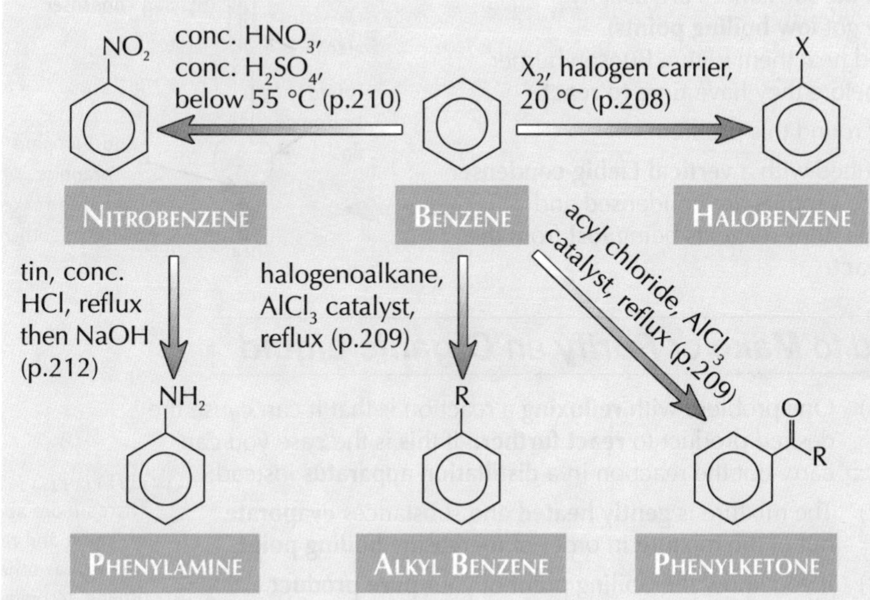

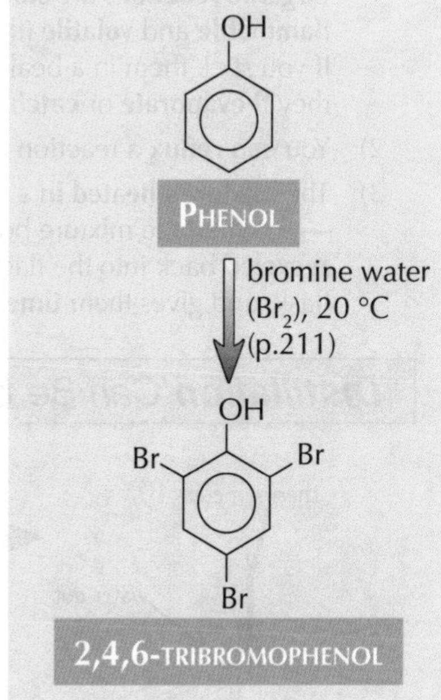

Practice Questions

Q1 What type of reactions do alkenes typically take part in?

Q2 What is shown in a synthetic route?

Q3 How do you make an alkene from an aldehyde?

Q4 How do you make phenylamine from benzene?

Exam Questions

Q1 Ethyl methanoate is one of the compounds responsible for the smell of raspberries.
Outline, with reaction conditions, how it could be synthesised in the laboratory from methanol. [2 marks]

Q2 How would you synthesise propanol starting with propane?
State the reaction conditions and reagents needed for each step. [2 marks]

Q3 The diagram below shows a possible reaction pathway for the two-step synthesis of a ketone from a halogenoalkane.

$H_3C{-}CHX{-}CH_3$ (**P**) $\xrightarrow[\text{NaOH}]{\text{Step 1}}$ $H_3C{-}CH(OH){-}CH_3$ (**Q**) $\xrightarrow{\text{Step 2}}$ $H_3C{-}C(=O){-}CH_3$ (**R**)

a) Give the conditions needed to carry out Step 1. [1 mark]

b) Give the reagents and the conditions needed to carry out Step 2. [2 marks]

Q4 A chemist synthesises compound **A** in three steps, starting from benzene.
Given that, in the second step, a Grignard reagent is formed, suggest a synthesis route the chemist could have taken. Give the reagents and conditions, as well as the organic compounds formed, at each step of the synthesis. [6 marks]

OH

A

Big red buses are great at Organic Synthesis — they're Route Masters...

There's loads of information here. Tons and tons of it. But you've covered pretty much all of it before, so it shouldn't be too hard to make sure it's firmly embedded in your head. If it's not, you know what to do — go back over it again. Then cover the diagrams up and try to draw them out from memory. Keep going until you can do it perfectly.

Practical Techniques

You can't call yourself a chemist unless you know these practical techniques. Not unless your name's Boots.

Reactions** Often Need to be **Heated** to **Work

1) **Organic reactions** are **slow** and the substances are usually **flammable** and **volatile** (they've got **low boiling points**). If you stick them in a beaker and heat them with a Bunsen burner they'll **evaporate** or **catch fire** before they have **time to react.**
2) You can **reflux** a reaction to get round this problem.
3) The mixture's **heated in a flask** fitted with a **vertical Liebig condenser** — so when the mixture boils, the vapours are condensed and **recycled** back into the flask. This stops reagents being **lost** from the flask, and gives them **time to react**.

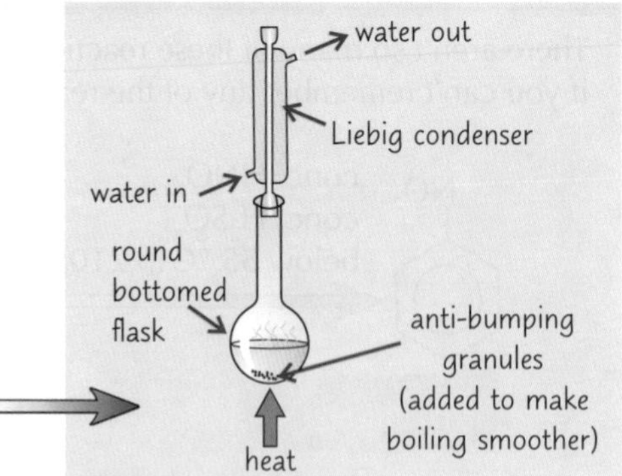

Distillation** Can Be Used to **Make** or **Purify** an **Organic Liquid

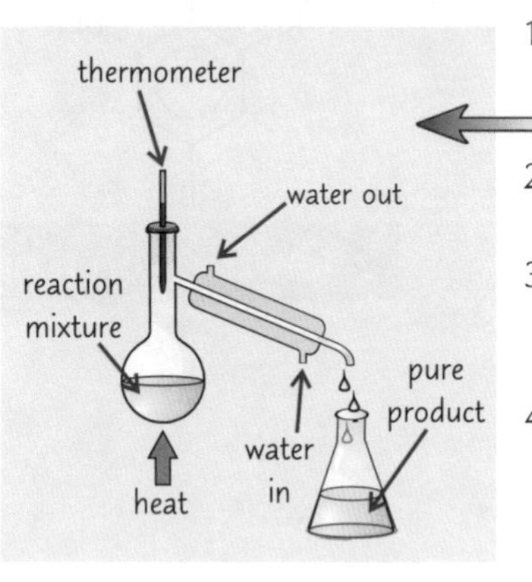

1) One problem with **refluxing** a reaction is that it can cause the desired product to **react further**. If this is the case you can carry out the reaction in a **distillation apparatus** instead.
2) The mixture is **gently heated** and substances **evaporate** out of the mixture in order of **increasing boiling point**.
3) If you know the boiling point of your **pure product**, you can use the thermometer to tell you when it's evaporating, and therefore when it's condensing.
4) If the **product** of a reaction has a **lower boiling point** than the **starting materials** then the reaction mixture can be **heated** so that the product **evaporates** from the reaction mixture as it forms. The **starting materials** will stay in the reaction mixture as long as the temperature is **controlled**.

There's more about distillation and reflux, as well as other organic techniques, back in Topic 6.

- If a product and its impurities have **different boiling points**, then distillation can be used to **separate** them. You use the distillation apparatus shown above, but this time you're heating an **impure product**, instead of the reaction mixture.
- When the liquid you want **boils** (this is when the thermometer is at the boiling point of the liquid), you place a flask at the open end of the condenser ready to collect your product.
- When the thermometer shows the temperature is changing, put another flask at the end of the condenser because a **different liquid** is about to be delivered.

David had no need for distillation — he was pure class.

***Steam Distillation Lowers** the Boiling Point of an Organic Liquid*

1) Some organic liquids have **high** boiling points or **decompose** when they're **heated**. This means you **can't** purify them using the distillation technique shown above. Instead, if the product you're collecting is immiscible with water, you can use **steam distillation**.
2) In steam distillation, the presence of steam **lowers** the **boiling point** of the immiscible product, allowing it to be distilled out of the impure mixture below its boiling point, and before it decomposes.
3) Using the apparatus shown on the right, you heat **water** in a flask until it evaporates, and then allow it to pass, as **steam**, into a flask containing the impure organic mixture.
4) The steam **lowers** the **boiling points** of the compounds in the mixture, so they will evaporate at a **lower temperature**.

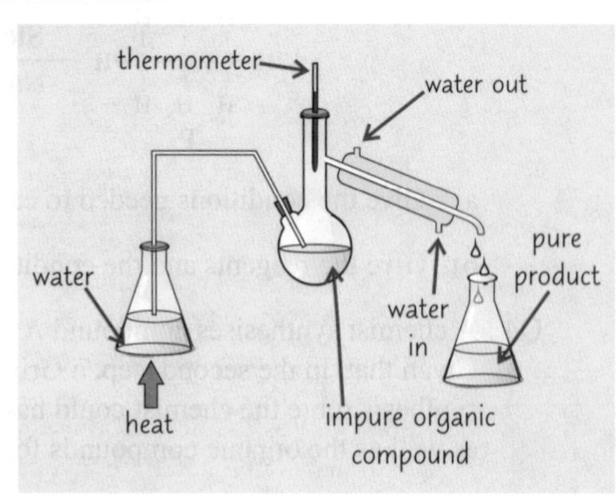

5) If the organic product you're trying to collect is less volatile than the components in the mixture you're separating it from, the organic product and the steam will evaporate out of the impure mixture **together**. You can then condense and collect them in a clean flask.
6) You can separate the organic product from water using a **separating funnel** (you may have to use the **solvent extraction** technique on the next page if the compound is slightly miscible with water).

Practical Techniques

Solvent Extraction Removes **Partially Soluble** Compounds from **Water**

You saw back on page 98 that if a product is **insoluble** in water then you can use **separation** to remove any impurities that **do dissolve** in water.

But, if your product and the impurities are **both** soluble in water, there's a similar separation method called **solvent extraction** that you can use.

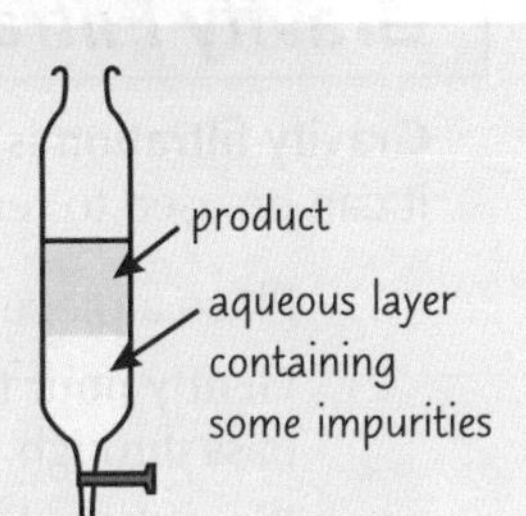

1) Add the impure compound to a separating funnel and add some water. Shake well.
2) Then add an **organic solvent** in which the product is **more soluble** than it is in water. Shake the separating funnel well. The product will **dissolve** into the organic solvent, leaving the impurities dissolved in the water.
3) You could also add a **salt** (such as NaCl) to the mixture. This will cause the organic product to move into the organic layer, as it will be less soluble in the very polar salt and water layer.
4) You can then open the tap and run each layer off into a separate container. (In the example on the right, the impurities will be run off first, and the product collected second.)

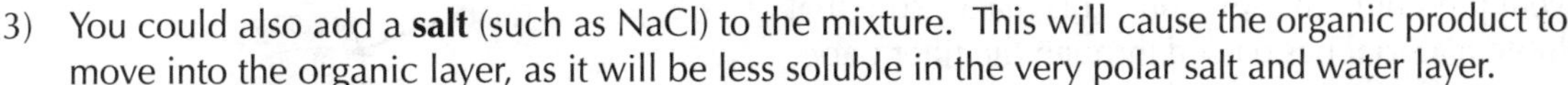

Remove Other **Impurities** by **Washing**

The product of a reaction can be **contaminated** with leftover reagents or unwanted side products. You can **remove** some of these by **washing** the product (which in this case means adding another liquid and shaking).

For example, if one of your reactants was an **organic acid**, it might be dissolved as an impurity in the **organic layer**, along with your product. To remove it, you could add aqueous **sodium hydrogencarbonate** which will react with the acid to give CO_2 gas and a **salt** of the acid. The salt will then dissolve in the **aqueous layer**. The organic **product** will be left in the organic layer, and can be separated from the aqueous layer containing the reactant impurities using a **separating funnel** (as above).

Remove Water from a Purified Product by **Drying** it

1) If you use separation to purify a product, the organic layer will end up containing **trace amounts** of **water** — so it has to be **dried**.
2) To do this, you add an **anhydrous salt** such as **magnesium sulfate** ($MgSO_4$) or **calcium chloride** ($CaCl_2$). The salt is used as a **drying agent** — it **binds** to any water present to become **hydrated**.
3) When you first add the salt to the organic layer it will **clump** together. You keep adding drying agent until it disperses **evenly** when you swirl the flask.
4) Finally, you **filter** the mixture to remove the solid drying agent — pop a piece of filter paper into a funnel that feeds into a flask and pour the mixture into the filter paper.

The filter paper can be fluted (concertina folded) to increase its surface area.

Practice Questions

Q1 Why is refluxing needed in many organic reactions?

Q2 Draw the set-up that you could use to carry out a simple distillation.

Q3 How could you remove an organic acid from the organic layer in a separating funnel?

Exam Question

Q1 A chemist synthesises phenylamine by refluxing nitrobenzene with tin and concentrated hydrochloric acid and then adding sodium hydroxide.

a) Phenylamine is immiscible with water and decomposes before it boils. Draw and label a diagram to show the distillation set-up the chemist should use to separate pure phenylamine from the impure mixture. [3 marks]

b) Describe a method that could be used to separate the condensed phenylamine from water after distillation, given that phenylamine is slightly soluble in water and also soluble in ether. [4 marks]

My organic compound isn't volatile — it's just highly strung...

Scientists need to know why they do the things they do — that way they can plan new experiments to make new compounds. Learning the details of how experiments are carried out and how products are purified may not be the most interesting thing in the world, but you should get to try out some of these methods in practicals, which is a lot more fun.

More Practical Techniques

Don't take your lab coat off or put down your safety specs just yet. There are more practical techniques coming up...

Gravity Filtration** is Used to Remove a **Solid** From a **Liquid

Gravity filtration is normally used when you want to keep the **liquid** (the filtrate) and discard the **solid**. For example, it can be used to remove the solid drying agent from the organic layer of a liquid that has been purified by separation.

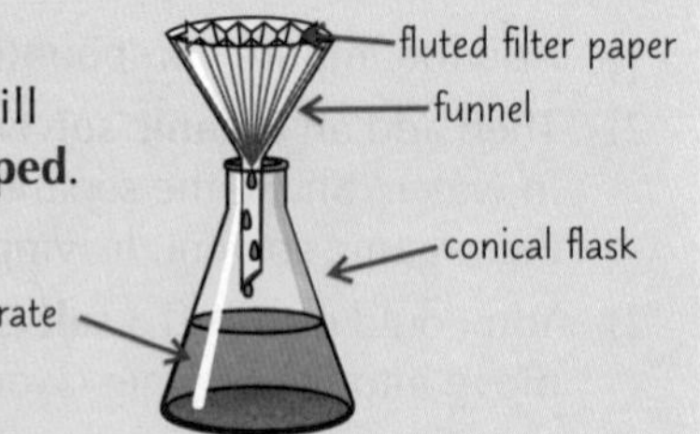

1) Place a piece of **fluted filter paper** in a funnel that feeds into a conical flask.
2) **Gently pour** the mixture to be separated into the filter paper. The solution will pass through the filter paper into the conical flask, and the **solid** will be **trapped**.
3) **Rinse** the solid left in the filter paper with a **pure sample** of the solvent present in the solution. This makes sure that all the **soluble material** has passed through the filter paper and has been collected in the conical flask.

Filtration Under Reduced Pressure** is Used to Remove a **Liquid** From a **Solid

Filtration under reduced pressure is normally used when you want to keep the **solid** and discard the **liquid** (filtrate).

1) Place a piece of **filter paper**, slightly smaller than the diameter of the funnel, on the bottom of the Büchner funnel so that it lies flat and covers all the holes.
2) **Wet** the paper with a little solvent, so that it **sticks** to the bottom of the funnel, and doesn't slip around when you pour in your mixture.
3) Turn the **vacuum** on, and then pour your mixture into the funnel. As the flask is under **reduced pressure**, the **liquid** is sucked through the funnel into the flask, leaving the **solid** behind.
4) **Rinse** the solid with a little of the solvent that your mixture was in. This will **wash off** any of the original liquid from the mixture that stayed on your crystals (and also any soluble impurities), leaving you with a **more pure** solid.

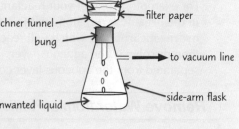

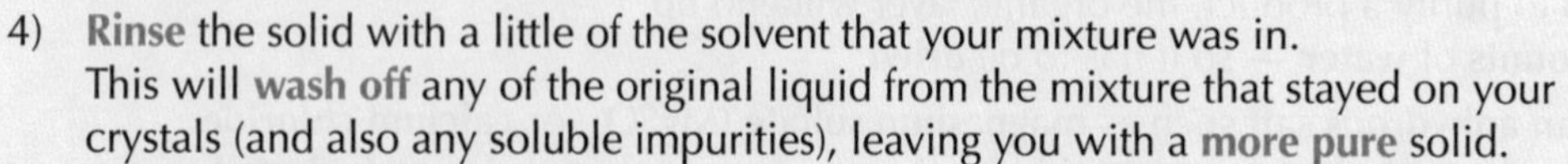

5) Disconnect the vacuum line from the side-arm flask and then turn off the vacuum.
6) The solid will be a bit wet from the solvent, so leave it to **dry completely**.

Organic Solids** can be **Purified** by **Recrystallisation

If the product of an organic reaction is a solid, then the simplest way of purifying it is a process called **recrystallisation**. First you dissolve your solid in a **hot** solvent to make a **saturated** solution. Then you let the solution cool. As the solution cools, the solubility of the product falls. When it reaches the point where it can't stay in solution, it starts to form crystals. Here's how it's done:

In a saturated solution, the maximum possible amount of solid is dissolved in the solvent.

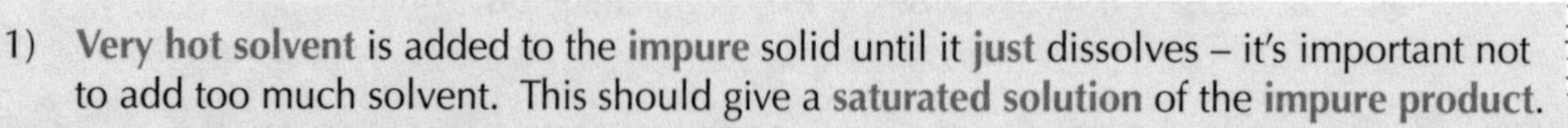

1) **Very hot solvent** is added to the **impure** solid until it **just** dissolves – it's important not to add too much solvent. This should give a **saturated solution** of the **impure product**.
2) Filter the solution while it's still hot by **gravity filtration** to remove any insoluble impurities.
3) This solution is left to **cool** down **slowly**. **Crystals** of the **product** form as it cools. The **impurities** stay in solution as they're present in much smaller amounts than the product, so take much longer to crystallise out.
4) The crystals are removed by **filtration** under **reduced pressure** (see above) and **washed** with ice-cold solvent. Then they are dried, leaving you with crystals of your product that are **much purer** than the original solid.

*The **Choice of Solvent** for Recrystallisation is **Very Important***

1) When you **recrystallise** a product, you must use an **appropriate solvent** for that particular substance. It will only work if the solid is **very soluble** in the **hot** solvent, but **nearly insoluble** when the solvent is **cold**.
2) If your product **isn't soluble enough** in the hot solvent you **won't** be able to dissolve it at all.
3) If your product **is too soluble** in the cold solvent, most of it will **stay in the solution** even after cooling. When you filter it, you'll **lose** most of your product, giving you a very low **yield**.

More Practical Techniques

Measuring **Boiling Point** is a Good Way to **Determine** the **Purity** of a Liquid

1) You can measure the purity of an organic, liquid product by looking at its boiling point.
2) If you've got a reasonable volume of liquid, you can determine its boiling point using a **distillation apparatus**, like the one shown on page 224.
3) If you **gently heat** the liquid in the distillation apparatus, until it evaporates, you can read the temperature at which it is distilled, using the thermometer in the top of the apparatus. This temperature is the **boiling point**.
4) You can then look up the boiling point of the substance in **data books** and compare it to your measurement.
5) If the sample contains **impurities**, then your measured boiling point will be **higher** than the recorded value. You may also find your product boils over a range of temperatures, rather than all evaporating at a single temperature.

Different organic liquids can have similar boiling points, so you should use other analytical techniques (see Topics 7 and 19) to help you determine your product's purity too.

Melting Points are Good Indicators of the **Purity** of an Organic Solid

Pure substances have a **specific melting point**. If they're **impure**, the **melting point's lowered**. If they're **very impure**, melting will occur across a wide range of temperatures.

1) You can use **melting point apparatus** to accurately determine the melting point of an **organic solid**.
2) Pack a small sample of the solid into a **glass capillary tube** and place it inside the **heating element**.
3) **Increase the temperature** until the sample turns from solid to **liquid**.
4) You usually measure a **melting range**, which is the range of temperatures from where the solid **begins to melt** to where it has **melted completely**.

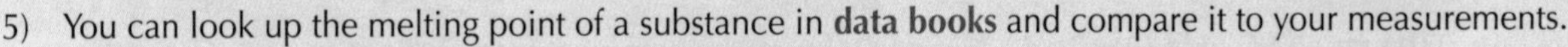

5) You can look up the melting point of a substance in **data books** and compare it to your measurements.
6) **Impurities** in the sample will **lower** the **melting point** and **broaden** the **melting range**.

Practice Questions

Q1 How could you separate a solid product from liquid impurities? And a liquid product from solid impurities?

Q2 Give two factors you should consider when choosing a solvent for recrystallisation.

Exam Questions

Q1 Two samples of impure stearic acid melt at 69 °C and 64 °C respectively.
Stearic acid dissolves in hot propanone but not in water.

a) Explain which sample is purer. [1 mark]

b) Suggest a method that could be used to purify the impure sample. [1 mark]

c) How could the sample from b) be tested for purity? [1 mark]

Q2 A scientist has produced some impure solid sodium ethanoate, which she wants to purify using recrystallisation. She begins by dissolving the impure sodium ethanoate in the minimum possible amount of hot solvent.

a) Explain why the scientist used the minimum possible amount of hot solvent. [1 mark]

b) Outline the rest of the procedure that the scientist would need to follow to recrystallise the solid. [5 marks]

c) Describe the melting point range of the impure sodium ethanoate compared to the pure product. [1 mark]

Q3 A student is carrying out an experiment using the apparatus shown on the right.
What type of experiment is she doing?

A reflux **B** filtration under reduced pressure

C distillation **D** recrystallisation [1 mark]

I hope that everything's now crystal clear...

Nobody wants loads of impurities in their reaction products. But now you're kitted out to get rid of them using these purification techniques. It doesn't even matter whether you have to purify a solid or a liquid — no excuses now.

Empirical and Molecular Formulae

It's the end of the Topic — hurray!!! But it's full of maths — boooo. But you've seen it before in Year 1— hurray!!! I can't keep doing this — boooo. Oh go on then, one more — hurray!!! And don't forget to brush your teeth — ????

Empirical and **Molecular** Formulae Can Help Identify **Organic Compounds**

You first met calculations to find empirical and molecular formulae in Topic 5. You can use empirical and molecular formulae, along with other data from, e.g. IR spectroscopy, to help you work out the structure of an unknown chemical.

In case you're feeling a bit hazy about what these formulae are, here's a quick reminder...

1) The **empirical formula** gives just the smallest whole number ratio of atoms in a compound.
   E.g. The empirical formula of ethane is CH_3.
2) The **molecular formula** gives the **actual** numbers of atoms in a molecule.
   It's made up of a **whole number** of empirical units. E.g. The molecular formula of ethane is C_2H_6.

Find **Empirical** and **Molecular** Formulae From **Percentage Compositions**

You saw calculations like this all the way back on page 56. So, here's a reminder...

Example: A compound has a molecular mass of 88. It is found to have percentage composition 54.5% carbon, 9.1% hydrogen and 36.4% oxygen by mass. Calculate its empirical and molecular formulae.

If you assume you've got 100 g of the compound, you can turn the % straight into mass, and then work out the number of moles as normal.

In **100 g** of compound there are:

Use $n = \frac{\text{mass}}{M}$

$\frac{54.5}{12.0} = 4.54$ moles of C $\quad \frac{9.1}{1.0} = 9.1$ moles of H $\quad \frac{36.4}{16.0} = 2.275$ moles of O

Divide each number of moles by the **smallest number** — in this case it's 2.275.

O: $\frac{4.54}{2.275} = 2.00$ $\quad$ H: $\frac{9.1}{2.275} = 4.00$ $\quad$ O: $\frac{2.275}{2.275} = 1.00$

The ratio of C : H : O = 2 : 4 : 1. So you know the empirical formula's got to be C_2H_4O.

The molecular mass of one empirical formula is (2 × 12.0) + (4 × 1.0) + (1 × 16.0) = 44.

This is half the molecular mass of the compound, so the compound must contain two of the empirical formula and have the molecular formula $C_4H_8O_2$.

Combustion Analysis Uses Information From **Burning** an Organic Compound

When an organic compound containing carbon, hydrogen and oxygen combusts completely in oxygen, **water** and **carbon dioxide** are produced. All the **carbon atoms** in the carbon dioxide and all the **hydrogen atoms** in the water will have come from the organic compound. If you burn a **known amount** of the organic compound, you can use the amounts of water and carbon dioxide produced to help you work out its **empirical formula**.

Example: When 7.2 g of a carbonyl compound is burnt in excess oxygen, it produces 17.6 g of carbon dioxide and 7.2 g of water. Calculate the empirical formula for the carbonyl compound.

No. of moles of $CO_2 = \frac{\text{mass}}{M} = \frac{17.6}{44.0} = 0.40$ moles
1 mole of CO_2 contains 1 mole of C. So, 0.40 moles of CO_2 contains **0.40 moles of C.**

No. of moles $H_2O = \frac{\text{mass}}{M} = \frac{7.2}{18.0} = 0.40$ moles
1 mole of H_2O contains 2 moles of H. So, 0.40 moles of H_2O contain **0.80 moles of H.**

Mass of C = no. of moles × M = 0.40 × 12.0 = 4.8 g
Mass of H = no. of moles × M = 0.80 × 1.0 = 0.80 g
Mass of O = 7.2 – (4.8 + 0.80) = 1.6 g
Number of moles of O = $\frac{\text{mass}}{M} = \frac{1.6}{16.0} = 0.10$ moles

Now work out the mass of carbon and hydrogen in the alcohol. The rest of the mass of the carbonyl must be oxygen — so work out that too. Once you know the mass of O, you can work out how many moles there are of it.

Molar Ratio = C : H : O = 0.40 : 0.80 : 0.10 = 4 : 8 : 1
Empirical formula = C_4H_8O

When you know the number of moles of each element, you've got the molar ratio. Divide each number by the smallest.

Empirical and Molecular Formulae

Combustion Analysis Data Might Be Given As **Volumes**

1) Combustion reactions can happen between **gases**.
2) All gases at the same temperature and pressure have the same **molar volume**. This means you can use the **ratio** of the **volumes** of gases reacting together to calculate the **molar ratios**, and then work out the **molecular formula** of the **organic compound** that is combusting.

Example: 30 cm³ of hydrocarbon X combusts completely with 180 cm³ oxygen. 120 cm³ carbon dioxide is produced. What is the molecular formula of hydrocarbon X?

- Using the volumes provided, the reaction equation can be written:
  $$30X + 180O_2 \rightarrow 120CO_2 + ?H_2O$$
- This can be simplified by dividing everything by 30:
  $$X + 6O_2 \rightarrow 4CO_2 + nH_2O$$
- 6 moles of oxygen reacts to form 4 moles of carbon dioxide and n moles of water. So any oxygen atoms (from O_2) that don't end up in CO_2, must be in H_2O. This means that **n = (6 × 2) – (4 × 2) = 4**.
- So, the combustion equation is: $X + 6O_2 \rightarrow 4CO_2 + 4H_2O$. You can use this to identify X.
- All the carbon atoms from X end up in carbon dioxide molecules, and all the hydrogen atoms from X end up in water, so the number of **carbon** atoms in X is **4** and the number of **hydrogen** atoms in X is **8**.
- The molecular formula of X is C_4H_8.

This method is really handy because it gives you the molecular formula straight away, rather than the empirical formula (which in this example is CH_2).

Practice Questions

Q1 What's the difference between empirical and molecular formulae?

Q2 What's the empirical formula of ethane?

Q3 Where do the carbon atoms in carbon dioxide produced by burning an organic compound completely in oxygen come from?

Exam Questions

Q1 A carbonyl compound contains only carbon, hydrogen and oxygen. When it is burnt in excess oxygen 0.100 g of the compound gives 0.228 g of carbon dioxide and 0.0930 g of water.

a) Calculate the empirical formula of this compound. [4 marks]

b) What percentage of the compound by mass is hydrogen? [2 marks]

c) If the molecular mass is 58.0, what is the molecular formula? [1 mark]

d) When a sample of the compound is heated with Tollens' reagent, a silver mirror is formed. Predict, with reasoning, the structure of the molecule. [1 mark]

Q2 A common explosive contains 37.0% carbon, 2.2% hydrogen, 18.5% nitrogen and 42.3% oxygen, by mass. It has a molecular mass of 227 and can be made from benzene.

a) Calculate the empirical formula of the compound and hence its molecular formula. [4 marks]

b) Suggest a possible structure of the molecule. [1 mark]

Q3 A student was trying to identify an unknown hydrocarbon, X. When she combusted 25 cm³ of X, completely with 125 cm³ of oxygen, 75 cm³ of carbon dioxide was produced.

a) Calculate the molecular formula of X. [2 marks]

b) The mass spectrum of X has an M peak at $m/z = 88$. What is the molecular formula of X? [2 marks]

These pages contain the formulae for A-Level Chemistry success...

These calculations aren't the only things you can use to work out the identity of an unknown molecule. Oh no. Coming up next there's loads more on analytical techniques. NMR and infrared spectroscopy, along with mass spectrometry, can really help to work out exactly what a certain substance is. Structure and all. Bet you can't wait.

High Resolution Mass Spectrometry

You met mass spectrometry back in Year 1 of the course, but who said the fun had to stop there? Time for more...

Mass Spectrometry Can Help to Identify Compounds

1) In a mass spectrometer, a **molecular ion** is formed when a molecule loses an **electron**.
2) The molecular ion produces a **molecular ion peak** on the mass spectrum of the compound.
3) For any compound, the **mass/charge** (*m/z*) value of the molecular ion peak will be the same as the **molecular mass** of the compound (assuming the ion has a +1 charge, which it normally will have).

Look back at your pages 7 and 100 for a reminder on how to work out atomic masses and molecular masses from mass spectra.

High Resolution Mass Spectrometry Measures **Masses Precisely**

1) Some mass spectrometers can measure atomic and molecular masses **extremely accurately** (to several decimal places). These are known as **high resolution mass spectrometers.**
2) This can be useful for identifying compounds that appear to have the **same M_r** when they're **rounded** to the nearest whole number.
3) For example, **propane** (C_3H_8) and **ethanal** (CH_3CHO) both have an M_r of **44** to the nearest whole number. But on a **high resolution mass spectrum**, propane has a molecular ion peak with m/z = **44.0624** and ethanal has a molecular ion peak with m/z = **44.0302**.

Example: On a high resolution mass spectrum, a compound had a molecular ion peak of 98.0448. What was its molecular formula?

A $C_5H_{10}N_2$ B $C_6H_{10}O$ C C_7H_{14} D $C_5H_6O_2$

Use these precise atomic masses to work out your answer:

^{1}H — 1.0078 ^{12}C — 12.0000 ^{14}N — 14.0064 ^{16}O — 15.9990

1) Work out the precise molecular mass of each compound:

$C_5H_{10}N_2$: $M_r = (5 \times 12.0000) + (10 \times 1.0078) + (2 \times 14.0064) = 98.0908$

$C_6H_{10}O$: $M_r = (6 \times 12.0000) + (10 \times 1.0078) + 15.9990 = 98.0770$

C_7H_{14}: $M_r = (7 \times 12.0000) + (14 \times 1.0078) = 98.1092$

$C_5H_6O_2$: $M_r = (5 \times 12.0000) + (6 \times 1.0078) + (2 \times 15.9990) = 98.0448$

2) So the answer is D, $C_5H_6O_2$.

On a normal (low resolution) mass spectrum, all of these molecules would show up as having an M_r of 98.

Practice Questions

Q1 Explain how you could find the molecular mass of a compound by looking at its mass spectrum.

Q2 Why is high resolution mass spectrometry useful for when studying molecules with similar molecular masses?

Exam Questions

Use the following precise atomic masses to answer the questions below:

^{1}H — 1.0078 ^{12}C — 12.0000 ^{14}N — 14.0064 ^{16}O — 15.9990

Q1 a) The high resolution mass spectrum of a compound has a molecular ion peak with m/z = 74.0908. Which of the following could be the molecular formula of the compound?

A $C_3H_6O_2$ B $C_4H_{10}O$ C $C_3H_{10}N_2$ D $C_2H_6N_2O$ [1 mark]

b) Explain why low resolution mass spectrometry would not allow you to distinguish between the options given in part a). [1 mark]

Q2 A sample of an unknown hydrocarbon is injected into a high resolution mass spectrometer. It produces a molecular ion peak at m/z = 56.0624. Draw a possible structure for and name the unknown hydrocarbon. [2 marks]

I am highly resolved to improve my understanding of Chemistry...

And you should be too if you want to ace your exams. This page is pretty easy. The only new bit is that stuff on high resolution mass spectrometry. But fear not — it's just like normal mass spectrometry, but with more decimal places.

NMR Spectroscopy

NMR isn't the easiest of things, so ingest this information one piece at a time — a bit like eating a bar of chocolate.

NMR *Gives You* ***Information*** *about the* ***Structure of Molecules***

Nuclear magnetic resonance (**NMR**) **spectroscopy** is an analytical technique that you can use to work out the **structure** of an organic molecule. The way that NMR works is pretty **complicated**, but here are the **basics**:

1) A sample of a compound is placed in a **strong magnetic field** and exposed to a range of different **frequencies** of **radio waves**.
2) The **nuclei** of certain atoms within the molecule **absorb energy** from the radio waves.
3) The amount of energy that a nucleus absorbs at each frequency will depend on the **environment** that it's in — there's more about this further down the page.
4) The **pattern** of these absorptions gives you information about the **positions** of certain atoms within the molecule, and about **how many** atoms of that type the molecule contains.
5) You can piece these bits of information together to work out the **structure of the molecule**.

Radiowaves.

The two types of NMR spectroscopy you need to know about are **carbon-13 NMR** and **high resolution proton NMR**.

Carbon-13 (or ^{13}C) **NMR** gives you information about the **number of carbon atoms** that are in a molecule, and the **environments** that they are in.

High resolution proton NMR gives you information about the **number of hydrogen atoms** that are in a molecule, and the **environments** that they're in.

Nuclei in ***Different Environments*** *Absorb* ***Different Amounts of Energy***

1) A nucleus is partly **shielded** from the effects of external magnetic fields by its **surrounding electrons**.
2) Any **other atoms** and **groups of atoms** that are around a nucleus will also affect its amount of electron shielding. E.g. if a carbon atom bonds to a more electronegative atom (like oxygen) the amount of electron shielding around its nucleus will decrease.
3) This means that the nuclei in a molecule feel different magnetic fields depending on their **environments**. Nuclei in different environments will absorb **different amounts** of energy at **different frequencies**.
4) It's these **differences in absorption** of energy between environments that you're looking for in **NMR spectroscopy**.
5) An atom's **environment** depends on **all** the groups that it's connected to, going **right along the molecule** — not just the atoms it's actually bonded to. To be in the **same environment**, two atoms must be joined to **exactly the same things**.

```
  H H
  | |
H-C-C-Cl
  | |
  H H
```

Chloroethane has **2** carbon environments — its carbons are bonded to different atoms.

```
  H Cl H
  |  | |
H-C--C-C-H
  |  | |
  H  H H
```

2-chloropropane has **2** carbon environments:
- **1** C in a CHCl group, bonded to $(CH_3)_2$
- **2** Cs in CH_3 groups, bonded to $CHCl(CH_3)$

```
  H H H H
  | | | |
H-C-C-C-C-Cl
  | | | |
  H H H H
```

1-chlorobutane has **4** carbon environments. (The two carbons in CH_2 groups are **different distances** from the **electronegative** Cl atom — so their **environments** are **different**.)

Tetramethylsilane *is Used as a* ***Standard***

The diagram below shows a typical **carbon-13 NMR spectrum**. The **peaks** show the **frequencies** at which **energy was absorbed** by the carbon nuclei. **Each peak** represents one **carbon environment** — so this molecule has two.

1) The **differences in absorption** are measured relative to a **standard substance** — **tetramethylsilane** (**TMS**).
2) TMS produces a **single absorption peak** in both types of NMR because all its carbon and hydrogen nuclei are in the **same environment**.
3) It's chosen as a standard because the **absorption peak** is at a **lower frequency** than just about everything else.
4) This peak is given a value of **0** and all the peaks in other substances are measured as **chemical shifts** relative to this.

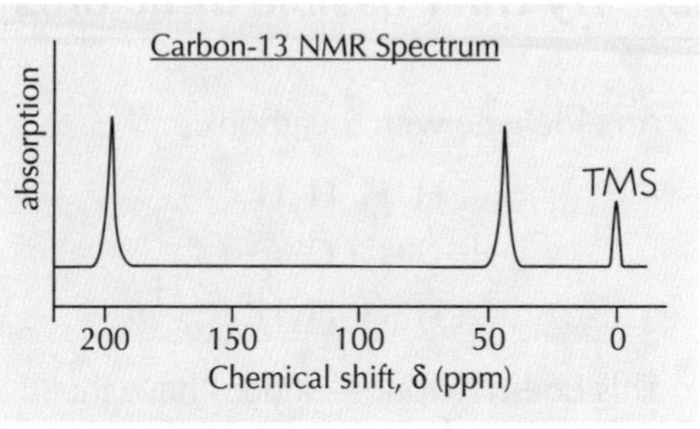

Chemical shift is the **difference in the radio frequency** absorbed by the nuclei (hydrogen or carbon) in the molecule being analysed and that absorbed by the same nuclei in **TMS**. It's given the symbol δ and is measured in **parts per million**, or **ppm**. A small amount of TMS is often added to samples to give a **reference peak** on the spectrum.

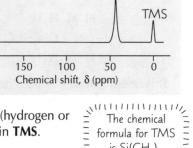

The chemical formula for TMS is $Si(CH_3)_4$.

NMR Spectroscopy

^{13}C NMR Spectra Tell You About Carbon Environments

It's very likely that you'll be given one or more **carbon-13 NMR spectra** to **interpret** in your exams. Here's a **step-by-step guide** to interpreting them:

1) Count the Number of Carbon Environments

First, count the **number of peaks** in the spectrum — this is the **number of carbon environments** in the molecule. If there's a peak at **δ = 0**, **don't count it** — it's the reference peak from **TMS**.

The spectrum on the right has **three peaks** — so the molecule must have **three different carbon environments**. This **doesn't** necessarily mean it only has **three carbons**, as it could have **more than one** in the **same environment**. In fact the molecular formula of this molecule is **$C_5H_{10}O$**, so it must have **several carbons** in the **same environment**.

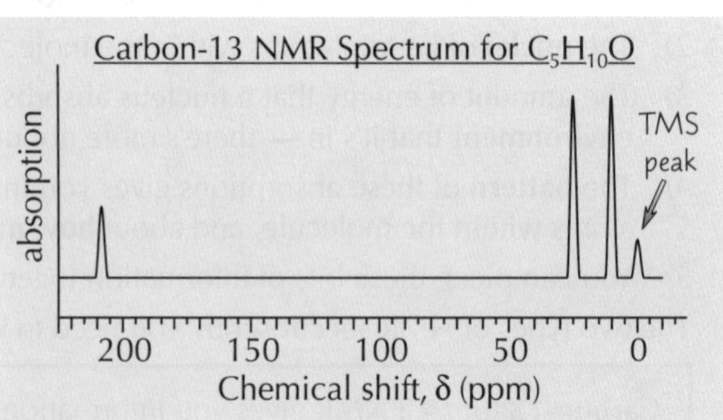

2) Look Up the Chemical Shifts in a Shift Diagram

In your exams you'll get a **data sheet** that will include a **diagram** a bit like the one below. The diagram shows the **chemical shifts** experienced by **carbon nuclei** in **different environments**. The boxes show the range of shift values a carbon in that environment could have, e.g. **C=C** could have a shift value anywhere between 115 – 140 ppm.

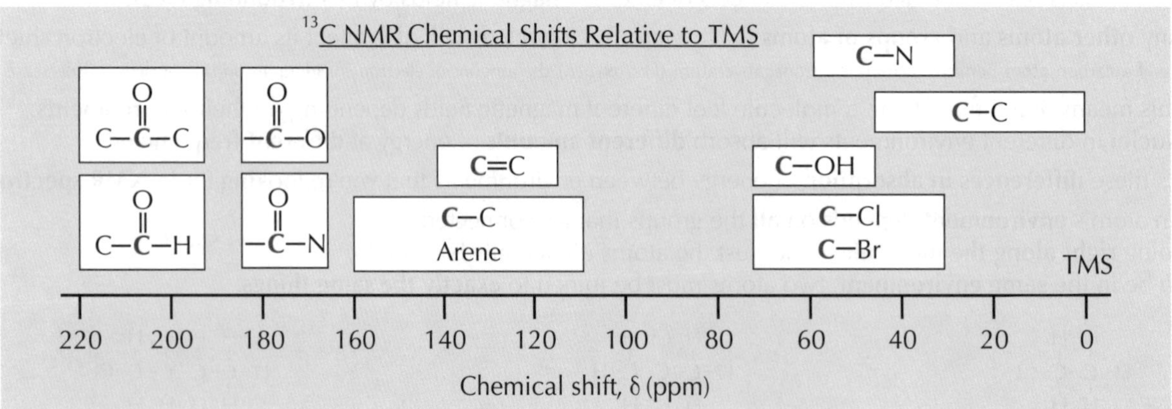

You need to **match up** the **peaks** in the spectrum with the **chemical shifts** in the diagram to work out which **carbon environments** they could represent. For example, the peak at **δ ≈ 10** in the spectrum above represents a **C–C** bond. The peak at **δ ≈ 25** is also due to a **C–C** bond. The carbons causing this peak have a different chemical shift to those causing the first peak — so they must be in a slightly different environment. The peak at **δ ≈ 210** is due to a **C=O** group, but you don't know whether it could be an aldehyde or a ketone.

Matching peaks to the groups that cause them isn't always straightforward, because the chemical shifts can overlap. For example, a peak at δ ≈ 40 might be caused by C–C, C–Cl, C–N or C–Br.

3) Try Out Possible Structures

An **aldehyde** with 5 carbons:

This doesn't work — it does have the right **molecular formula** ($C_5H_{10}O$), but it also has **five carbon environments**.

A **ketone** with five carbons:

This works. **Pentan-3-one** has **three** carbon environments — two CH_3 carbons, each bonded to $CH_2COCH_2CH_3$, two CH_2 carbons, each bonded to CH_3 and $COCH_2CH_3$, and one CO carbon bonded to $(CH_2CH_3)_2$. It has the right **molecular formula** ($C_5H_{10}O$) too.

It can't be pentan-2-one — that has 5 carbon environments.

So, the molecule analysed was **pentan-3-one**.

NMR Spectroscopy

Interpreting NMR Spectra Gets Easier with *Practice*

Example: The diagram shows the carbon-13 NMR spectrum of an alcohol with the molecular formula $C_4H_{10}O$. Analyse and interpret the spectrum to identify the structure of the alcohol.

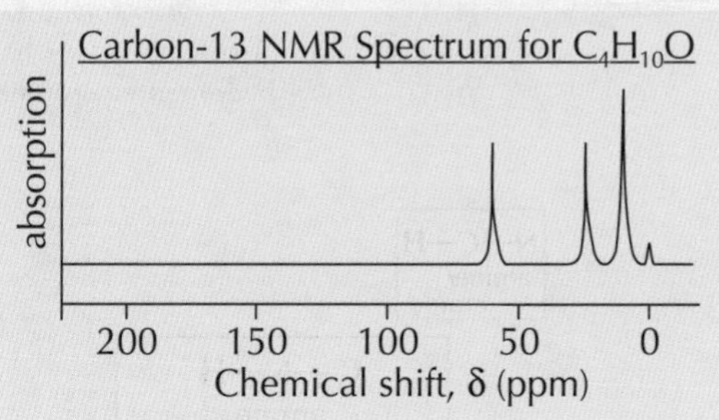

1) Looking at the **diagram** on the **previous page**, the peak with a **chemical shift** of **δ ≈ 65** is likely to be due to a **C–O** bond. Remember, the alcohol doesn't contain any **chlorine** or **bromine**, so you know the peak can't be caused by C–Cl or C–Br bonds.
2) The two peaks around **δ ≈ 20** probably both represent carbons in **C–C** bonds, but with slightly different environments.
3) The spectrum has **three peaks**, so the alcohol must have three **carbon environments**. There are **four carbons** in the alcohol, so two of the carbons must be in the **same environment**.
4) Put together all the **information** you've got so far, and try out some **structures**:

```
   H  H  H  H
   |  |  |  |
H–C–C–C–C–OH
   |  |  |  |
   H  H  H  H
```

This has a C–O bond, and some C–C bonds, which is right. But all four carbons are in different environments.

```
   H  H  H  H
   |  |  |  |
H–C–C–C–C–H
   |  |  |  |
   H  H  OH H
```

Again, this has a C–O bond, and some C–C bonds. But the carbons are still all in different environments.

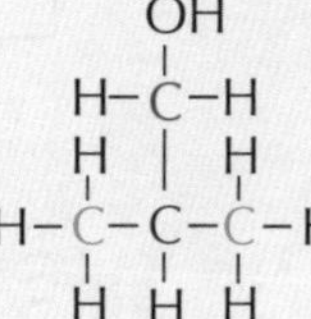

This molecule has a C–O bond and C–C bonds and two of the carbons are in the same environment. So this must be the correct structure.

You'll also need to be able to predict what the carbon-13 NMR spectrum of a molecule may look like. This isn't as hard as it sounds — just identify the number of **unique carbon environments**, then use the **shift diagram** in your data booklet to work out **where** the peaks of each carbon environment would appear.

Practice Questions

Q1 What part of the electromagnetic spectrum does NMR spectroscopy use?

Q2 What is meant by chemical shift? What compound is used as a reference for chemical shifts?

Q3 How can you tell from a carbon-13 NMR spectrum how many carbon environments a molecule contains?

Q4 Which type of bond could a shift of δ ≈ 150 correspond to?

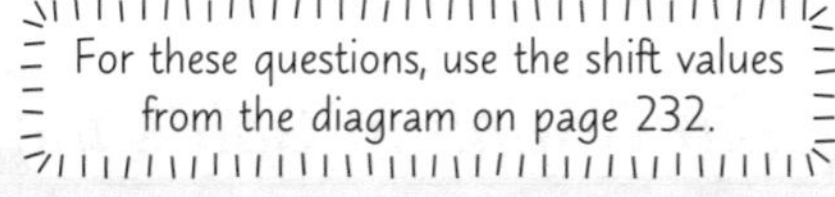

For these questions, use the shift values from the diagram on page 232.

Exam Questions

Q1 The carbon-13 NMR spectrum shown on the right was produced by a compound with the molecular formula C_3H_9N.

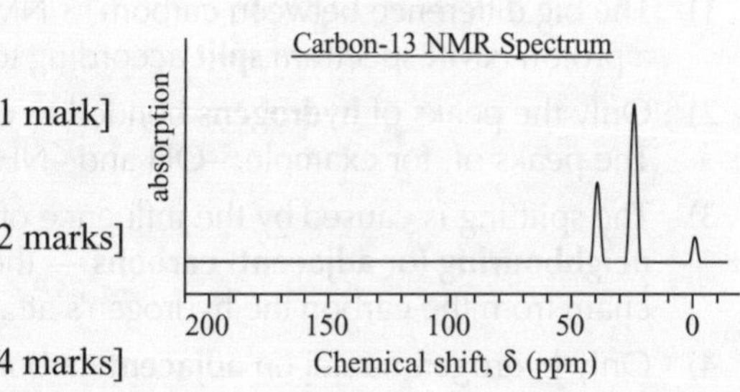

a) Explain why there is a peak at δ = 0. [1 mark]

b) The compound does not have the formula $CH_3CH_2CH_2NH_2$. Explain how the spectrum shows this. [2 marks]

c) Suggest and explain, using evidence from the carbon-13 NMR spectrum, a possible structure for the compound. [4 marks]

Q2 Look at molecule X on the right. Which of the following statements is/are true?

```
    H  O     H
H   |  ‖     |
 \C=C–C–O–C–H
H/           |
             H
```

1. The carbon-13 NMR spectrum of X has a peak in the region of 165 - 185.
2. Molecule X has three different carbon environments.
3. The carbon-13 NMR spectrum of X shows four peaks.

A 1, 2 and 3 **B** Only 1 and 2 **C** Only 1 and 3 **D** Only 3 [1 mark]

Why did the carbon peak? Because it saw the radio wave...

The ideas behind NMR are difficult, but don't worry too much if you don't really understand them. The important thing is to know how to interpret a spectrum — that's what will get you marks in the exam. If you're having trouble, go over the examples and practice questions a few more times. You should have the "ahh... I get it" moment sooner or later.

Proton NMR Spectroscopy

So, you know how to interpret carbon-13 NMR spectra — now it's time for some high resolution proton NMR spectra.

¹H NMR Spectra *Tell You About* Hydrogen Environments

Interpreting **proton** (or ¹H) **NMR spectra** is similar to interpreting carbon-13 NMR spectra:

1) Each peak represents one **hydrogen environment**.
2) Look up the **chemical shifts** on a **data diagram** to identify possible environments. They're different from ¹³C NMR, so make sure you're looking at the **correct data diagram**.

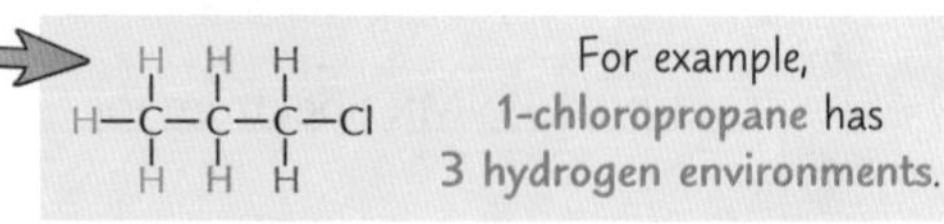

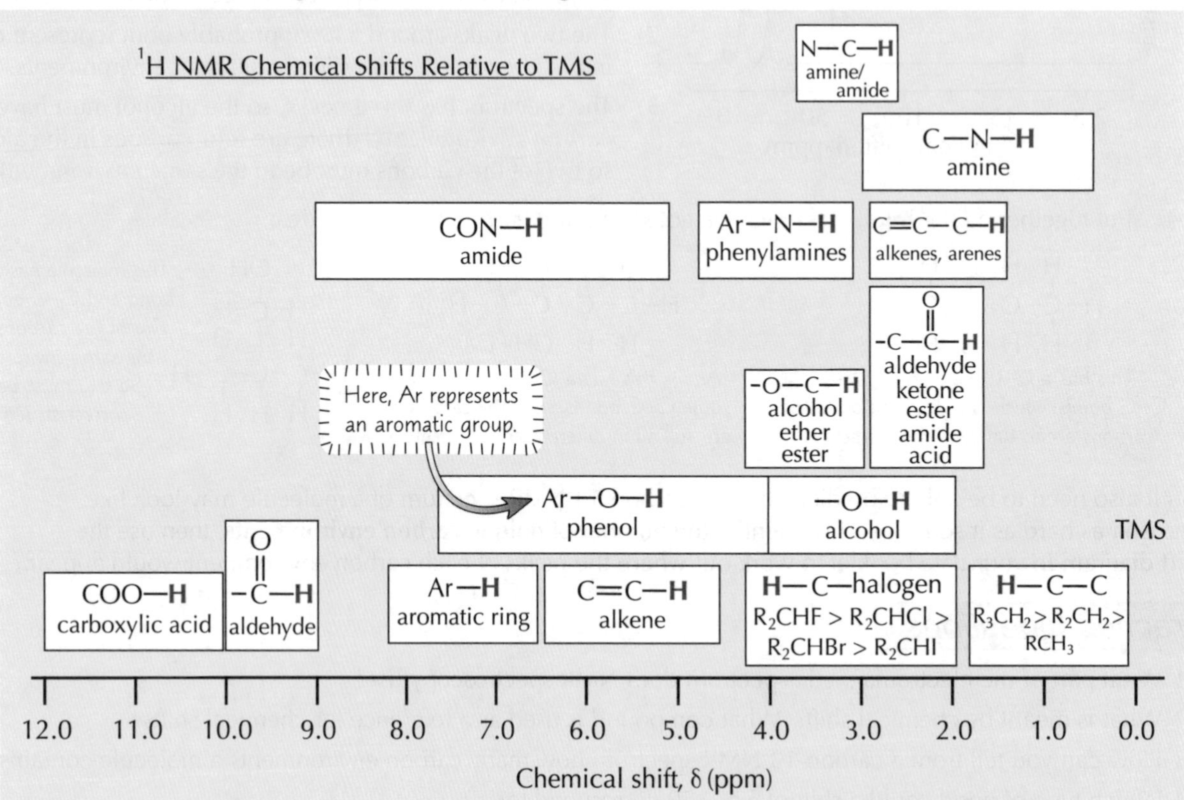

Spin-Spin Coupling *Splits the* Peaks *in a Proton NMR Spectrum*

1) The big difference between carbon-13 NMR and proton NMR spectra is that the peaks in a proton NMR spectrum **split** according to how the **hydrogen environments are arranged**.
2) Only the peaks of **hydrogens** bonded to **carbon** atoms split. The peaks of, for example, –OH and –NH hydrogens are not split.
3) The splitting is caused by the influence of hydrogen atoms that are bonded to **neighbouring** (or **adjacent**) **carbons** — these are carbons one along in the carbon chain from the carbon the hydrogen's attached to. This effect is called **spin-spin coupling**.
4) Only hydrogen nuclei on **adjacent** carbon atoms affect each other.
5) These **split peaks** are called **multiplets**. They always split into one more than the number of hydrogens on the neighbouring carbon atoms — it's called the **n+1 rule**. For example, if there are **2 hydrogens** on the adjacent carbon atoms, the peak will be split into 2 + 1 = 3.

The splitting of the peak for this H...

H H
C—C—H
O H

...tells you about the hydrogens on this adjacent carbon.

Type of Peak	Number of Hydrogens on Adjacent Carbon(s)
Singlet (not split)	0
Doublet (split into two)	1
Triplet (split into three)	2
Quartet (split into four)	3

6) You need to consider the hydrogens on **all** the adjacent carbons — if a hydrogen is attached to a carbon in the middle of a carbon chain, there could be **two neighbouring carbon atoms**, each bonded to hydrogens. They'll all contribute to the **splitting**.

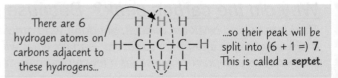

There are 6 hydrogen atoms on carbons adjacent to these hydrogens...

H H H
H—C—C—C—H
H H H

...so their peak will be split into (6 + 1 =) 7. This is called a **septet**.

Proton NMR Spectroscopy

***Integration Traces** Tell You the **Ratio** of **Protons** in Each Environment*

1) In ^{1}H NMR, the **relative area** under each peak tells you the relative number of H atoms in each environment. For example, if the area under two peaks is in the **ratio** 2:1, there will be **two** H atoms in the first environment for every **one** in the second environment.
2) Areas can be shown using **numbers** above the peaks or with an **integration trace.**

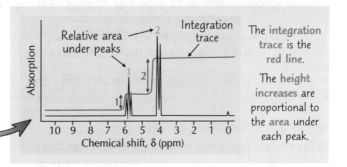

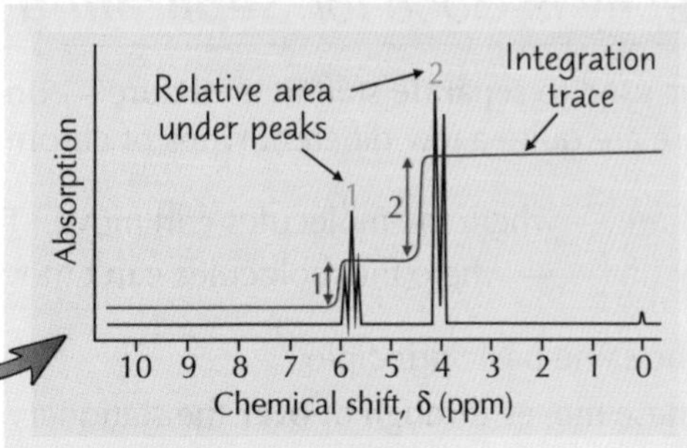

The **integration trace** is the **red line.**

The **height increases** are proportional to the **area** under each peak.

Proton NMR** Can Be Used to Work Out **Structures

Now it's time to put it all together. You'll have to use all the clues from **integration traces** or **numbers** above the peaks, **chemical shift** values and **splitting patterns** to work out what a molecule could be from a proton NMR spectrum.

You might also be asked to predict the proton NMR spectrum for a molecule.

Example: Look at the ^{1}H NMR spectrum of **propanoic acid**:

The peak due to the blue hydrogens is split into **four** because there's **three hydrogens** on the adjacent carbon atom.

The peak due to the red hydrogens is split into **three** because there are **two hydrogens** on the adjacent carbon.

The peak due to the purple hydrogen **isn't** split because there are **no hydrogens** on the adjacent carbon atom.

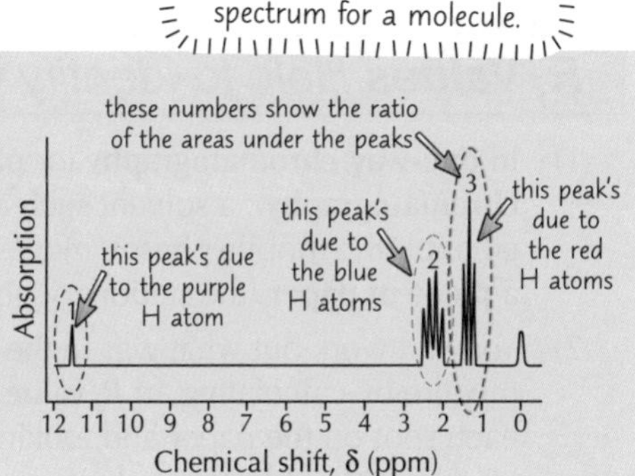

Practice Questions

Q1 What causes the peaks on a high resolution proton NMR spectrum to split?

Q2 What causes a triplet of peaks on a high resolution proton NMR spectrum?

Q3 What do the relative areas under each of the peaks on an NMR spectrum tell you?

Exam Questions

Q1 The proton NMR spectrum below is for an organic compound.
Use the diagram of chemical shifts on page 234 to answer this question.

a) Explain the splitting patterns of the two peaks. [2 marks]

b) What is the likely environment of the protons with a shift of 3.6 ppm? [1 mark]

c) What is the likely environment of the protons with a shift of 1.3 ppm? [1 mark]

d) The molecular mass of the molecule is 64.5. Suggest a possible structure and explain your suggestion. [2 marks]

Q2 A sample of pure 3-chlorobut-1-ene was fed into a high resolution proton NMR spectroscopy machine.

a) Predict the number of peaks that will appear on the spectrum (excluding a TMS peak). [1 mark]

b) Predict the chemical shifts and splitting patterns of each peak. [4 marks]

Never mind splitting peaks — this stuff's likely to cause splitting headaches...

Is your head spinning yet? I know mine is. Round and round like a merry-go-round. It's a hard life when you're tied to a desk trying to get NMR spectroscopy firmly fixed in your head. You must be looking quite peaky by now... so go on, learn this stuff, take the dog around the block, then come back and see if you can still remember it all.

Chromatography

You've probably tried chromatography with a spot of ink on a piece of filter paper — it's a classic experiment.

*Chromatography is Good for **Separating** and **Identifying** Things*

Chromatography is used to **separate** stuff in a mixture — once it's separated out, you can often **identify** the components. There are quite a few different types of chromatography — but they all have the same basic set up:

- A **mobile phase** — where the molecules can move. This is always a liquid or a gas.
- A **stationary phase** — where the molecules can't move. This must be a solid, or a liquid on a solid support.

And they all use the same basic principle:

1) The mobile phase **moves through** or **over** the stationary phase.
2) The **distance** each substance moves up the plate depends on its **solubility** in the mobile phase and its **retention** by or **adsorption** to the stationary phase.
3) Components that are **more soluble** in the mobile phase will **travel further** up the plate, or faster through the column. It's these **differences** in solubility and retention by the stationary phase that **separate** out the different substances.

Claire was going through a bit of a stationery phase.

***R_f* Values** *Help to Identify* **Components** *in a* **Mixture**

1) In **one-way chromatography** (or **paper chromatography**), a solvent such as ethanol (the mobile phase), moves over a **piece of paper** (the stationary phase).
2) You can work out what was in the mixture by calculating an **R_f value** for each spot on the paper and looking them up in a **table of known values**.
3) To work out R_f values, just use this formula:

$$R_f \text{ value} = \frac{\text{distance travelled by spot}}{\text{distance travelled by solvent}}$$

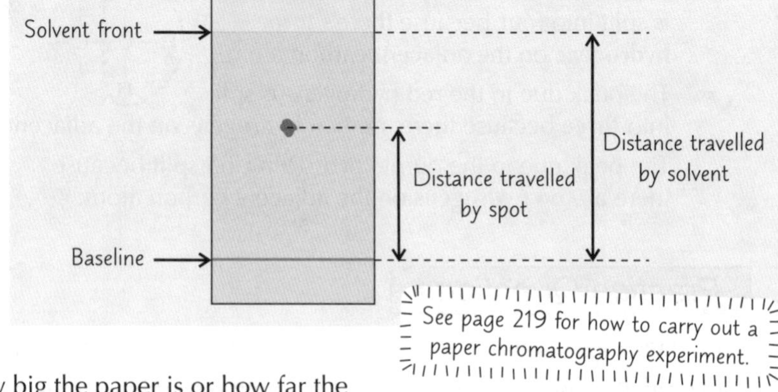

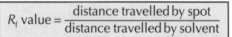

See page 219 for how to carry out a paper chromatography experiment.

4) R_f values are **always the same** no matter how big the paper is or how far the solvent travels — they're properties of the chemicals in the mixture and so can be used to identify those chemicals.
5) BUT if the composition of the paper, the solvent, or the temperature change even slightly, you'll get **different R_f values**.
6) It's hard to keep the conditions identical. So, if you suspect that a mixture contains, say, chlorophyll, it's best to put a spot of chlorophyll on the baseline of the **same paper** as the mixture and run them both at the **same time**.

HPLC *is Done Under* ***High Pressure***

1) In **high-performance liquid chromatography** (HPLC) the stationary phase is small particles of a **solid** packed into a column (or tube). This is often **silica** bonded to various **hydrocarbons**.
2) The **liquid** mobile phase is often a **polar mixture** such as **methanol and water**. It's forced through the column under **high pressure**, which is why it used to be called high-pressure liquid chromatography. The mixture to be separated is injected into the stream of solvent and is carried through the column as a **solution**.
3) The mixture is separated because the different parts are **attracted** by **different amounts** to the solid, so they take different lengths of time to travel through the column.
4) As the liquid leaves the column, **UV light** is passed through it. The UV is **absorbed** by the parts of the mixture as they come through, and a **UV detector** measures the UV light absorbed by the mixture. A graph (called a **chromatogram**) is produced.

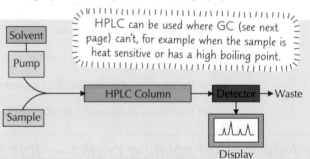

HPLC can be used where GC (see next page) can't, for example when the sample is heat sensitive or has a high boiling point.

Solvent
Pump
Sample
HPLC Column
Detector
Waste
Display

5) The chromatogram shows the **retention times** of the components of the mixture — this is the **time taken** for a **substance** to pass through the **column** and reach the **detector**. You can compare experimental retention times with those from **reference books** or **databases** to identify the different substances in the mixture.

Chromatography

In Gas Chromatography the Mobile Phase is a Gas

1) In **gas chromatography** (GC) the **sample** to be analysed is **injected** into a stream of **gas**, which carries it through a coiled **column** coated with a **viscous liquid** (such as an oil) or a **solid**.
2) The components of the mixture constantly **dissolve in the oil** or **adsorb onto the solid**, **evaporate back** into the gas and then **redissolve** as they travel through the **column**.
3) As with HPLC, the different components in the mixture can be **identified** by their time taken to travel through the column (their **retention times**).

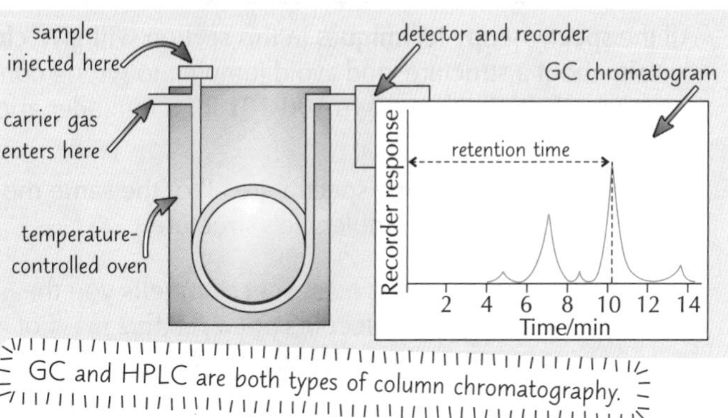

GC and HPLC are both types of column chromatography.

Mass Spectrometry can be Combined with GC and HPLC

1) **Mass spectrometry** is a technique used to identify substances from their mass/charge ratio (see page 100). It is very good at **identifying** unknown compounds, but would give confusing results from a mixture of substances.
2) **Gas chromatography** and **HPLC**, on the other hand, are both very good at **separating** a mixture into its individual components, but not so good at identifying those components.
3) If you put HPLC or GC and mass spectrometry **together**, you get an **extremely useful** analytical tool. For example:

Gas chromatography-mass spectrometry (or GC-MS for short) **combines** the **benefits** of gas chromatography and mass spectrometry to make a super analysis tool.
The sample is **separated** using **gas chromatography**, but instead of going to a detector, the separated components are fed into a **mass spectrometer**.
The spectrometer produces a **mass spectrum** for each **component**, which can be used to **identify** each one and show what the original **sample** consisted of.

HPLC and GC combined with mass spectrometry are often used in forensics. Together, they can separate and detect trace amounts of illegal substances in samples, e.g. testing for drugs in blood samples of athletes.

Practice Questions

Q1 Explain what is meant by the terms 'mobile phase' and 'stationary phase'.

Q2 State the formula used to calculate the R_f value of a substance.

Exam Questions

Q1 Look at this diagram of a chromatogram produced using one-way chromatography on a mixture of substances A and B.

Solvent front
A
B
Initial spot
8 cm
7 cm

a) Calculate the R_f value of spot A. [2 marks]

b) Explain why substance A has moved further up the plate than substance B. [1 mark]

Q2 HPLC is a useful technique for separating mixtures.

a) Describe the key features of HPLC apparatus. [3 marks]

b) Explain how the resulting chromatogram may be used to identify the components of the mixture. [3 marks]

Q3 GC can be used to detect the presence and quantity of alcohol in the blood or urine samples of suspected drink-drivers.

a) What do the letters GC stand for? [1 mark]

b) Explain how 'retention time' is used to identify ethanol in a sample of blood or urine. [2 marks]

Cromer-tography — pictures from my holiday in Norfolk...

Loads of techniques to learn here, and don't forget to check p.219 to remind yourself about thin-layer chromatography and how to carry out a paper chromatography experiment. Good news is the theory behind all these different types of chromatography is the same. You've got a mobile phase, a stationary phase and a mixture that wants separating.

Combined Techniques

Yes, I know, it's yet another page on spectra — but it's the last one (alright, two) I promise.

You Can Use Data From Several Spectra to Work Out a Structure

All the **spectroscopy techniques** in this section will **give clues** to the **identity of a mystery molecule**, but you can be more **certain** about a structure (and avoid jumping to wrong conclusions) if you look at **data from several different types of spectrum**. Look back at pages 100-101 for a reminder about mass spectroscopy, and pages 102-103 for IR spectroscopy.

Example: The following spectra are all of the same molecule. Deduce the molecule's structure.

The **mass spectrum** tells you the molecule's got a **relative mass** of **44** and it's likely to contain a **CH_3 group**.

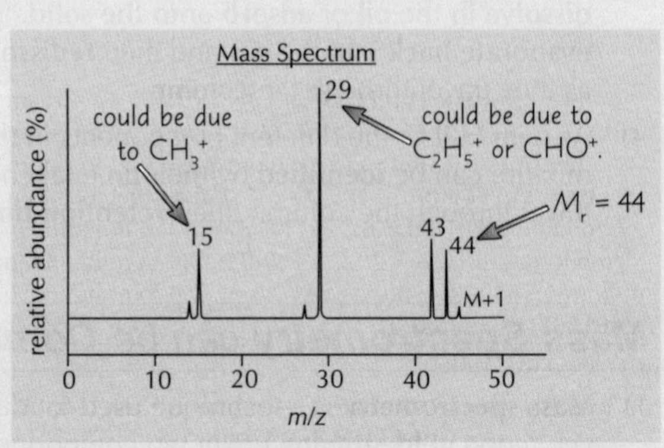

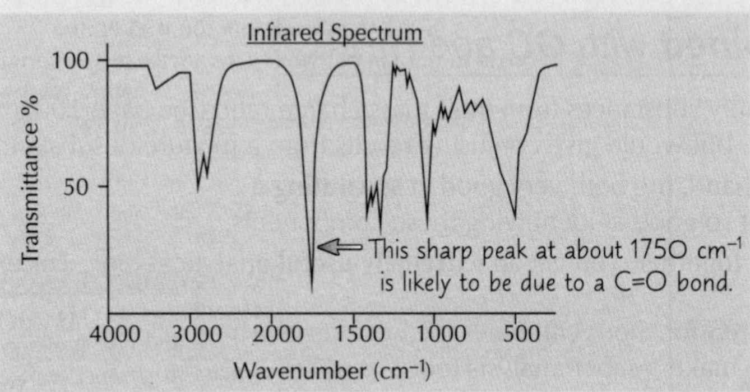

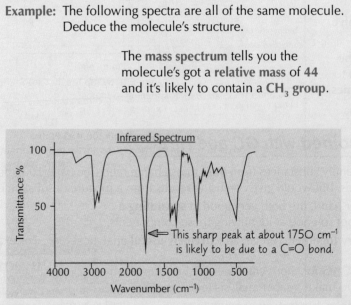

The **IR spectrum** strongly suggests a **C=O** bond in an aldehyde, ketone, ester, carboxylic acid, amide, acyl chloride or acid anhydride.

But since it **doesn't** also have a broad absorption between 2500 and 3300, the molecule **can't** be a carboxylic acid. And there is no peak between 3300 and 3500, so it can't be an amide.

The **high resolution proton NMR spectrum** shows that there are **hydrogen nuclei in 2 environments**.

The peak at **δ ≈ 9.5** is due to a **CHO group** and the one at **δ ≈ 2.5** is probably the hydrogen atoms in **$COCH_3$**.

(You know that these can't be any other groups with similar chemical shifts thanks to the mass spectrum and IR spectrum.)

The **area** under the peaks is in the ratio **1 : 3**, which makes sense as there's **1 hydrogen in CHO** and **3 in $COCH_3$**.

The **splitting pattern** shows that the protons are on **adjacent carbon atoms**, so the group must be **$HCOCH_3$**.

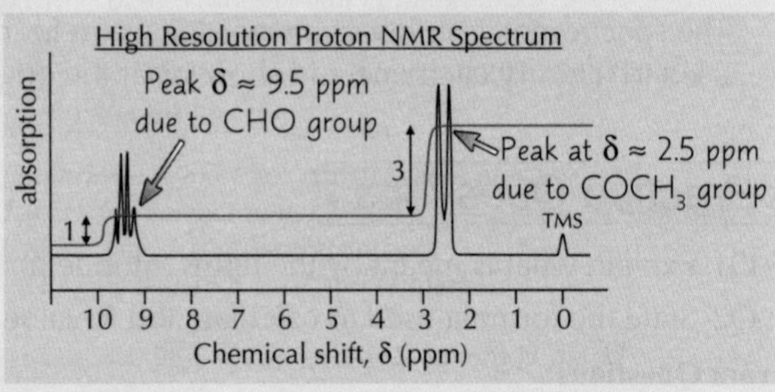

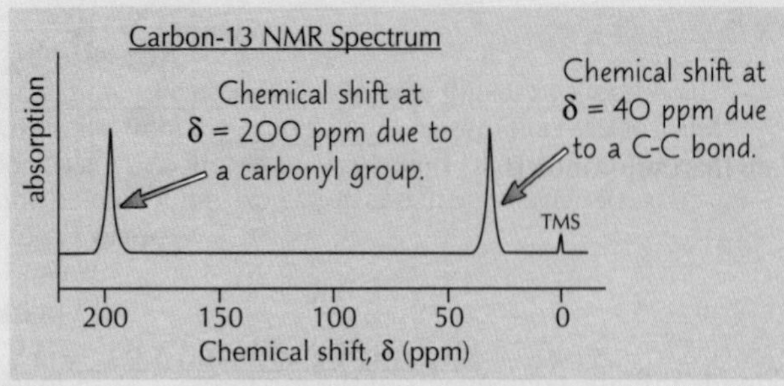

The **carbon-13 NMR spectrum** shows that the molecule has carbon nuclei in **2 different environments**.

The peak at **δ = 200** corresponds to a carbon in a **carbonyl group** and the other peak is due to a **C–C bond**.

Putting all this together we have a molecule with a **mass of 44**, which contains a **CH_3** group, a **C=O** bond, and an **$HCOCH_3$** group.

So, the structure of the molecule must be: $H_3C-C(=O)H$ which is the aldehyde **ethanal**.

You probably could have worked the molecule's structure out **without** using all the spectra, but in more **complex examples** you might well need all of them, so it's good practice.

Combined Techniques

Elemental Analysis also Helps to Work Out a Structure

1) In elemental analysis, experiments determine the **masses** or **percentage compositions** of different elements in a compound.
2) This data can help you to work out the **empirical** and **molecular formulae** of a compound. See pages 56-57 and page 228 to remind yourself how to do this.
3) Knowing the molecular formula is useful in working out the **structure** of the compound from different spectra.

Jim has a good knowledge of specs. Do you?

Practice Questions

Q1 Which type of spectrum gives you the relative mass of a molecule?

Q2 Which spectrum can tell you how many different hydrogen environments there are in a molecule?

Q3 Which spectrum can tell you how many carbon environments are in a molecule?

Exam Questions

Q1 The four spectra shown were produced by running different tests on samples of the same pure organic compound. Use them to work out:

a) The molecular mass of the compound. [1 mark]

b) The probable structure of the molecule. Explain your reasoning. [6 marks]

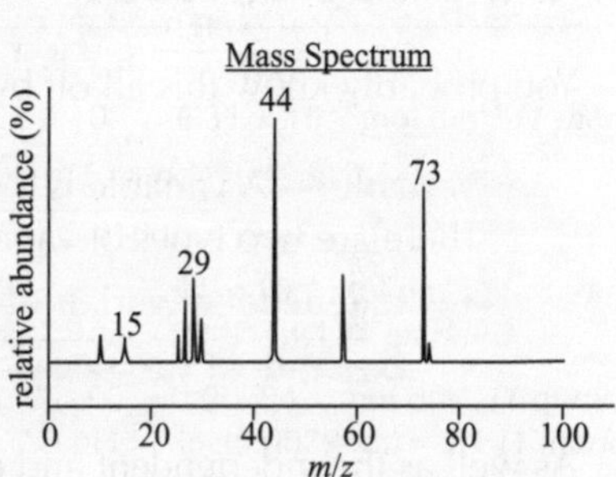

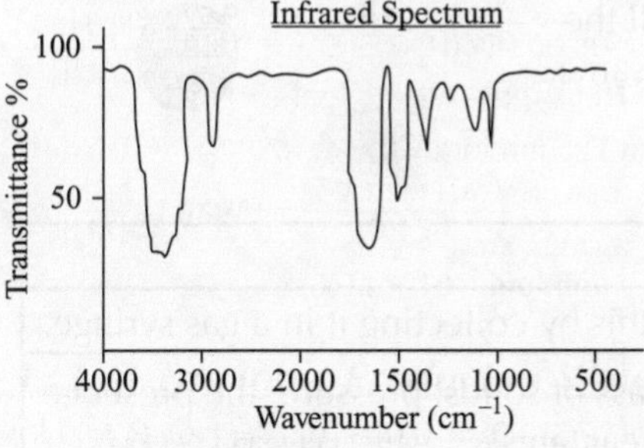

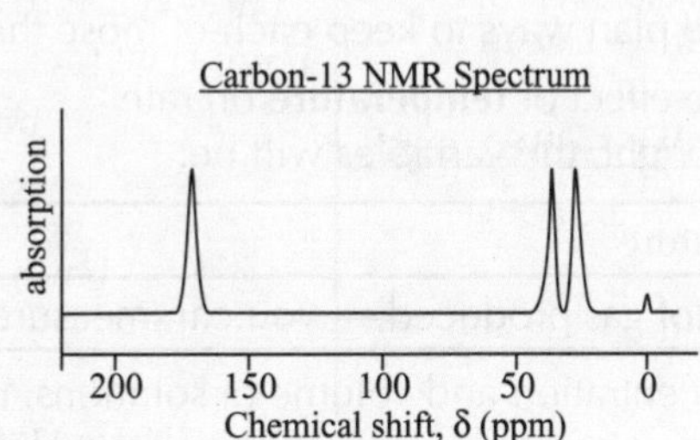

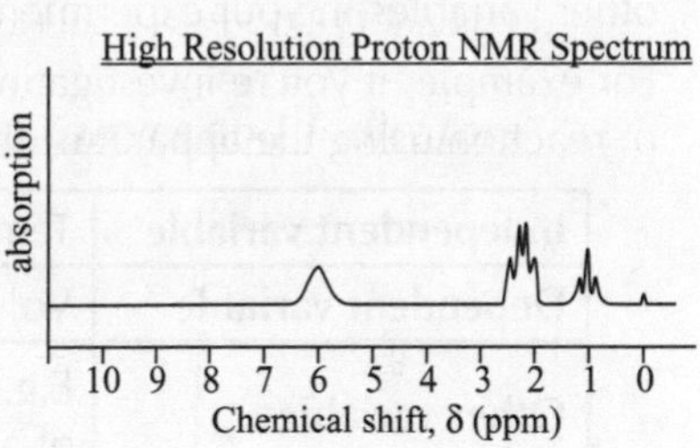

Q2 The four spectra shown were produced by running different tests on samples of the same pure organic compound. Use them to work out:

a) The molecular mass of the compound. [1 mark]

b) The probable structure of the molecule. Explain your reasoning. [6 marks]

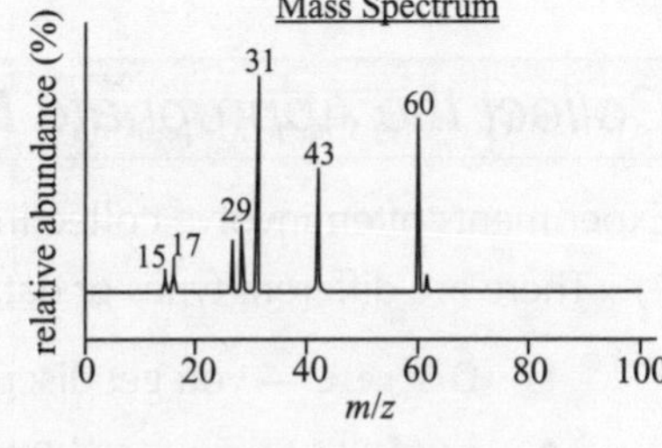

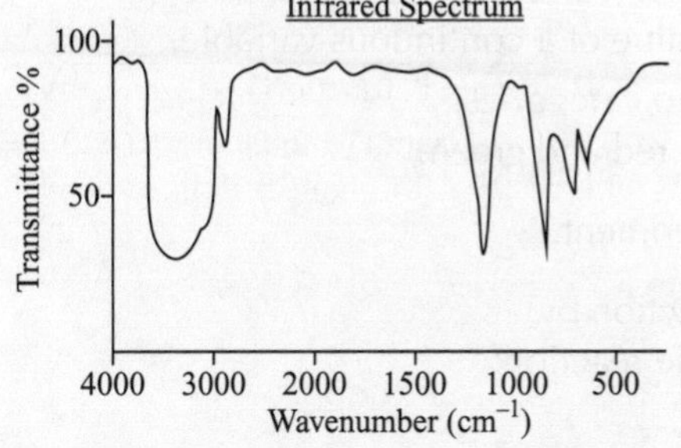

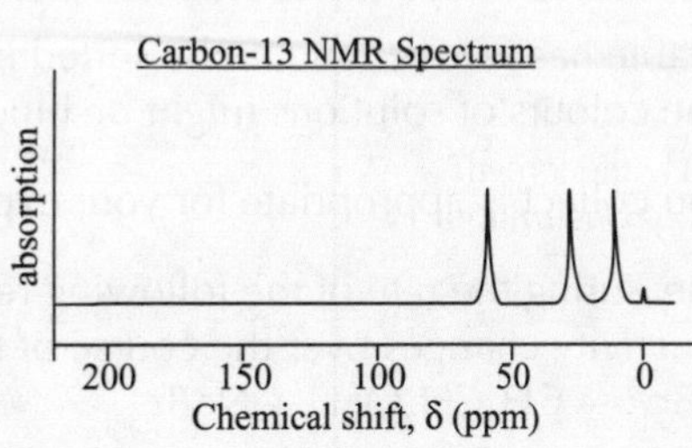

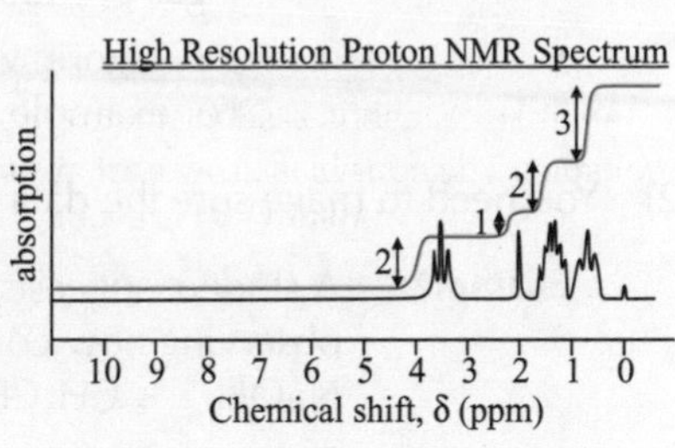

Spectral analysis — psychology for ghosts...

So that's analysis done and dusted, you'll be pleased to hear. But before you celebrate reaching the final topic in the book, take a moment to check that you really know how to interpret all the different spectra. You might want to have a look back at page 221 if you're struggling to remember what all the different functional groups look like.

Planning Experiments

As well as doing practical work in class, you can get asked about it in your exams too. Harsh I know, but that's how it goes. You need to be able to plan the perfect experiment and make improvements to ones other people have planned.

Make Sure You **Plan** Your **Experiment Carefully**

It's really important to plan an experiment well if you want to get accurate and precise results. Here's how to go about it...

Have a peek at page 248 to find out more about accurate and precise results.

1) Work out the **aim** of the experiment — what are you trying to find out?
2) Identify the **independent**, **dependent** and other **variables** (see below).
3) Decide what **data** to collect.
4) Select **appropriate equipment** which will give you accurate results.
5) Make a **risk assessment** and plan any safety precautions.
6) Write out a **detailed method**.
7) Carry out **tests** — to gather **evidence** to address the aim of your experiment.

Make it a **Fair Test** — Control your **Variables**

You probably know this all off by heart but it's easy to get mixed up sometimes. So here's a quick recap:

Variable — A variable is a **quantity** that has the **potential to change**, e.g. mass. There are two types of variable commonly referred to in experiments:

- **Independent variable** — the thing that you **change** in an experiment.
- **Dependent variable** — the thing that you **measure** in an experiment.

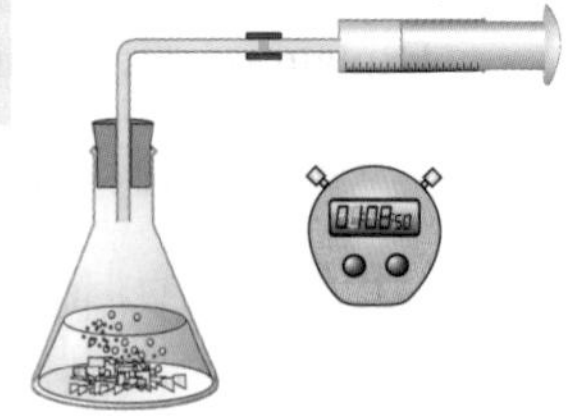

As well as the independent and dependent variables, you need to think of all the other variables in your experiment and plan ways to keep each of those the same.

For example, if you're investigating the effect of **temperature** on rate of reaction using the apparatus on the right, the variables will be:

Independent variable	Temperature
Dependent variable	Volume of gas produced — you can measure this by collecting it in a gas syringe.
Other variables	E.g. concentration and volume of solutions, mass of solids, pressure, the presence of a catalyst and the surface area of any solid reactants.

You MUST control your other variables so they're always the same.

Collect the Appropriate **Data**

Experiments often involve collecting **data** and you need to decide what data to collect.

1) There are different types of data, so it helps to know what they are:
   - **Discrete** — you get discrete data by **counting**. E.g. the number of bubbles produced in a reaction.
   - **Continuous** — a continuous variable can have **any value** on a scale. For example, the volume of gas produced. You can never measure the exact value of a continuous variable.
   - **Categoric** — a categoric variable has values that can be sorted into **categories**. For example, the colours of solutions might be blue, red and green.
2) You need to make sure the data you collect is appropriate for your experiment.

Example: A student suggests measuring the rate of the following reaction by observing how conductivity changes over the course of the reaction:

$NaOH_{(aq)} + CH_3CH_2Br_{(l)} \rightarrow CH_3CH_2OH_{(l)} + NaBr_{(aq)}$

Suggest what is wrong with the student's method, and how it could be improved.

You couldn't collect data about how the **conductivity changes** over the course of the reaction, because there are **salts** in both the reactants and the products.

Instead you could use a **pH meter** to measure how the **pH changes** from basic (due to sodium hydroxide) to neutral.

Planning Experiments

Choose **Appropriate** Equipment — Think about **Size** and **Precision**

Selecting the right apparatus may sound easy but it's something you need to think carefully about.

1) The equipment has to be **appropriate** for the specific experiment.

   For example, if you want to measure the volume of gas produced in a reaction, you need to make sure you use apparatus which will collect the gas, without letting any escape.

2) The equipment needs to be the right **size.**

   For example, if you're using a gas syringe to collect a gas, it needs to be big enough to collect **all** the gas produced during the experiment, or the plunger will just fall out the end. You might need to do some **calculations** to work out what size of syringe to use.

3) The equipment needs to be the right level of **precision.**

   If you want to measure 10 cm^3 of a liquid, it will be more precise to use a measuring cylinder that is graduated to the nearest 0.5 cm^3 than to the nearest 1 cm^3. A burette would be most precise though (they can measure to the nearest 0.1 cm^3).

Risk Assessments Help You to Work **Safely**

1) When you're planning an experiment, you need to carry out a **risk assessment**. To do this, you need to identify:
   - All the **dangers** in the experiment, e.g. any hazardous compounds or naked flames.
   - **Who** is at **risk** from these dangers.
   - What can be done to **reduce the risk**, such as wearing goggles or working in a fume cupboard.
2) You need to make sure you're working **ethically** too. This is most important if there are other people or animals involved. You have to put their welfare first.

There's more about risks and hazards on page 62.

Methods Must be **Clear** and **Detailed**

When **writing** or **evaluating** a method, you need to think about all of the things on these two pages. The method must be **clear** and **detailed** enough for anyone to follow — it's important that **other people** can recreate your experiment and get the **same** results. Make sure your method includes:

1) All **substances** and **quantities** to be used.
2) How to **control** variables.
3) The exact **apparatus** needed (a diagram is usually helpful to show the set up).
4) Any **safety precautions** that should be taken.
5) What **data** to collect and **how** to collect it.

Practice Questions

Q1 Briefly outline the steps involved in planning an experiment.

Q2 What three things should you consider when choosing the best apparatus for your experiment?

Exam Question

Q1 A student carries out an experiment to investigate how the rate of the following reaction changes with the concentration of hydrochloric acid: $Mg_{(s)} + 2HCl_{(aq)} \rightarrow MgCl_{2\,(aq)} + H_{2\,(g)}$

The student decides to measure how the pH changes over time using litmus paper.
Explain why this method of measuring pH is unsuitable, and suggest an alternative method. [2 marks]

Revision time — independent variable. Exam mark — dependent variable...

I wouldn't advise you to investigate the effect of revision on exam marks. Just trust me — more revision = better marks. But if you were to investigate it, there are all manner of variables that you'd need to control. The amount of sleep you had the night before, how much coffee you drank in the morning, your level of panic on entering the exam hall...

Practical Techniques

The way you carry out your experiment is important, so here's a nice round up of some of the techniques chemists use all the time. You've probably met some of them before, which should hopefully make it all a bit easier. Hopefully... :-)

Results Should be ***Repeatable*** *and* ***Reproducible***

1) **Repeatable** means that if the **same** person does the experiment again using the same methods and equipment, they'll get the same results. **Reproducible** means that if someone **else** does the experiment, or a different **method** or piece of **equipment** is used, the results will still be the same.
2) To make sure your results can be consistently repeated and reproduced, you need to **minimise** any **errors** that might sneak into your data. This includes:
   - using **apparatus** and **techniques** correctly,
   - taking **measurements** correctly,
   - **repeating** your experiments and calculating a **mean**.

Make Sure You ***Measure*** *Substances* ***Correctly***

The **state** (solid, liquid or gas) that your substance is in will determine **how** you decide to measure it.

1) You weigh **solids** using a **balance**. Here are a couple of things to look out for:
   - Put the container you are weighing your substance into on the balance, and make sure the balance is set to exactly zero before you start weighing out your substance.
   - If you need to **transfer** the solid into another container, make sure that it's **all** transferred. For example, if you're making up a standard solution you could wash any remaining solid into the new container using the solvent. Or, you could **reweigh** the weighing container after you've transferred the solid so you can work out **exactly** how much you added to your experiment.
2) There are a few methods you might use to measure the volume of a liquid. Whichever method you use, always read the volume from the **bottom** of the **meniscus** (the curved upper surface of the liquid) when it's at **eye level**.

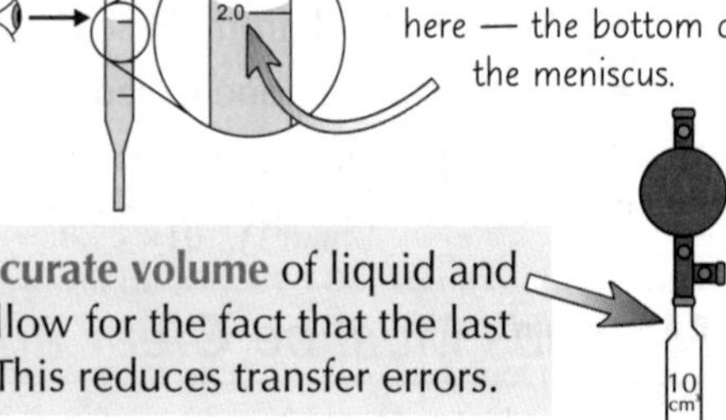

Pipettes are long, narrow tubes that are used to **suck up** an **accurate volume** of liquid and transfer it to another container. They are often **calibrated** to allow for the fact that the last drop of liquid stays in the pipette when the liquid is ejected. This reduces transfer errors.

Burettes measure from **top** to **bottom** (so when they are **full**, the scale reads **zero**). They have a **tap** at the bottom which you can use to release the liquid into another container (you can even release it drop by drop). To use a burette, take an **initial reading**, and once you've released as much liquid as you want, take a **final reading**. The **difference** between the readings tells you how much liquid you used.

Burettes are used a lot for titrations. There's loads more about titrations on pages 62-65.

Volumetric flasks allow you to **accurately** measure a very **specific** volume of liquid. They come in various **sizes** (e.g. 100 cm^3, 250 cm^3) and there's a **line** on the neck that marks the volume that they measure. They're used to make **accurate dilutions** and **standard solutions**. To use them, first measure out and add the liquid or solid that is being diluted or dissolved. Rinse out the measuring vessel into the volumetric flask with a little solvent to make sure everything's been transferred. Then fill the flask with solvent to the **bottom** of the neck. Fill the neck **drop by drop** until the bottom of the meniscus is **level** with the line.

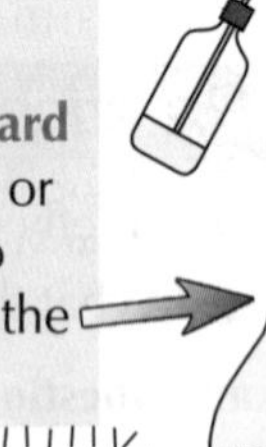

A standard solution is a solution with a precisely known concentration. You can find out how they're made on page 62.

3) Gases can be measured with a **gas syringe**. They should be measured at **room temperature** and **pressure** as the **volume** of a gas **changes** with temperature and pressure. Before you use the syringe, you should make sure it's completely **sealed** and that the **plunger** moves **smoothly**.

Once you've measured a quantity of a substance you need to be careful you don't **lose** any. In particular, think about how to minimise losses as you transfer it from the measuring equipment to the reaction container.

Practical Techniques

Measure **Temperature** Accurately

I'm sure you've heard this before, so I'll be quick... You can use a **thermometer** or a **temperature probe** to measure the temperature of a substance (a temperature probe is like a thermometer but it will always have a **digital display**).

- Make sure the **bulb** of your thermometer or temperature probe is **completely submerged** in any mixture you're measuring.
- Wait for the temperature to **stabilise** before you take an initial reading
- If you're using a thermometer with a scale, read off your measurement at **eye level** to make sure it's accurate.

Qualitative Tests Can be Harder to **Reproduce**

Qualitative tests measure **physical qualities** (e.g. colour) while **quantitative** tests measure numerical data, (e.g. mass).

So if you carried out a reaction and noticed that heat was produced, this would be a **qualitative** observation. If you **measured** the temperature change with a thermometer, this would be **quantitative**.

Qualitative tests can be harder to **reproduce** because they're often **subjective** (based on **opinion**), such as describing the **colour** or **cloudiness** of a solution. There are ways to **reduce** the subjectivity of qualitative results though. For example:

- If you're looking for a **colour change**, put a **white background** behind your reaction container.
- If you're looking for a **precipitate** to form, mark an **X** on a piece of paper and place it under the reaction container. Your solution is 'cloudy' when you can **no longer see** the X.

There are Specific Techniques for Synthesising **Organic Compounds**

Synthesis is used to **make** one **organic compound** from another. There are a number of techniques that chemists use to help them make and purify their products:

These techniques are covered in more detail on pages 98-99.

1) **Reflux** — heating a reaction mixture in a flask fitted with a **condenser** so that any materials that **evaporate**, condense and drip back into the mixture.
2) **Distillation** — gently heating a mixture so that the compounds evaporate off in order of **increasing boiling point** and can be collected separately. This can be done **during** a reaction to collect a product as it forms, or **after** the reaction is **finished** to purify the mixture.
3) **Removing water soluble impurities** — adding **water** to an organic mixture in a separating funnel. Any **water soluble impurities** move out of the organic layer and dissolve in the aqueous layer. The layers have different **densities** so are easy to separate.

Practice Questions

Q1 Give three ways that you could ensure your experiment is repeatable and reproducible.

Q2 How would you measure out a desired quantity of a solid? And a gas?

Q3 How could you make the results of an experiment measuring time taken for a precipitate to form less subjective?

Exam Question

Q1 A student dilutes a 1 mol dm^{-3} solution of sodium chloride to 0.1 mol dm^{-3} as follows:

He measures 10 cm^3 of 1 mol dm^{-3} sodium chloride solution in a pipette and puts this into a 100 cm^3 volumetric flask. He then tops up the volumetric flask with distilled water until the top of the meniscus is at 100 cm^3.

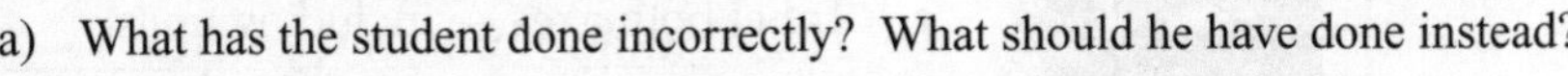

a) What has the student done incorrectly? What should he have done instead? [1 mark]

b) Which of the arrows in the diagram on the right indicates the level to which you should fill a volumetric flask? [1 mark]

A

B

C

Reflux, take it easy...

It might seem like there's a lot to do to make sure your results are accurate, but you should get lots of practice in practicals. Before long you'll be measuring temperatures and volumes with your eyes shut (metaphorically speaking).

Presenting Results

Once you've collected the data from your experiment, it's not time to stop, put your feet up and have a cup of tea — you've got some presenting to do. Results tables need converting into graphs and other pretty pictures.

Organise Your Results in a **Table**

It's a good idea to set up a table to **record** the **results** of your experiment in. When you draw a table, make sure you **include** enough **rows** and **columns** to **record all of the data** you need. You might also need to include a column for **processing** your data (e.g. working out an average).

Make sure each **column** has a **heading** so you know what's going to be recorded where.

The **units** should be in the **column heading**, not the table itself.

Temperature (°C)	Time (s)	Volume of gas evolved (cm^3)			Average volume of gas evolved (cm^3)
		Run 1	Run 2	Run 3	
20	10	8.1	7.6	8.5	(8.1 + 7.6 + 8.5) ÷ 3 = 8.1
	20	17.7	19.0	20.1	(17.7 + 19.0 + 20.1) ÷ 3 = 18.9
	30	28.5	29.9	30.0	(28.5 + 29.9 + 30.0) ÷ 3 = 29.5

You'll need to repeat each test **at least three** times to check your results are **repeatable.**

You can find the **mean result** by **adding up** the data from each repeat and **dividing** by the number of repeats.

Graphs: **Scatter** or **Bar** — Use the **Best Type**

When drawing graphs, the dependent variable should go on the *y*-axis, the independent on the *x*-axis.

You'll often need to make a **graph** of your results.
Graphs make your data **easier to understand** — so long as you choose the right type.

Scatter plots are great for showing how two sets of continuous data are related (or **correlated** — see page 246). Don't try to join all the points on a scatter plot — draw a straight or curved **line of best fit** to show the **trend**.

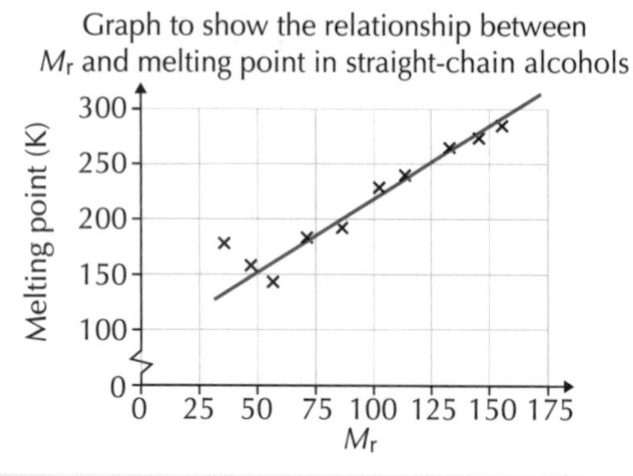

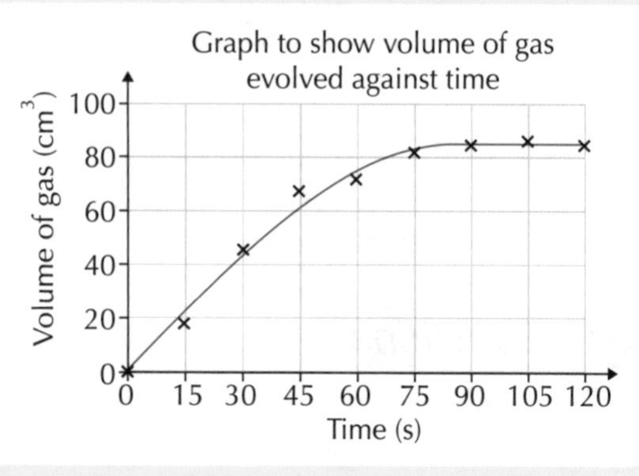

You should use a **bar chart** when one of your data sets is **categoric**. For example:

Graph to Show Chlorine Concentration in Water Samples

Chlorine concentration (ppm): 0, 0.1, 0.2, 0.3, 0.4, 0.5

Water samples: A, B, C

Pie charts are also used to display categoric data.

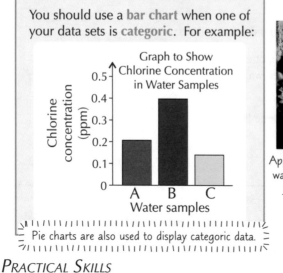

Apple and blackberry was number one on Jane's pie chart

Whatever type of graph you make, you'll ONLY get full marks if you:

- Choose a sensible **scale** — don't do a tiny graph in the corner of the paper, or massive axes where the data only takes up a tiny part of the graph.
- **Label** both **axes** — including units.
- Plot your points accurately — use a **sharp pencil**.

Sometimes you might need to work out the gradient of a graph, e.g. to work out the rate of a reaction. There are details of how to do this on page 114.

Presenting Results

Don't Forget About **Units**

Units are really important — 10 g is a bit different from 10 kg, so make sure you don't forget to add them to your **tables** and **graphs**. It's often a good idea to write down the units on each line of any **calculations** you do — it makes things less confusing, particularly if you need to convert between two different units.

Here are some useful examples:

Concentration can be measured in **mol dm^{-3}** and **mol cm^{-3}**.

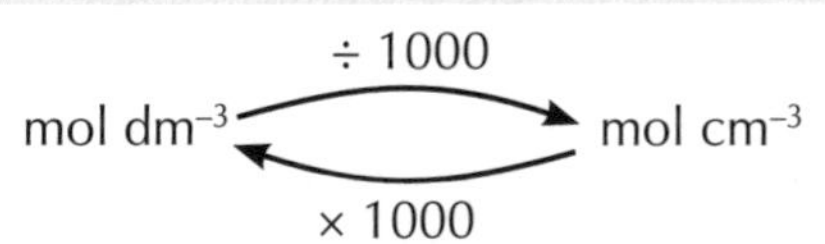

Example: Write 0.2 mol dm^{-3} in mol cm^{-3}.

To convert 0.2 mol dm^{-3} into mol cm^{-3} you divide by 1000.

0.2 mol dm^{-3} ÷ 1000 = **2 × 10^{-4} mol cm^{-3}**

Standard form is useful for writing very big or very small numbers.

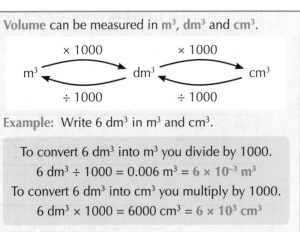

Volume can be measured in **m^3**, **dm^3** and **cm^3**.

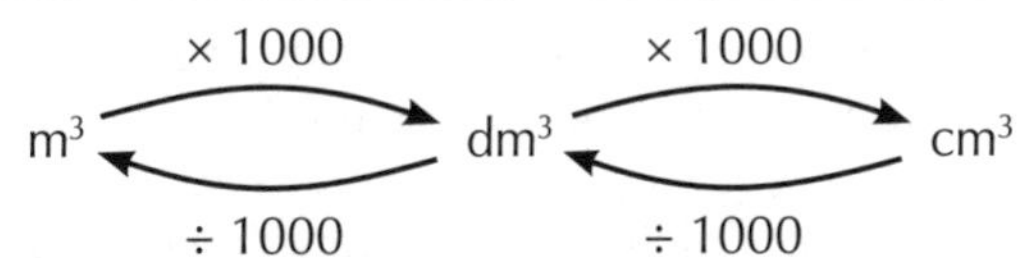

Example: Write 6 dm^3 in m^3 and cm^3.

To convert 6 dm^3 into m^3 you divide by 1000.

6 dm^3 ÷ 1000 = 0.006 m^3 = **6 × 10^{-3} m^3**

To convert 6 dm^3 into cm^3 you multiply by 1000.

6 dm^3 × 1000 = 6000 cm^3 = **6 × 10^3 cm^3**

Round to the **Lowest Number** of **Significant Figures**

You always need to be aware of **significant figures** when working with data.

1) The rule is the same for when doing calculations with the results from your experiment, or when doing calculations in the exam — you have to round your answer to the **lowest number of significant figures** (s.f.) given in the question.
2) It always helps to write down the number of significant figures you've rounded to after your answer — it shows you really know what you're talking about.
3) If you're converting between **standard** and **ordinary form**, you have to keep the **same number** of significant figures. For example, 0.0060 mol dm^{-3} is the same as 6.0 × 10^{-3} mol dm^{-3} — they're both given to 2 s.f..

The first significant figure of a number is the first digit that isn't a zero. The second, third and fourth significant figures follow on immediately after the first (even if they're zeros).

Example: 13.5 cm^3 of a 0.51 mol dm^{-3} solution of sodium hydroxide reacts with 1.5 mol dm^{-3} hydrochloric acid. Calculate the volume of hydrochloric acid required to neutralise the sodium hydroxide

3 s.f. 2 s.f.

No. of moles of NaOH: (13.5 cm^3 × 0.51 mol dm^{-3}) ÷ 1000 = 6.885 × 10^{-3} mol

You don't need to round intermediate answers. Rounding too early will make your final answer less accurate.

Volume of HCl: (6.885 × 10^{-3}) mol × 1000 ÷ 1.5 mol dm^{-3} = 4.59 cm^3 = **4.6 cm^3 (2 s.f.)**

Final answer should be rounded to 2 s.f.

Make sure all your units match when you're doing calculations.

Practice Questions

Q1 Why is it always a good idea to repeat your experiments?

Q2 How would you convert an answer from m^3 to dm^3?

Q3 How do you decide how many significant figures you should round your answer to?

Exam Question

Q1 10 cm^3 sodium hydroxide solution is titrated with 0.50 mol dm^{-3} hydrochloric acid to find its concentration. The titration is repeated three times and the volumes of hydrochloric acid used are: 7.30 cm^3, 7.25 cm^3, 7.25 cm^3.

a) What is the mean volume of hydrochloric acid recorded in dm^3? [1 mark]

b) What is the concentration of hydrochloric acid in mol cm^{-3}? [1 mark]

Significant figures — a result of far too many cream cakes...

When you draw graphs, always be careful to get your axes round the right way. The thing you've been changing (the independent variable) goes on the x-axis, and the thing you've been measuring (the dependent variable) is on the y-axis.

Analysing Results

You're not quite finished yet... there's still time to look at your results and try and make sense of them. Graphs can help you to see patterns but don't try and read too much in to them — they won't tell you what grade you're going to get.

Watch Out For ***Anomalous*** *Results*

1) Anomalous results are ones that **don't fit** in with the other values and are likely to be wrong.
2) They're often due to **random errors**, e.g. if a drop in a titration is too big and shoots past the end point, or if a syringe plunger gets stuck whilst collecting gas produced in a reaction.
3) When looking at results in tables or graphs, you always need to look to see if there are any anomalies — you need to **ignore** these results when calculating means or drawing lines of best fit.

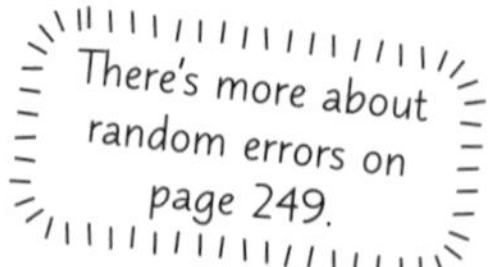

There's more about random errors on page 249.

Example: Calculate the mean volume from the results in the table below.

Titration Number	1	2	3	4
Titre Volume (cm^3)	15.20	15.30	15.25	15.50

Titre **4** isn't **concordant** (doesn't match) the other results so you need to ignore it and just use the other three:

$$\frac{15.20 + 15.30 + 15.25}{3} = \mathbf{15.25\ cm^3}$$

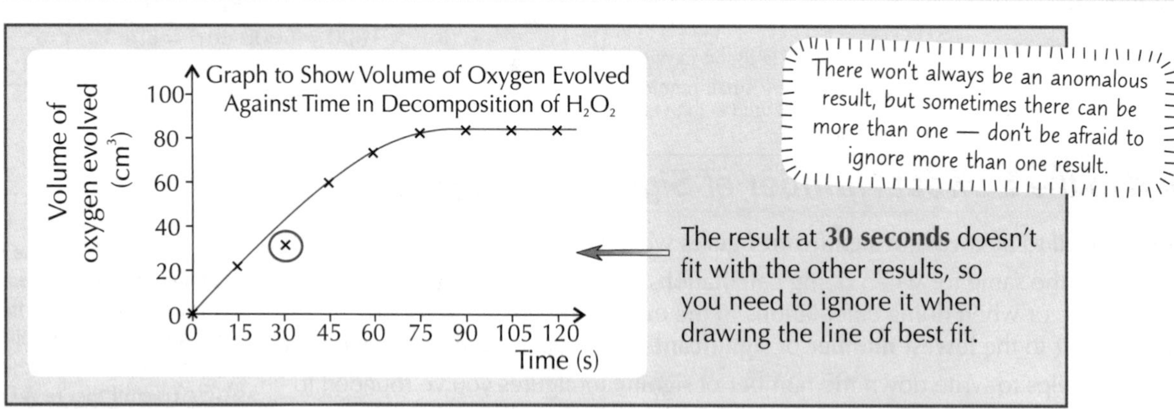

Graph to Show Volume of Oxygen Evolved Against Time in Decomposition of H_2O_2

There won't always be an anomalous result, but sometimes there can be more than one — don't be afraid to ignore more than one result.

Scatter Graphs *Show The* ***Relationship*** *Between Variables*

Correlation describes the **relationship** between two variables — the independent one and the dependent one. Data can show:

1) **Positive correlation**
As one variable **increases** the other **increases.**

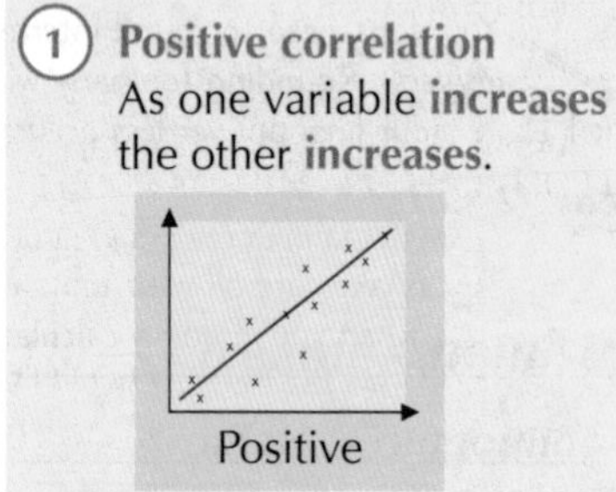

2) **Negative correlation**
As one variable **increases** the other **decreases.**

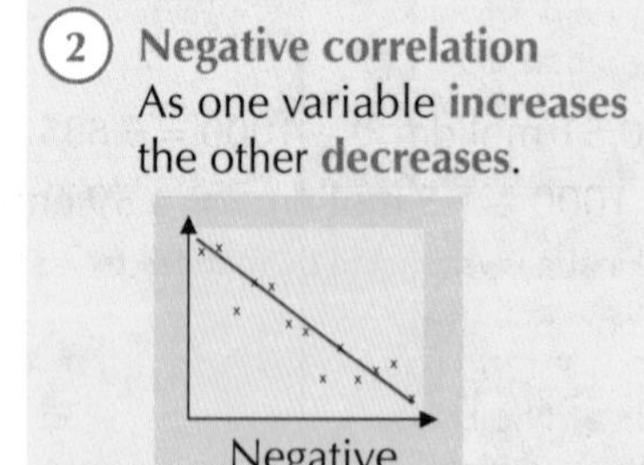

3) **No correlation**
There is **no relationship** between the two variables.

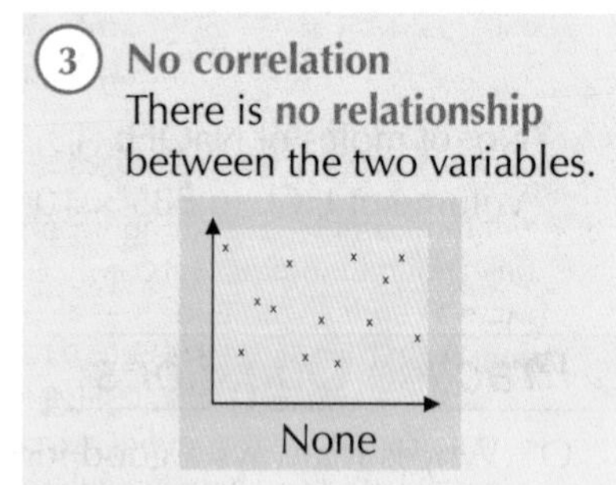

Correlation ***Doesn't*** *Mean* ***Cause*** *— Don't Jump to Conclusions*

1) Ideally, only **two** quantities would **ever** change in any experiment — everything else would remain **constant**.
2) But in experiments or studies outside the lab, you **can't** usually control all the variables. So even if two variables are correlated, the change in one may **not** be causing the change in the other. Both changes might be caused by a **third variable**.

Example:
Some studies have found a correlation between **drinking chlorinated tap water** and the risk of developing certain cancers. So some people argue that water shouldn't have chlorine added.
BUT it's hard to control all the **variables** between people who drink tap water and people who don't.
It could be due to other lifestyle factors.
Or, the cancer risk could be affected by something else in tap water — or by whatever the non-tap water drinkers drink instead...

Analysing Results

Don't Get **Carried Away** When Drawing Conclusions

The **data** should always **support** the conclusion. This may sound obvious but it's easy to **jump** to conclusions. Conclusions have to be **specific** — not make sweeping generalisations.

Example:

1) The rate of an enzyme-controlled reaction was measured at **10 °C, 20 °C, 30 °C, 40 °C, 50 °C** and **60 °C.** All other variables were kept constant, and the results are shown in the graph below.

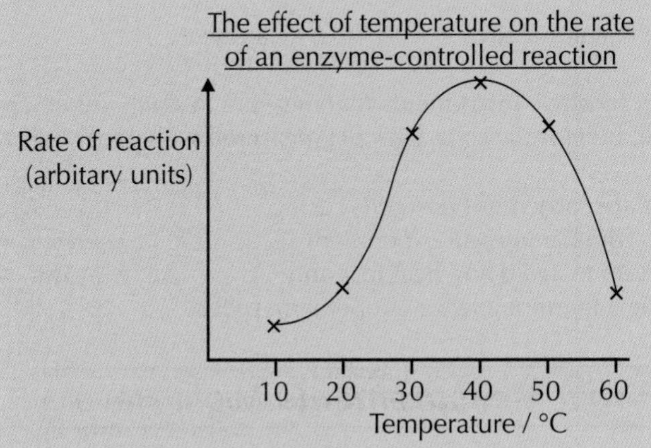

2) A science magazine **concluded** from this data that this enzyme works best at **40 °C.**
3) The data **doesn't** support this. The enzyme **could** work best at 42 °C or 47 °C but you can't tell from the data because **increases** of **10 °C** at a time were used. The rate of reaction at in-between temperatures **wasn't** measured.
4) All you know is that it's faster at **40 °C** than at any of the other temperatures tested.
5) The experiment **ONLY** gives information about this particular enzyme-controlled reaction. You can't conclude that **all** enzyme-controlled reactions happen faster at a particular temperature — only this one. And you can't say for sure that doing the experiment at, say, a different constant pressure, wouldn't give a different optimum temperature.

Practice Questions

Q1 How do you treat anomalous results when calculating averages? And when drawing lines of best fit?

Q2 What is negative correlation?

Exam Question

Q1 A student carried out an investigation to study how the rate of a reaction changed with temperature. He plotted his results on the graph shown on the right.

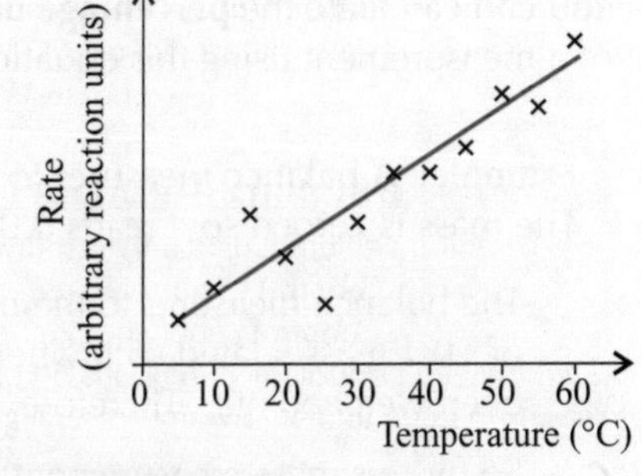

a) 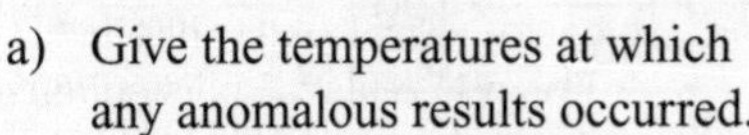
Give the temperatures at which any anomalous results occurred. [1 mark]

b) 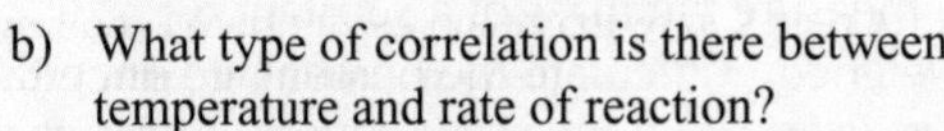
What type of correlation is there between temperature and rate of reaction? [1 mark]

c) Which of the following statements are appropriate conclusions to draw from this experiment?

1. The rate of the reaction is highest at 60 °C.
2. Increasing the temperature causes the rate of the reaction to increase.
3. Between 5 °C and 60 °C, the rate of the reaction increased as temperature increased.

A Statements 1, 2 and 3. **B** Statements 2 and 3 only.

C Statement 3 only. **D** Statement 2 only. [1 mark]

Correlation Street — my favourite programme...

Watch out for bias when you're reading about the results of scientific studies. People often tell you what they want you to know. So a bottled water company might say that studies have shown that chlorinated tap water can cause cancer, without mentioning any of the doubts in the results. After all, they want to persuade you to buy their drinks.

Evaluating Experiments

So you've planned an experiment, collected your data (no less than three times, mind you) and put it all onto a lovely graph. Now it's time to sit back, relax and... work out everything you did wrong. That's science, I'm afraid.

You Need to Look **Critically** at Your Experiment

There are a few terms that'll come in handy when you're evaluating how convincing your results are...

1) **Valid results** — Valid results answer the **original question**. For example, if you haven't **controlled all the variables** your results won't be valid, because you won't be testing just the thing you wanted to.

2) **Accurate results** — Accurate results are those that are **really close** to the **true** answer.

3) **Precise results** — These are results taken using **sensitive instruments** that measure in **small increments**, e.g. pH measured with a meter (pH 7.692) will be **more precise** than pH measured with paper (pH 7).

4) **Reliable experiments** — Reliable experiments are carried out **correctly**, using **suitable equipment** and with **minimal errors**. For example, an experiment measuring a temperature change would be set up to avoid any heat loss and temperature changes would be measured using a thermometer or temperature probe.

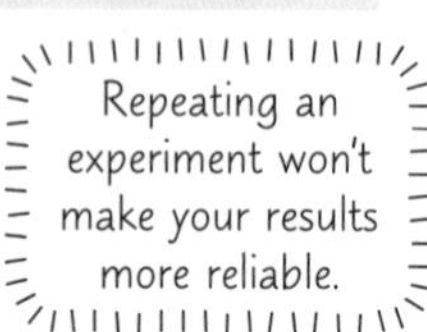

Repeating an experiment won't make your results more reliable.

Uncertainty is the Amount of **Error** Your **Measurements** Might Have

1) Any measurements you make will have **uncertainty** in them due to the limits to the **precision** of the equipment you used.
2) If you use a weighing scale that measures to the nearest 0.1 g, then the **true** weight of any substance you weigh could be up to 0.05 g **more than** or **less than** your reading. Your measurement has an **uncertainty** (or error) of ±0.05 g in either direction.
3) The ± sign tells you the **range** in which the true value could lie. The range can also be called the **margin of error**.
4) For any piece of equipment you use, the uncertainty will be **half** the **smallest increment** the equipment can measure, in either direction.
5) If you're **combining measurements**, you'll need to combine their **uncertainties**. For example, if you're calculating a temperature change by measuring an initial and a final temperature, the **total** uncertainty for the temperature change will be the uncertainties for both measurements added together.

The **Percentage Uncertainty** in a Result Should be Calculated

You can calculate the **percentage uncertainty** of a measurement using this equation:

$$\text{percentage uncertainty} = \frac{\text{uncertainty}}{\text{reading}} \times 100$$

You may see percentage uncertainty called percentage error.

Example: A balance measures to the nearest 0.2 g, and is used to measure the **mass** of a substance. The mass is zeroed so it reads 0.0 g. Then, 18.4 g of a solid are weighed. Calculate the percentage uncertainty.

The balance measures to the nearest 0.2 g, so **each reading** has an uncertainty of ±0.1 g. There is an error of ±0.1 g associated with when the balance reads 0.0 g (when it's zeroed), and when the mass of solid has been weighed out. Therefore, there are two sources of error, so the **total uncertainty** is 0.1 × 2 = 0.2 g.

So for this mass measurement, percentage uncertainty $= \frac{0.2}{18.4} \times 100 = \mathbf{1.1\%}$

This stuff's really important, so there are more examples on pages 66 and 67.

You Can **Minimise** the **Percentage Uncertainty**

1) One obvious way to **reduce errors** in your measurements is to use the most **precise equipment** available to you.
2) A bit of clever **planning** can also improve your results. If you measure out **5 cm³** of liquid in a measuring cylinder that has increments of 0.1 cm³ then the percentage uncertainty is (0.05 ÷ 5) × 100 = **1%**.
   But if you measure **10 cm³** of liquid in the same measuring cylinder the percentage uncertainty is (0.05 ÷ 10) × 100 = **0.5%**. Hey presto — you've just halved the percentage uncertainty.
   So the percentage uncertainty can be reduced by planning an experiment so you use a **larger volume** of liquid.
3) The general principle is that the **smaller** the measurement, the **larger** the percentage uncertainty.

Evaluating Experiments

Errors Can Be Systematic or Random

1) **Systematic errors** are the same every time you repeat the experiment. They may be caused by the **set-up** or **equipment** you used. For example, if the 10.00 cm^3 pipette you used to measure out a sample for titration actually only measured 9.95 cm^3, your sample would have been about 0.05 cm^3 too small **every time** you repeated the experiment.
2) **Random errors** vary — they're what make the results a bit **different** each time you repeat an experiment. The errors when you make a reading from a burette are random. You have to estimate or round the level when it's between two marks — so sometimes your figure will be **above** the real one, and sometimes it will be **below**.
3) **Repeating an experiment** and finding the mean of your results helps to deal with **random errors**. The results that are a bit high will be **cancelled out** by the ones that are a bit low. But repeating your results won't get rid of any **systematic errors**, so your results won't get more **accurate**.

This should be a photo of a scientist. I don't know what happened — it's a random error...

Think About How the Experiment Could Be Improved

In your evaluation you need to think about anything that you could have done differently to improve your results. Here are some things to think about...

1) **Whether your method gives you valid results.**
   - Will the data you collected answer the question your experiment aimed to answer?
   - Did you control all your variables?
2) **How you could improve the accuracy of your results.**
   - Was the apparatus you used on an appropriate scale for your measurements?
   - Could you use more precise equipment to reduce the random errors and uncertainty of your results?
3) **Whether your results are repeatable and reproducible.**
   - Did you repeat the experiment, and were the results you got similar?

There's more about repeatable and reproducible results on page 242.

Practice Questions

Q1 What's the difference between the accuracy and precision of results?

Q2 What's the uncertainty of a single reading on a balance that reads to the nearest 0.1 g?

Q3 How do you calculate percentage uncertainty?

Q4 Give two ways of reducing percentage uncertainty.

Q5 How can you reduce the random errors in your experiments?

Exam Question

Q1 A student carried out an experiment to determine the temperature change in the reaction between citric acid and sodium bicarbonate using the following method:

1. Measure out 25.0 cm^3 of 1.00 mol dm^{-3} citric acid solution in a measuring cylinder and put it in a polystyrene cup.
2. Weigh out 2.10 g sodium bicarbonate and add it to the citric acid solution.
3. Place a thermometer in the solution and measure the temperature change over one minute.

a) The measuring cylinder the student uses measures to the nearest 0.5 cm^3. What is the percentage uncertainty of the student's measurement? [1 mark]

b) The student's result is different to the documented value. How could you change the method to give a more accurate measurement for the change in temperature of the complete reaction? [2 marks]

Repeat your results: Your results, your results, your results, your results...

So there you have it. All you need to know about planning, carrying out and analysing experiments. Watch out for errors creeping in to your experimental methods. It may not seem obvious that there's an error when you're taking a measurement that's zero (e.g. on a balance or a burette), so remember to include this when calculating errors.

Do Well In Your Exams

Revision is really important when it comes to exams, but it's not the only thing that can help. Good exam technique and knowing what to expect in each exam can make a big difference to your mark, so you'd better check this out...

*Make Sure You Know the **Structure** of Your **Exams***

For A-Level Chemistry, you'll be sitting **three papers**. Knowing what's going to come up in each paper and how much time you'll have will be really useful when you are preparing for your exams, so here's what you'll be up against:

Paper		Time	No. of marks	% of total mark	Topics assessed	Paper details
1	Advanced Inorganic and Physical Chemistry	1 hr 45 mins	90	30	1-5, 8 and 10-15	A mixture of multiple choice, short answer, calculations and extended writing questions.
2	Advanced Organic and Physical Chemistry	1 hr 45 mins	90	30	2, 3, 5-7, 9 and 16-19	A mixture of multiple choice, short answer, calculations and extended writing questions.
3	General and Practical Principles in Chemistry	2 hrs 30 mins	120	40	All topics, including Practical Skills.	A mixture of short answer, calculations and extended writing questions.

1) **All three papers** cover theory from **both years** of your course — this means you need to make sure you **revise** your **Year 1 topics** (**1-10**) as well as your **Year 2 topics** (**11-19**) for these exams.
2) Each paper will include some **extended writing questions** which are marked on the **quality** of the response, as well as their **scientific content**. These questions will be shown by an **asterisk** (*) next to their number. Your answer needs to:
   - Have a **clear** and **logical structure**.
   - Include the right **scientific terms**, spelt correctly.
   - Include **detailed information** that's **relevant** to the question.

*Some Questions Will Test Your Knowledge of **Carrying Out Practicals***

Some of the marks in your A-Level Chemistry exams will focus on how to carry out **experiments**, analyse **data** and **work scientifically**. This means you will be given questions where you're asked to do things like comment on the **design** of **experiments**, make **predictions**, **draw graphs**, **calculate** percentage **errors** — basically, anything related to planning experiments or analysing results. These skills are covered in the Practical Skills section of this book on pages 240-249, and in the relevant topics.

Although Paper 3 covers the Practical Skills section of this book, you could be asked about practical techniques in any of your exams.

***Manage** Your **Time** Sensibly*

1) **How long** you spend on **each question** is important in an exam — it could make all the difference to your grade.
2) The **number of marks** tells you roughly **how long** to spend on a question. But some questions will require **lots of work** for a few marks while others will be **quicker**.

Example:
1) Define the term 'enthalpy change of neutralisation'. (2 marks)
2) Compounds A and B are hydrocarbons with relative molecular masses of 78 and 58 respectively. In their ^{1}H NMR spectra, A has only one peak and B has two peaks. Draw a possible structure for each compound. (2 marks)

Question 1 only requires you to write down a **definition** — if you can remember it this shouldn't take too long.

Question 2 requires you to **apply your knowledge** of NMR spectra and **draw the structure** of two compounds — this may take you a lot longer, especially if you have to draw out a few structures before getting it right.

So if **time's running out**, it makes sense to do questions like Q1 **first** and **come back** to Q2 if there's time at the end.

3) If you get stuck on a question for too long, it may be best to **move on** and come back to it later. If you skip any questions the first time round, don't forget to **go back** to do them.
4) You don't have to work through the paper **in order** — you might decide not to do all the multiple choice questions first, or leave questions on topics you find harder till the end.

Do Well In Your Exams

Make Sure You **Read the Question**

1) It sounds obvious, but it's really important you read each question **carefully**, and give an answer that fits.
2) **Command words** in the question give you an idea of the **kind of answer** you should write. You'll find answering exam questions much easier if you understand exactly what they mean. Here's a summary of the **common** ones:

Command word	What to do
Give / Name / State	Give a brief one or two word answer, or a short sentence.
Identify	Say what something is.
Compare / Contrast	Look at the similarities and differences between two or more things.
Explain	Give an explanation, including reasoning, for something.
Predict	Use your scientific knowledge to work out what the answer might be.
Describe	Write an account or a description of something, e.g. an experiment, some observations or a chemical trend.
Calculate	Work out the solution to a mathematical problem.
Deduce / Determine	Use the information given in the question to work something out.
Discuss	Explore and investigate a topic, as presented in the question.
Sketch	Produce a rough drawing of a diagram or graph.

From the looks on his classmates' faces, Ivor deduced that he had gone a bit overboard when decorating his lucky exam hat.

Remember to Use the **Data Booklet**

When you sit your exams, you'll be given a data booklet. It will contain lots of **useful information**, including:

- the **characteristic infrared absorptions**, **^{13}C NMR shifts** and **^{1}H NMR shifts** of some common functional groups.
- some electronegativity information, including the **Pauling electronegativity index**.
- some useful **scientific constants**.
- the **standard electrode potentials** of some electrochemical half-cells.
- some information about the **colours** and **pH ranges** of common **indicators**.
- a copy of the **periodic table**.

Use a copy of the data booklet while you're revising. It will get you used to using it, and show you the facts you don't need to memorise.

Be **Careful** With **Calculations**

20% of the marks up for grabs in A-Level Chemistry will require maths skills, so make sure you know your stuff.

1) In calculation questions you should always **show your working** — you may get some marks for your **method** even if you get the answer wrong.
2) Don't **round** your answer until the **very end**. Some of the calculations in A-Level Chemistry can be quite **long**, and if you round too early you could introduce errors into your final answer.
3) Be careful with **units**. Lots of formulae require quantities to be in specific units (e.g. temperature in kelvin), so it's best to **convert** any numbers you're given into these before you start. And obviously, if the question **tells** you which units to give your **answer** in, don't throw away marks by giving it in different ones.
4) You should give your final answer to the correct number of **significant figures**. This is usually the same as the data with the **lowest number** of significant figures in the question — see page 245 for more on significant figures.
5) It can be easy to mistype numbers into your calculator when you're under pressure in an exam, so always **double-check** your calculations and make sure that your answer looks **sensible**.

I'd tell you another Chemistry joke, but I'm not sure it'd get a good reaction...

The key to preparing for your exams is to practise, practise, practise. Get your hands on some practice papers and try to do each of them in the time allowed. This'll flag up any topics that you're a bit shaky on, so you can go back and revise.

Answers

Topic 1 — Atomic Structure and the Periodic Table

Page 5 — The Atom

1 a) Similarity — They've all got the same number of protons/electrons ***[1 mark]***.
Difference — They all have different numbers of neutrons ***[1 mark]***.
b) 1 proton, 1 neutron (2 – 1), 1 electron ***[1 mark]***.
c) ${}^{3}_{1}H$ ***[1 mark]***

2 a) i) Same number of electrons. ${}^{32}S^{2-}$ has 16 + 2 = 18 electrons. ${}^{40}Ar$ has 18 electrons too ***[1 mark]***.
ii) Same number of protons. Each has 16 protons ***[1 mark]***.
iii) Same number of neutrons. ${}^{40}Ar$ has 40 – 18 = 22 neutrons. ${}^{42}Ca$ has 42 – 20 = 22 neutrons ***[1 mark]***.
b) **A** and **C** ***[1 mark]***. They have the same number of protons but different numbers of neutrons ***[1 mark]***.
It doesn't matter that they have a different number of electrons because they are still the same element.

3 H has 1 proton, O has 8 protons and C has 6 protons, so the total number of protons in C_3H_7OH is (3 × 6) + (8 × 1) + 8 = **34**.
H has 1 electron, O has 8 electrons and C has 6 electrons, so the total number of electrons in C_3H_7OH is (3 × 6) + (8 × 1) + 8 = **34** ***[1 mark for correct numbers of protons and electrons]***.
For neutral molecules, the number of electrons is equal to the number of protons.
H has 1 – 1 = 0 neutrons, O has 16 – 8 = 8 neutrons and C has 12 – 6 = 6 neutrons.
So C_3H_7OH has (3 × 6) + (8 × 0) + 8 = **26** neutrons ***[1 mark]***.

Page 7 — Relative Mass

1 a) First multiply each relative abundance by the relative mass — 120.8 × 63 = 7610.4, 54.0 × 65 = 3510.0
Next add up the products: 7610.4 + 3510.0 = 11 120.4 ***[1 mark]***
Now divide by the total abundance (120.8 + 54.0 = 174.8)

$$A_r(\text{Cu}) = \frac{11\,120.4}{174.8} = \mathbf{63.6}$$ ***[1 mark]***

You can check your answer by seeing if A_r(Cu) is in between 63 and 65 (the lowest and highest relative isotopic masses).
b) A sample of copper is a mixture of 2 isotopes in different abundances ***[1 mark]***. The relative atomic mass is an average mass of these isotopes which isn't a whole number ***[1 mark]***.

2 You use pretty much the same method here as for question 1 a).
93.1 × 39 = 3630.9, 0.120 × 40 = 4.8, 6.77 × 41 = 277.57
3630.9 + 4.8 + 277.57 = 3913.27 ***[1 mark]***
This time you divide by 100 because they're percentages.

$$A_r(\text{K}) = \frac{3913.27}{100} = \mathbf{39.1}$$ ***[1 mark]***

Again check your answer's between the lowest and highest relative isotopic masses, 39 and 41. A_r(K) is closer to 39 because most of the sample (93.1 %) is made up of this isotope.

Page 9 — More on Relative Mass

1 a)

	${}^{16}O$	${}^{18}O$
${}^{16}O$	${}^{16}O-{}^{16}O$: 0.98 × 0.98 = **0.9604**	${}^{16}O-{}^{18}O$: 0.98 × 0.02 = **0.0196**
${}^{18}O$	${}^{18}O-{}^{16}O$: 0.02 × 0.98 = **0.0196**	${}^{18}O-{}^{18}O$: 0.02 × 0.02 = **0.0004**

[2 marks — 2 marks for a correct abundances for all molecules, 1 mark if three correct abundances]
${}^{16}O-{}^{18}O$ and ${}^{18}O-{}^{16}O$ are the same, so the relative abundance is 0.0196 + 0.0196 = **0.0392** ***[1 mark]***.
b) Divide each by 0.0004 to get the simplified relative abundances.

Molecule	M_r	Relative Abundance
${}^{16}O-{}^{16}O$	16 + 16 = **32**	0.9604 ÷ 0.0004 = **2401**
${}^{16}O-{}^{18}O$	16 + 18 = **34**	0.0392 ÷ 0.0004 = **98**
${}^{18}O-{}^{18}O$	18 + 18 = **36**	0.0004 ÷ 0.0004 = **1**

[2 marks — 1 mark for correct relative abundances, 1 mark for correct relative molecular masses]
So the mass spectrum for the sample of O_2 will be:

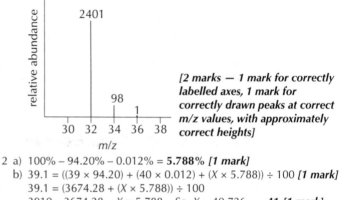

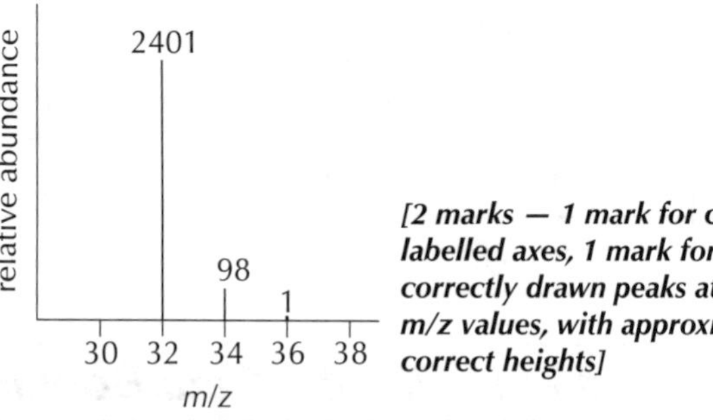

[2 marks — 1 mark for correctly labelled axes, 1 mark for correctly drawn peaks at correct m/z values, with approximately correct heights]

2 a) 100% – 94.20% – 0.012% = **5.788%** ***[1 mark]***
b) 39.1 = ((39 × 94.20) + (40 × 0.012) + (X × 5.788)) ÷ 100 ***[1 mark]***
39.1 = (3674.28 + (X × 5.788)) ÷ 100
3910 – 3674.28 = X × 5.788. So, X = 40.726... = **41** ***[1 mark]***

3 a) 58 ***[1 mark]***
b) E.g.

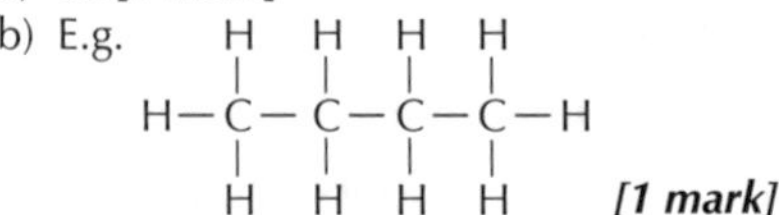

[1 mark]

Page 11 — Electronic Structure

1 a) K atom: $1s^2\ 2s^2\ 2p^6\ 3s^2\ 3p^6\ 4s^1$ or [Ar] $4s^1$ ***[1 mark]***
K^+ ion: $1s^2\ 2s^2\ 2p^6\ 3s^2\ 3p^6$ or [Ar] ***[1 mark]***
b) $1s^2\ 2s^2\ 2p^4$ ***[1 mark]***

2 a) Germanium ($1s^2\ 2s^2\ 2p^6\ 3s^2\ 3p^6\ 3d^{10}\ 4s^2\ 4p^2$ or [Ar] $3d^{10}\ 4s^2\ 4p^2$) ***[1 mark]***.
The 4p sub-shell is partly filled, so it must be a p block element.
b) Ar (atom) ***[1 mark]***, K^+ (positive ion) ***[1 mark]***, Cl^- (negative ion) ***[1 mark]***.
You also could have suggested Ca^{2+}, S^{2-} or P^{3-}.
c) $1s^2\ 2s^2\ 2p^6\ 3s^2\ 3p^6\ 3d^{10}\ 4s^1$ ***[1 mark]***

Page 13 — Atomic Emission Spectra

1 a) The movement of electrons/an electron ***[1 mark]*** from higher to lower energy levels ***[1 mark]***.
b) Line E (because it is at the highest frequency) ***[1 mark]***.
c) Because the energy levels get closer together with increasing energy ***[1 mark]***.

Answers

2 a) Energy is released/emitted ***[1 mark]***.

b) The lines represent the frequencies of light that are emitted/released when an electron drops from a higher energy level to a lower one ***[1 mark]***.

c) Emission spectra show that specific amounts of energy are emitted when electrons drop down from higher energy levels to lower energy levels ***[1 mark]***. In-between amounts of energy are never emitted, which suggests that electrons only exist at very specific energy levels (they're discrete) ***[1 mark]***.

d) E.g. ionisation energy ***[1 mark]***

Page 15 — Ionisation Energies

1 a) $C_{(g)} \rightarrow C^{+}_{(g)} + e^{-}$

Correct equation ***[1 mark]***. Both state symbols showing gaseous state ***[1 mark]***.

b) First ionisation energy increases as nuclear charge increases ***[1 mark]***.

c) As the nuclear charge increases there is a stronger force of attraction between the nucleus and the electron ***[1 mark]*** and so more energy is required to remove the electron ***[1 mark]***.

2 a) Group 3 ***[1 mark]***

There are three electrons removed before the first big jump in energy.

b) The electrons are being removed from an increasingly positive ion ***[1 mark]*** so there's less repulsion amongst the remaining electrons so they're held more strongly by the nucleus ***[1 mark]***.

c) When an electron is removed from a different shell there is a big increase in the energy required (since that shell is closer to the nucleus) ***[1 mark]***.

d) There are 3 shells ***[1 mark]***.

You can tell there are 3 shells because there are 2 big jumps in energy. There is always one more shell than big jumps.

Page 18 — Periodicity

1 a) C ***[1 mark]*** b) B ***[1 mark]*** c) C ***[1 mark]***

2 a) Si has a giant covalent lattice structure ***[1 mark]*** consisting of lots of very strong covalent bonds which require a lot of energy to break ***[1 mark]***.

b) Sulfur (S_8) has more electrons than phosphorus (P_4) ***[1 mark]*** which results in stronger London forces of attraction between molecules ***[1 mark]***.

Topic 2 — Bonding and Structure

Page 21 — Ionic Bonding

1 a) Giant ionic lattice ***[1 mark]***.

b) Sodium chloride will have a high melting point ***[1 mark]***, because a lot of energy is required to overcome the strong electrostatic attraction between the positive and negative ions ***[1 mark]***.

c) Sodium bromide would have a lower melting point than sodium chloride ***[1 mark]***. Bromide ions have one more electron shell than chloride ions, so have a larger ionic radius. This means the ions in sodium bromide can't pack as closely together as the ions in sodium chloride ***[1 mark]***. Ionic bonding gets weaker as the distance between the ions increases, so the ionic bonding in sodium bromide is weaker than in sodium chloride / less energy is required to break the ionic bonds in sodium bromide than sodium chloride ***[1 mark]*** (so the ionic melting point is lower).

2 a)

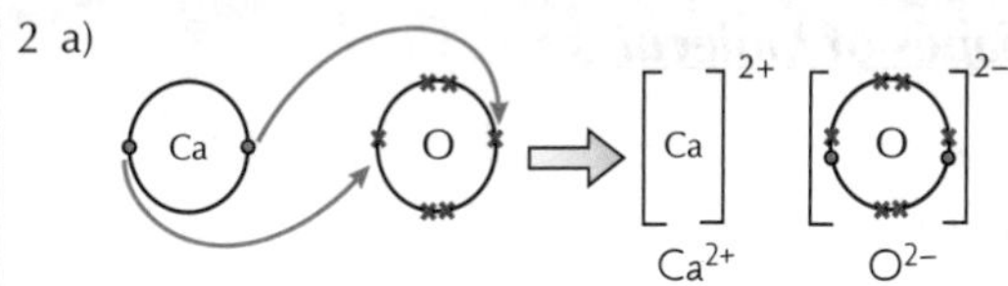

[2 marks — 1 mark for correct electron arrangement, 1 mark for correct charges]

b) In a solid, ions are held in place by strong ionic bonds ***[1 mark]***. When molten, the ions are mobile ***[1 mark]*** and so carry charge (and hence electricity) through the substance ***[1 mark]***.

3 Sodium loses one (outer) electron to form Na^{+} ***[1 mark]***. Fluorine gains one electron to form F^{-} ***[1 mark]***. Electrostatic forces of attraction between oppositely charged ions forms an ionic lattice ***[1 mark]***.

4 C ***[1 mark]***

Page 23 — Covalent Bonding

1

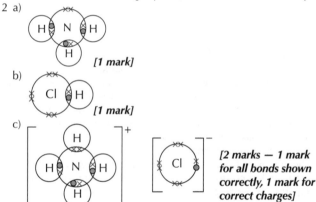

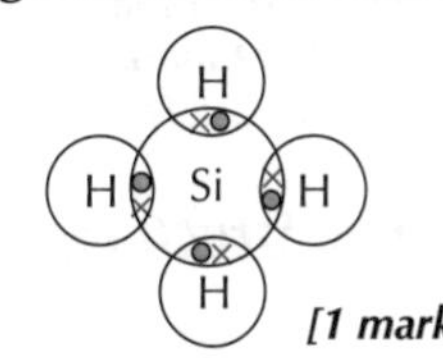

[1 mark]

Because Si is in the same group as C, it will often form similar compounds.

2 a)

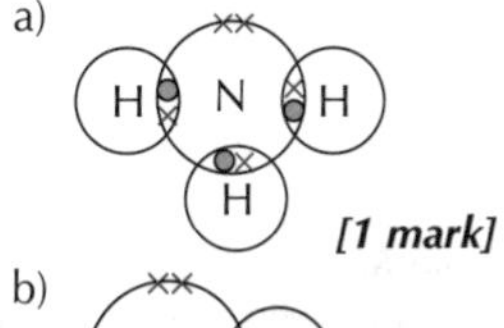

[1 mark]

b)

[1 mark]

c)

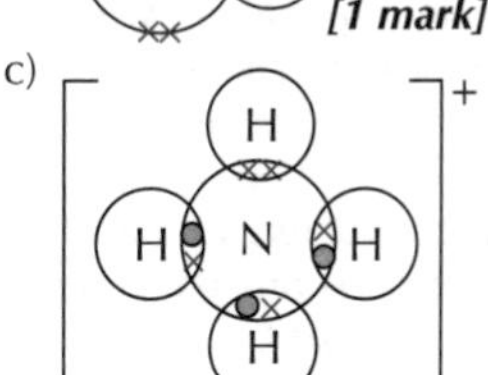

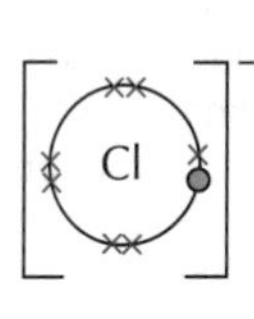

[2 marks — 1 mark for all bonds shown correctly, 1 mark for correct charges]

3 a) An N–N bond is longer than an N=N bond ***[1 mark]*** as there are four shared electrons in an N=N bond and only two shared electrons in an N–N bond, meaning the electron density between the two nitrogen atoms in the nitrogen double bond is greater than in the nitrogen single bond ***[1 mark]***. This increases the strength of the electrostatic attraction between the positive nuceli and the negative electrons in the N=N bond, making the bond shorter ***[1 mark]***.

b)

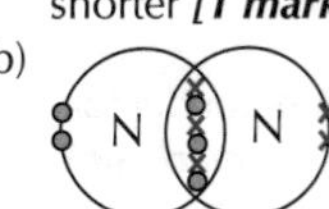

[1 mark]

c) The bond enthalpy of the bond in N_2 would be larger than the bond enthalpy of a nitrogen single bond or a nitrogen double bond ***[1 mark]***. The bond in N_2 is a nitrogen triple bond. There are six shared electrons in this bond, leading to a higher electron density than in N–N or N=N bonds (where there are two and four shared electrons respectively) ***[1 mark]***. This means there's a stronger electrostatic attraction between the two nitrogen nuclei and the bonding electrons, so stronger covalent bonding ***[1 mark]***.

Answers

Page 25 — Shapes of Molecules

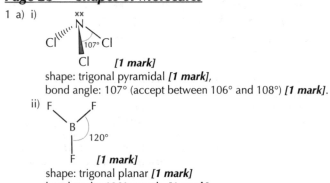

1 a) i) *[1 mark]*

shape: trigonal pyramidal *[1 mark]*,
bond angle: 107° (accept between 106° and 108°) *[1 mark]*.

ii) 120° *[1 mark]*

shape: trigonal planar *[1 mark]*
bond angle: 120° exactly *[1 mark]*.

b) BCl_3 has three electron pairs only around B. *[1 mark]*
NCl_3 has four electron pairs around N *[1 mark]*, including one lone pair. *[1 mark]*

2 Atom A: shape: trigonal planar, bond angle: 120° *[1 mark]*
Atom B: shape: tetrahedral, bond angle: 109.5° *[1 mark]*
Atom C: shape: non-linear/bent, bond angle: 104.5° *[1 mark]*

Page 27 — Giant Covalent and Metallic Structures

1 a) delocalised electron sea, lattice of +ve metal ions *[1 mark]*

Metallic bonding results from the attraction between positive metal ions and a sea of delocalised electrons between them *[1 mark]*.

b) Calcium (Ca^{2+}) has two delocalised electrons per atom, while potassium (K^+) has only one delocalised electron per atom. So calcium has more delocalised electrons and therefore stronger metallic bonding *[1 mark]*.

2 Silicon dioxide has a giant covalent lattice structure *[1 mark]* so, to melt it, lots of strong covalent bonds must be broken, which requires lots of energy/high temperatures *[1 mark]*.

3 Graphite consists of sheets of carbon atoms, where each carbon atom is bonded to three others *[1 mark]*. This means that each atom has one free electron not involved in bonds, and it is these free electrons that allow graphite to conduct electricity *[1 mark]*.

4 Copper is metallically bonded and so delocalised electrons are free to move (carry electric charge) *[1 mark]*. Oxygen and sulfur form copper oxide/sulfide, fixing some electrons (as anions) *[1 mark]*. This prevents them from moving and carrying charge *[1 mark]*.

5 a) Giant covalent *[1 mark]*

b) Any two from: high melting point / electrical non-conductor (insulator) / insoluble / good thermal conductor. *[1 mark for each]*

Page 29 — Electronegativity and Polarisation

1 a) The ability of an atom to attract the bonding electrons in a covalent bond *[1 mark]*.

b) Electronegativity increases across a period and decreases down a group *[1 mark]*.

c) A *[1 mark]*

2 a) i) ii) *[2 marks each — in each part, 1 mark for correct shape, 1 mark for correct partial charges]*

b) The polar bonds in BCl_3 are arranged so that they cancel each other out, so the molecule has no overall dipole *[1 mark]*. CH_2Cl_2 does have an overall dipole because the polar bonds are not orientated so they are pointing in opposite directions so they don't cancel each other out *[1 mark]*.

To help you decide if the molecule's polar or not, imagine the atoms are having a tug of war with the electrons. If they're all pulling the same amount in different directions, the electrons aren't going to go anywhere.

Page 31 — Intermolecular Forces

1 The boiling point of a substance depends on the energy needed to overcome the intermolecular forces between the molecules *[1 mark]*. Pentane is the most linear molecule so it has the greatest surface contact, and so has the strongest London forces. This gives it the highest boiling point *[1 mark]*. The surface contact of 2-methylbutane is less than that of pentane and that of 2,2-dimethylpropane is smaller still, meaning that these substances have weaker London forces and consequently lower boiling points *[1 mark]*.

2 London forces/instantaneous dipole-induced dipole bonds and permanent dipole-permanent dipole bonds *[1 mark]*.

3 NO has a higher boiling point. Both molecules have a similar number of electrons, so the strength of the London forces will be similar *[1 mark]*. NO is a polar molecule, so can also form permanent dipole-permanent dipole bonds. This means there are stronger intermolecular forces between molecules in NO than in N_2, which can only form London forces, so NO has a higher boiling point *[1 mark]*.

Page 33 — Hydrogen Bonding

1 a) Water contains hydrogen covalently bonded to oxygen, so it is able to form hydrogen bonds *[1 mark]*. These hydrogen bonds are stronger than the other types of intermolecular forces, so more energy is needed to break them *[1 mark]*.

b)

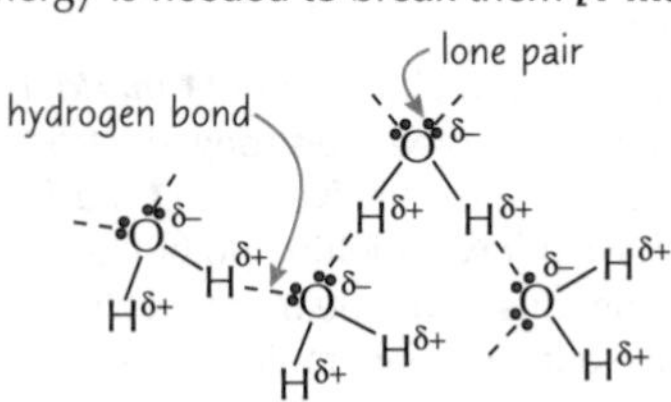

[2 marks — 1 mark for correctly drawn molecules showing partial charges and lone pairs, 1 mark for at least 3 correctly drawn hydrogen bonds]

2 a) i) Ammonia will have the higher boiling point *[1 mark]*.
ii) Water will have the higher boiling point *[1 mark]*.
iii) Propan-1-ol will have the higher boiling point *[1 mark]*.

b) The molecules of ammonia, water and propan-1-ol can form hydrogen bonds *[1 mark]*. These are stronger/take more energy to overcome than the intermolecular forces between the molecules of the other compounds *[1 mark]*.

3 Ethane-1,2-diol has stronger intermolecular forces because there are two alcohol groups, twice as many as in ethanol. Therefore ethane-1,2-diol can form twice as many hydrogen bonds as ethanol *[1 mark]*.

Answers

Page 35 — Solubility

1 a) i) Hydrogen bonds ***[1 mark]*** form between the alcohol and water molecules ***[1 mark]***. The (hydrogen) bonds between water molecules are stronger ***[1 mark]*** than bonds that would form between water and the halogenoalkane molecules ***[1 mark]***.
For the last two marks, you could also say that the halogenoalkanes do not contain strong enough dipoles to form hydrogen bonds with water.

ii)

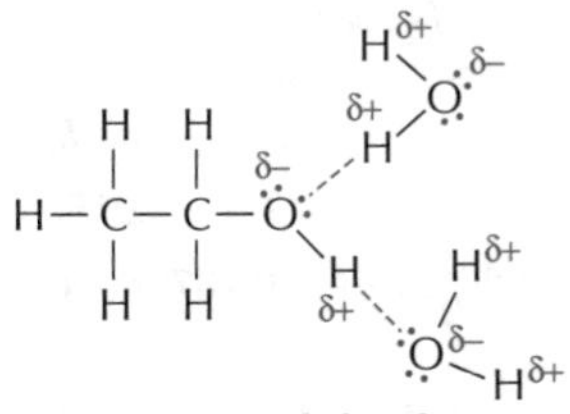

[2 marks — 1 mark for the two substances with relevant δ+ and δ– marked correctly, 1 mark for showing at least one correctly drawn hydrogen bond between propan-1-ol and a molecule of water]

b) K^+ ions are attracted to the δ– ends of the water molecules ***[1 mark]*** and I^- ions are attracted to the δ+ ends ***[1 mark]***. This overcomes the ionic bonds in the lattice/the ions are pulled away from the lattice ***[1 mark]***, and surrounded by water molecules ***[1 mark]***, forming hydrated ions:

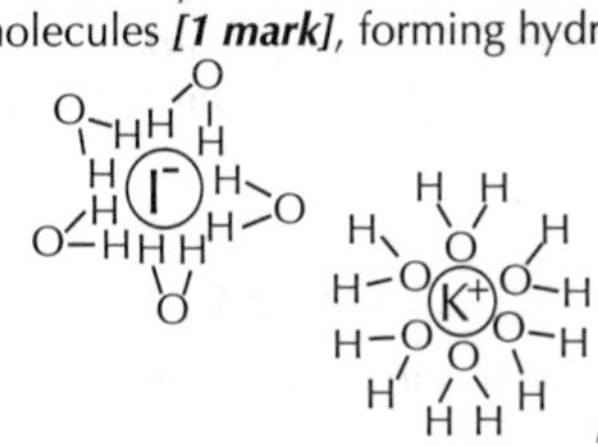

[1 mark]

2 a) Try to dissolve the substance in water ***[1 mark]*** and hexane (or other non-polar solvent) ***[1 mark]***. If X is non-polar, it is likely to dissolve in hexane, but not in water ***[1 mark]***.
Remember 'like dissolves like' — in other words, substances usually dissolve best in solvents that have similar intermolecular forces.

b) X and hexane have London forces/instantaneous dipole-induced dipole bonds between their molecules ***[1 mark]*** and form similar bonds with each other ***[1 mark]***. Water has hydrogen bonds ***[1 mark]*** which are much stronger than the bonds it could form with a non-polar compound ***[1 mark]***.

Page 37 — Predicting Structures and Properties

1 A = ionic ***[1 mark]***, B = simple molecular/covalent ***[1 mark]***, C = metallic ***[1 mark]***, D = giant covalent ***[1 mark]***.

2 Iodine is a simple molecular substance ***[1 mark]***. To melt or boil iodine, you only need to overcome the weak intermolecular forces holding the molecules together, which doesn't need much energy ***[1 mark]***. Graphite is a giant covalent substance ***[1 mark]***. Graphite will remain solid unless you can overcome the strong covalent bonds between atoms, which needs a lot of energy ***[1 mark]***.

3 B ***[1 mark]***

Topic 3 — Redox I

Page 39 — Oxidation Numbers

1 a) 0 b) +4 c) +6 d) –2 ***[4 marks — 1 mark for each]***

2 a) i) +1 ***[1 mark]*** ii) –1 ***[1 mark]***

b) +4 ***[1 mark]***
The oxidation number of combined oxygen is –2, so the total charge from the oxygens in Na_2SO_3 is (–2 × 3) = –6. Sodium forms ions with a +1 charge, so the total charge from sodium in the compound is (2 × +1) = +2. The contribution to the charge from non-sodium ions is therefore: –6 + 2 = –4. The overall charge on the compound is O, so the total charge from sulfur ion/the oxidation number of sulfur must be +4 (since –4 + 4 = O).

Page 41 — Redox Reactions

1 a) Oxidation is the loss of electrons ***[1 mark]***.

b) Oxygen is being reduced ***[1 mark]***. $O_2 + 4e^- \rightarrow 2O^{2-}$ ***[1 mark]***

2 a) An oxidising agent accepts electrons and gets reduced ***[1 mark]***.

b) $2In + 3Cl_2 \rightarrow 2InCl_3$ ***[2 marks — 1 mark for correct reactants and products, 1 mark for correct balancing]***
To do this question, you'll have to write out the half-equation for the oxidation of In first. It's $In \rightarrow In^{3+} + 3e^-$.

3 In a disproportionation reaction, an element in a single species is simultaneously oxidised and reduced ***[1 mark]***. In the reaction shown, oxygen has an oxidation state of –1 in H_2O_2/hydrogen peroxide ***[1 mark]***. In the reactants, oxygen has an oxidation state of –2 in H_2O (it's been reduced) and an oxidation state of 0 in O_2 (it's been oxidised) ***[1 mark]*** (so oxygen's been both oxidised and reduced).

4 $VO^{2+} + 2H^+ + e^- \rightarrow V^{3+} + H_2O$ ***[1 mark]***
$Sn^{2+} \rightarrow Sn^{4+} + 2e^-$ ***[1 mark]***
$2VO^{2+} + 4H^+ + Sn^{2+} \rightarrow 2V^{3+} + 2H_2O + Sn^{4+}$ ***[1 mark]***

Topic 4 — Inorganic Chemistry and the Periodic Table

Page 43 — Group 2

1 a) B ***[1 mark]***

b) Calcium ***[1 mark]***. Barium has more electron shells than calcium, meaning that the outer electrons are further away from the nucleus and more shielded by inner shells ***[1 mark]***, reducing the strength of the attraction between the outer electrons and the nucleus ***[1 mark]***. This makes it easier to remove outer electrons, resulting in barium having a lower combined first and second ionisation energy ***[1 mark]***.

c) $Ca_{(s)} + Cl_{2(g)} \rightarrow CaCl_{2(s)}$ ***[1 mark]***

2 a) $Mg(OH)_2 + 2HCl \rightarrow MgCl_2 + 2H_2O$
[2 marks — 1 mark for correct reactants and products, 1 mark if equation correctly balanced]

b) $CaO + H_2O \rightarrow Ca^{2+} + 2OH^-$ / $CaO + H_2O \rightarrow Ca(OH)_2$
[2 marks — 1 mark for correct reactants and products, 1 mark if equation correctly balanced]

Page 45 — Group 1 and 2 Compounds

1 a) $CaCO_{3(s)} \rightarrow CaO_{(s)} + CO_{2(g)}$
[1 mark for correct equation, and 1 mark for state symbols]

b) Barium carbonate is more thermally stable ***[1 mark]***. This is because barium has a larger ionic radius than calcium/has a lower charge density than calcium, so it has weaker polarising power ***[1 mark]***. The weaker polarising power of the barium ion causes less distortion of the carbonate ion ***[1 mark]*** (making it more thermally stable).
You'd also get the marks if you used the reverse argument to explain why $CaCO_3$ is less thermally stable.

2 a) $2NaNO_{3(s)} \rightarrow 2NaNO_{2(s)} + O_{2(g)}$ ***[1 mark]***

b) E.g. O_2 gas relights a glowing splint ***[1 mark]***.

c) magnesium nitrate, sodium nitrate, potassium nitrate ***[1 mark]***
Group 2 nitrates decompose more easily than Group 1 as they have a +2 charge on their cations, compared to the 1+ charge on Group 1 cations. The greater the charge on the cation, the less stable the nitrate compound ***[1 mark]***. The further down the group, the more stable the nitrate as the cations increase in size down the group, and the larger the cation, the less distortion to the nitrate anion ***[1 mark]***.

3 a) Energy is absorbed and electrons move to higher energy levels. ***[1 mark]*** Energy is released in the form of coloured light when the electrons fall back to the lower levels ***[1 mark]***.

b) caesium ***[1 mark]***

Answers

Page 47 — Halogens

1 a) $Cl_2 + 2Br^- \rightarrow 2Cl^- + Br_2$ ***[1 mark]***

b) The boiling points of the halogens increase down the group ***[1 mark]***. There is an increase in electron shells (and therefore electrons) the further down the group you go, and so the London forces also increase down the group ***[1 mark]***. Larger London forces make it harder to overcome the intermolecular forces, and so melting and boiling points increase down the group ***[1 mark]***.

2 a) (potassium) iodide ***[1 mark]***

b) brown ***[1 mark]***

Page 49 — Reactions of Halogens

1 a) $2OH^- + Br_2 \rightarrow OBr^- + Br^- + H_2O$ ***[1 mark]***

b) A disproportionation reaction ***[1 mark]***.

c) $3Br_2 + 6KOH \rightarrow KBrO_3 + 5KBr + 3H_2O$
[2 marks — 1 mark for correct reactants and products, 1 mark if equation correctly balanced]

Page 51 — Reactions of Halides

1 A ***[1 mark]***

2 Sodium chloride — misty fumes ***[1 mark]***
$NaCl + H_2SO_4 \rightarrow NaHSO_4 + HCl$ ***[1 mark]***
Sodium bromide — misty fumes ***[1 mark]***
$NaBr + H_2SO_4 \rightarrow NaHSO_4 + HBr$ ***[1 mark]***
$2HBr + H_2SO_4 \rightarrow Br_2 + SO_2 + 2H_2O$ ***[1 mark]***
Orange/brown vapour ***[1 mark]***

3 Potassium bromide reacts with sulfuric acid to produce hydrogen bromide, which is seen as misty fumes:
$KBr + H_2SO_4 \rightarrow KHSO_4 + HBr$ ***[1 mark]***
Bromide ions are a reducing agent, and are strong enough to reduce H_2SO_4 as part of a redox reaction:
$2HBr + H_2SO_4 \rightarrow Br_2 + SO_2 + 2H_2O$ ***[1 mark]***.
Potassium iodide reacts with sulfuric acid in a similar way:
$KI + H_2SO_4 \rightarrow KHSO_4 + HI$ ***[1 mark]***
$2HI + H_2SO_4 \rightarrow I_2 + SO_{(g)} + 2H_2O$ ***[1 mark]***
But iodide ions are a stronger reducing agent than bromide ions ***[1 mark]***, so go onto reduce SO_2 to H_2S:
$6HI + SO_2 \rightarrow H_2S + 3I_2 + 2H_2O$ ***[1 mark]***

Page 53 — Tests for Ions

1 Add dilute hydrochloric acid to the solution ***[1 mark]*** and then test to see whether the gas given off is carbon dioxide by bubbling it through limewater. If the limewater goes cloudy, the solution contains carbonates ***[1 mark]***.

2 a) C ***[1 mark]***

b) $Ba^{2+}_{(aq)} + SO_4{}^{2-}_{(aq)} \rightarrow BaSO_{4(s)}$ ***[2 marks — 1 mark for correct equation, 1 mark for correct state symbols]***

3 Add some sodium hydroxide to the solution in a test tube and gently heat the mixture ***[1 mark]***. Test the gas produced with a damp piece of red litmus paper. If there's ammonia given off this means there are ammonium ions in the solution. If there's ammonia present, the paper will turn blue ***[1 mark]***.

Topic 5 — Formulae, Equations & Amounts of Substances

Page 55 — The Mole

1 M of $CaSO_4 = 40.1 + 32.1 + (4 \times 16.0) = 136.2$ g mol^{-1}
number of moles $= \frac{34.05}{136.2} = \mathbf{0.2500}$ **moles** ***[1 mark]***

2 M of $CH_3COOH = (2 \times 12.0) + (4 \times 1.0) + (2 \times 16.0)$
$= 60.0$ g mol^{-1}
mass $= 60.0 \times 0.360 = \mathbf{21.6}$ **g** ***[1 mark]***

3 M of $HCl = 1.0 + 35.5 = 36.5$ g mol^{-1}
mass $= 0.100 \times 36.5 = 3.65$ g ***[1 mark]***
volume of water in dm^3 $= 100 \div 1000 = 0.100$ dm^3
concentration $= \frac{\text{mass}}{\text{volume}} = \frac{3.65}{0.100} = \mathbf{36.5}$ **g dm^{-3}** ***[1 mark]***

4 number of moles $= 0.250 \times \frac{60.0}{1000} = 0.0150$ moles ***[1 mark]***
M of $H_2SO_4 = (2 \times 1.0) + 32.1 + (4 \times 16.0) = 98.1$ g mol^{-1}
mass $= 0.0150 \times 98.1 = \mathbf{1.47}$ **g** ***[1 mark]***

5 M of $AgI = 107.9 + 126.9 = 234.8$ g mol^{-1}
number of moles $= \frac{1.01}{234.8} = 0.00430...$ mol ***[1 mark]***
volume of nitric acid in dm^3 $= 15.0 \div 1000 = 0.0150$ dm^3
concentration $= \frac{\text{moles}}{\text{volume}} = \frac{0.00430...}{0.0150} = \mathbf{0.287}$ **mol dm^{-3}** ***[1 mark]***

Page 57 — Empirical and Molecular Formulae

1 The mass 'lost' during the experiment must have been oxygen.
$2.80 - 2.50 = 0.300$ g oxygen was present in the oxide ***[1 mark]***.
Moles of Cu $= 2.50 \div 63.5 = 0.0394$
Moles of O $= 0.300 \div 16.0 = 0.0188$ ***[1 mark]***
Dividing both these values by the smaller one:
Ratio Cu : O $= (0.0394 \div 0.0188) : (0.0188 \div 0.0188)$
$= 2.09... : 1$ ***[1 mark]***
So, rounding off, empirical formula $= Cu_2O$ ***[1 mark]***

2 Assume you've got 100 g of the compound so you can turn the % straight into mass.
No. of moles of C $= \frac{92.3}{12.0} = 7.69$ moles
No. of moles of H $= \frac{7.70}{1.00} = 7.70$ moles ***[1 mark]***
Divide both by the smallest number, in this case 7.69.
So ratio C : H = 1 : 1
So, the empirical formula = CH ***[1 mark]***
The empirical mass $= 12.0 + 1.0 = 13.0$
No. of empirical units in molecule $= \frac{78.0}{13.0} = 6$
So the molecular formula $= \mathbf{C_6H_6}$ ***[1 mark]***

3 The magnesium is burning, so it's reacting with oxygen and the product is magnesium oxide.
First work out the number of moles of each element.
No. of moles Mg $= \frac{1.20}{24.0} = 0.0500$ moles
Mass of O is everything that isn't Mg: $2.00 - 1.20 = 0.800$ g
No. of moles O $= \frac{0.800}{16.0} = 0.0500$ moles ***[1 mark]***
Ratio Mg : O = 0.0500 : 0.0500
Divide both by the smallest number, in this case 0.0500.
So ratio Mg : O = 1 : 1
So the empirical formula is **MgO** ***[1 mark]***

4 First calculate the no. of moles of each product and then the mass of C and H:
No. of moles of $CO_2 = \frac{33.0}{44.0} = 0.0750$ moles
Mass of C $= 0.750 \times 12.0 = 9.00$ g
No. of moles of $H_2O = \frac{10.8}{18.0} = 0.600$ moles
0.600 moles H_2O = 1.20 moles H
Mass of H $= 1.20 \times 1.0 = 1.20$ g ***[1 mark]***
Organic acids contain C, H and O, so the rest of the mass must be O.
Mass of O $= 19.8 - (9.00 + 1.20) = 9.60$ g
No. of moles of O $= \frac{9.60}{16.0} = 0.600$ moles ***[1 mark]***
Mole ratio = C : H : O = 0.750 : 1.20 : 0.600
Divide by smallest 1.25 : 2 : 1
The carbon part of the ratio isn't a whole number, so you have to multiply them all up until it is. As its fraction is ¼, multiply them all by 4.
So, mole ratio = C : H : O = 5 : 8 : 4
Empirical formula $= \mathbf{C_5H_8O_4}$ ***[1 mark]***
Empirical mass $= (12.0 \times 5) + (1.0 \times 8) + (16.0 \times 4) = 132$ g
This is the same as what we're told the molecular mass is, so the molecular formula is also $\mathbf{C_5H_8O_4}$ ***[1 mark]***.

Answers

Page 59 — Chemical Equations

1 On the LHS, you need 2 each of K and I, so use 2KI
This makes the final equation:
$\mathbf{2KI + Pb(NO_3)_2 \rightarrow PbI_2 + 2KNO_3}$ ***[1 mark]***
In this equation, the NO_3 group remains unchanged, so it makes balancing much easier if you treat it as one indivisible lump.

2 The equation for the reaction is: $C_2H_4 + HCl \rightarrow C_2H_5Cl$
M of $C_2H_5Cl = (2 \times 12.0) + (5 \times 1.0) + (1 \times 35.5) = 64.5$ g mol^{-1} ***[1 mark]***
Number of moles of $C_2H_5Cl = \frac{258}{64.5} = 4.00$ moles ***[1 mark]***
From the equation, 1 mole C_2H_5Cl is made from 1 mole C_2H_4 so, 4 moles C_2H_5Cl is made from 4 moles C_2H_4 ***[1 mark]***.
M of $C_2H_4 = (2 \times 12.0) + (4 \times 1.0) = 28.0$ g mol^{-1}
so, the mass of 4 moles $C_2H_4 = 4 \times 28.0 =$ **112 g** ***[1 mark]***

3 $Ag^+_{(aq)} + Cl^-_{(aq)} \rightarrow AgCl_{(s)}$ ***[2 marks — 1 mark for correct equation, 1 mark for correct state symbols]***
The question tells you that the reaction is a precipitation reaction, and that magnesium nitrate solution is formed. So the other product, silver chloride, must be the solid precipitate.

Page 61 — Calculations with Gases

1 Moles of $Cl_2 = \frac{1.28}{35.5 \times 2} = 0.0180...$ moles ***[1 mark]***
Rearranging $pV = nRT$ to find T gives $T = \frac{pV}{nR}$.
So, $T = \frac{175 \times (98.6 \times 10^{-3})}{0.0180 \times 8.314} =$ **115 K** ***[1 mark]***

2 M of $C_3H_8 = (3 \times 12.0) + (8 \times 1.0) = 44.0$ g mol^{-1}
No. of moles of $C_3H_8 = \frac{88}{44.0} = 2.0$ moles ***[1 mark]***
At r.t.p. 1 mole of gas occupies 24 dm^3, so 2.0 moles of gas occupies $2.0 \times 24 =$ **48 dm³** ***[1 mark]***
You could also use the equation $pV = nRT$ to answer this question, where at r.t.p, $T = 293$ K, and $p = 101\,300$ Pa. In this case, your answer would be $V = \frac{nRT}{p} = \frac{2.0 \times 8.31 \times 293}{101300} = 0.048$ m^3 = 48 dm^3.

3 Start by writing the balanced equation for the combustion of butane:
$C_4H_{10} + 6\frac{1}{2}O_2 \rightarrow 4CO_2 + 5H_2O$ ***[1 mark]***
So, moles of O_2 required $= 3.50 \times 10^{-2} \times 6.5 = 0.2275$ mol
At room temperature and pressure, 1 mole of gas occupies 24 dm^3.
So $0.2275 \times 24 =$ **5.46 dm³** ***[1 mark]***.

4 $MgCO_3 \rightarrow MgO + CO_2$
1 mole of $MgCO_3$ produces 1 mole of CO_2.
At r.t.p., 6.00 dm^3 of $CO_2 = 6.00 \div 24.0 = 0.250$ mol ***[1 mark]***.
So 0.250 mol of CO_2 is produced by 0.250 mol of $MgCO_3$.
M_r of $MgCO_3 = 24.3 + 12.0 + (3 \times 16.0) = 84.3$
0.250 mol of $MgCO_3 = 84.3 \times 0.250 =$ **21.1 g** ***[1 mark]***

Page 63 — Acid-Base Titrations

1 Moles $= \frac{\text{Concentration} \times \text{Volume}}{1000} = \frac{0.500 \times 200}{1000} = 0.100$ moles ***[1 mark]***
Mass = moles × molar mass
$= 0.100 \times [(3 \times 1.0) + 14.0 + 32.1 + (16.0 \times 3)]$
$= 0.100 \times 97.1 =$ **9.71 g** ***[1 mark]***

2 ***A maximum of two marks can be awarded for structure and reasoning of the written response:***
2 marks: The answer is constructed logically, and displays clear reasoning and links between points throughout.
1 mark: The answer is mostly logical, with some reasoning and links between points.
0 marks: The answer has no structure and no links between points.
Here are some points your answer may include:
Indicators change colour when the solution reaches a particular pH to mark an end point. They are used in acid/alkali titrations to mark the end point of the reaction. Indicators used in titrations need to change colour quickly over a very small pH range.
A few drops of indicator solution are added to the analyte.
The analyte/indicator solution can be placed on a white surface to make a colour change easy to see. Methyl orange and phenolphthalein are both good indicators for titrations as they quickly change colour when the solution turns from alkali to acid. Universal indicator is a poor indicator to use for titrations as its colour changes gradually over a wide pH range.
[4 marks — 4 marks if 6 points mentioned covering all areas of the question, 3 marks if 4-5 points covered, 2 marks if 2-3 points covered, 1 mark if 1 point covered]

Page 65 — Titration Calculations

1 First write down what you know:
$CH_3COOH + NaOH \rightarrow CH_3COONa + H_2O$
25.4 cm^3 14.6 cm^3
? 0.500 mol dm^{-3}
No. of moles of NaOH $= \frac{0.500 \times 14.6}{1000} = 0.00730$ moles ***[1 mark]***
From the equation, you know 1 mole of NaOH neutralises 1 mole of CH_3COOH, so if you've used 0.00730 moles NaOH you must have neutralised 0.00730 moles CH_3COOH ***[1 mark]***.
Concentration of $CH_3COOH = \frac{0.00730 \times 1000}{25.4} =$ **0.287 mol dm⁻³** ***[1 mark]***

2 First write down what you know again:
$CaCO_3 + H_2SO_4 \rightarrow CaSO_4 + H_2O + CO_2$
0.750 g 0.250 mol dm^{-3}
M of $CaCO_3 = 40.1 + 12.0 + (3 \times 16.0) = 100.1$ g mol^{-1} ***[1 mark]***
No. of moles of $CaCO_3 = \frac{0.750}{100.1} = 7.49... \times 10^{-3}$ moles ***[1 mark]***
From the equation, 1 mole $CaCO_3$ reacts with 1 mole H_2SO_4 so, $7.49... \times 10^{-3}$ moles $CaCO_3$ reacts with $7.49... \times 10^{-3}$ moles H_2SO_4 ***[1 mark]***.
Volume needed is $= \frac{(7.49... \times 10^{-3}) \times 1000}{0.250} =$ **30.0 cm³** ***[1 mark]***

3 a) $Ca(OH)_2 + 2HCl \rightarrow CaCl_2 + 2H_2O$ ***[1 mark]***

b) Number of moles of HCl $= \frac{0.250 \times 17.1}{1000}$
$= 4.275 \times 10^{-3}$ moles ***[1 mark]***
From the equation in a), 2 moles HCl reacts with 1 mole $Ca(OH)_2$, so, 4.275×10^{-3} moles HCl reacts with 2.1375×10^{-3} moles $Ca(OH)_2$ ***[1 mark]***.
So concentration of $Ca(OH)_2$ solution =
$\frac{(2.1375 \times 10^{-3}) \times 1000}{25.0} =$ **0.0855 mol dm⁻³** ***[1 mark]***.

Answers

Page 67 — Uncertainty and Errors

1 a) The titre is calculated by subtracting the initial volume from the final volume. Each of these has an uncertainty of 0.05 cm^3, so the total uncertainty is 0.1 cm^3.
percentage uncertainty = (0.1 ÷ 3.1) × 100 = **3.23%**
[2 marks — 1 mark for correct use of percentage uncertainty formula, 1 mark for using uncertainty of 0.1 cm³]

b) The percentage uncertainty will decrease if the titres are larger ***[1 mark]***. Using a less concentrated solution will result in larger titres ***[1 mark]***.

2 % uncertainty in pipette = (0.06 ÷ 25.00) × 100 = 0.24% ***[1 mark]***
% uncertainty in titre = (0.1 ÷ 19.25) × 100 = 0.519...% ***[1 mark]***
Total % uncertainty = 0.24 + 0.519... = 0.759...% ***[1 mark]***
So uncertainty of concentration = 0.759...% of 0.0770
= **0.00058 mol dm^{-3} (5.8 × 10^{-4} mol dm^{-3})** ***[1 mark]***

Page 69 — Atom Economy and Percentage Yield

1 a) 2 is an addition reaction ***[1 mark]***

b) For reaction 1: % atom economy
= $M_r(C_2H_5Cl) \div [M_r(C_2H_5Cl) + M_r(POCl_3) + M_r(HCl)] \times 100\%$ ***[1 mark]***
= [(2 × 12.0) + (5 × 1.0) + 35.5] ÷ [(2 × 12.0) + (5 × 1.0) + 35.5 + 31.0 + 16.0 + (3 × 35.5) + 1.0 + 35.5] × 100%
= (64.5 ÷ 254.5) × 100% = **25.3%** ***[1 mark]***

c) The atom economy is 100% because there is only one product (there are no by-products) ***[1 mark]***

2 a) Number of moles = mass ÷ molar mass
Moles PCl_3 = 0.275 ÷ 137.5 = 0.002 moles
Chlorine is in excess, so there must be 0.002 moles of product ***[1 mark]***. Mass of PCl_5 = 0.002 × 208.5 = **0.417 g** ***[1 mark]***

b) percentage yield = (0.198 ÷ 0.417) × 100% = **47.5%** ***[1 mark]***

c) Changing reaction conditions will have no effect on atom economy ***[1 mark]***. Since the equation shows that there is only one product, the atom economy will always be 100% ***[1 mark]***.
Atom economy is related to the type of reaction — addition, substitution, etc. — not to the quantities of products and reactants.

Topic 6 — Organic Chemistry I

Page 71 — The Basics

1 a)

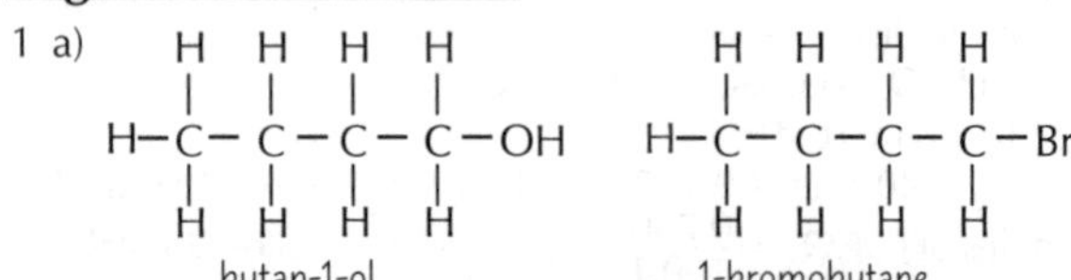

[2 marks — 1 mark for each correct structure]

b) It tells you that the main functional group (-OH) is attached to the first carbon in the chain ***[1 mark]***. The number is necessary because the main functional group could be attached to the first or second carbon/butan-2-ol also exists ***[1 mark]***.

2 a) i) 1-chloro-2-methylpropane ***[1 mark]***
Remember to put the substituents in alphabetical order.
ii) 3-methylbut-1-ene ***[1 mark]***
iii) 2,4-dibromo-but-1-ene ***[1 mark]***

b) i) C_7H_{16} ***[1 mark]***
ii) $CH_3CH_2CH(CH_2CH_3)CH_2CH_3$ ***[1 mark]***

Page 73 — Organic Reactions

1 C ***[1 mark]***

2 a) polymerisation ***[1 mark]***
b) hydrolysis / substitution ***[1 mark]***
c) substitution ***[1 mark]***

Page 75 — Isomerism

1 a) B ***[1 mark]***
b) Isomers that have the same molecular formula but different structural formulae ***[1 mark]***.

2 a) OR  ***[1 mark]***

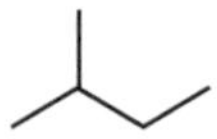

b) OR 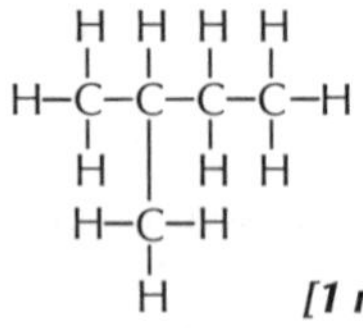 ***[1 mark]***

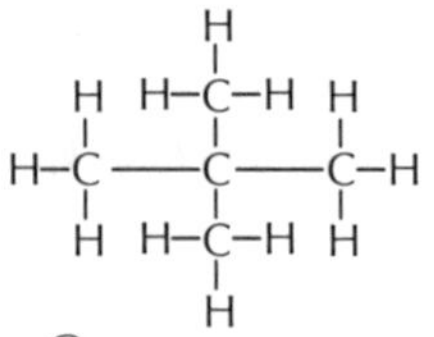

3 a) ***[1 mark]*** 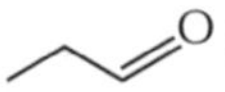 ***[1 mark]***

b) CH_3COCH_3 ***[1 mark]*** and CH_3CH_2CHO ***[1 mark]***

4 D ***[1 mark]***

Page 77 — Alkanes

1 a) Radical substitution ***[1 mark]***.
b) $CH_4 + Br_2 \xrightarrow{U.V.} CH_3Br + HBr$ ***[1 mark]***
c) $Br\bullet + CH_4 \rightarrow HBr + \bullet CH_3$ ***[1 mark]***
$\bullet CH_3 + Br_2 \rightarrow CH_3Br + Br\bullet$ ***[1 mark]***
d) i) Two methyl radicals bond together to form an ethane molecule ***[1 mark]***. The equation for the reaction is:
$\bullet CH_3 + \bullet CH_3 \rightarrow CH_3CH_3$ ***[1 mark]***
ii) termination step ***[1 mark]***
e) tetrabromomethane ***[1 mark]***

Page 79 — Crude Oil

1 a) i) E.g. There's greater demand for smaller fractions for things such as motor fuels ***[1 mark]***. / There's greater demand for alkenes to make petrochemicals/polymers ***[1 mark]***.
ii) E.g. $C_{12}H_{26} \rightarrow C_2H_4 + C_{10}H_{22}$ ***[1 mark]***.
There are loads of possible answers — just make sure the C's and H's balance and there's an alkane and an alkene.

b) i) Any two from: Cycloalkanes / arenes / aromatic hydrocarbons / branched alkanes ***[2 marks — 1 mark for each]***
ii) They promote efficient combustion/reduce knocking (autoignition) ***[1 mark]***.

Page 81 — Fuels

1 a) $C_5H_{12} + 8O_2 \rightarrow 5CO_2 + 6H_2O$ ***[2 marks — 1 mark for reactants and products correct, 1 mark for correct balancing]***

b) The products of incomplete combustion include carbon monoxide gas which is toxic ***[1 mark]***. This is because it binds to haemoglobin in the blood, meaning less oxygen can be transported around the body and leading to oxygen deprivation ***[1 mark]***.

2 a) Sulfur dioxide and nitrogen oxides (NO_x) ***[1 mark]***.
b) Catalytic converters convert nitrogen oxides into harmless gases, such as nitrogen and water vapour ***[1 mark]***.

3 E.g. Advantage: it's carbon neutral / can be made from waste that would otherwise go to landfill / is renewable ***[1 mark]***.
Disadvantage: engines would have to be converted to run off biodiesel / growing crops for biodiesel uses land that could otherwise be used to grow food ***[1 mark]***.

Page 82 — Alkenes

1 a) E.g. Both bonds form when two atomic orbitals overlap / when the nuclei of two atoms form electrostatic attractions to a bonding pair of electrons ***[1 mark]***.

b) E.g. σ-bonds form when two atomic orbitals overlap directly between two nuclei, whereas π-bonds form when both lobes of two p-orbitals overlap side-on / in σ-bonds, the electron density lies directly between the two nuclei, whereas in π-bonds, the electron density lies above and below the molecular axis / σ-bonds have a higher bond enthalpy than π-bonds ***[1 mark]***.

Answers

Page 85 — Stereoisomerism

1 a) 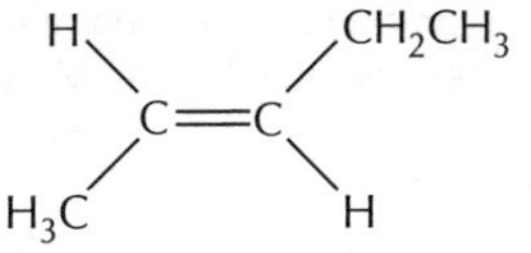 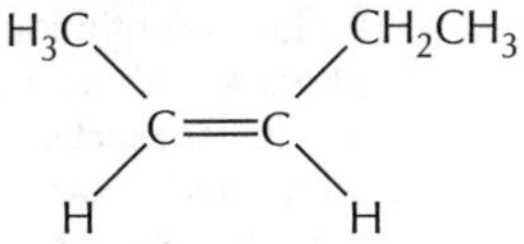 [structure: H and H_3C on one carbon, CH_2CH_3 and H on the other, C=C]
E-pent-2-ene *[1 mark]*
[structure: H_3C and H on one carbon, CH_2CH_3 and H on the other, C=C]
Z-pent-2-ene *[1 mark]*

b) E/Z isomers occur because atoms can't rotate about C=C double bonds ***[1 mark]***. Alkenes contain C=C double bonds and alkanes don't, so alkenes can form E/Z isomers and alkanes can't ***[1 mark]***.

2 B ***[1 mark]***

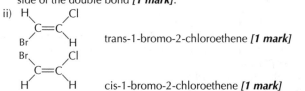

3 a) i) 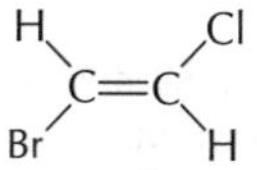 H(Br)C=C(Cl)(H) E-1-bromo-2-chloroethene ***[1 mark]*** 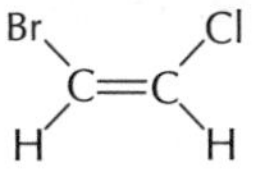
Br(H)C=C(Cl)(H) Z-1-bromo-2-chloroethene ***[1 mark]***
ii) 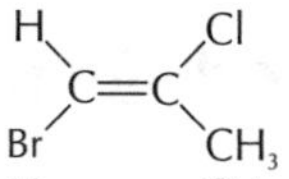 H(Br)C=C(Cl)(CH_3) E-1-bromo-2-chloroprop-1-ene ***[1 mark]*** 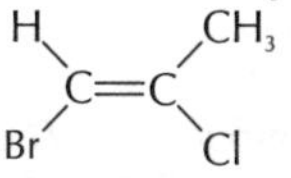
H(Br)C=C(CH_3)(Cl) Z-1-bromo-2-chloroprop-1-ene ***[1 mark]***

b) i) 1-bromo-2-chloroethene ***[1 mark]*** because there is a hydrogen atom / an identical group attached to the carbons on either side of the double bond ***[1 mark]***.
ii) 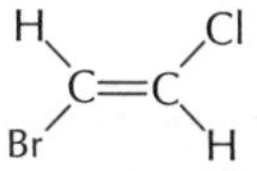 H(Br)C=C(Cl)(H) trans-1-bromo-2-chloroethene ***[1 mark]*** 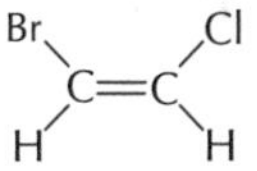
Br(H)C=C(Cl)(H) cis-1-bromo-2-chloroethene ***[1 mark]***

Page 87 — Reactions of Alkenes

1 a) Shake the alkene with bromine water, and the solution goes from brown to colourless if a double bond is present ***[1 mark]***.

b) Electrophilic addition ***[1 mark]***.
E.g. [mechanism: but-1-ene + $Br^{\delta+}$–$Br^{\delta-}$ → carbocation intermediate H–C(H)(Br)–C⁺(H)–C(H)(H)–C(H)(H)–H with Br^- → H–C(H)(Br)–C(H)(Br)–C(H)(H)–C(H)(H)–H]

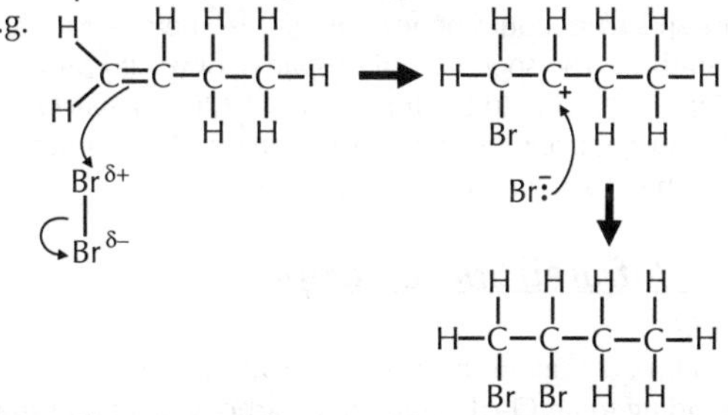

[4 marks — 1 mark for correct partial charges on bromine molecule, 1 mark for correct curly arrows showing bromine attacking the C=C double bond and the Br–Br bond breaking heterolytically, 1 mark for structure of intermediate, 1 mark for curly arrow showing attack of Br^- on the carbocation]

This reaction can go via a primary or a secondary carbocation. You'd get the marks for the mechanism for showing it going by either one.

c) 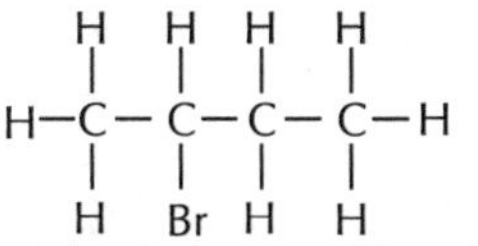 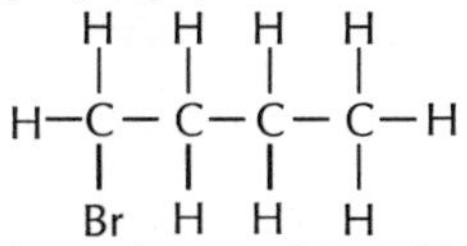 [structure: $CH_3CHBrCH_2CH_3$] 2-bromobutane ***[1 mark]***
[structure: $CH_2BrCH_2CH_2CH_3$] 1-bromobutane ***[1 mark]***
The major product will be 2-bromobutane ***[1 mark]*** since the formation of this product goes via the more stable carbocation intermediate ***[1 mark]***.

Page 89 — Polymers

1 a) 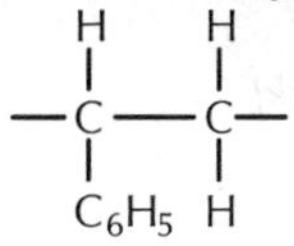 [repeat unit: –C(H)(C_6H_5)–C(H)(H)–] ***[1 mark]***

b) 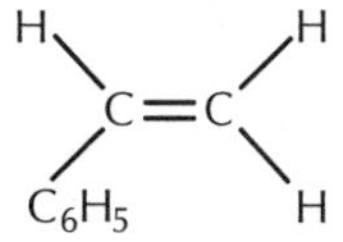 [structure: H(C_6H_5)C=C(H)(H)] ***[1 mark]***

2 a) E.g. Saves on landfill / Energy can be used to generate electricity ***[1 mark]***.

b) E.g. Toxic gases produced ***[1 mark]***. Scrubbers can be used to remove these toxic gases / polymers that might burn to produce toxic gases can be separated out before incineration ***[1 mark]***.

3 ***A maximum of two marks can be awarded for structure and reasoning of the written response:***
2 marks: The answer is constructed logically, and displays clear reasoning and links between points throughout.
1 mark: The answer is mostly logical, with some reasoning and links between points.
0 marks: The answer has no structure and no links between points.
Here are some points your answer may include:
Chemists could use reactant molecules that are as safe and as environmentally friendly as possible. Chemists should aim to use as few materials as possible in the manufacture process (e.g. limit the use of solvents). Chemists should aim to use renewable raw materials wherever possible. Chemists should minimise energy usage (e.g. by using catalysts) during the manufacturing process. Chemists should minimise the amount of waste products made during the process, especially those which are hazardous to human health or the environment. Polymers should be made with a lifespan that is appropriate for their use. Chemists could create biodegradable polymers which, when disposed of, are less damaging to the environment.
[4 marks — 4 marks if 6 points covered, 3 marks if 4-5 points covered, 2 marks if 2-3 points covered, 1 mark if 1 point covered]

Page 91 — Halogenoalkanes

1 a) 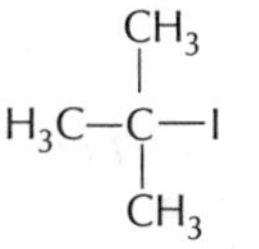 [structure: $(CH_3)_3C$–I] ***[1 mark]*** 2-iodo-2-methylpropane ***[1 mark]***

b) AgI ***[1 mark]***

c) The tertiary alcohol with formula C_4H_9Cl will be hydrolysed more slowly than 2-methyl-2-iodopropane under the same conditions ***[1 mark]***. This is because C–Cl bonds are shorter so have a higher bond enthalpy that C–I bonds ***[1 mark]***, and are therefore harder to break than C–I bonds ***[1 mark]*** (resulting in a slower rate of hydrolysis).

Answers

Page 93 — More on Halogenoalkanes

1 a) $CH_3CHOHCH_3$ ***[1 mark]***

b) i) ethanolic ammonia ***[1 mark]***, warm ***[1 mark]***

ii) Step 1:

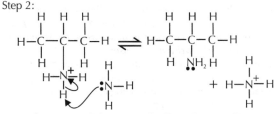

```
    H  H  H                          H   H   H
    |  |  |                          |   |   |
 H—C—C^δ+—C—H    ——————→        H—C—C—C—H
    |  |  |       ethanol            |   |   |
  H H  Br^δ- H                        H  NH3 H
  |                                      +        :Br⁻
H—N:
  |
  H
```

[2 marks — 1 mark for NH_3 attacking δ+ carbon, 1 mark for C–Br bond breaking]

Step 2:

```
   H   H   H                 H   H   H
   |   |   |                 |   |   |
H—C—C—C—H      ⇌      H—C—C—C—H
   |   |   |                 |   |   |
   H   |   H    H            H  NH2  H           H
   H—N+—H       |                ••               |+
     |       :N—H                         + H—N—H
     H          |                                 |
                H                                 H
```

[2 marks — 1 mark for correctly drawn intermediate, 1 mark for showing ammonia attacking a positive nitrogen centre]

c) CH_3CHCH_2 ***[1 mark]***

Page 95 — Alcohols

1 a) primary: e.g.

```
   H  H  H  H  H
   |  |  |  |  |
H—C—C—C—C—C—OH
   |  |  |  |  |
   H  H  H  H  H
```

pentan-1-ol ***[1 mark]***

secondary: e.g

```
   H  H  H  H  H
   |  |  |  |  |
H—C—C—C—C—C—H
   |  |  |  |  |
   H  H  H  OH H
```

pentan-2-ol ***[1 mark]***

tertiary:

```
          H
          |
        H—C—H
   H  H   |   H
   |  |   |   |
H—C—C—C—C—H
   |  |   |   |
   H  H  OH   H
```

2-methylbutan-2-ol ***[1 mark]***

b) E.g. React ethanol with sodium bromide (KBr) with a 50% concentrated sulfuric acid catalyst ***[1 mark]***.

2 a) Elimination reaction OR dehydration reaction ***[1 mark]***.

b) C ***[1 mark]***

Page 97 — Oxidation of Alcohols

1 a) i) Propanoic acid (CH_3CH_2COOH) ***[1 mark]***

ii) $CH_3CH_2CH_2OH + [O] \rightarrow CH_3CH_2CHO + H_2O$ ***[1 mark]***
$CH_3CH_2CHO + [O] \rightarrow CH_3CH_2COOH$ ***[1 mark]***

iii) Distillation. This is so aldehyde is removed immediately as it forms ***[1 mark]***.

If you don't get the aldehyde out quick-smart, it'll be a carboxylic acid before you know it.

b) i)

```
        H
        |
      H—C—H
   H    |    H
   |    |    |
H—C—C—C—H
   |    |    |
   H   OH    H
```

[1 mark]

ii) 2-methylpropan-2-ol is a tertiary alcohol ***[1 mark]***.

2 D ***[1 mark]***

3 React 2-methylpropan-1-ol ($CH_3CH(CH_3)CH_2OH$) ***[1 mark]*** with a controlled amount of acidified potassium dichromate(VI) and heat gently in distillation apparatus to distil off the aldehyde ***[1 mark]***.

Page 99 — Organic Techniques

1 a) i) Reflux is continuous boiling/evaporation and condensation ***[1 mark]***. It's done to prevent loss of volatile liquids while heating ***[1 mark]***.

ii) Unreacted hexan-1-ol ***[1 mark]***

iii) Pour the reaction mixture into a separating funnel and add water ***[1 mark]***. Shake the funnel and allow the layers to settle ***[1 mark]***. To separate the layers, open the tap to run the lower layer out of the separating funnel into a container. Then, collect the upper layer in a separate container ***[1 mark]***.

b) i) The alkene product may dehydrate again to form a diene ***[1 mark]***.

ii) Carry out the experiment in a distillation apparatus ***[1 mark]*** so the singly dehydrated product is removed immediately from the reaction mixture and doesn't react a second time ***[1 mark]***.

Topic 7 — Modern Analytical Techniques I

Page 101 — Mass Spectrometry

1 a) 44 ***[1 mark]***

b) X has a mass of 15. It is probably a methyl group/CH_3^+ ***[1 mark]***.
Y has a mass of 29. It is probably an ethyl group/$C_2H_5^+$ ***[1 mark]***.

c)

```
   H  H  H
   |  |  |
H—C—C—C—H
   |  |  |
   H  H  H
```

[1 mark]

d) If the compound was an alcohol, you would expect a peak with m/z ratio of 17, caused by the OH fragment ***[1 mark]***.

2 a) 56 ***[1 mark]***

b) CH_3CHCH^+ ***[1 mark]***

c) E.g. $m/z = 15$ ***[1 mark]***, CH_3^+ ***[1 mark]*** or
$m/z = 28$ ***[1 mark]***, CH_3CH^+ ***[1 mark]***.

3

```
   H  H  OH
   |  |  |
H—C—C—C—H
   |  |  |
   H  H  H
```

[1 mark], propan-1-ol ***[1 mark]***

The mass spectrum could be for one of 2 isomers — propan-1-ol or propan-2-ol. The spectrum of propan-1-ol would produce a peak at $m/z = 31$, due to the fragment CH_2OH^+ ***[1 mark]***. This would be absent from the spectrum of propan-2-ol ***[1 mark]*** (therefore the unknown alcohol is propan-1-ol).

Page 103 — Infrared Spectroscopy

1 a) A ***[1 mark]***

b) There is a broad peak in the region of 3300-2500 cm^{-1}, corresponding to an O–H stretch in a carboxylic acid ***[1 mark]***. There is also a strong peak in the region of 1725-1700 cm^{-1}, corresponding to a C=O stretch in a carboxylic acid ***[1 mark]***.

2 a) A: O–H group in a carboxylic acid ***[1 mark]***.
B: C=O as in an aldehyde, ketone or carboxylic acid ***[1 mark]***.

b) The spectrum suggests that the compound is a carboxylic acid, so it must be propanoic acid ***[1 mark]*** (CH_3CH_2COOH) ***[1 mark]***.

Answers

Topic 8 — Energetics I

Page 105 — Enthalpy Changes

1 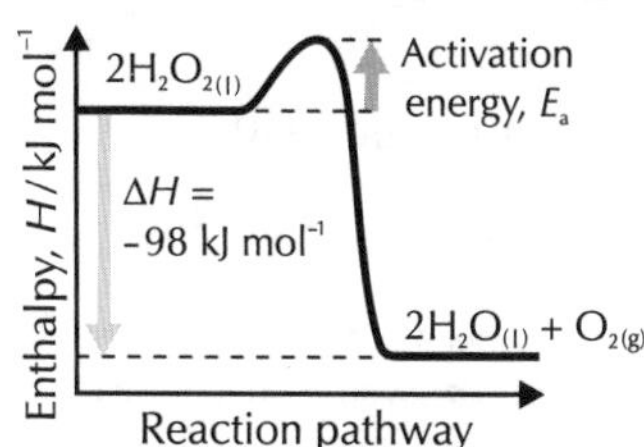

[3 marks — 1 mark for having reactants lower in energy than products, 1 mark for labelling activation energy correctly, 1 mark for labelling ΔH correctly, with arrow pointing downwards]

For an exothermic reaction, the ΔH arrow points downwards, but for an endothermic reaction it points upwards. The activation energy arrow always points upwards though.

2 a) $CH_3OH_{(l)} + 1\frac{1}{2}O_{2(g)} \rightarrow CO_{2(g)} + 2H_2O_{(l)}$ ***[1 mark]***
Make sure that only 1 mole of CH_3OH is combusted, as it says in the definition for $\Delta_c H^\circ$.
b) $C_{(s)} + 2H_{2(g)} + \frac{1}{2}O_{2(g)} \rightarrow CH_3OH_{(l)}$ ***[1 mark]***
c) Only 1 mole of C_3H_8 should be shown according to the definition of $\Delta_c H^\circ$ ***[1 mark]***.
You really need to know the definitions of the standard enthalpy changes off by heart. There are loads of nit-picky little details they could ask you questions about.

3 a) $C_{(s)} + O_{2(g)} \rightarrow CO_{2(g)}$ ***[1 mark]***
b) It has the same value because it is the same reaction ***[1 mark]***.
c) 1 tonne = 1 000 000 g
1 mole of carbon is 12.0 g
so 1 tonne is 1 000 000 ÷ 12.0 = 83 333... moles ***[1 mark]***
1 mole releases 393.5 kJ
so 1 tonne will release 83 333... × 393.5 = **32 800 000 kJ** (32.8×10^7 kJ) ***[1 mark]***
The final answer is rounded to 3 significant figures because the number with the fewest significant figures in the whole calculation is 12.0.

Page 107 — More on Enthalpy Changes

1 $\Delta T = 25.8 - 19.0 = 6.80$ °C = 6.80 K
$m = 25.0 + 25.0 = 50.0$ cm^3 of solution, which has a mass of 50.0 g.
Assume density to be 1.00 g cm^{-3}.
Heat produced by reaction = $mc\Delta T$
= 50.0 × 4.18 × 6.80 = 1421.2 J ***[1 mark]***
No. of moles of HCl = 1 × (25.0 ÷ 1000) = 0.0250
No. of moles of NaOH = 1 × (25.0 ÷ 1000) = 0.0250
Therefore, no. of moles of water = 0.0250 ***[1 mark]***
Producing 0.0250 mol of water takes 1421.2 J of heat, therefore producing 1 mol of water takes 1421.2 ÷ 0.0250 = 56 848 J
≈ 56.8 kJ (3 s.f.)
So the enthalpy change is **–56.8 kJ mol^{-1}** ***[1 mark]***
You need the minus sign because it's exothermic.

2 No. of moles of $CuSO_4$ = 0.200 × (50.0 ÷ 1000) = 0.0100 mol
From the equation, 1 mole of $CuSO_4$ reacts with 1 mole of Zn.
So, 0.0100 mol of $CuSO_4$ reacts with 0.0100 mol of Zn ***[1 mark]***.
Heat produced by reaction = $mc\Delta T$
= 50.0 × 4.18 × 2.00 = 418 J ***[1 mark]***
0.0100 mol of zinc produces 418 J of heat, therefore 1 mol of zinc produces 418 ÷ 0.0100 = 41 800 J = 41.8 kJ
So the enthalpy change is **–41.8 kJ mol^{-1}** ***[1 mark]***.
You need the minus sign because it's exothermic.
It'd be dead easy to work out the heat produced by the reaction, breathe a sigh of relief and sail on to the next question. But you need to find out the enthalpy change when 1 mole of zinc reacts. It's always a good idea to reread the question and check you've actually answered it.

Page 109 — Hess's Law

1 $\Delta_r H^\circ$ = sum of $\Delta_f H^\circ$(products) – sum of $\Delta_f H^\circ$(reactants) ***[1 mark]***
$\Delta_r H^\circ = [0 + (3 \times -602)] - [-1676 + 0]$
$\Delta_r H^\circ$ = **–130 kJ mol^{-1}** ***[1 mark]***
Don't forget the units. It's a daft way to lose marks.

2 $\Delta_f H^\circ = \Delta_c H^\circ$(glucose) – 2 × $\Delta_c H^\circ$(ethanol) ***[1 mark]***
$\Delta_f H^\circ = [-2820] - [(2 \times -1367)]$
$\Delta_f H^\circ$ = **–86 kJ mol^{-1}** ***[1 mark]***

Page 111 — Bond Enthalpy

1 Sum of bond enthalpies of reactants = (4 × 435) + (2 × 498)
= 2736 kJ mol^{-1}
Sum of bond enthalpies of products = (2 × 805) + (4 × 464)
= 3466 kJ mol^{-1} ***[1 mark]***
Enthalpy change of reaction = 2736 + (–3466)
= **–730 kJ mol^{-1}** ***[1 mark]***

2 Sum of bond enthalpies of reactants = (½ × 498) + 436
= 685 kJ mol^{-1}
Sum of bond enthalpies of products = (2 × 460)
= 920 kJ mol^{-1} ***[1 mark]***
Enthalpy change of formation = 685 – 920
= **–235 kJ mol^{-1}** ***[1 mark]***

3 a) Sum of bond enthalpies of reactants = (4 × 435) + 243
= 1983 kJ mol^{-1}
Sum of bond enthalpies of products = (3 × 397) + 432 + E(C–Cl)
= 1623 + E(C–Cl) kJ mol^{-1} ***[1 mark]***
–101 = 1983 – (1623 + E(C–Cl))
E(C–Cl) = 1983 – 1623 + 101 = **461 kJ mol^{-1}** ***[1 mark]***
b) The values differ because the data book value of C–Cl is an average of C–Cl bond energies in many molecules, while 461 kJ mol^{-1} is the C–Cl bond energy in chloromethane ***[1 mark]***.

Topic 9 — Kinetics I

Page 113 — Collision Theory

1 Increasing the pressure will increase the rate of reaction ***[1 mark]*** because there will be more particles in a given volume, so they will collide more frequently and therefore are more likely to react ***[1 mark]***.

2 The particles in a liquid move freely and all of them are able to collide with the solid particles ***[1 mark]***. Particles in solids just vibrate about fixed positions, so only those on the touching surfaces between the two solids will be able to react ***[1 mark]***.

3 a) X ***[1 mark]***
The X curve shows the same total number of molecules as the 25 °C curve, but more of them have lower energy.
b) The shape of the curve shows fewer molecules have the required activation energy ***[1 mark]***.

Answers

Page 115 — Reaction Rates

1 E.g.

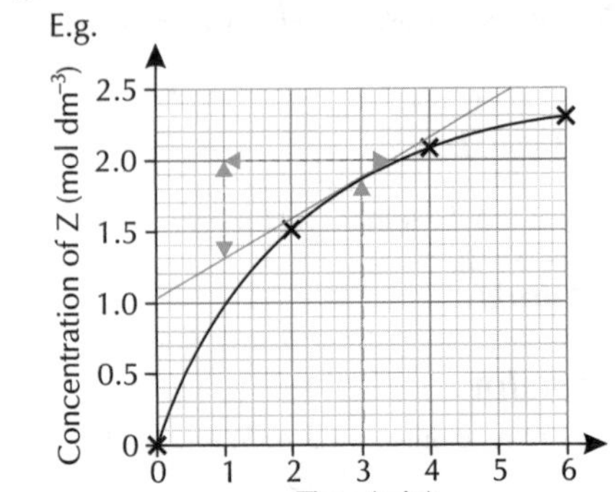

[1 mark for tangent drawn at 3 mins]

rate of reaction = gradient of tangent at 3 mins

gradient = change in y ÷ change in x

e.g. = (2.0 – 1.3) ÷ (3.4 – 1.0)

= **0.29 (± 0.06) mol dm^{-3} min^{-1}**

[2 marks — 1 mark for answer within margin of error, 1 mark for units]

Different people will draw slightly different tangents and pick different spots on the tangent so there's a margin of error in this answer. 0.29 (± 0.06) mol dm^{-3} min^{-1} means any answer between 0.35 mol dm^{-3} min^{-1} and 0.23 mol dm^{-3} min^{-1} is worth the mark.

Page 117 — Catalysts

1 a) A ***[1 mark]***

A catalyst only lowers activation energy. It doesn't affect the enthalpy change.

b) The catalyst lowers the activation energy ***[1 mark]***, meaning there are more particles with enough energy to react when they collide ***[1 mark]***. So, in a certain amount of time, more particles react ***[1 mark]***.

c) The vanadium(V) oxide catalyst is heterogeneous because it's in a different physical state to the reactants ***[1 mark]***.

Topic 10 — Equilibrium I

Page 119 — Dynamic Equilibrium

1 a) At dynamic equilibrium, the rate of the forwards and backwards reactions are the same ***[1 mark]*** and the concentrations of the reactants and the products are constant ***[1 mark]***.

b) $K_c = \frac{[NH_3]^2}{[N_2][H_2]^3}$ ***[1 mark]***

2 The reaction is heterogeneous so pure liquids / water should be excluded from the expression ***[1 mark]***. The reactants and products are also the wrong way round / the reactants should be on the bottom of the expression and the products should be on the top ***[1 mark]***.

3 B ***[1 mark]***

Page 121 — Le Chatelier's Principle

1 a) i) There's no change as there's the same number of molecules/ moles of gas on each side of the equation ***[1 mark]***.

ii) Reducing temperature removes heat. The equilibrium shifts in the exothermic direction to release heat, so the position of equilibrium shifts left ***[1 mark]***.

iii) Removing nitrogen monoxide reduces its concentration. The equilibrium position shifts right to try and increase the nitrogen monoxide concentration again ***[1 mark]***.

2 For an exothermic reaction, a low temperature means a high yield ***[1 mark]***. But a low temperature also means a slow reaction rate, so moderate temperatures are chosen as a compromise ***[1 mark]***.

Topic 11 — Equilibrium II

Page 123 — Calculations Involving K_c

1 C ***[1 mark]***

2 $K_c = \frac{[Cu^{2+}]}{[Ag^+]^2}$ ***[1 mark]*** $= \frac{0.193}{(0.431)^2} =$ **1.04 mol^{-1}dm^3**

[2 marks — 1 mark for correct value of K_c, 1 mark for correct units]

(Units = (mol dm^{-3})/ (mol dm^{-3})^2 = 1/mol dm^{-3} = mol^{-1} dm^3)

Don't forget, solids aren't included in the expression for the equilibrium constant.

3 a) i) mass ÷ M_r = 42.5 ÷ 46.0 = **0.923...** ***[1 mark]***

ii) moles of O_2 = mass ÷ M_r = 14.1 ÷ 32.0 = 0.440... ***[1 mark]***

moles of NO = 2 × moles of O_2 = 0.881... ***[1 mark]***

moles of NO_2 = 0.923... – 0.881... = **0.0427** ***[1 mark]***

b) Concentration of O_2 = 0.441 ÷ 22.8 = 0.0193... mol dm^{-3}

Concentration of NO = 0.881 ÷ 22.8 = 0.0386... mol dm^{-3}

Concentration of NO_2 = 0.0427 ÷ 22.8 = 0.00187... mol dm^{-3}

$K_c = \frac{[NO]^2[O_2]}{[NO_2]^2}$ ***[1 mark]*** $\Rightarrow K_c = \frac{(0.0386...)^2 \times (0.0193...)}{(0.00187...)^2}$ ***[1 mark]***

= **8.23 mol dm^{-3}** ***[2 marks — 1 mark for correct value of K_c, 1 mark for correct units]***

(Units = (mol dm^{-3})^2 × (mol dm^{-3}) /(mol dm^{-3})^2 = mol dm^{-3})

You might get a slightly different answer depending on how you rounded your intermediate answers throughout this question. As long as your answer is between 8.16 and 8.23, you'll still get the mark.

Page 125 — Gas Equilibria

1 a) $K_p = \frac{p(SO_2)p(Cl_2)}{p(SO_2Cl_2)}$ ***[1 mark]***

b) Cl_2 and SO_2 are produced in equal amounts so $p(Cl_2) = p(SO_2)$ = 0.594 atm ***[1 mark]***

Total pressure = $p(SO_2Cl_2) + p(Cl_2) + p(SO_2)$ so

$p(SO_2Cl_2)$ = 1.39 – 0.594 – 0.594 = **0.202 atm** ***[1 mark]***

c) $K_p = \frac{0.594 \times 0.594}{0.202}$ = **1.75 atm**

[2 marks — 1 mark for correct value of K_p, 1 mark for correct units]

(Units = (atm × atm)/ atm = atm)

2 a) $p(O_2)$ = ½ × 0.36 = 0.18 atm ***[1 mark]***

b) $p(NO_2)$ = total pressure – $p(NO)$ – $p(O_2)$

= 0.98 – 0.36 – 0.18 = **0.44 atm** ***[1 mark]***

c) $K_p = \frac{p(NO_2)^2}{p(NO)^2 p(O_2)}$ ***[1 mark]***

$= \frac{0.44^2}{0.36^2 \times 0.18}$ = **8.3 atm^{-1}** ***[2 marks — 1 mark for correct value of K_p, 1 mark for correct units]***

(Units = atm^2/(atm^2 × atm) = atm^{-1})

Page 127 — Le Chatelier's Principle and Equilibrium Constants

1 a) T_2 is lower than T_1 ***[1 mark]***. A decrease in temperature shifts the position of equilibrium in the exothermic direction, producing more product ***[1 mark]***. More product (and less reactant) means K_c increases ***[1 mark]***.

A negative ΔH means the forward reaction is exothermic — it gives out heat.

b) A decrease in volume means an increase in pressure. This shifts the equilibrium position to the right where there are fewer moles of gas. The yield of ammonia increases ***[1 mark]***.

K_c is unchanged ***[1 mark]***.

2 a) $K_p = \frac{p(CO)p(H_2)^3}{p(CH_4)p(H_2O)}$ ***[1 mark]***

b) A ***[1 mark]***

Answers

Topic 12 — Acid-Base Equilibria

Page 129 — Acids and Bases

1 a) $HCN \rightleftharpoons H^+ + CN^-$ OR $HCN + H_2O \rightleftharpoons H_3O^+ + CN^-$ ***[1 mark]***

b) Strongly to the left ***[1 mark]*** as it is a weak acid so it is only partially dissociated ***[1 mark]***.

c) CN^- ***[1 mark]***

2 a) The enthalpy of neutralisation is the enthalpy change when solutions of an acid and a base react together, under standard conditions ***[1 mark]***, to produce 1 mole of water ***[1 mark]***.

b) He is incorrect/the values for the enthalpy change of neutralisation will be different ***[1 mark]***. This is because nitric acid is a strong acid, so will fully dissociate in solution. Therefore, the value for the standard enthalpy change of neutralisation for the reaction of nitric acid and potassium hydroxide only includes the enthalpy of reaction between the H^+ and OH^- ions ***[1 mark]***. Ethanoic acid is a weak acid, so only dissociates slightly in solution. Therefore, the value for the enthalpy change of neutralisation for the reaction of ethanoic acid and potassium hydroxide includes the enthalpy of dissociation of the ethanoic acid, as well as enthalpy for the reaction of the H^+ and OH^- ions ***[1 mark]***.

Page 131 — pH

1 a) It's a strong monobasic acid, so $[H^+] = [HBr] = 0.32$ mol dm^{-3}.
$pH = -\log_{10} 0.32 = \mathbf{0.49}$ ***[1 mark]***

b) HF is a weaker acid than HCl, so will be less dissociated in solution. This means the concentration of hydrogen ions will be lower, so the pH will be higher ***[1 mark]***.

2 a) $K_a = \frac{[H^+][A^-]}{[HA]}$ ***[1 mark]***

b) $K_a = \frac{[H^+]^2}{[HA]}$ $[H^+] = \sqrt{(5.60 \times 10^{-4}) \times 0.280} = 0.0125...$ ***[1 mark]***
$pH = -\log_{10}[H^+] = -\log_{10}(0.0125...) = \mathbf{1.90}$ ***[1 mark]***

3 $[H^+] = 10^{-2.65} = 2.23... \times 10^{-3}$ mol dm^{-3} ***[1 mark]***
$K_a = \frac{[H^+]^2}{[HX]}$ ***[1 mark]*** $= \frac{(2.23... \times 10^{-3})^2}{0.150}$
$= \mathbf{3.34 \times 10^{-5}}$ **mol dm^{-3}** ***[1 mark]***

Page 133 — The Ionic Product of Water

1 a) Moles of NaOH = 2.50 ÷ 40.0 = 0.0625 moles ***[1 mark]***
1 mole of NaOH gives 1 mole of OH^-.
So $[OH^-] = [NaOH] = \mathbf{0.0625}$ **mol dm^{-3}** ***[1 mark]***.

b) $K_w = [H^+][OH^-]$
$[H^+] = 1 \times 10^{-14} \div 0.0625 = 1.60 \times 10^{-13}$ ***[1 mark]***
$pH = -\log_{10}(1.60 \times 10^{-13}) = \mathbf{12.80}$ ***[1 mark]***

2 $K_w = [H^+][OH^-]$
$[OH^-] = [NaOH] = 0.0370$
$[H^+] = K_w \div [OH^-] = (1 \times 10^{-14}) \div 0.0370 = 2.70 \times 10^{-13}$ ***[1 mark]***
$pH = -\log_{10}[H^+] = -\log_{10}(2.70 \times 10^{-13}) = \mathbf{12.57}$ ***[1 mark]***

3 $K_a = 10^{-pK_a} = 10^{-4.20} = 6.3 \times 10^{-5}$ ***[1 mark]***
$K_a = \frac{[H^+]^2}{[HA]}$ so $[H^+] = \sqrt{K_a \times [HA]}$
$= \sqrt{(6.3 \times 10^{-5}) \times (1.60 \times 10^{-4})} = \sqrt{1.0 \times 10^{-8}}$
$= 1.0 \times 10^{-4}$ mol dm^{-3} ***[1 mark]***
$pH = -\log_{10}[H^+] = -\log_{10} 1.0 \times 10^{-4} = \mathbf{4.00}$ ***[1 mark]***

Page 135 — Experiments Involving pH

1 a) E.g. pH meter / pH probe connected to a data logger ***[1 mark]***

b) Substance A is a acidic, and $[H^+] = 10^{-3.20} = 0.00063$ mol dm^{-3}, which means only a tiny fraction of the molecules in A dissociate ***[1 mark]***.
Substance B is alkali, so $[H^+] = 10^{-13.80} = 1.58... \times 10^{-14}$ mol dm^{-3}.
Since $K_w = [H^+][OH^-] = 1.0 \times 10^{-14}$,
$[OH^-] = 1.0 \times 10^{-14} \div 1.58... \times 10^{-14} = 0.63$ mol dm^{-3}.
This means there's more dissociation in B than in A / a larger number of molecules dissociate in B than in A ***[1 mark]***.
Substance C is slightly acidic, so $[H^+] = 10^{-6.80}$
$= 1.6 \times 10^{-7}$ mol dm^{-3}.
This means a tiny fraction of molecules dissociate in C ***[1 mark]***.
So, substance B dissociates the most in solution ***[1 mark]***.

2 a) Moles of benzoic acid in solution = 1.22 ÷ 122 = 0.0100 moles
Concentration of benzoic acid solution $= \frac{0.0100 \times 1000}{100}$
$= 0.100$ mol dm^{-3} ***[1 mark]***
$[H^+] = 10^{-2.60} = 0.00251...$ mol dm^{-3} ***[1 mark]***
Assume that [HA] at equilibrium is 0.100 because only a very small amount of HA will dissociate ***[1 mark]***.
$K_a = \frac{[H^+]^2}{[C_6H_5COOH]}$ ***[1 mark]*** $= \frac{(0.00251...)^2}{0.100}$
$= 6.309... \times 10^{-5} = \mathbf{6.31 \times 10^{-5}}$ **mol dm^{-3}** ***[1 mark]***

b) $[H^+] = \sqrt{K_a[C_6H_5COOH]}$ ***[1 mark]***
$= \sqrt{(6.309... \times 10^{-5}) \times 0.0100} = 7.94... \times 10^{-4}$
$= \mathbf{7.94 \times 10^{-4}}$ **mol dm^{-3}** ***[1 mark]***

c) $pH = -\log_{10}[H^+] = -\log(7.94... \times 10^{-4}) = \mathbf{3.1}$ ***[1 mark]***

d) $[H^+] = \sqrt{(6.309... \times 10^{-5}) \times 1.00} = 0.00794...$ mol dm^{-3} ***[1 mark]***
So $pH = -\log(0.00794...) = \mathbf{2.1}$ ***[1 mark]***

e) The pH would be (3.1 + 0.5 =) 3.6 ***[1 mark]*** since, as the solution is diluted by 10, the pH increases by 0.5 ***[1 mark]***.

Page 138 — Titration Curves and Indicators

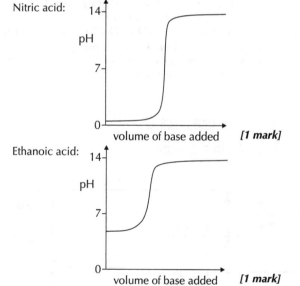

1 Nitric acid:

14
pH
7
0
volume of base added ***[1 mark]***

Ethanoic acid:

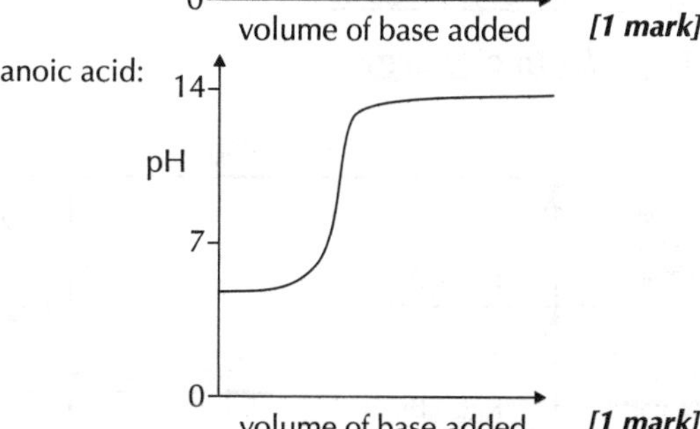

[1 mark]

2 Thymol blue ***[1 mark]***. It's a weak acid/strong base titration so the equivalence point is above pH 8 ***[1 mark]***.

Answers

3 a) 9 (accept values in the range 8 – 10) ***[1 mark]***
b) 15 cm^3 ***[1 mark]***
c) E.g. phenolphthalein ***[1 mark]*** because the pH range where it changes colour lies entirely on the vertical part of the titration curve ***[1 mark]***.
d)

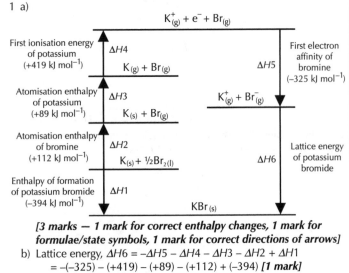

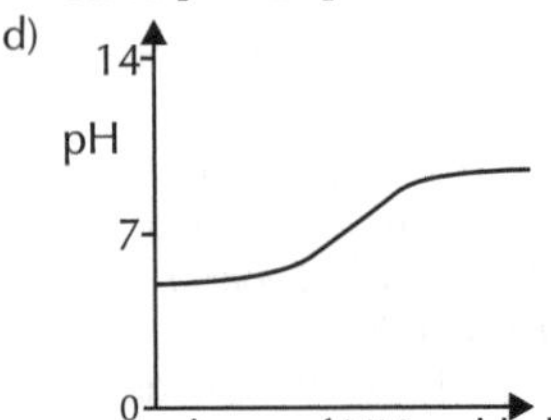

[1 mark]

e) The change in pH is gradual, so is difficult to see with an indicator ***[1 mark]***.

4 a) i) 8 (accept values in the range 7 – 9) ***[1 mark]***
ii) 3.5 (accept values in the range 3.0 – 4.0) ***[1 mark]***
b) $K_a = \frac{[H^+][HCOO^-]}{[HCOOH]}$ ***[1 mark]***
c) It is reduced to half its original value, 0.05 mol dm^{-3} ***[1 mark]***.
d) At the half-equivalence point pK_a = pH = 3.5 ***[1 mark]***
so $K_a = 10^{-3.5}$ = **3×10^{-4} mol dm^{-3}** ***[1 mark — allow marks for correct method with value from 2a)ii) if answer is not 3.5]***

Page 141 — Buffers

1 a) $K_a = \frac{[C_6H_5COO^-][H^+]}{[C_6H_5COOH]}$ ***[1 mark]***
$[H^+] = 6.40 \times 10^{-5} \times \frac{0.400}{0.200}$ = 0.000128 mol dm^{-3} ***[1 mark]***
pH = $-\log_{10}(0.000128)$ = 3.892... = **3.893** ***[1 mark]***
b) The buffer solution contains benzoic acid and benzoate ions in equilibrium: $C_6H_5COOH \rightleftharpoons H^+ + C_6H_5COO^-$ ***[1 mark]***.
Adding H_2SO_4 increases the concentration of H^+ ***[1 mark]***.
The equilibrium shifts left to reduce concentration of H^+, so the pH will only change very slightly ***[1 mark]***.

2 a) $CH_3(CH_2)_2COOH \rightleftharpoons H^+ + CH_3(CH_2)_2COO^-$ ***[1 mark]***
b) $[CH_3(CH_2)_2COOH] = [CH_3(CH_2)_2COO^-]$,
so $[CH_3(CH_2)_2COOH] \div [CH_3(CH_2)_2COO^-] = 1$ and $K_a = [H^+]$.
pH = $-\log_{10}(1.5 \times 10^{-5})$ ***[1 mark]*** = **4.8** ***[1 mark]***
If the concentrations of the weak acid and the salt of the weak acid are equal, they cancel from the K_a expression and the buffer pH = pK_a.

Topic 13 — Energetics II

Page 143 — Lattice Energy

1 a)

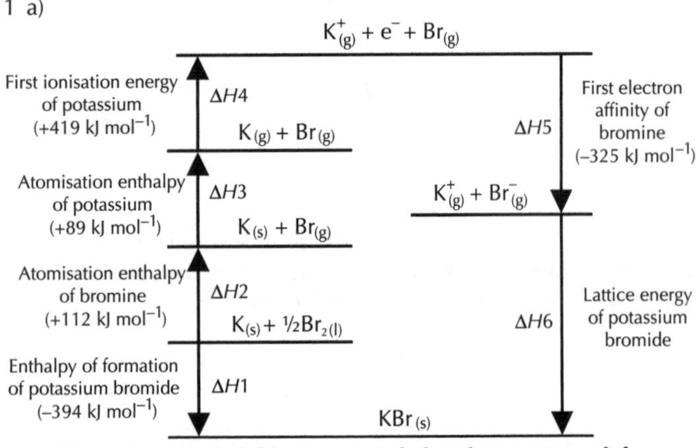

[3 marks — 1 mark for correct enthalpy changes, 1 mark for formulae/state symbols, 1 mark for correct directions of arrows]

b) Lattice energy, $\Delta H6 = -\Delta H5 - \Delta H4 - \Delta H3 - \Delta H2 + \Delta H1$
= –(–325) – (+419) – (+89) – (+112) + (–394) ***[1 mark]***
= **–689 kJ mol^{-1}** ***[1 mark]***

2 a)

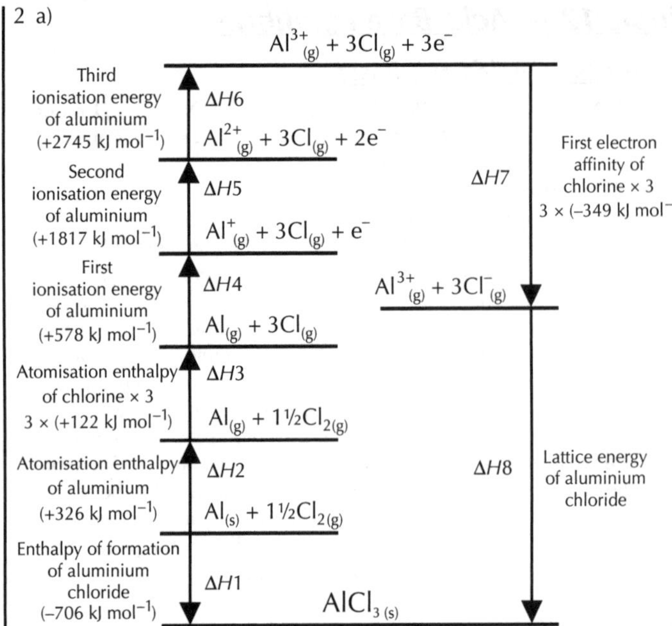

[3 marks — 1 mark for correct enthalpy changes and correctly multiplying all the enthalpies, 1 mark for formulae/state symbols, 1 mark for correct directions of arrows]

b) Lattice energy, $\Delta H8$
$= -\Delta H7 - \Delta H6 - \Delta H5 - \Delta H4 - \Delta H3 - \Delta H2 + \Delta H1$
= –3(–349) – (+2745) – (+1817) – (+578) – 3(+122) – (+326) + (–706) ***[1 mark]***
= **–5491 kJ mol^{-1}** ***[1 mark]***

3 a)

$2Al^{3+}_{(g)} + 3O_{(g)} + 6e^-$
Third ionisation energy of aluminium × 2
2 × (+2745 kJ mol^{-1})
$\Delta H6$
$2Al^{2+}_{(g)} + 3O_{(g)} + 4e^-$
Second ionisation energy of aluminium × 2
2 × (+1817 kJ mol^{-1})
$\Delta H5$
$2Al^+_{(g)} + 3O_{(g)} + 2e^-$
First ionisation energy of aluminium × 2
2 × (+578 kJ mol^{-1})
$\Delta H4$
$2Al_{(g)} + 3O_{(g)}$
Atomisation enthalpy of oxygen × 3
3 × (+249 kJ mol^{-1})
$\Delta H3$
$2Al_{(g)} + 1\frac{1}{2}O_{2(g)}$
Atomisation enthalpy of aluminium × 2
2 × (+326 kJ mol^{-1})
$\Delta H2$
$2Al_{(s)} + 1\frac{1}{2}O_{2(g)}$
Enthalpy of formation of aluminium oxide (–1676 kJ mol^{-1})
$\Delta H1$
$Al_2O_{3(s)}$
$\Delta H7$
First electron affinity of oxygen × 3
3 × (–141 kJ mol^{-1})
$2Al^{3+}_{(g)} + 3O^-_{(g)} + 3e^-$
$\Delta H8$
Second electron affinity of oxygen × 3
3 × (844 kJ mol^{-1})
$2Al^{3+}_{(g)} + 3O^{2-}_{(g)}$
$\Delta H9$
Lattice energy of aluminium oxide

[3 marks — 1 mark for correct enthalpy changes and correctly multiplying all the enthalpies, 1 mark for formulae/state symbols, 1 mark for correct directions of arrows]

b) Lattice energy, $\Delta H9$
$= -\Delta H8 - \Delta H7 - \Delta H6 - \Delta H5 - \Delta H4 - \Delta H3 - \Delta H2 + \Delta H1$
= –3(+844) – 3(–141) – 2(+2745) – 2(+1817) – 2(+578) – 3(+249) – 2(+326) + (–1676) ***[1 mark]***
= **–15 464 kJ mol^{-1}** ***[1 mark]***

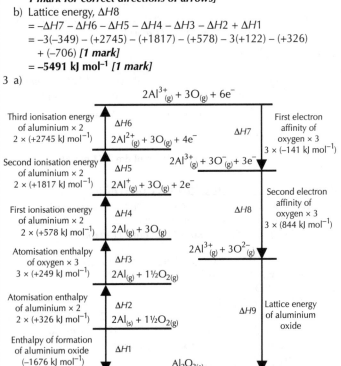

Answers

Page 145 — Polarisation

1 Al^{3+} has a high charge/volume ratio (or a small radius AND a large positive charge) ***[1 mark]***, so it has a high polarising ability ***[1 mark]*** and can pull electron density away from Cl^- ***[1 mark]*** to create a bond with mostly covalent characteristics ***[1 mark]***. (Alternatively Cl^- is relatively large ***[1 mark]*** and easily polarised ***[1 mark]*** so its electrons can be pulled away from Cl^- ***[1 mark]*** to create a bond with mostly covalent characteristics ***[1 mark]***.)

2 a) Increasing covalent character: NaBr, $MgBr_2$, MgI_2 ***[1 mark]***. Covalent character is greatest when cations are small and have large charge, which applies more to Mg^{2+} than to Na^+ ***[1 mark]***, and when anions are large, which applies more to I^- than to Br^- ***[1 mark]***.

b) Experimental and theoretical lattice energies match well when a compound has a high degree of ionic character ***[1 mark]***. NaI has a higher degree of ionic character than MgI_2 because Na^+ has a smaller charge density / smaller charge and isn't much smaller than Mg^{2+} ***[1 mark]***.

Page 147 — Dissolving

1 a)

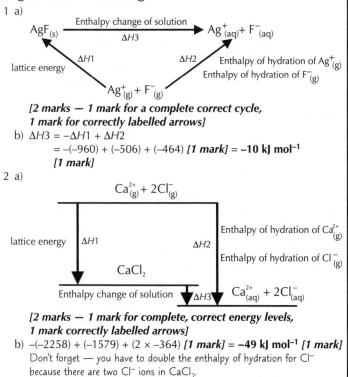

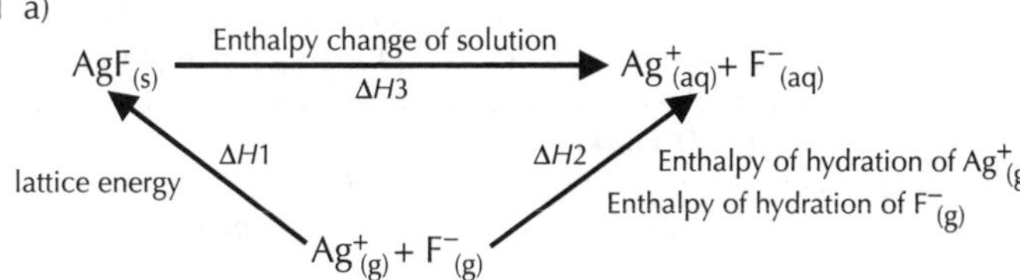

[2 marks — 1 mark for a complete correct cycle, 1 mark for correctly labelled arrows]

b) $\Delta H3 = -\Delta H1 + \Delta H2$
$= -(-960) + (-506) + (-464)$ ***[1 mark]*** $=$ **-10 kJ mol^{-1}** ***[1 mark]***

2 a)

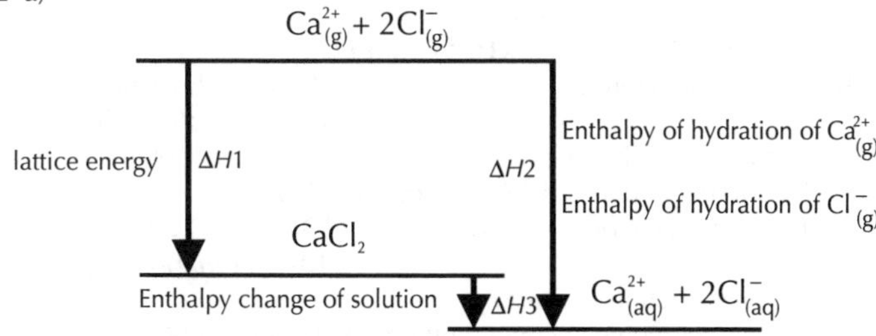

[2 marks — 1 mark for complete, correct energy levels, 1 mark correctly labelled arrows]

b) $-(-2258) + (-1579) + (2 \times -364)$ ***[1 mark]*** $=$ **-49 kJ mol^{-1}** ***[1 mark]***
Don't forget — you have to double the enthalpy of hydration for Cl^- because there are two Cl^- ions in $CaCl_2$.

3 By Hess's law:
Enthalpy change of solution ($MgCl_{2(s)}$)
$=$ –lattice energy ($MgCl_{2(s)}$) + enthalpy of hydration ($Mg^{2+}_{(g)}$) + [2 × enthalpy of hydration ($Cl^-_{(g)}$)] ***[1 mark]***
So enthalpy of hydration ($Cl^-_{(g)}$)
$=$ [enthalpy change of solution ($MgCl_{2(s)}$) + lattice energy ($MgCl_{2(s)}$) – enthalpy of hydration ($Mg^{2+}_{(g)}$)] ÷ 2
$= [(-122) + (-2526) - (-1920)] \div 2$ ***[1 mark]***
$= -728 \div 2 =$ **-364 kJ mol^{-1}** ***[1 mark]***

4 Ca^{2+} will have a greater enthalpy of hydration ***[1 mark]*** because it is smaller and has a higher charge / has a higher charge density than K^+ ***[1 mark]***. This means there is a stronger attraction between Ca^{2+} and the water molecules, so more energy is released when bonds are formed between them ***[1 mark]***.

Page 149 — Entropy

1 a) The reaction is not likely to be feasible ***[1 mark]*** because there are fewer moles of product than moles of reactants / there's a gas in the reactants and only a solid product, and therefore a decrease in entropy ***[1 mark]***.
Remember — more particles means more entropy. There's 1½ moles of reactants and only 1 mole of product.

b) $\Delta S = 26.9 - [32.7 + (\frac{1}{2} \times 205)]$ ***[1 mark]***
$=$ **-108 J K^{-1} mol^{-1}** ***[1 mark]***

c) The reaction is not likely to be feasible because ΔS is negative/there is a decrease in entropy ***[1 mark]***.

2 a) $\Delta S = 48 - 70 =$ **-22 J K^{-1} mol^{-1}** ***[1 mark]***

b) Despite the negative entropy change, the reaction might still be feasible because other factors such as enthalpy, temperature and kinetics also play a part in whether or not a reaction occurs ***[1 mark]***.

Page 151 — More on Entropy Change

1 a) You would expect an increase in the entropy of the system ***[1 mark]*** because a solid is combining with a substance in solution to produce another solution, a liquid and a gas — this leads to an increase in disorder ***[1 mark]***. There is also an increase in the number of molecules which will also lead to an increase in disorder ***[1 mark]***.

b) The reaction is endothermic, so the entropy change of the surroundings will be negative ***[1 mark]***. However, if the entropy change of the system has a large enough positive value then this will override the negative entropy change of the surroundings and result in an overall positive entropy change ***[1 mark]***.

2 a) $\Delta S_{system} = S_{products} - S_{reactants}$ ***[1 mark]***
$= (2 \times 26.9) - ((2 \times 32.7) + 205) = 53.8 - 270.4$ ***[1 mark]***
$=$ **-217 J K^{-1} mol^{-1}** (3 s.f.) ***[1 mark, include units]***

b) $\Delta S_{surroundings} = -\Delta H/T = -(-1\,204\,000 \div 298)$ ***[1 mark]***
$=$ **$+4040$ J K^{-1} mol^{-1}** (3 s.f.) ***[1 mark]***
$\Delta S_{total} = \Delta S_{system} + \Delta S_{surroundings} = (-216.6) + 4040.3$ ***[1 mark]***
$=$ **$+3824$ J K^{-1} mol^{-1}** (3 s.f.) ***[1 mark]***

Page 153 — Free Energy

1 a) $\Delta S = [214 + (2 \times 69.9)] - [186 + (2 \times 205)]$
$= -242.2$ J K^{-1} mol^{-1} ***[1 mark]***
$\Delta G = -730\,000 - (298 \times -242.2)$
$\approx$ **$-658\,000$ J mol^{-1}** (3 s.f.) (= **-658 kJ mol^{-1}**) ***[1 mark]***

b) The reaction is feasible at 298 K because ΔG is negative ***[1 mark]***.

c) $T = \frac{\Delta H}{\Delta S} = -730\,000 \div -242.2 =$ **3010 K** (3 s.f.) ***[1 mark]***

2 a) $\Delta G = -[8.31 \times 723] \times \ln(60)$
$=$ **-24600 J mol^{-1}** (3 s.f.) (= **-246 kJ mol^{-1}**) ***[1 mark]***

b) As $\Delta G = \Delta H - T\Delta S$ ***[1 mark]*** and the change in entropy for the reaction is negative, an increase in temperature will result in a less negative value for the free energy change of reaction ***[1 mark]***.

Answers

Topic 14 — Redox II

Page 155 — Electrochemical Cells

1 a) Get a strip each of zinc and iron metal. Clean the surfaces of the metals using a piece of emery paper (or sandpaper).
Clean any grease or oil from the electrodes using some propanone ***[1 mark]***. Place each electrode into a beaker filled with a solution containing ions of that metal (e.g. $ZnSO_{4(aq)}$ and $FeSO_{4(aq)}$) ***[1 mark]***. Create a salt bridge to link the two solutions together by soaking a piece of filter paper in salt solution, e.g. $KCl_{(aq)}$ or $KNO_{3(aq)}$, and draping it between the two beakers. The ends of the filter paper should be immersed in the solutions ***[1 mark]***.
Connect the electrodes to a voltmeter, using crocodile clips and wires ***[1 mark]***.

b) 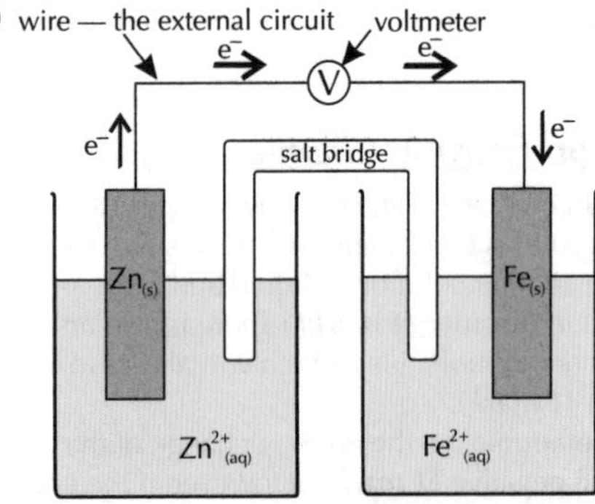

[4 marks — 1 mark for complete circuit of wires and salt bridge, 1 mark for zinc electrode drawn on the left, 1 mark for a correct aqueous solution of ions in each half-cell, 1 mark for correct direction of electron flow]

2 a) The salt bridge completes the circuit ***[1 mark]*** and allows the salt ions to flow between the half-cells to balance the charges ***[1 mark]***.
b) E.g. Soak a piece of filter paper in a salt solution, e.g. $KNO_{3(aq)}$ ***[1 mark]***.
c) silver ***[1 mark]***

Page 157 — Electrode Potentials

1 a) Iron ***[1 mark]*** as it has a more negative electrode potential/it loses electrons more easily than lead ***[1 mark]***.
b) Standard cell potential = –0.13 – (–0.44) = **+0.31 V** ***[1 mark]***

2 a) +0.80 V – (–0.76 V) = **+1.56 V** ***[1 mark]***
b) The concentration of Zn^{2+} ions or Ag^+ ions was not 1.00 mol dm^{-3} ***[1 mark]***. The pressure wasn't 100 kPa ***[1 mark]***.

Page 159 — The Electrochemical Series

1 a) $Zn_{(s)} + Ni^{2+}_{(aq)} \rightleftharpoons Zn^{2+}_{(aq)} + Ni_{(s)}$ ***[1 mark]***
$E^\ominus$ = (–0.25) – (–0.76) = **+0.51 V** ***[1 mark]***
b) $2MnO_4^-{}_{(aq)} + 16H^+_{(aq)} + 5Sn^{2+}_{(aq)} \rightleftharpoons 2Mn^{2+}_{(aq)} + 8H_2O_{(l)} + 5Sn^{4+}_{(aq)}$ ***[1 mark]***
$E^\ominus$ = (+1.51) – (+0.14) = **+1.37 V** ***[1 mark]***
c) No reaction ***[1 mark]***. Both reactants are in their oxidised form ***[1 mark]***.

2 $KMnO_4$ ***[1 mark]*** because it has a more positive/less negative electrode potential ***[1 mark]***.

3 a) $Cu^{2+}_{(aq)} + Ni_{(s)} \rightleftharpoons Cu_{(s)} + Ni^{2+}_{(aq)}$ ***[1 mark]***
b) If the copper solution was more dilute, the $E^\ominus$ of the copper half-cell would be lower (the equilibrium would shift to the left/ the copper would lose electrons more easily), so the overall cell potential would be lower ***[1 mark]***.

Page 161 — Storage and Fuel Cells

1 a) i) and ii)

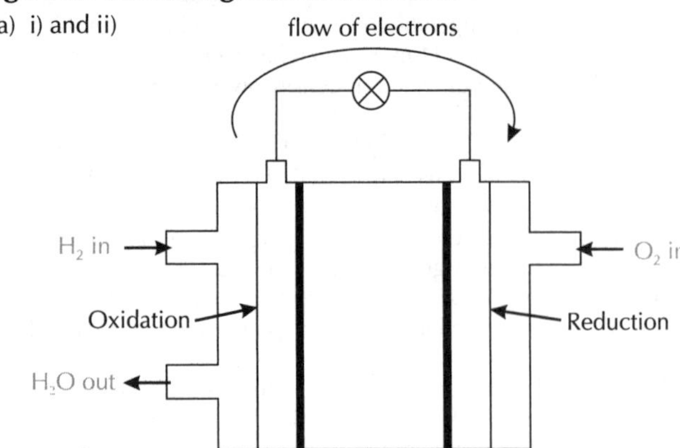

[2 marks — 1 mark for labelling the sites of reduction and oxidation correctly, 1 mark for drawing the arrow showing the direction of electron flow correctly]

b) Negative electrode: $H_{2(g)} + 4OH^-_{(aq)} \rightarrow 4H_2O_{(l)} + 4e^-$ ***[1 mark]***
Positive electrode: $O_{2(g)} + 2H_2O_{(l)} + 4e^- \rightarrow 4OH^-_{(aq)}$ ***[1 mark]***
c) It only allows the OH^- across and not O_2 and H_2 gases ***[1 mark]***.

2 a) The PEM only allows H^+ ions across it ***[1 mark]***, forcing the electrons around the circuit to get to the cathode. This creates an electrical current ***[1 mark]***.
b) Anode reaction: $H_2 \rightarrow 2H^+ + 2e^-$ ***[1 mark]***
Cathode reaction: $2H^+ + ½O_2 + 2e^- \rightarrow H_2O$ ***[1 mark]***

Page 164 — Redox Titrations

1 a) 15.0 cm^3 of manganate(VII) solution contains:
(15.0 × 0.00900) ÷ 1000 = 1.35 ×10^{-4} moles of manganate(VII) ions ***[1 mark]***
From the equation the number of moles of iron = 5 × the number of moles of manganate(VII). So the number of moles of iron = 5 × 1.35 ×10^{-4} = **6.75 ×10^{-4}** ***[1 mark]***
b) In the tablet there will be 250 ÷ 25.0 = 10 times this amount = **6.75 × 10^{-3} moles** ***[1 mark]***
c) 1 mole of iron has a mass of 55.8 g, so the tablet contains:
6.75 ×10^{-3} × 55.8 = 0.37665 g of iron ***[1 mark]***
The percentage of iron in the tablet = (0.37665 ÷ 3.20) × 100 = **11.8%** ***[1 mark]***

2 a) A redox reaction ***[1 mark]***.
b) Number of moles = (concentration × volume) ÷ 1000
= (0.500 × 10.0) ÷ 1000 ***[1 mark]*** = **0.00500 moles** ***[1 mark]***
c) Number of moles = (concentration × volume) ÷ 1000
= (0.100 × 20.0) ÷ 1000 ***[1 mark]*** = **0.00200 moles** ***[1 mark]***
d) 1 mole of MnO_4^- ions needs 5 moles of electrons to be reduced. So to reduce 0.00200 moles of MnO_4^-, you need (0.00200 × 5) = 0.0100 moles of electrons ***[1 mark]***.
The 0.00500 moles of tin ions must have lost 0.0100 moles of electrons as they were oxidised OR all of these electrons must have come from the tin ions ***[1 mark]***. Each tin ion changed its oxidation number by 0.01 ÷ 0.005 = 2 ***[1 mark]***. So, the oxidation number of the oxidised tin ions is (+2) + 2 = **+4** ***[1 mark]***.

Page 167 — More on Redox Titrations

1 a) $IO_3^- + 5I^- + 6H^+ \rightarrow 3I_2 + 3H_2O$ ***[1 mark]***
b) Number of moles = (concentration × volume) ÷ 1000
Number of moles of thiosulfate = (0.150 × 24.0) ÷ 1000 = **3.60 × 10^{-3}** ***[1 mark]***
c) 2 moles of thiosulfate react with 1 mole of iodine, so there were (3.60 × 10^{-3}) ÷ 2 = **1.80 × 10^{-3}** moles of iodine ***[1 mark]***
d) 1/3 mole ***[1 mark]***
e) There must be 1.80 × 10^{-3} ÷ 3 = **6.00 × 10^{-4} moles** of iodate(V) in the solution ***[1 mark]***. So concentration of potassium iodate(V) = (6.00 × 10^{-4}) ÷ (10.0 ÷ 1000) = **0.0600 mol dm^{-3}** ***[1 mark]***

Answers

2 Number of moles = (concentration × volume) ÷ 1000
Number of moles of thiosulfate = (0.300 × 12.5) ÷ 1000
$= 3.75 \times 10^{-3}$ ***[1 mark]***
2 moles of thiosulfate react with 1 mole of iodine.
So there must have been $(3.75 \times 10^{-3}) \div 2 = 1.875 \times 10^{-3}$ moles of iodine produced ***[1 mark]***
2 moles of manganate(VII) ions produce 5 moles of iodine molecules, so there must have been
$(1.875 \times 10^{-3}) \times (2 \div 5) = 7.50 \times 10^{-4}$ moles of manganate(VII) in the solution ***[1 mark]***
Concentration of potassium manganate(VII)
$= (7.50 \times 10^{-4}$ moles$) \div (18.0 \div 1000) =$ **0.0417 mol dm^{-3}** ***[1 mark]***

3 a) The number of moles of thiosulfate used =
(19.3 × 0.150) ÷ 1000 = 0.002895 moles ***[1 mark]***
From the iodine-thiosulfate equation, the number of moles of I_2 = half the number of moles of thiosulfate, so in this case the number of moles of I_2 = 0.002895 ÷ 2 = 0.0014475
= **0.00145 moles** ***[1 mark]***

b) From the equation, 2 copper ions produce 1 iodine molecule ***[1 mark]***, so the number of moles of copper ions
= 0.0014475 × 2 = 0.002895 = **0.00290 moles** ***[1 mark]***

c) In 250 cm^3 of the copper solution there are:
(250 ÷ 25.0) × 0.002895 = 0.02895 moles of copper ***[1 mark]***
1 mole of copper has a mass of 63.5 g, so in the alloy there are:
0.02895 × 63.5 = 1.8383... g of copper ***[1 mark]***
% of copper in alloy = (1.8383... ÷ 4.20) × 100 = **43.8%** ***[1 mark]***

Topic 15 — Transition Metals

Page 169 — Transition Metals

1 Manganese has the electronic configuration [Ar] $4s^2 3d^5$ so its outer electrons are in the 4s and 3d subshells. These subshells are very close in energy ***[1 mark]***, so there is no great difference between removing electrons from the 4s subshell (e.g. to make Mn^{2+}) or from the 3d subshell (e.g. to make MnO_4^-) ***[1 mark]***.
The energy released when manganese forms compounds or complexes containing manganese in variable oxidation numbers is greater than the energy required to remove these outer electrons ***[1 mark]***, (so manganese can exist with variable oxidation numbers).

2 a) Iron: $1s^2 2s^2 2p^6 3s^2 3p^6 3d^6 4s^2$ OR [Ar] $3d^6 4s^2$ ***[1 mark]***
Copper: $1s^2 2s^2 2p^6 3s^2 3p^6 3d^{10} 4s^1$ OR [Ar] $3d^{10} 4s^1$ ***[1 mark]***

b) Copper has only one 4s electron ***[1 mark]*** because it is more stable with a full 3d subshell ***[1 mark]***.

c) Iron loses the 4s electrons to form Fe^{2+} ***[1 mark]***.
It loses the 4s electrons and an electron from the 3d orbital containing 2 electrons to form Fe^{3+} ***[1 mark]***.

Page 171 — Complex Ions

1 a) Coordination number: 6 ***[1 mark]***
Shape: octahedral ***[1 mark]***

b) Coordination number: 4 ***[1 mark]***
Shape: tetrahedral ***[1 mark]***
Bond angles: 109.5° ***[1 mark]***
Formula: $[CuCl_4]^{2-}$ ***[1 mark]***

c) Cl^- ligands are larger than water ligands ***[1 mark]***, so only 4 Cl^- ligands can fit around the Cu^{2+} ion ***[1 mark]***.

Page 173 — Complex Ions and Colour

1 a) i) [Ar] $3d^{10}$ ***[1 mark]***
ii) [Ar] $3d^9$ ***[1 mark]***

b) Cu^{2+} because it has an incomplete d-subshell ***[1 mark]***.

2 ***A maximum of two marks can be awarded for structure and reasoning of the written response:***
2 marks: The answer is constructed logically, and displays clear reasoning and links between points throughout.
1 mark: The answer is mostly logical, with some reasoning and links between points.
0 marks: The answer has no structure and no links between points.
Here are some points your answer may include:
Normally, all the 3d orbitals have the same energy. When ligands form dative covalent bonds with a metal ion, the 3d electron orbitals split in energy. Electrons tend to occupy the lower orbitals and energy is required to move an electron from an lower 3d orbital to a higher one. The energy needed to make an electron jump from the lower 3d orbital to the higher 3d orbital is equal to a certain frequency of light. This frequency gets absorbed. All the other frequencies are transmitted and it is these frequencies that give the transition metal colour.
[4 marks — 4 marks if 6 points mentioned covering all areas of the question, 3 marks if 4-5 points covered, 2 marks if 2-3 points covered, 1 mark if 1 point covered]

Page 175 — Chromium

1 a) The solution changes from orange to green ***[1 mark]***.

b) Cr is reduced from +6 to +3 ***[1 mark]***.
Zn is oxidised from 0 to +2 ***[1 mark]***.
$Cr_2O_7^{2-} + 14H^+ + 3Zn \rightarrow 2Cr^{3+} + 7H_2O + 3Zn^{2+}$ ***[1 mark]***

c) The solution turns blue ***[1 mark]*** because the Cr^{3+} is reduced further to Cr^{2+} ***[1 mark]***. It is not oxidised back to Cr^{3+} because it is in an inert atmosphere ***[1 mark]***.

2 a) Amphoteric means something can react with both an acid and a base ***[1 mark]***.
In acid: $[Cr(OH)_3(H_2O)_3]_{(s)} + 3H^+_{(aq)} \rightarrow [Cr(H_2O)_6]^{3+}_{(aq)}$ ***[1 mark]***
In base: $[Cr(OH)_3(H_2O)_3]_{(s)} + 3OH^-_{(aq)} \rightarrow [Cr(OH)_6]^{3-}_{(aq)} + 3H_2O_{(l)}$ ***[1 mark]***

b) $[Cr(OH)_3(H_2O)_3]_{(s)} + 6NH_{3(aq)} \rightarrow [Cr(NH_3)_6]^{3+}_{(aq)} + 3OH^-_{(aq)} + 3H_2O_{(l)}$ ***[1 mark]***
The grey-green precipitate would dissolve to form a purple solution ***[1 mark]***.

Page 177 — Reactions of Ligands

1 a) $[Fe(H_2O)_6]^{3+} + EDTA^{4-} \rightarrow [FeEDTA]^- + 6H_2O$ ***[1 mark]***

b) The formation of $[FeEDTA]^-$ results in an increase in entropy, because the number of particles increases from two to seven ***[1 mark]***.

2 a) $[Co(H_2O)_6]^{2+}_{(aq)}$ ***[1 mark]***

b) $[Co(H_2O)_6]^{2+}_{(aq)} + 2NH_{3(aq)} \rightarrow [Co(OH)_2(H_2O)_4]_{(s)} + 2NH_4^+{}_{(aq)}$ ***[1 mark]***
This is an acid-base reaction ***[1 mark]***.
$[Co(OH)_2(H_2O)_4]_{(s)} + 6NH_{3(aq)} \rightarrow [Co(NH_3)_6]^{2+}_{(aq)} + 2OH^-_{(aq)}\ 4H_2O_{(l)}$ ***[1 mark]***
This is a ligand exchange reaction ***[1 mark]***.

Page 179 — Transition Metals and Catalysts

1 a) Heterogeneous means 'in a different phase from the reactants'.
Homogeneous means 'in the same phase as the reactants' ***[1 mark]***.

b) The orbitals allow reactant molecules to make weak bonds to the catalyst ***[1 mark]***.

c) By changing oxidation state easily, transition metals can take in or give out electrons ***[1 mark]*** and so they can help transfer electrons from one reactant to another ***[1 mark]***.
You could also give an answer that describes a catalyst in terms of helping to oxidise and reduce.

Answers

2 The overall equation for the reaction is:
$2MnO_4^-{}_{(aq)} + 16H^+_{(aq)} + 5C_2O_4^{2-}{}_{(aq)} \rightarrow$
$2Mn^{2+}_{(aq)} + 8H_2O_{(l)} + 10CO_{2(g)}$ ***[1 mark]***.
This is slow to begin with, because the MnO_4^- and $C_2O_4^{2-}$ ions are both negatively charged, so repel each other and don't collide very frequently ***[1 mark]***. The Mn^{2+} product, however, is able to catalyse the reaction. It reduces MnO_4^- to Mn^{3+}:
$MnO_4^-{}_{(aq)} + 4Mn^{2+}_{(aq)} + 8H^+_{(aq)} \rightarrow 5Mn^{3+}_{(aq)} + 4H_2O_{(l)}$ ***[1 mark]***.
The Mn^{3+} ions are reduced back to Mn^{2+} by reaction with $C_2O_4^{2-}$:
$2Mn^{3+}_{(aq)} + C_2O_4^{2-}{}_{(aq)} \rightarrow 2Mn^{2+}_{(aq)} + 2CO_{2(g)}$ ***[1 mark]***.
This means the reaction is an autocatalysis reaction. As more Mn^{2+} is produced, there is more catalyst available and so the reaction rate will increase ***[1 mark]***.

3 a) When molecules stick to the surface of a solid ***[1 mark]***.
b) The surface of the catalyst activates the molecules, weakening the bonds between the atoms in the reactants ***[1 mark]***, making them easier to break and reform as the products ***[1 mark]***.

Topic 16 — Kinetics II

Page 181 — Reaction Rates

1 a) E.g there is an increase in number of ions so follow the reaction by measuring electrical conductivity ***[1 mark]***.
b) Plot a graph of concentration of propanone against time ***[1 mark]*** and find out the rate at any time by working out the gradient of the graph at that time ***[1 mark]***.
c)

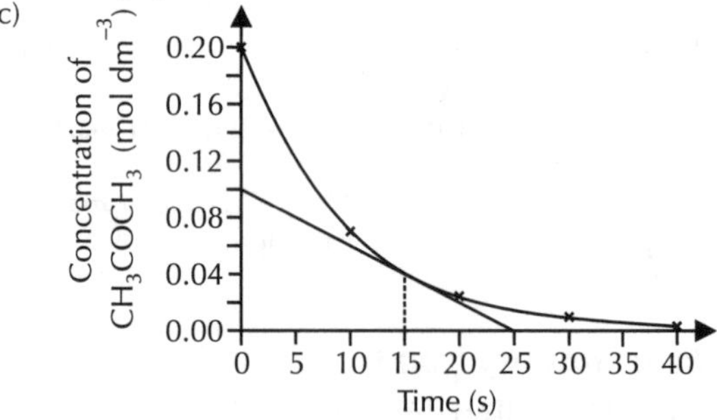

Rate after 15 s = 0.1 ÷ 25 = **0.004 mol dm^{-3} s^{-1}**
[3 marks — 1 mark for labelled axes the correct way round, 1 mark for points plotted accurately, smooth best-fit curve and a tangent drawn at 15 s, 1 mark for rate within range 0.004 ±0.001 and correct units]

Page 183 — Orders of Reactions

1 a)

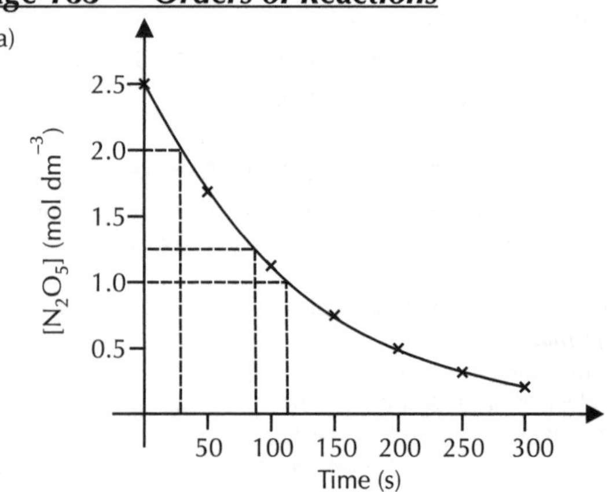

[2 marks — 1 mark for $[N_2O_5]$ on y-axis, time on x-axis, and points plotted accurately, 1 mark for a smooth best-fit curve]

b) i) Time value = 85 s ***[1 mark, allow 85 ±2]***
(Horizontal line from 1.25 on y-axis to curve and vertical line from curve to x-axis.)
ii) Time value difference = 113 (±2) – 28 (±2) = **85 s** ***[1 mark, allow 85 ±4]***
(Vertical lines from curve at 2.0 mol dm^{-3} and 1.0 mol dm^{-3}.)
c) Half life for 0.625 mol dm^{-1} from 1.25 mol dm^{-1}= 170 – 85 = 85 s
Half life for 1.25 mol dm^{-1} from 2.5 mol dm^{-1} = 85 – 0 = 85 s
So, the half lives remain constant and are independent of concentration so the order of reaction is 1 ***[1 mark]***.

2 a) The reaction rate would double ***[1 mark]***.
b) The overall order is 3 ***[1 mark]***.

Page 185 — The Initial Rates Method

1 a) All the sodium thiosulfate that has been added has been used up so any more iodine that is formed will stay in solution turning the starch indicator blue-black ***[1 mark]***.
b) The time it would take for the colour change to occur would increase as there would be a greater amount of thiosulfate instantaneously removing iodine from solution meaning it would take longer for it to be used up ***[1 mark]***.

2 Take samples of the reaction mixture at regular intervals and stop the reaction using sodium hydrogen carbonate ***[1 mark]***. Titrate the samples against sodium thiosulfate, using starch as the indicator, to calculate the concentration of iodine ***[1 mark]***. Repeat the experiment several times changing the concentration of the iodine ***[1 mark]***.

Page 187— Rate Equations

1 a) Rate = $k[NO_{(g)}]^2\,[H_{2(g)}]$ ***[1 mark]***
Sum of individual orders = 2 + 1 = **3rd order overall** ***[1 mark]***.
b) i) $0.0027 = k \times (0.004)^2 \times 0.002$ ***[1 mark]***
$k = 0.0027 \div ((0.004)^2 \times 0.002)$
k = **84 000 dm^6 mol^{-2} s^{-1}** (2 s.f.) ***[1 mark]***
(Units: k = mol dm^{-3} s^{-1}/[(mol dm^{-3})^2 × (mol dm^{-3})]
= dm^6 mol^{-2} s^{-1})
ii) The rate constant would decrease ***[1 mark]***.

2 a) When [X] is doubled and [Y] and [Z] remain constant between experiment 1 and 2, there is no change in the initial rate so the rate is zero order with respect to [X] ***[1 mark]***.
When [Y] is doubled and [X] and [Z] remain constant between experiment 1 and 3, the initial rate quadruples so the rate is second order with respect to [Y] ***[1 mark]***.
When [Z] is doubled and [X] and [Y] remain constant between experiment 3 and 4, the initial rate doubles so the rate is first order with respect to [Z] ***[1 mark]***.
b) $1.30 \times 10^{-3} \times 3$ = **3.90 × 10^{-3} mol dm^{-3} s^{-1}** ***[1 mark]***
c) rate = $k[Z][Y]^2$ ***[1 mark]***

Page 189— The Rate-Determining Step

1 H^+ is acting as a catalyst ***[1 mark]***. You know this because it is not one of the reactants in the chemical equation, but it does affect the rate of reaction/appear in the rate equation ***[1 mark]***.

2 a) If the molecule is in the rate equation, it must be involved in the reaction in or before the rate-determining step. The orders of the reaction tell you how many molecules of each reactant are involved up to the rate-determining step ***[1 mark]***. So the rate-determining step is affected by one molecule of H_2 and one molecule of ICl ***[1 mark]***.
b) Incorrect ***[1 mark]***. H_2 and ICl are both in the rate equation, so they must both be involved in the reaction in or before the rate-determining step. / The order of the reaction with respect to ICl is 1, so there must be only one molecule of ICl in the rate-determining step ***[1 mark]***.

Answers

Page 191 — Halogenoalkanes and Reaction Mechanisms

1 D ***[1 mark]***

1-chloropropane is a primary halogenoalkane, which means it will react using an S_N2 mechanism. So both 1-chloropropane and sodium hydroxide must be in the rate equation, as the rate will depend on the concentration of both them.

2 a) 1-iodobutane is a primary iodoalkane ***[1 mark]***.

b) Rate = $k[CH_3CH_2CH_2CH_2I][OH^-]$ ***[1 mark]***

c) Mechanism is S_N2 ***[1 mark]***

d)
```
  CH3CH2CH2              [CH3CH2CH2  H  ]−          CH3CH2CH2
       \  δ+↷  δ−        [      \   /   ]               /
HO:⁻ ↷ C — I    ——>      [ HO-- C --- I ]  ——>  HO — C        + :I⁻
      / |                [      |       ]             \ \
     H  H                [      H       ]              H  H
```

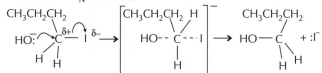

[3 marks — 1 mark for each curly arrow, 1 mark for correct transition molecule]

3 a) Rate = $k[CH_3CBr(CH_3)C_3H_7]$

b) Step 1— Rate determining step
```
          C3H7                     C3H7
           |δ+↷ δ−                  |
    H3C — C — Br    ⇌     H3C — C⁺   + :Br⁻
           |                        |
          CH3                      CH3
```
Step 2
```
          C3H7                      C3H7
           |                         |
    H3C — C⁺ ↶ :OH⁻  ——>     H3C — C — OH
           |                         |
          CH3                       CH3
```

[3 marks — 1 mark for each correct step in the mechanism, 1 mark for correct identification of rate determining step]

Page 193 — Activation Energy

1 a)

T (K)	*k*	1/*T* (K⁻¹)	ln *k*
305	0.181	0.00328	-1.709
313	0.468	**0.00319**	**-0.759**
323	1.34	**0.00310**	**0.293**
333	3.29	0.00300	1.191
344	10.1	**0.00291**	**2.313**
353	22.7	0.00283	**3.127**

[2 marks — 1 mark for all 1/T values, 1 mark for all ln k values]

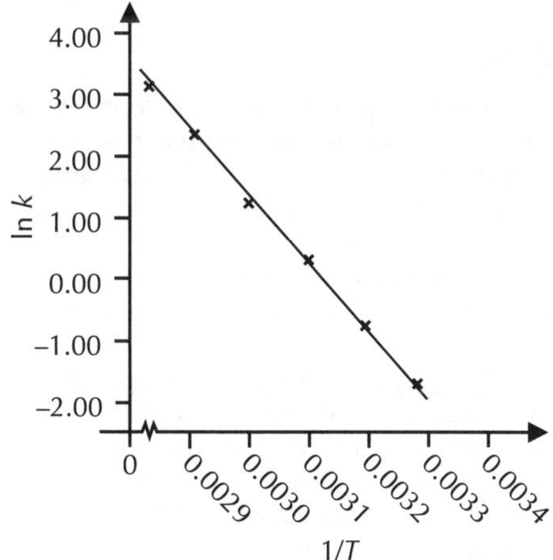

[2 marks — 1 mark for at least 5 accurate points, 1 mark for line of best fit]

b) Value = −10750 ±250 ***[1 mark]***

c) $-E_a/R = -10750$ ***[1 mark]***.

$E_a = 10750 \times 8.31 =$ **89 300 J mol⁻¹** OR **89.3 kJ mol⁻¹** ***[1 mark]***

2 Homogeneous catalysts are in the same state as the reactants, homogeneous however, are in a different physical state than the reactants ***[1 mark]***.

Topic 17 — Organic Chemistry II

Page 195 — Optical Isomerism

1 a)
```
    H   H   Br  H
    |   |   |   |
H — C — C — C*— C — H
    |   |   |   |
    H   H   H   H
```
[1 mark]

It doesn't really matter how you mark the chiral centre, as long as you've made it clear which carbon you've marked.

b) Since the butan-2-ol solution is a racemic mixture, it must contain equal amounts of both optical isomers. The two optical isomers will exactly cancel out each other's light-rotating effect ***[1 mark]***.

c) The reaction has proceeded via an S_N1 mechanism ***[1 mark]***. You know this because the original solution contained a single optical isomer, but the product is a racemic mixture ***[1 mark]***.

Page 197 — Aldehydes and Ketones

1 a) C ***[1 mark]***

b) B and C ***[1 mark]***

c) Compound B is a ketone and is therefore not oxidised by acidified dichromate(VI) ions and no colour change occurs ***[1 mark]***.

Page 199 — Reactions of Aldehydes and Ketones

1 a) E.g.
```
    H   H   H   H   H   O   H
    |   |   |   |   |   ||  |
H — C — C — C — C — C — C — C — H
    |   |   |   |   |       |
    H   H   H   H   H       H
```
[1 mark]

The reaction with 2,4-DNPH tells you that the molecule contains a carbonyl group ***[1 mark]***. The reduction to a secondary alcohol tells you it must be a ketone ***[1 mark]***. The result of the reaction with iodine tells you that the molecule contains a methyl carbonyl group ***[1 mark]***.

b) You can measure the melting point of the precipitate formed with 2,4-DNPH ***[1 mark]***. Each carbonyl compound gives a precipitate with a specific melting point which can be looked up in tables ***[1 mark]***.

c) E.g.
```
    H   H   H   H   H   OH  H
    |   |   |   |   |   |   |
H — C — C — C — C — C — C — C — H
    |   |   |   |   |   |   |
    H   H   H   H   H   H   H
```
[1 mark]

2 a) Nucleophilic addition ***[1 mark]***

b) i)
```
       OH
       |
H3C — C — CH3
       |
       C≡N
```
[1 mark]

ii)
```
     ↶O^δ−              O:⁻ ↷ H⁺                 OH
     ||                 |                        |
H3C — C^δ+   ——>  H3C — C — CH3   ——>    H3C — C — CH3
   ↗   \                |                        |
 :CN⁻   CH3             C≡N                      C≡N
```

[4 marks — 1 mark for correct structures, 1 mark for each correct curly arrow]

c) Depending on which side the CN^- attacks from, one of two optical isomers is formed ***[1 mark]***. Because the groups around the C=O bond are planar, there is an equal chance that the CN^- will attack from either direction ***[1 mark]***, meaning an equal amount of each optical isomer, i.e. a racemic mixture, will form ***[1 mark]***.

Page 201 — Carboxylic Acids

1 a) Reflux ***[1 mark]*** propan-1-ol with acidified potassium dichromate(VI) ***[1 mark]***.

b) Add a carbonate/hydrogencarbonate ***[1 mark]***. Propan-1-ol will show no reaction, but propanoic acid will produce bubbles of carbon dioxide ***[1 mark]***.

Answers

2 a) 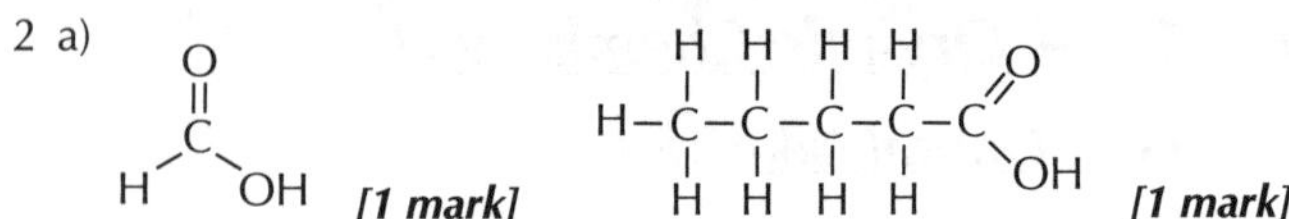

b) Pentanoic acid has a longer carbon chain than methanoic acid ***[1 mark]***. This means the chain is more likely to get in the way of the hydrogen bonds forming between pentanoic acid and water. The energy released from formation of the water–acid hydrogen bonds for pentanoic acid is less than that for methanoic acid . This leads to less energy to compensate for the breaking of water–water hydrogen bonds and therefore a reduction in solubility ***[1 mark]***.

c) $C_7H_{14}O_2 + PCl_5 \rightarrow C_7H_{14}OCl + POCl_3 + HCl$ ***[1 mark]***

Page 203 — Esters

1 a) 2-methylpropyl ethanoate ***[1 mark]***

b)
```
     H   O
     |  //
   H-C-C
     |  \
     H   OH
```
[1 mark] Ethanoic acid ***[1 mark]***
```
       H  H   H
       |  |   |
   HO–C – C – C–H
       |  |   |
       H CH3  H
```
[1 mark] 2-methylpropan-1-ol ***[1 mark]***

This is an acid hydrolysis reaction ***[1 mark]***.

2 a)
```
      O     H
     //     |
   H-C      |
      \     |
       O – C – CH3
            |
           CH3
```
[1 mark]

b) $HCOOH + CH_3CH(CH_3)OH \overset{H^+}{\rightleftharpoons} HCOOCH(CH_3)_2 + H_2O$
[1 mark for correct reactants, 1 mark for correct products, 1 mark for reversible reaction]

c) An esterification reaction ***[1 mark]***.

Page 204 — Acyl Chlorides

1 a)
```
     H   H   H  CH3
     |   |   |   |     O
   H–C – C – C – C – C//
     |   |   |   |     \
     H   H   H   H      Cl
```
[1 mark]

b) i)
```
      H   H   H
      |   |   |
   H– C – C – C –NH3
      |   |   |
      H   H   H
```
[1 mark]

ii) $C_5H_9OCl + C_3H_9N \rightarrow C_5H_9ONHC_3H_7 + HCl$ ***[1 mark]***

Topic 18 — Organic Chemistry III

Page 207 — Aromatic Compounds

1 a) i) 2 moles ***[1 mark]***

ii) 2 × 120 = **240 kJ** ***[1 mark]***

b) You would expect 3 moles of H_2 to react with a molecule with the Kekulé structure. Each mole should release 120 kJ, so there should be 3 × 120 = 360 kJ released in the reaction ***[1 mark]***.

c) The delocalisation of electrons makes benzene more stable (it lowers the energy of the molecule) ***[1 mark]*** and so it releases less energy when it reacts ***[1 mark]***.

d) E.g. The Kekulé structure cannot explain why the bonds between carbons in benzene are all the same length ***[1 mark]***, since C=C double bonds are shorter than single bonds ***[1 mark]***. The benzene molecule represented by the Kekulé structure should react in the same way as alkenes ***[1 mark]*** (i.e. by electrophilic addition), but benzene is actually much less reactive ***[1 mark]*** (and tends to react via electrophilic substitution).

2 Cyclohexene would decolourise the brown bromine water, benzene would not ***[1 mark]***. This is because bromine water reacts in an electrophilic addition reaction with cyclohexene, due to the localised electrons in the double bond ***[1 mark]***, to form a colourless dibromocycloalkane, leaving a clear solution. Benzene has a ring of delocalised π-bonds which spreads out the negative charge and makes it very stable, so it doesn't react with bromine water and the solution stays brown ***[1 mark]***.

Page 210 — Electrophilic Substitution Reactions

1 a) i) A: Nitrobenzene ***[1 mark]***
B + C: Concentrated nitric acid ***[1 mark]*** and concentrated sulfuric acid ***[1 mark]***
D: Warm, not more than 55 °C ***[1 mark]***

When you're asked to name a compound, write the name, not the formula.

ii) $HNO_3 + H_2SO_4 \rightarrow H_2NO_3^+ + HSO_4^-$ ***[1 mark]***
$H_2NO_3^+ \rightarrow NO_2^+ + H_2O$ ***[1 mark]***

iii) 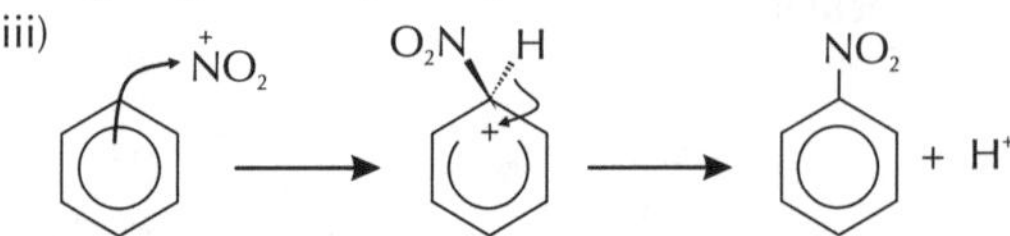

[2 marks — 1 mark for each step]

b) i) J: Bromobenzene ***[1 mark]***

ii) E + F: Bromine ***[1 mark]*** and $FeBr_3$ ***[1 mark]***
G: Room temperature ***[1 mark]***

2 a) Conditions: non-aqueous solvent (e.g. dry ether), reflux ***[1 mark]***

b) The acyl chloride molecule isn't polarised enough/isn't a strong enough electrophile to attack the benzene ***[1 mark]***. The halogen carrier makes the acyl chloride electrophile stronger ***[1 mark]***.

c) $H_3C{-}\overset{+}{C}{\equiv}O$ ***[1 mark]***

Page 211 — Phenols

1 a) With benzene, there will be no reaction but with phenol a reaction will occur which decolourises the brown bromine water and forms a precipitate ***[1 mark]***. The product from the reaction with phenol is 2,4,6-tribromophenol ***[1 mark]***.

b) Electrons from one of oxygen's p-orbitals overlap with the benzene ring's delocalised system, increasing its electron density ***[1 mark]***. This makes the ring more likely to be attacked by electrophiles ***[1 mark]***.

c) Electrophilic substitution ***[1 mark]***.

Page 214 — Amines

1 a) The amine molecules remove protons/H^+/H ions from the water molecules ***[1 mark]***. This gives alkyl ammonium ions and hydroxide ions, which make the solution alkaline ***[1 mark]***.

b) $CH_3COCl + C_4H_9NH_2 \rightarrow CH_3CONH(C_4H_9) + HCl$ ***[1 mark]***
$C_4H_9NH_2 + HCl \rightarrow C_4H_9NH_3^+ + Cl^-$ ***[1 mark]***

2 a) The lone pair of electrons on the nitrogen atom can accept protons/H^+ ions, or it can donate a lone pair of electrons ***[1 mark]***.

b) Methylamine is stronger, as the methyl group/CH_3 pushes electrons onto/increases electron density on the nitrogen, making the lone pair more available ***[1 mark]***. Phenylamine is weaker, as the nitrogen lone pair is less available — nitrogen's electron density is decreased as it's partially delocalised around the benzene ring ***[1 mark]***.

3 a) $LiAlH_4$ and a non-aqueous solvent (e.g. dry ether), followed by dilute acid ***[1 mark]***.

b) Hydrogen gas ***[1 mark]***, metal catalyst such as platinum or nickel and high temperature and pressure ***[1 mark]***.

Page 215 — Amides

1 a) N-propylbutanamide ***[1 mark]***

b) Butanoyl chloride ***[1 mark]***, propan-1-amine ($CH_3CH_2CH_2NH_2$) ***[1 mark]***, room temperature ***[1 mark]***.

Answers

Page 217 — Condensation Polymers

1 a) E.g. $-\overset{\text{O}}{\overset{\|}{\text{C}}}-(CH_2)_2-\overset{\text{O}}{\overset{\|}{\text{C}}}-\text{O}-\underset{\text{H}}{\underset{|}{\overset{\text{H}}{\overset{|}{\text{C}}}}}-(CH_2)_2-\underset{\text{H}}{\underset{|}{\overset{\text{H}}{\overset{|}{\text{C}}}}}-\text{O}-$

[2 marks — 1 mark for ester link correct, 1 mark for rest of structure correct]

The oxygen atom at the right-hand end of the repeat unit could just as easily go on the left-hand end instead. As long as you have it there, it doesn't really matter which side it's on.

b) ester link ***[1 mark]***

2 a) E.g. $-\overset{\text{O}}{\overset{\|}{\text{C}}}-(CH_2)_4-\overset{\text{O}}{\overset{\|}{\text{C}}}-\underset{\text{H}}{\underset{|}{\text{N}}}-(CH_2)_6-\underset{\text{H}}{\underset{|}{\text{N}}}-$

[2 marks — 1 mark for amide link correct, 1 mark for rest of structure correct]

b) For each link formed, one small molecule (water) is eliminated ***[1 mark]***.

Page 219 — Amino Acids

1 a) Cysteine is chiral but glycine isn't ***[1 mark]***. So a mixture containing just one enantiomer of cysteine will rotate the plane of plane-polarised light, but glycine won't ***[1 mark]***.

b) ***A maximum of two marks can be awarded for structure and reasoning of the written response:***

2 marks: The answer is constructed logically, and displays clear reasoning and links between points throughout.

1 mark: The answer is mostly logical, with some reasoning and links between points.

0 marks: The answer has no structure and no links between points.

Here are some points your answer may include:

Draw a line near the bottom of a piece of chromatography paper, and put a spot of the amino acid mixture on it. Put the paper into a beaker containing a small amount of solvent that lies below the level of the spot of mixture. Put a watch glass on the beaker and leave until the solvent has nearly reached the top of the paper, then remove the paper and mark the distance the solvent has moved. Each amino acid will have a different solubility in the solvent, so as the solvent spreads up the paper the different amino acids will separate out. Leave the paper to dry and spray with ninhydrin (to reveal location of spots), then measure how far the solvent front and the spots have travelled. Calculate the R_f values of the amino acid spots using the equation $R_f \text{ value} = \frac{\text{distance travelled by spot}}{\text{distance travelled by solvent}}$ and compare to a table of known amino acid R_f values ***[1 mark]***.

[4 marks — 4 marks if 6 points mentioned covering all areas of the question, 3 marks if 4-5 points covered, 2 marks if 2-3 points covered, 1 mark if 1 point covered]

2 a) An amino acid's isoelectric point is the pH where its average overall charge is zero ***[1 mark]***.

b) i) $H_2N-\underset{\text{H}}{\underset{|}{\overset{CH_2OH}{\overset{|}{\text{C}}}}}-COOH$ ***[1 mark]***

ii) $H_2N-\underset{\text{H}}{\underset{|}{\overset{CH_2OH}{\overset{|}{\text{C}}}}}-COO^-$ ***[1 mark]***

It might seem a bit obvious to say this, but if you've drawn these out in more detail — like drawing the NH_2 group out with all its bonds shown — you'd get the mark.

Page 220 — Grignard Reagents

1 a) 1-bromobutane, magnesium, dry ether ***[1 mark]***

b) i) Ethanal and dry ether ***[1 mark]***, then dilute HCl ***[1 mark]***.

ii) CO_2 and dry ether ***[1 mark]***, then dilute HCl ***[1 mark]***.

Page 223 — Organic Synthesis

1 E.g. Step 1: The methanol is refluxed with $K_2Cr_2O_7$ and acid to form methanoic acid ***[1 mark]***.
Step 2: The methanoic acid is heated with ethanol using an acid catalyst to make ethyl methanoate ***[1 mark]***.

2 E.g. Step 1: React propane with bromine in the presence of UV light to form bromopropane ***[1 mark]***.
Step 2: Bromopropane is then refluxed with aqueous sodium hydroxide solution to form propanol ***[1 mark]***.

3 a) Heat under reflux ***[1 mark]***.

b) $K_2Cr_2O_7$/potassium dichromate and H_2SO_4/sulfuric acid ***[1 mark]***, reflux ***[1 mark]***.

4 E.g. Step 1: benzene $\xrightarrow[\text{heat}]{Br_2,\ FeBr_3\text{ (cat.)}}$ bromobenzene

[2 marks — 1 mark for reagents, 1 mark for product]

Step 2:

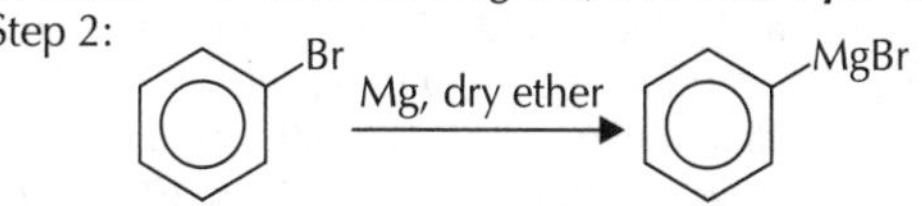

[2 marks — 1 mark for reagents, 1 mark for product]

Step 3: phenylmagnesium bromide (MgBr) $\xrightarrow[\text{2) dilute HCl}]{\text{1) propanal, dry ether}}$ product (OH)

[2 marks — 1 mark for reagents at each stage]

Page 225 — Practical Techniques

1 a)

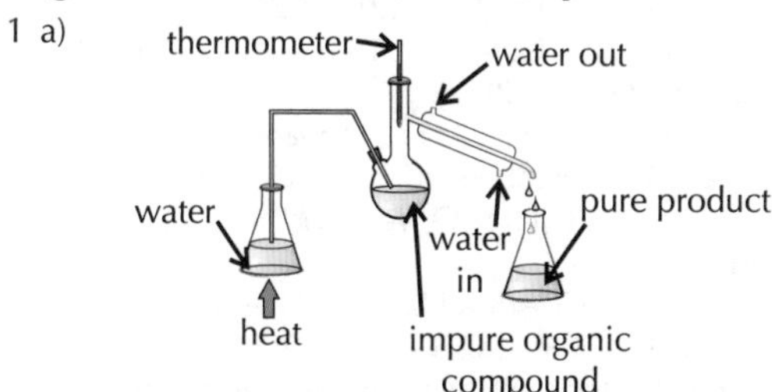

[3 marks — 1 mark showing steam distillation apparatus, 1 mark for a correct set-up, 1 mark for correct labels]

b) Put the mixture in a separating funnel and add ether ***[1 mark]***. Add some salt (e.g. NaCl) to the mixture, as this makes the aqueous layer very polar, ensuring that all the phenylamine is dissolved in the ether layer ***[1 mark]***. Put a stopper on the funnel, and shake it, then remove the stopper and let the mixture settle into layers ***[1 mark]***. Open the tap and run each layer off into a separate container ***[1 mark]***.

Page 227 — More Practical Techniques

1 a) The purer sample will have the higher melting point, so the sample that melts at 69 °C is purer ***[1 mark]***.

b) E.g. recrystallisation in propanone ***[1 mark]***.

c) E.g. the purity could be checked by measuring the melting point and comparing it against the known melting point of stearic acid ***[1 mark]***.

2 a) The scientist used the minimum possible amount of hot solvent to make sure that the solution would be saturated ***[1 mark]***.

b) Filter the hot solution through a heated funnel to remove any insoluble impurities ***[1 mark]***. Leave the solution to cool down slowly until crystals of the product have formed ***[1 mark]***. Filter the mixture under reduced pressure ***[1 mark]***. Wash the crystals with ice-cold solvent ***[1 mark]***. Leave the crystals to dry ***[1 mark]***.

c) The melting point range of the impure product will be lower and broader than that of the pure product ***[1 mark]***.

3 B ***[1 mark]***

Answers

Page 229 — Empirical and Molecular Formulae

1 a) 0.100 g of the carbonyl gives 0.228 g of CO_2.
$0.228 \div 44.0 = 0.00518$ moles of CO_2.
1 mole of CO_2 contains 1 mole of carbon, so 0.100 g of the carbonyl must contain 0.00518 moles of C ***[1 mark]***.
0.100 g of the carbonyl makes 0.0930 g of H_2O.
$0.0930 \div 18.0 = 0.00517$ moles of H_2O.
1 mole of H_2O contains 2 moles of H, so 0.100 g of the carbonyl must contain $2 \times 0.00517 = 0.0103$ moles of H ***[1 mark]***.
0.00518 moles of C has a mass of $0.00518 \times 12.0 = 0.0622$ g
0.0103 moles of H has a mass of $0.0103 \times 1.0 = 0.0103$ g
$0.0622 + 0.0103 = 0.0725$g
So 0.100 g of the compound contains $0.100 - 0.0725 = 0.0275$ g of O ***[1 mark]***.
0.0275 g of O = $0.0275 \div 16.0 = 0.00172$ moles
So the mole ratio is C = 0.00518, H = 0.0103, O = 0.00172
Divide by the smallest (0.00172): The ratio of C : H : O is 3 : 6 : 1.
So the empirical formula = C_3H_6O ***[1 mark]***.

b) Mass of empirical formula: $(3 \times 12.0) + 6.0 + 16.0 = 58.0$ ***[1 mark]***
So by mass, hydrogen is $(6.0 \div 58.0) \times 100$ = **10.3%** ***[1 mark]***

c) Molecular formula is the same as the empirical formula as they have the same mass ***[1 mark]***.

d) The carbonyl reacts with Tollens' reagent to form a silver mirror, so it must be an aldehyde. So, the structure is:

```
  H H  H
  | | /
H-C-C-C
  | |  \\
  H H   O
```
[1 mark]

2 a) To get the mole ratio, divide each % by atomic mass:
C: $37.0 \div 12.0 = 3.08$ H: $2.2 \div 1.0 = 2.2$
N: $18.5 \div 14.0 = 1.32$ O: $42.3 \div 16.0 = 2.64$ ***[1 mark]***
Then divide by the smallest (1.32):
The ratio of C : H : N : O is 2.33 : 1.67 : 1 : 2 ***[1 mark]***
Multiply by 3 to get whole numbers: C : H : N : O = 7 : 5 : 3 : 6
So the empirical formula = $C_7H_5N_3O_6$ ***[1 mark]***
The molecular mass = 227
The empirical mass = $(7 \times C) + (5 \times H) + (3 \times N) + (6 \times O)$
$= (7 \times 12.0) + (5 \times 1.0) + (3 \times 14.0) + (6 \times 16.0) = 227$
The empirical formula is the same as the molecular formula as they have the same mass ***[1 mark]***.

b) E.g.

```
        CH3
  O2N         NO2
       (ring)
        NO2
```
[1 mark, allow different placing of groups around ring]

3 a) $25X_{(g)} + 125O_{2(g)} \rightarrow 75CO_{2(g)} + ?H_2O$
Dividing by 25 gives: $X_{(g)} + 5O_2 \rightarrow 3CO_2 + nH_2O$
5 moles of O_2 reacts to give 3 moles of CO_2 and n moles of H_2O, so $n = (5 \times 2) - (3 \times 2) = 4$.
$X_{(g)} + 5O_2 \rightarrow 3CO_2 + 4H_2O$ ***[1 mark]***
All the C atoms in CO_2 come from X, so X contains 3 C atoms.
All the H atoms in H_2O come from X, so X contains $(4 \times 2) = 8$ H atoms. The molecular formula of X is $\mathbf{C_3H_8}$ ***[1 mark]***.

b) The empirical mass is $(3 \times 12.0) + (8 \times 1.0) = 44$ ***[1 mark]***.
The mass spectrum of X has an M peak at $m/z = 88$, so the molecular mass of X is 88. So X contains $88 \div 44 = 2$ empirical units. The molecular formula of X is $\mathbf{C_6H_{16}}$ ***[1 mark]***.

Topic 19 — Modern Analytical Techniques II

Page 230 — High Resolution Mass Spectrometry

1 a) C ***[1 mark]***
The relative molecular mass of the compound = the m/z value of the molecular ion, so calculate the precise M_r of each possible molecular formula:
A: $(3 \times 12.0000) + (6 \times 1.0078) + (2 \times 15.9990) = 74.0448$
B: $(4 \times 12.0000) + (10 \times 1.0078) + 15.9990 = 74.077$
C: $(3 \times 12.0000) + (10 \times 1.0078) + (2 \times 14.0064) = 74.0908$
D: $(2 \times 12.0000) + (6 \times 1.0078) + (2 \times 14.0064) + 15.9990$
$= 74.0586$

b) The four options given in part a) all have the same M_r to the nearest whole number, so their molecular ions would all have the same m/z value on a low resolution mass spectrum ***[1 mark]***.

2 E.g.

```
  H H       H              H     H
  | |      /               |     |
H-C-C-C=C        OR      H-C-C=C-C-H
  | | |    \               | | | |
  H H H     H              H H H H
 but-1-ene                but-2-ene

         H
         |     H
   OR  H-C-C=C
         | |   \
         H CH3  H
     methylpropene
```

[2 marks — 1 mark for correct structure, 1 mark for correct name]
Answering questions like this can involve a bit of trial and error. Here, there was a big clue in the question — it's a hydrocarbon, so it only contains H and C atoms. There are actually two other hydrocarbons with the formula C_4H_8, so well done if you thought of cyclobutane or methylcyclopropane.

Page 233 — NMR Spectroscopy

1 a) The peak at $\delta = 0$ is produced by the reference compound, tetramethylsilane/TMS ***[1 mark]***.

b) All three carbon atoms in the molecule $CH_3CH_2CH_2NH_2$ are in different environments ***[1 mark]***. There are only two peaks on the carbon-13 NMR spectrum shown ***[1 mark]***.
The ^{13}C NMR spectrum of $CH_3CH_2CH_2NH_2$ would have three peaks because this molecule has three carbon environments.

c) The peak at $\delta \approx 25$ represents carbons in C–C bonds ***[1 mark]***.
The peak at $\delta \approx 40$ represents a carbon in a C–N bond ***[1 mark]***.
The spectrum has two peaks, so the molecule must have two carbon environments ***[1 mark]***.
So the structure of the molecule must be:

```
  H  NH2 H
  |   |  |
H-C---C--C-H
  |   |  |
  H   H  H
```
[1 mark]

The two carbon environments are $\mathbf{C}H_3$–$CH(NH_2)$–$\mathbf{C}H_3$ and $\mathbf{C}H(NH_2)$–$(CH_3)_2$.

2 C ***[1 mark]***

Page 235 — Proton NMR Spectroscopy

1 a) The quartet at 3.6 ppm is caused by 3 protons on the adjacent carbon. The n+1 rule tells you that 3 protons give 3 + 1 = 4 peaks ***[1 mark]***.
Similarly the triplet at 1.3 ppm is due to 2 adjacent protons giving 2 + 1 = 3 peaks ***[1 mark]***.

b) A CH_2 group adjacent to a halogen or oxygen (in an alcohol, ether or ester) or a CH_2 group adjacent to a nitrogen (in an amine or amide) ***[1 mark]***.

c) A CH_3 group ***[1 mark]***.

d) CH_2 added to CH_3 gives a mass of 29, which leaves a mass of $64.5 - 29 = 35.5$ for the rest of the molecule. This is the relative atomic mass of chlorine ***[1 mark]***, so a likely structure is CH_3CH_2Cl ***[1 mark]***.

2 a) 4 ***[1 mark]***
With questions like this, it really helps to draw out the structure of the molecule you're dealing with. That way you can clearly see how many different H environments there are.
Here's the structure of 3-chlorobut-1-ene:

```
 H     H H H
  \    | | |
   C=C-C-C-H
  /      | |
 H       Cl H
```

b) There will be a doublet with a chemical shift of $\delta \approx$ 4.5-6.5 ppm (corresponding to the H in the alkene environment) ***[1 mark]***, a quartet with a chemical shift of $\delta \approx$ 4.5-6.5 ppm (corresponding to the other H in the alkene environment) ***[1 mark]***, a quintet with a chemical shift of $\delta \approx$ 2.0-4.0 ppm (corresponding to the H in the halogen environment) ***[1 mark]*** and a doublet with a chemical shift of $\delta \approx$ 0.2-1.9 ppm (corresponding to the H in the alkane environment) ***[1 mark]***.

Answers

Page 237 — Chromatography

1 a) R_f value = $\frac{\text{Distance travelled by spot}}{\text{Distance travelled by solvent}}$ ***[1 mark]***

R_f value of spot A = 7 ÷ 8 = 0.875 ***[1 mark]***

The R_f value has no units, because it's a ratio.

b) Substance A has moved further up the plate because it's less strongly adsorbed onto the surface / more soluble in the solvent than substance B ***[1 mark]***.

2 a) E.g. the stationary phase consists of small solid particles packed in a tube ***[1 mark]***. The sample is injected into a stream of high pressure liquid — this is the mobile phase ***[1 mark]***. The detector monitors the output from the tube ***[1 mark]***.

b) The chromatogram shows a peak for each component of the mixture ***[1 mark]***. UV light is passed through the liquid leaving the tube and the detector measures the absorbance ***[1 mark]***. From these, the retention time can be seen and compared to reference books or databases to identify the substances ***[1 mark]***.

3 a) Gas chromatography ***[1 mark]***

b) Different substances have different retention times ***[1 mark]***. The retention time of substances in the sample is compared against that for ethanol ***[1 mark]***.

Page 239 — Combined Techniques

1 a) Relative mass of molecule = 73 ***[1 mark]***

You can tell this from the mass spectrum — the *m/z* value of the molecular ion is 73.

b) Structure of the molecule:

```
     H  H
     |  |      NH2
  H-C--C--C<
     |  |      O
     H  H
```

[1 mark]

Explanation: ***[Award 1 mark each for the following pieces of reasoning, up to a total of 5 marks]***:

The infrared spectrum of the molecule shows a strong absorbance at about 3200 cm^{-1}, which suggests that the molecule contains an amine or amide group.

It also has a trough at about 1700 cm^{-1}, which suggests that the molecule contains a C=O group.

The ^{13}C NMR spectrum tells you that the molecule has three carbon environments.

One of the ^{13}C NMR peaks has a chemical shift of about 170, which corresponds to a carbonyl group in an amide.

The ^{1}H NMR spectrum has a quartet at $\delta \approx 2$, and a triplet at $\delta \approx 1$ — to give this splitting pattern the molecule must contain a CH_2CH_3 group.

The ^{1}H NMR spectrum has a singlet at $\delta \approx 6$, corresponding to H atoms in an amine or amide group.

The mass spectrum shows a peak at *m/z* = 15 which corresponds to a CH_3^+ group.

The mass spectrum shows a peak at *m/z* = 29 which corresponds to a $CH_2CH_3^+$ group.

The mass spectrum shows a peak at *m/z* = 44 which corresponds to a $CONH_2^+$ group.

2 a) Relative mass of molecule = 60 ***[1 mark]***

You can tell this from the mass spectrum — the *m/z* value of the molecular ion is 60.

b) Structure of the molecule:

```
     H  H  H
     |  |  |
  H-C--C--C-OH
     |  |  |
     H  H  H
```

[1 mark]

Explanation: ***[Award 1 mark each for the following pieces of reasoning, up to a total of 5 marks]***:

The ^{13}C NMR spectrum tells you that the molecule has three carbon environments.

One of the ^{13}C NMR peaks has a chemical shift of 60 — which corresponds to a C–O group.

The infrared spectrum of the molecule has a trough at about 3300 cm^{-1}, which suggests that the molecule contains an alcoholic OH group.

It also has a trough at about 1200 cm^{-1}, which suggests that the molecule also contains a C–O group.

The mass spectrum shows a peak at *m/z* = 15 which corresponds to a CH_3^+ group.

The mass spectrum shows a peak at *m/z* = 17 which corresponds to an OH^+ group.

The mass spectrum shows a peak at *m/z* = 29 which corresponds to a $C_2H_5^+$ group.

The mass spectrum shows a peak at *m/z* = 31 which corresponds to a CH_2OH^+ group.

The mass spectrum shows a peak at *m/z* = 43 which corresponds to a $C_3H_7^+$ group.

The ^{1}H NMR spectrum has 4 peaks, showing that the molecule has 4 proton environments.

The ^{1}H NMR spectrum has a singlet at $\delta \approx 2$, corresponding to H atoms in an OH group.

The ^{1}H NMR spectrum has a sextet with an integration trace of 2 at $\delta \approx 1.5$, a triplet with an integration trace of 2 at $\delta \approx 3.5$, and a triplet with an integration trace of 3 at $\delta \approx 0.5$ — to give this splitting pattern the molecule must contain a $CH_3CH_2CH_2$ group.

Practical Skills

Page 241 — Planning Experiments

1 Using litmus paper is not a particularly accurate method of measuring pH / not very sensitive equipment ***[1 mark]***. It would be better to use a pH meter ***[1 mark]***.

Page 243 — Practical Techniques

1 a) The student measured the level of the liquid from the top of the meniscus, when he should have measured it from the bottom ***[1 mark]***.

b) B ***[1 mark]***.

Page 245 — Presenting Results

1 a) mean volume = $\frac{7.30 + 7.25 + 7.25}{3}$ = 7.26666... cm^3

= **0.00727 dm^3** or **7.27 × 10^{-3} dm^3** (3 s.f.) ***[1 mark]***

b) 0.50 ÷ 1000 = **0.00050 mol cm^{-3}** or **5.0 × 10^{-4} mol cm^{-3}** ***[1 mark]***

Page 247 — Analysing Results

1 a) 15 °C and 25 °C ***[1 mark]***.

b) Positive correlation ***[1 mark]***.

c) C ***[1 mark]***

Page 249 — Evaluating Experiments

1 a) The volumetric flask reads to the nearest 0.5 cm^3, so the uncertainty is ±0.25 cm^3.

percentage error = $\frac{\text{uncertainty}}{\text{reading}} \times 100 = \frac{0.25}{25} \times 100 =$ **1.0 %** ***[1 mark]***

b) E.g. The student should add the thermometer to the citric acid solution and allow it to stabilise before adding the sodium bicarbonate to give an accurate value for the initial temperature ***[1 mark]***. The student should then measure the temperature change until the solution stops reacting to give a valid result for the temperature change of the entire reaction ***[1 mark]***.

Index

Index

Index

CER73